W9-CSA-879

70I

PROPERTIES OF POLYMERS

THEIR ESTIMATION AND CORRELATION WITH CHEMICAL STRUCTURE

PROPERTIES OF POLYMERS

THEIR ESTIMATION AND CORRELATION WITH CHEMICAL STRUCTURE

By

D.W. VAN KREVELEN

*Professor at the University of Technology, Delft, The Netherlands
and Director of Research, Akzo N.V., Arnhem, The Netherlands*

With the collaboration of

P.J. HOFTYZER

Research Associate, Akzo N.V., Arnhem, The Netherlands

ELSEVIER SCIENTIFIC PUBLISHING COMPANY
AMSTERDAM – OXFORD – NEW YORK
1976

ELSEVIER SCIENCE PUBLISHERS B.V.
Sara Burgerhartstraat 25
P.O. Box 211, 1000 AE Amsterdam, The Netherlands

Distributors for the United States and Canada:

ELSEVIER SCIENCE PUBLISHING COMPANY INC.
52, Vanderbilt Avenue
New York, NY 10017

First edition 1972
Second, completely revised edition 1976
Second impression 1980
Third impression 1986
Fourth impression 1987

Library of Congress Cataloging in Publication Data

Krevelen, Dirk Willem van.
    Properties of polymers, their estimation and correla-
tion with chemical structure.

    Includes bibliographies and index.
    1. Polymers and polymerization. I. Hoftyzer, P. J.,
joint author. II. Title.
TA455.P58K74 1976   620.1'92   76-18203
ISBN 0-444-41467-3

ISBN 0-444-41467-3

Printed in The Netherlands

FROM THE PREFACE TO THE FIRST EDITION

This book is intended for those who work on *practical* problems in the field of polymers and who are in need of *orienting* numerical information on polymer properties; for
the organic chemist who is faced with the task of synthesizing new polymers and wonders
if the structures he wants to realize will actually have the properties he has as a target; for
the chemical engineer who is often forced to execute his designs without having enough
data at his disposal and who looks in vain for numerical values of the quantities needed
under the conditions of the process; for the polymer processer who tries to predict and
understand how certain physical parameters will react to changes in process conditions;
for the polymer technologist who tries to get a better insight into the interrelationships
of the many disciplines in his branch; and finally for all students who are interested in
the correlation between chemical structure and properties and in the mutual relation of
the properties.

With the chemical constitution as the basis, our aim has consistently been to show
that each functional group in the molecular structure actually performs a function that is
reflected in *all* properties. Ample use has been made of the *empricial fact* that a number
of quantities and combinations of quantities have additive properties — within certain
limits of precision — so that these quantities can be calculated in a simple manner from
empirically derived group contributions or increments. Many readers will be surprised to
see how far one can get by setting out from this simple starting point.

Theoretical expositions have purposely been omitted, except where some elucidation
is indispensable for a proper understanding of quantities that are less widely known.

It follows that this book has not been written for the polymer scientist proper, notably the polymer physicist and physical chemist, its design being too empirical for him and
too much directed to practice. In this book the expert will find no data that are not available elsewhere. Many experts may even have great objections, some of them justified, to
the design of this book and its approach.

Unfortunately, the gap between polymer scientists and practicians is not narrowing
but constantly widening. The work in the field of polymer science is becoming increasingly sophisticated, in the experimental as well as in the theoretical disciplines.

This book is meant to be a modest contribution towards narrowing the gap between
polymer science and polymer practice. Time will have to show whether this attempt has
been successful.

V

PREFACE TO THE SECOND EDITION

On its appearance this book was given such a good welcome that a second edition proved to be necessary within four years. For this purpose the book was completely revised, updated and considerably extended. The scope of the chapters dealing with the mechanical and rheological properties was much enlarged, as were the sections discussing polymer solutions. An improved system for the assessment of the transition temperatures was introduced. SI units are used throughout the book.

While the first impression confined itself to the intrinsic properties, the second edition also covers the processing and product properties, if to a limited extent and on a selective basis.

The objectives have remained the same, viz. (1) correlating properties with chemical structure and (2) describing methods that permit the prediction of properties from the structure. The reader will find that these methods rapidly yield results; the only tool he needs is a slide rule or a simple electronic pocket calculator. The basic philosophy of the book is summarized in Chapters 1, 3 and 23. The book consists of seven parts.

Part I   —   Introduction — discusses polymers and polymer properties from the widest possible viewpoint. Its aim is to provide a basis for the characteristic line of approach followed in this book.

Part II   —   Thermophysical Properties of Polymers — deals with the basic physical properties, such as the volumetric and calorimetric ones; it also considers the transition temperatures and the "interaction" properties.

Part III   —   Properties of Polymers in Fields of Force — concerns the behaviour of polymers in mechanical and electromagnetic fields of force.

Part IV   —   Transport Properties of Polymers — gives a survey of the quantities controlling the transport of heat, momentum and matter; especially the important properties of heat conductivity, viscosity and diffusivity are discussed; also the combined transport processes as encountered in crystallization and dissolving are considered.

Part V   —   Properties Determining the Chemical Stability and Breakdown of Polymers — starts with a chapter on thermochemical properties of a more general nature and deals with the phenomena of thermal and chemical degradation and their influence on the properties.

Part VI   —   Polymer Properties as an Integral Concept — starts with a brief retrospect of the intrinsic properties, discusses the processing and product properties, and concludes with an illustrative example of end use properties, viz. article properties of textile materials.

Part VII — Comprehensive Tables — gives valuable numerical data on the conversion factors relating the different measuring systems, on physical properties of the most important polymers and the most important solvents, etc. The last Comprehensive Table (VII) marks the culminating points of the book in that it offers a complete survey of the values of the group contributions of all additive quantities used.

Although consistency of nomenclature has been pursued, it has proved unavoidable that many symbols have several meanings; this drawback has largely been obviated by the use of subscripts that will be readily understood.

ACKNOWLEDGEMENTS

Above all I want to thank Mr. P.J. Hoftyzer, my collaborator for almost 35 years, who has critically read and examined the whole book and has substantially contributed to chapters 4–7, 9, 15, 16 and 24.

Thanks are also due to a number of colleagues in the Akzo Research Laboratories at Arnhem, who kindly read special chapters critically and made welcome suggestions for improvements and amplifications of the text. The names mentioned in the first edition (Dr. J. Boon, Dr. R. Bonn, Dr. H. De Vries, Dr. H.J. Hageman, Ing. F.J. Huntjens, Drs. E.P. Magré, Dr. W.J. Mijs, Dr. S. Opschoor, Dr. J.J. Van Aartsen, Dr. S.J. Van der Meer, Dr. D. Vermaas and Ir. H.G. Weijland) have to be extended by those of Dr. H.G. Bruil, Mr. D.J. Goedhart, Drs. H.M. Heuvel, Dr. J. Hoogschagen, Dr. H.G.B. Huysmans and Dr. M.G. Northolt. The suggestions of Dr. D.B. Holmes, Polaroid Corp., are also gratefully acknowledged.

Special thanks are due to Mr. G.A. Hanekamp for a number of valuable literature surveys, to Mr. W.J.A. Van der Eijk and Mr. R. Timmer for welcome linguistic help, criticisms and improvements; to Mr. M. Hogeweg and Mr. A.F. De Visser who made most of the drawings; to Mr. J. Blommers and Miss I.A.G. Saveur for their help in various calculations and in preparing an extensive card index system of all the available polymer properties.

Finally I want to express my gratitude to Miss L. Harteman and Miss I.A.G. Saveur (once more) who shared the task of typing the manuscript.

In particular I am deeply grateful to my wife, Frieda, for the patience she has displayed; she aided and sustained me in many ways and her presence made this undertaking a joy and pleasure.

ACKNOWLEDGEMENTS FOR USE OF ILLUSTRATIONS

Furthermore, thanks are due to the following publishers for their permission to reproduce in this second edition some figures from copyright books and journals.

The American Chemical Society
Fig. 2.12 from Journal of Physical Chemistry 75 (1971) p. 3928, fig. 6. Fig. 26.8 and 26.9 from Macromolecules 1 (1968) p. 395, fig. 4 and p. 397, fig. 5.

Deutsche Bunsen-Gesellschaft
Fig. 2.10 from Berichte der Bunsengesellschaft 74 (1970) p. 772, Abb. 11.

Imperial Chemical Industries Ltd.

Figs. 15.13 and 15.14 and tables 15.8 and 15.10 from "Thermoplastics, Properties and Design", R.M. Ogorkiewicz (Editor), p. 182, fig. 11.14; p. 195, fig. 11.15; p. 182, table 11.1; p. 198, table 11.2.

IPC Business Press Ltd.

Fig. 2.9 from Polymer 3 (1962) p. 387, fig. 46. Fig. 19.3 from Polymer 13 (1972) p. 596, fig. 2. Figs. 26.10 a–c from Polymer 13 (1972) pp. 286 and 287, figs. 2, 3 and 4.

John Wiley and Sons Inc.

Fig. 16.1 from "The Flow of High Polymers", by S. Middleman, 1968, p. 9, table 1.6. Fig. 18.9 from J. Polymer Science, Polymer Letters 7 (1969) p. 406, fig. 1. Fig. 25.1 and Table 25.2 from "Testing of Polymers", by J.V. Schmitz, 1965, p. 323, fig. 1 and p. 329, table I. Fig. 26.2, 26.3, 26.4 from J. Applied Polymer Science, 18 (1974) p. 500, fig. 8; p. 502, figs. 9 and 10. Table 26.5 from "The Chemistry and Uses of Fire Retardants", by J.W. Lyons, 1970, p. 23, table 1.10.

CONTENTS

Part VII. Comprehensive tables

SYMBOLS OF QUANTITIES

		Used in chapter
a	constant	general
a	activity	18
a	exponent of the Mark–Houwink equation	7, 9, 16
a	lattice spacing	13
a	surface per unit volume	3
a_T	WLF shift factor	13
A	constant	general
A	area	general
A	atomic weight	3
A	temperature or concentration dependent quantity	23
A_R	reference value of A	23
A_0	original area	24
A_0	value of A for zero concentration	23
A_2	second virial coefficient	9, 10
A	constant in eq. (20.13)	20
$\mathcal{A}$	temperature dependence of viscosity	15
b	constant	general
b	bond angle factor	9
b	thickness, width	19, 25
b_0	thickness of chain molecules	19
B	constant	general
B	bulk modulus	4, 13, 23
B	interaction parameter	9
B	constant in eq. (20.13)	20
c	concentration	general
c_{cr}	critical value of concentration	16
c_p	specific heat capacity at constant pressure	general
c_p^a	specific heat capacity of amorphous polymer	19
c_p^c	specific heat capacity of crystalline polymer	19

XVII

E	modulus of elasticity (Young's modulus)	general
E_{act}	activation energy	general
E_c	tensile modulus of crystalline polymer	13
E_d	contribution of dispersion forces to the cohesive energy	7
E_D	activation energy of diffusion	18, 19
$E_{D,0}$	value of E_D for zero concentration	18
E_{Dg}	activation energy of diffusion in the glassy state	18
E_{diss}	bond dissociation energy	21
E_{Dr}	activation energy of diffusion in the rubbery state	18
E_g	tensile modulus of glassy polymer	13
E_h	contribution of the hydrogen bonding forces to the cohesive energy	7
E_{iso}	value of E for isotropic material	14
E_{max}	maximum value of tensile modulus	14
E_p	contribution of the polar forces to the cohesive energy	7
E_P	activation energy of permeability	18
E_R	reference value of E	13, 25
E_{r1}	relaxation modulus	13
E_{subl}	sublimation energy	13
E_η	activation energy for viscous flow	15, 16, 24
$E_\eta(\infty)$	value of E_η for $T \gg T_g$	3, 15, 16, 23
E_0	initial value of E	13, 14
E_0	Newtonian value of E	15
E^*	complex tensile modulus	13, 14
$|E^*|$	absolute value of E^*	13
E'	real component of E^*	13, 14
E''	imaginary component of E^*	13, 14
$\mathbf{E}$	molar thermal expansivity	3, 4, 13, 23
$\mathbf{E}_c$	molar thermal expansivity of crystalline polymer	4
$\mathbf{E}_{coh}$	cohesive energy	general
$\mathbf{E}_g$	molar thermal expansivity of a glass	4, 23
$\mathbf{E}_1$	molar thermal expansivity of a liquid	4, 7
f	cross section of rodlet	19
f	force per unit volume	3
f_{el}	electric field per unit volume	3
f_{or}	orientation factor	14
F	force	13, 24, 25
F_{max}	maximum force	24
$\mathbf{F}$	additive function	3
$\mathbf{F}$	molar attraction function	3, 7, 23
$\mathbf{F}_d$	dispersion component of the molar attraction function	7

ΔH_M	enthalpy of mixing	7
ΔH_s	heat of solution	18
ΔH_{sg}	heat of solution for a glassy polymer	18
ΔH_{sr}	heat of solution for a rubbery polymer	18
$\Delta H_{1/2}$	line width at half height	12
$\mathbf{H}$	molar enthalpy	5
$\mathbf{H_c}$	molar enthalpy of crystalline substance	5
$\mathbf{H_\eta}$	molar viscosity–temperature function	3, 15, 23
$\mathbf{H_l}$	molar enthalpy of liquid	5
$\mathbf{\Delta H_f^\circ}$	standard enthalpy of formation	20
$\mathbf{\Delta H_m}$	molar enthalpy of fusion	5, 6, 7, 13, 19
$\mathbf{\Delta H_{vap}}$	molar enthalpy of evaporation	3, 7
$\mathbf{\Delta H^\circ}$	standard enthalpy of reaction	20
$\mathbf{\Delta H_{xy}^\circ}$	standard molar enthalpy difference when monomer in state x is transformed into polymer in state y	20
$\mathbf{\Delta H_\circ^*}$	standard enthalpy of activation	20
i_ϑ	intensity of light per unit volume at angle ϑ	10
I	impact strength	14, 25
I	intensity of light	10, 19
I	ionic strength	9
I	moment of inertia	25
I_a	intensity of radiation for amorphous polymer	19
I_c	intensity of radiation for crystalline polymer	19
I_x	interaction factor for group X	6
I_0	original value of I	10
$\mathcal{I}$	intensity of magnetization	12
J	rate of nucleation per unit volume	19
J	shear compliance	13
J_0	reference value of rate of nucleation	19
J^*	complex shear compliance	13
$|J^*|$	absolute value of complex shear compliance	13
J'	real component of complex shear compliance	13
J''	imaginary component of complex shear compliance	13
k	constant	general
$k\ (k)$	Boltzmann constant	10, 11, 19, 20
k	reaction rate constant	3, 20, 22
k_D	concentration coefficient of diffusion	16
k_H	Huggins constant	16, 23
k_I	rate constant of first order reaction	3
k_K	Kraemer constant	16
k_m	mass transfer coefficient	3

k_s	concentration coefficient of sedimentation	16
k_{tr}	transfer constant	21
K	constant	12, 13
K'	constant	12, 13
K	Mark–Houwink constant	9, 16
K	absorption index	10
K	slope	18
K_D	constant in eq. (9.56)	9
K_{eq}	equilibrium constant	3, 20
K_f	equilibrium constant of formation reaction	20
K_h	constant in eq. (9.10)	9
K_s	constant in eq. (9.52)	9
K_Θ	unperturbed viscosity coefficient	3, 9, 15, 19, 23
$\mathcal{K}$	pressure coefficient of viscosity	15
K	molar limiting viscosity number function	3, 9, 23
l	bond length	4, 9
l	length (per unit volume)	3, 10
L	average free path length	17
L	(characteristic) length	general
L_{eff}	effective flow length	15
L_{max}	maximum length	24
L_0	original length	13, 14, 15, 24
$(\Delta L)_e$	elastic elongation	15
m	constant	14
m	mass	18
M	molecular weight	general
M_b	molecular weight of branched polymer	9
M_{cr}	critical molecular weight	9, 13, 15, 16
M_l	molecular weight of linear polymer	9
M_u	molecular weight of the "interacting unit"	7
$\overline{M}_{crl}$	molecular weight of the polymer segment between cross-links	13
$\overline{M}_n$	number-average molecular weight	2, 3, 13
$\overline{M}_v$	viscosity-average molecular weight	2, 9, 24
$\overline{M}_w$	weight-average molecular weight	2, 3, 10, 15
$\overline{M}_z$	z-average molecular weight	2
M	molar weight per structural unit	general
n	constant	general
n	number	general

n	index of refraction	3, 10, 11, 14, 23
n	Ostwald–de Waele constant	15, 24
n_D	refractive index in sodium light	10, 11, 23
n_{iso}	refractive index of isotropic material	14
n_p	number of particles	9
n_P	refractive index of polymer	10
n_S	refractive index of solvent	10, 23
n_ϕ	number of phenylene groups per structural unit	6
$\bar{n}$	average index of refraction	10
$n*$	complex refractive index	11
$n_\parallel$	refractive index in parallel direction	10, 14
$n_\perp$	refractive index in perpendicular direction	10, 14
Δn	birefringence	10, 14, 15
N	number	general
N	number of nuclei per unit volume	19, 23
N_A	Avogadro number	general
N_{Bm}	Bingham number	3
N_{Bo}	Bodenstein number	3
N_{Da}	Damköhler number	3
N_{De}	Deborah number	3
N_{Fa}	Fanning number	3
N_{Fo}	Fourier number	3
N_{Le}	Lewis number	3
N_{Ma}	Mach number	3
N_{Me}	Merkel number	3
N_{MF}	melt fracture number	15
N_{Nu}	Nusselt number	3
N_{Pe}	Péclet number	3
N_{Po}	Poiseuille number	3
N_{Pr}	Prandtl number	3
N_{Re}	Reynolds number	3, 19, 24
N_{Sc}	Schmidt number	3
N_{Sh}	Sherwood number	3
N_{St}	Stanton number	3
N_{We}	Weber number	3, 24
N_{Wg}	Weissenberg number	3, 15
p	constant	14, 16
p	pressure	general
p	stress component	15
p_y	yield pressure	25
P	driving force	2
P	load	25

T_m	crystalline melting point	general
T_m^0	"effective" melting point	19
T_{mS}	melting point of solvent	16
T_R	reference temperature	13, 15, 18, 20, 23
T_S	standard temperature	15
$T_{\alpha c}$	premelting transition temperature	6
T_0	wall temperature	24
$T_{1/2}$	characteristic temperature for the half conversion	21
T_∞	characteristic temperature at which polymer chain segmental transport tends to zero	19
$\mathscr{T}$	torque	25
u	sound velocity	13, 17
u_{dist}	velocity of propagation of transverse waves	13
u_{long}	longitudinal sound velocity	3, 13, 17, 23
U	internal energy per mole	5, 7
ΔU_{vap}	energy of evaporation	7
$\mathbf{U}$	Rao function or molar sound velocity function	3, 13, 17, 23
v	rate of crystal growth	19, 23
v	specific volume	general
v	velocity	general
v_a	specific volume of amorphous polymer	19
v_c	specific volume of crystalline polymer	19
v_h	hydrodynamic volume per particle	9
v_{max}	maximum rate of growth	19
v_0	reference value of v	19, 24
V	volume	general
V_{cr}	critical volume	18
V_D	molar volume of diffusing molecule	18
V_R	retention volume	2
V_s	parameter with additive properties	6
V_{solv}	volume of a solvated polymer molecule	16
$\mathbf{V}$	molar volume per structural unit	general
$\mathbf{V}_a$	molar volume of amorphous polymer	4
$\mathbf{V}_c$	molar volume of crystalline polymer	4
$\mathbf{V}_g$	molar volume of glassy amorphous polymer	4, 23
$\mathbf{V}_l$	molar volume of organic liquids	4, 8
$\mathbf{V}_r$	molar volume of rubbery amorphous polymer	4
$\mathbf{V}_s$	molar volume of solid	8
$\mathbf{V}_S$	molar volume of solvent	7
$\mathbf{V}_{sc}$	molar volume of semi-crystalline polymer	4
$\mathbf{V}_W$	Van der Waals volume	4, 7

$\mathbf{V}_0$	reference value of $\mathbf{V}$	3, 13
$\mathbf{V}^0(0)$	zero point molar volume	4
$\Delta\mathbf{V}_g$	excess molar volume of glassy amorphous polymer	4
$\Delta\mathbf{V}_{g0}$	value of $\Delta\mathbf{V}_g$ at 0 K	4
$\Delta\mathbf{V}_m$	melting expansion	4
w	water content	18
w	weight factor	3
w	weight fraction of molecules	2
W	weight, load	general
W	width	24
W_{adh}	work of adhesion	8
W_{coh}	work of cohesion	8
W_0	original width	24
ΔW^*	work required to form a crystal nucleus	19
x	fraction of material	19
x	length coordinate	3, 9, 15, 18, 24
x_c	degree of crystallinity	general
X	property	general
$\mathbf{X}$	molar magnetic susceptibility	3, 12, 23
y	maximum beam deflection	25
$\mathbf{Y}_g$	molar glass transition function	3, 6, 23
$\mathbf{Y}_m$	molar melt transition function	3, 6, 23
z_{crl}	average number of cross-links per structural unit	13
Z_{cr}	critical value of the number of chain atoms in the polymer molecule	15
Z	number of backbone atoms per structural unit	6, 9, 19
α	constant	18
α	coefficient of thermal expansion	general
α	expansion factor	9, 19
α	exponent in eq. (16.17)	16
α	half angle of natural convergence	15
α_c	coefficient of thermal expansion of crystalline polymer	4
α_g	coefficient of thermal expansion of glassy polymer	4, 6, 16
α_{gP}	expansion coefficient of polymer below T_g	16
α_{gS}	expansion coefficient of solvent below T_g	16

γ_0	reference value of surface tension	3
γ_{12}	interfacial tension	8
$\gamma_{\parallel}$	interfacial free energy per unit area parallel to the chain	19
$\gamma_{\perp}$	interfacial free energy per unit area perpendicular to the chain	19
$\dot{\gamma}$	rate of shear	3, 9, 15, 24
$\dot{\gamma}_N$	shear rate of a Newtonian fluid	15
δ	chemical shift	12
δ	layer thickness	18, 19
δ	loss angle (phase angle)	2, 11, 13, 25
δ	solubility parameter	3, 7, 8, 11, 23
δ_a	contribution of polar and hydrogen bonding forces to the solubility parameter	7
δ_d	contribution of dispersion forces to the solubility parameter	7, 26
δ_{dP}	dispersion force component for the polymer	7, 9
δ_{dS}	dispersion force component for the solvent	7, 9
δ_E	loss angle in dynamic tensile deformation	13
δ_G	loss angle in dynamic shear deformation	13
δ_h	contribution of hydrogen bonding to the solubility parameter	7, 26
δ_{hP}	hydrogen bonding component for the polymer	9, 26
δ_{hS}	hydrogen bonding component for the solvent	9, 26
δ_p	contribution of polar forces to the solubility parameter	7, 26
δ_P	solubility parameter of a polymer	7, 9, 26
δ_{pP}	polar component for the polymer	7, 9
δ_{pS}	polar component for the solvent	7, 9
δ_S	solubility parameter of a solvent	7, 9, 26
δ_v	contribution of dispersion and polar forces to the solubility parameter	7, 26
δ_{vP}	dispersion and polar force component for the polymer	9, 26
δ_{vS}	dispersion and polar force component for the solvent	9, 26
δ_0	reference value of surface layer thickness	19
Δ	logarithmic decrement	13
ϵ	dielectric constant (permittivity)	3, 11, 23
ϵ	exponent in eq. (9.22)	9
ϵ	infrared mass extinction coefficient	19
ϵ	swelling factor	16
ϵ	tensile strain, elongation	13, 14, 15, 25
ϵ_{br}	elongation at break	13
ϵ_{cr}	critical strain	26

ϵ_e	elastic part of the tensile deformation	13, 15
ϵ_{max}	maximum tensile deformation	13, 14, 15, 25
ϵ_n	nominal strain	13, 14
ϵ_{obs}	observed tensile deformation	14
ϵ_{red}	reduced tensile deformation	14
ϵ_{tr}	true strain	13
ϵ_v	viscous part of tensile deformation	13
ϵ_λ	mass extinction coefficient at given wavelength	10, 19
$\epsilon_\lambda^{(a)}$	mass extinction coefficient of amorphous polymer	19
$\epsilon_\lambda^{(c)}$	mass extinction coefficient of crystalline polymer	19
ϵ_0	maximum amplitude of dynamic tensile deformation	13
ϵ_0	swelling at infinite dilution	16
ϵ^*	complex electric inductive capacity	11
ϵ^*	complex tensile deformation	13
$\dot{\epsilon}$	rate of extension	15
ϵ'	real component of ϵ^*	11, 13
ϵ''	imaginary component of ϵ^*	11, 13
η	shear viscosity	general
η_{cr}	viscosity at critical molecular weight	15
η_{inh}	inherent viscosity	9, 24
η_{MF}	viscosity at melt fracture	15
η_P	viscosity of polymer	16
η_P^*	viscosity of undiluted polymer	16
η_{red}	reduced viscosity	9, 23
η_{rel}	relative viscosity	9
η_S	viscosity of solvent	9, 16
η_{sp}	specific viscosity	9, 16
η_0	Newtonian viscosity	15, 16, 24
η_∞	second Newtonian viscosity	16
$\tilde{\eta}$	reduced viscosity	16
$[\eta]$	limiting viscosity number	2, 9, 16, 23, 24
$[\eta]_b$	limiting viscosity number of branched polymer	9
$[\eta]_{cr}$	limiting viscosity number at the critical molecular weight	9
$[\eta]_l$	limiting viscosity number of linear polymer	9
$[\eta]_R$	reference value of the limiting viscosity number	9
$[\eta]_{rod}$	limiting viscosity number of rod-like molecules	9
$[\eta]_\Theta$	limiting viscosity number of Θ-solution	3, 9, 23
η^*	complex shear viscosity	13, 15
$|\eta^*|$	absolute value of the complex shear viscosity	13, 15
η'	real component of complex shear viscosity	13
η''	imaginary component of complex shear viscosity	13
ϑ	angle	general

μ	coefficient of friction	25
μ	dipole moment	7, 11
μ	magnetic inductive capacity (magnetic permeability)	10
μ	shape factor	25
μ_{sh}	coefficient of shearing friction	25
ν	Poisson ratio	3, 15, 17, 23, 25
ν	resonance frequency	12
ν_e	cross-link density	13
ν_ω	frequency	13
$\Delta\nu$	hydrogen bonding number	7
ξ	deformation gradient	24
ξ	normal stress coefficient	15
π	internal pressure	7
π_{eq}	equilibrium spreading pressure	8
Π	osmotic pressure	10
ρ	density	general
ρ_a	density of amorphous polymer	4, 14, 17
ρ_c	density of crystalline polymer	4, 17, 19
ρ_g	density of glassy amorphous polymer	4
ρ_P	density of polymer	10
ρ_r	density of rubbery amorphous polymer	4
ρ_R	density at reference temperature	13
ρ_{sc}	density of semi-crystalline polymer	4, 14
ρ^*	relative density	19
σ	screening or shielding constant	12
σ	stiffness factor	9
σ	tensile stress	general
σ_{br}	stress-at-break	13
σ_c	compressive stress	25
σ_D	design stress	25
σ_e	elastic component of stress	13
σ_{el}	specific conductivity	10
σ_{Gr}	Griffith strength	13
σ_{max}	maximum tensile stress	13, 14, 25
σ_{obs}	observed stress	14
σ_{red}	reduced stress	14
σ_{th}	theoretical strength	13
σ_v	viscous component of stress	13
σ_y	yield stress	13, 25

PART I

INTRODUCTION

CHAPTER 1

POLYMER PROPERTIES

A. APPROACH

The continuous development of the modern process industries has made it increasingly important to have information about the properties of materials, including many new chemical substances whose physical properties have never been measured experimentally. This is especially true of polymeric substances. The design of manufacturing and processing equipment requires considerable knowledge of the processed materials and related compounds. Also for the application and final use of these materials this knowledge is essential.

In some handbooks, for instance the "Polymer Handbook" (Brandrup and Immergut, 1966, 1975), "Physical Constants of Linear Homopolymers" (Lewis, 1968) , and similar compilations, one finds part of the data required, but in many cases the property needed cannot be obtained from such sources. *The present book is intended to provide methods for the estimation of the more important properties of polymers, in the solid, liquid and dissolved states, in cases where experimental values are not to be found.*

Prediction is usually based on correlations of known information, with interpolation or extrapolation, as required. Reid and Sherwood (1958, 1966) distinguished correlations of three different types:

a. Purely empirical; on extrapolation these correlations are often unreliable or even arbitrary and useless.

b. Purely theoretical; these are seldom adequately developed.

c. Partly empirical, but based on theoretical concepts; these "semi-empirical" correlations are the most useful and reliable types for practical purposes.

Among scientists there is often a tendency to look down upon semi-empirical approaches for the estimation of properties. This is completely unjustified. There are almost no purely theoretical expressions for the properties in which practice is interested. One of the great triumphs of theoretical physics is the modern kinetic theory of gases. On the basis of a force function, e.g. the Lennard—Jones force function, it is possible to develop theoretical expressions for all the important properties of gases, such as the $p-v-T$ relationships, viscosity, molecular diffusivity, thermal conductivity and thermal-diffusion coefficient. The predicted variations of these properties with temperature are in excellent agreement with experimental data. But it should be realized that this extremely successful theoretical development has a purely empirical basis, viz. the force function. Except for the most simple cases, there is no sufficiently developed theory for a quantitative description of the forces between molecules. Whereas the theory of gases is relatively advanced, that of solids is less well understood, and the theory of liquids is still less developed.

In the relatively new field of macromolecular matter the semi-empirical approach is mostly necessary and sometimes even the only possible way.

Fundamental theory is generally too remote from the phenomena which have to be described. *What is needed in practice is a formulation which is designed to deal directly with the phenomena and makes use of the language of observation.* This is a pragmatic approach that is designed specifically for use; it is a completely non-speculative procedure.

In the low-molecular field Reid and Sherwood (1958, 1966) have performed this task in an admirable way, as far as gases and liquids are concerned. For solids and liquids Bondi (1968) gave a similar contribution which partly covers the polymeric field, too.

The amount of literature in the macromolecular field is already extremely large. Nevertheless one is very often confronted with the problem that neither directly measured properties, nor reliable methods to calculate them, can be found. This is the justification of this book. The value of estimation and correlation methods largely depends on their simplicity. Complicated methods have to be rejected. This has been one of our guiding principles.

It is obvious that reliable experimental data are always to be preferred to values obtained by an estimation method. In this respect all the methods proposed in this book have a restricted value.

B. THE CONCEPT: "POLYMER PROPERTIES"

The properties of materials can always be divided into three distinct, though inseparable, categories: intrinsic properties, processing properties and product or article properties. Fig. 1.1 (Van Krevelen, 1967) gives a survey. It should be emphasized that these three categories of properties are strongly interrelated. Whereas intrinsic properties always refer to a *substance,* product properties refer to an *entity*; they also depend on size and shape. One speaks of the conductivity of iron (an intrinsic property) and of the conductance of an iron wire of a certain size (a product property). Processing properties occupy an intermediate position. Here, too, the "form factor" may have an influence.

The *intrinsic properties* lend themselves to almost exact reproducible measurement. The *processing properties* are *combinations* of some intrinsic properties which determine the possibility of processing materials and the efficacy of this operation. During processing a number of properties are *added,* e.g. form and orientation. It is the combination of certain intrinsic properties and the added properties that constitutes the *product properties.*

A distinctive feature of polymeric materials is that the properties can be influenced decisively by the method of manufacturing and by processing. The sensitivity of polymers to processing conditions is much greater than that of other materials. This is because at a given chemical composition a polymeric material may show considerable differences in physical structure (e.g. orientation, degree and character of crystallinity). The physical

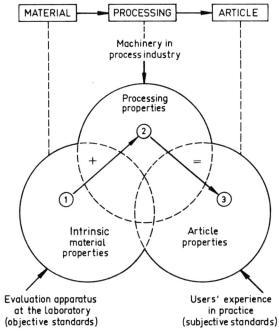

Fig. 1.1. The concept "Property".

structure is very much dependent on processing conditions. Moreover, both chemical composition and physical structure change with time owing to degradation or relaxation processes.

Intrinsic properties

As the actual material properties are anchored in the chemical and physical structure of the material, all intrinsic properties relate to a material with a distinct processing history. Usually the change in chemical structure during processing is small compared with the change in physical structure.

This poses a typical problem for the determination of intrinsic properties. A specimen prepared for the testing of its mechanical properties, for instance, has gone through a number of processing stages during which the structure may have been altered. Yet it is possible to systematize the sample preparation and the methods of measuring in such a way that an impression is obtained of the intrinsic material properties as such, hence largely unaffected by influences.

Processing properties

Fig. 1.2 presents a survey of processing techniques based on rheological aspects. Practically all polymers are processed via a *melt* or a (rather concentrated) *solution.* In every processing technique four phases may be distinguished, which are often closely connected:

Transportation of the material to the forming section of the processing machine (transport properties important);

6

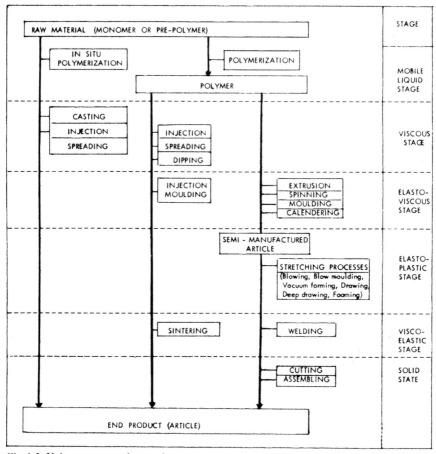

Fig. 1.2. Unit processes and operations.

Conditioning (mostly by heating) of the material to the forming process (thermal properties important);

Forming proper (rheological properties important);

Fixation of the imposed shape (thermal and rheological properties and especially transfer properties, like thermal conductivity, rate of crystallization, etc., are important).

In each of these phases the material is subject to changing temperatures, changing external and internal forces and varying retention times, all of which contribute to the ultimate structure. It is this fluctuating character of the conditions in processing which makes it so difficult to choose criteria for the processing properties.

In order to find answers to the problems of processability and to bridge the gap between research data (i.e. the behaviour expected) and the behaviour in practice, usually simulation experiments are carried out. As regards processing, the simulation experiment has to approach actual practice as closely as possible.

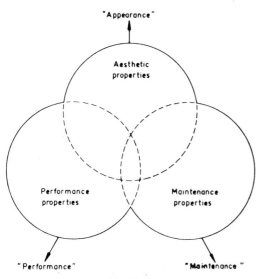

Fig. 1.3. The concept "Article properties".

Product (article) properties

For a product (article) "permanence" may be regarded as the most important aspect, whether this permanence relates to shape (dimensional stability), mechanical properties (tensile and impact strength, fatigue) or environment (resistance to ageing). Very little is as yet known about the fundamental background of these permanence properties.

The article (product) properties can be distinguished into three subgroups (fig. 1.3)

Aesthetic properties

Performance properties

Maintenance properties

Most of these are extremely subjective and depend on — often as yet unexplored — combinations of intrinsic and added properties. Nearly all the article (product) properties are connected with the *solid* polymeric state.

Since all the article properties depend on choice of materials, processing and application, it may be said that there are no bad materials as such, but only bad articles (products).

Bad products result from the wrong choice of material, poor processing, wrong application and often poor design. What we ultimately need are methods of predicting use properties from intrinsic material properties and processing parameters. *In this book attention will mainly be paid to the intrinsic material properties of polymers.*

BIBLIOGRAPHY, CHAPTER 1

Bondi, A., "Physical Properties of Molecular Crystals, Liquids and Glasses", Wiley, New York, 1968.
Brandrup, J. and Immergut, E.H. (Eds.), "Polymer Handbook", Wiley-Interscience, New York, 1st ed., 1966; 2nd ed., 1975.

8

Lewis, O. Griffin, "Physical Constants of Linear Homopolymers", Springer, Berlin, New York, 1968.

Reid, R.C. and Sherwood, Th.K., "The Properties of Gases and Liquids", McGraw-Hill, New York, 1st ed., 1958; 2nd ed., 1966.

Van Krevelen, D.W., "Processing Polymers to Products", International Congress 1966, 't Raedthuys, Utrecht, 1967, pp. 11–19.

CHAPTER 2

TYPOLOGY OF POLYMERS

Introduction

Macromolecules are giant molecules in which at least a thousand atoms are linked together by covalent bonds. They may be linear chains or three-dimensional networks.

Many natural substances, especially the biological construction materials, are macromolecules. Of these, proteins and cellulose are the most important. While cellulose (being made up of β-D-glucose units) has a relatively simple chemical structure, proteins are built up from many amino acids (varying from four to about twenty five), in a fixed sequence. This gives the proteins a very marked identity. In some cases the whole protein macromolecule is one single chemical unit, characterized by the nature and sequence of its amino acids.

In contrast with these complex natural macromolecules, many synthetic macromolecules have a relatively simple structure, since they consist of identical *constitutional repeating units* (*structural units*). This is the reason why they are called polymers [1].

In this book we confine ourselves to these synthetic macromolecules or polymers

In essence there are only two really *fundamental* characteristics of polymers: their *chemical structure* and their *molecular weight distribution pattern.*

The *chemical structure* (CS) of a polymer comprises:

    a. the nature of the repeating units
    b. the nature of the end groups
    c. the composition of possible branches and cross-links
    d. the nature of defects in the structural sequence.

The *molecular weight distribution* (MWD) informs us about the average molecular size and describes how regular (or irregular) the molecular size is. The MWD may vary greatly, depending on the method of synthesis of the polymer.

These two fundamental characteristics, CS and MWD, determine all the properties of the polymer. In a direct way they determine the *cohesive forces,* the *packing density* (and potential crystallinity) and the *molecular mobility* (with phase transitions). In a more indirect way they control the *morphology* and the *relaxation phenomena,* i.e. the total behaviour of the polymer.

In the geometrical arrangements of the atoms in a polymer chain two categories can be discerned:

---

[1] Only if the polymer is formed by copolymerization of more than one basic unit, may the composition of the macromolecule vary from ordered repetition to random distribution.

a. Arrangements fixed by the chemical bonding, known as *configurations*. The configuration of a chain cannot be altered unless chemical bonds are broken or reformed. Examples of configurations are cis- and trans-isomers or d- and l-forms.

b. Arrangements arising from rotation about single bonds, known as *conformations*.

In dilute solutions the molecules are in continuous motion and assume different conformations in rapid succession (random coils). In the solid state many polymers have typical conformations, such as folded chains and helical structures. In polypeptides helical structures containing two chains are found.

It is becoming increasingly clear that polymer molecules are "normal", and that only their chainlike nature is "different" and imposes restrictions, but also provides new properties.

In this chapter we shall consider the main aspects of polymer typology, viz. the chemical structure, the molecular weight distribution, the phase transition temperatures, the morphology, and the relaxation phenomena. Furthermore a short survey will be given on multicomponent polymer systems.

A. POLYMER STRUCTURE

The polymer molecule consists of a "skeleton" (which may be a linear or branched chain or a network structure) and peripheral atoms or atom groups.

Polymers of a finite size contain so-called *end groups* which do not form part of the repeating structure proper. Their effect on the chemical properties cannot be neglected, but their influence on the physical properties is usually small at degrees of polymerization as used in practice.

Structural groups

Every polymer structure can be considered as a summation of structural groups. A long chain may consist mainly of bivalent groups, but any bivalent group may also be replaced by a trivalent or tetravalent group, which in turn carries one or two monovalent groups, thus forming again a bivalent "composed" group, e.g.

$$-CH_2-\text{ may be replaced by }-\underset{\underset{CH_3}{|}}{\overset{}{CH}}-\text{ or }-\underset{\underset{CH_3}{|}}{\overset{\overset{CH_3}{|}}{C}}-$$

Table 2.1 gives the most important structural groups.

Somtimes it is better to regard a composed unit as one structural group. It is, e.g., often advisable to consider

$$-\underset{\underset{Cl}{|}}{\overset{\overset{F}{|}}{C}}-\text{ and }-C\overset{\nearrow O}{\underset{\searrow OH}{}}$$

TABLE 2.1
Main structural groups

Groups	Monovalent	Bivalent		Trivalent	Tetravalent
1. Hydrocarbon groups	$-CH_3$	$-CH_2-$		$>CH-$	$-\overset{\vert}{\underset{\vert}{C}}-$
	$-CH=CH_2$	$-CH=CH-$		$-CH=C<$	$>C=C<$

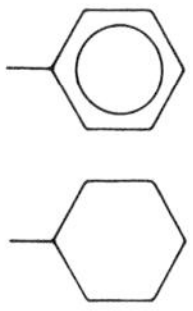

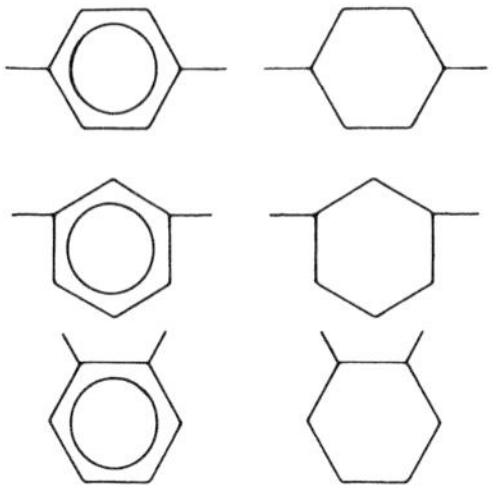

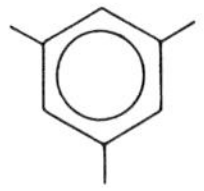

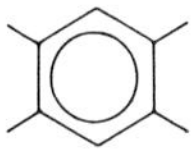

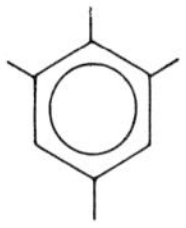

2. Non-hydro- carbon groups	$-OH$ $-SH$ $-NH_2$	$-O-$ $-S-$ $-NH-$			
	$-F$	$\overset{O}{\underset{\Vert}{-C-}}$		$-N<$	$-\overset{\vert}{\underset{\vert}{Si}}-$
	$-Cl$ $-Br$				
	$-I$	$\overset{O}{\underset{\underset{O}{\Vert}}{-\overset{\Vert}{S}-}}$			
	$-C\equiv N$				

3. Composed groups

$$-O-\overset{O}{\overset{\Vert}{C}}-$$

$$-NH-\overset{O}{\overset{\Vert}{C}}-$$

$-COOH$

$$-O-\overset{O}{\overset{\Vert}{C}}-O-$$

$$-O-\overset{O}{\overset{\Vert}{C}}-NH-$$

$$-NH-\overset{O}{\overset{\Vert}{C}}-NH-$$

$-CONH_2$

$$-\overset{O}{\overset{\Vert}{C}}-O-\overset{O}{\overset{\Vert}{C}}-$$

$$-O-\overset{O}{\overset{\Vert}{C}}-O-\overset{O}{\overset{\Vert}{C}}-O-$$

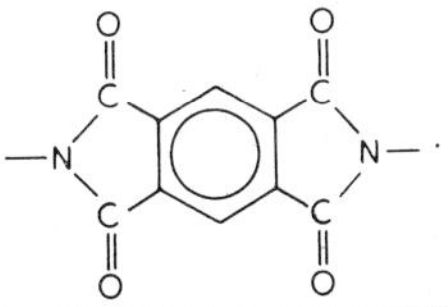

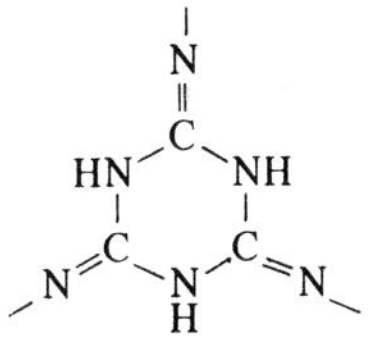

as individual structural groups and not as combinations of

$$-\overset{|}{\underset{|}{C}}- \text{ with } -F, -Cl \text{ and of } -\overset{|}{C}=O \text{ with } -OH$$

Linear chain polymers

Linear chain polymers can be distinguished into two main classes:

1. *Homochain polymers,* containing only carbon atoms in the main chain. These polymers are normally prepared by *addition or chain-reaction polymerization.*

2. *Heterochain polymers,* which may have other atoms (originating in the monomer functional groups) as part of the chain. These polymers are usually prepared by *condensation or step-reaction polymerization.*

Tables 2.2 and 2.3 give a survey of the principal polymer families belonging to these two classes.

Most of the homochain polymers are built up according to the following schemes (per structural unit):

$$\boxed{-\overset{}{\underset{R'}{\overset{|}{C}H}}-CH_2-} \quad \text{or} \quad \boxed{\overset{CH_3}{\underset{R'}{\overset{|}{\underset{|}{C}}}}-CH_2-}$$

where R′ is a monovalent side group. R′ may be composed of several structural groups, e.g.:

$$-\overset{}{\underset{O}{\overset{|}{C}}}-O-(CH_2)_2-CH_3$$

Heterochains are usually built up according to the following scheme (per structural unit):

$$\boxed{-AB-R''-}$$

where R″ is a bivalent hydrocarbon grouping and −AB− is a bivalent group originating from the original monomer functional groups (e.g. $-NH-\overset{}{\underset{O.}{\overset{|}{C}}}-$ from $-NH_2$ and $HO-\overset{}{\underset{O}{\overset{|}{C}}}-$).

Configurations of polymer chains

It may be useful to describe at this point the several *stereoregular* configurations which are observed in polymer chains. The possible regular structure of *poly-α-olefins* was recognized by Natta et al. (1955), who devised a nomenclature now accepted to describe stereoregular polymers of this type (Huggins et al., 1962). Fig. 2.1 shows the different possibilities.

Polymers of 1,3-dienes containing one residual double bond per repeat unit after polymerization can contain sequences with different configurations (fig. 2.2).

For further stereoregular configurations we refer to Corradini (1968).

Stereoregularity plays a very important role in the structure of proteins, nucleic acids and other substances of biological importance.

TABLE 2.2

Class of homochain polymers $\left[R'\equiv(CH_2)_n-B \text{ with } B\equiv \begin{cases} -CH_3 \\ -CH(CH_3)_2 \\ -C(CH_3)_3 \end{cases} \right]$

Polymer families	Basic unit	α-substituted basic unit	Derivatives of basic unit	Derivatives of α-substituted basic unit
Polyolefins	Polyethylene $-CH_2-CH_2-$	Polypropylene $-\underset{\overset{\mid}{CH_3}}{CH}-CH_2-$	$-\underset{\overset{\mid}{R'}}{CH}-CH_2-$	$-\overset{\overset{CH_3}{\mid}}{\underset{\underset{R'}{\mid}}{C}}-CH_2-$
Polystyrenes	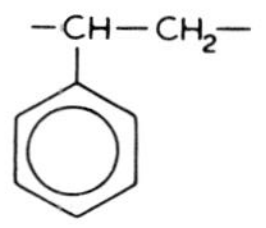 $-\underset{C_6H_5}{CH}-CH_2-$	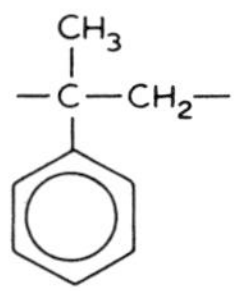 $-\overset{CH_3}{\underset{C_6H_5}{C}}-CH_2-$	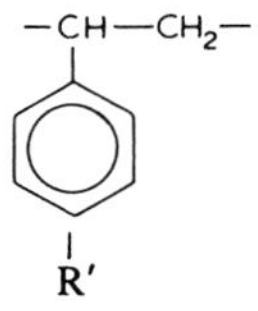 $-\underset{C_6H_4-R'}{CH}-CH_2-$	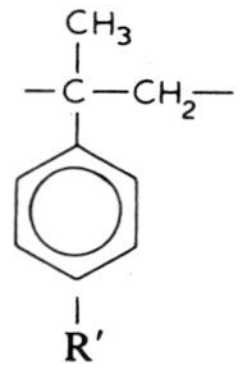 $-\overset{CH_3}{\underset{C_6H_4-R'}{C}}-CH_2-$
"Polyvinyls"	Poly(vinyl alcohol) $-\underset{\overset{\mid}{OH}}{CH}-CH_2-$		Polyvinyl ethers $-\underset{\overset{\mid}{O-R'}}{CH}-CH_2-$ Polyvinyl esters $-\underset{\overset{\mid}{O-C(=O)-R'}}{CH}-CH_2-$	

(Continued on p. 14)

TABLE 2.2 (continued)

Polymer families	Basic unit	α-substituted basic unit	Derivatives of basic unit	Derivatives of α-substituted basic unit
"Polyacrylics"	Poly(acrylic acid)[1] $-CH-CH_2-$ $\quad\mid$ $\quad C=O$ $\quad\mid$ $\quad NH_2$ (COOH)	Poly(methacrylic acid)[1] $\quad CH_3$ $\quad\mid$ $-C-CH_2-$ $\quad\mid$ $\quad COOH$	Polyacrylates $-CH-CH_2-$ $\quad\mid$ $\quad C=O$ $\quad\mid$ $\quad OR'$	Polymethacrylates $\quad CH_3$ $\quad\mid$ $-C-CH_2-$ $\quad\mid$ $\quad C=O$ $\quad\mid$ $\quad OR'$
	Polyacrylamide $-CH-CH_2-$ $\quad\mid$ $\quad C=O$ $\quad\mid$ $\quad NH_2$	Polymethacrylamide $\quad CH_3$ $\quad\mid$ $-C-CH_2-$ $\quad\mid$ $\quad C=O$ $\quad\mid$ $\quad NH_2$	Polyacrylamides $-CH-CH_2-$ $\quad\mid$ $\quad C=O$ $\quad\mid$ $\quad NHR'$	Polymethacrylamides $\quad CH_3$ $\quad\mid$ $-C-CH_2-$ $\quad\mid$ $\quad C=O$ $\quad\mid$ $\quad NHR'$
"Polyhalo-olefins"	X_1X_2 $\quad$ X=H $\;\mid\;\mid$ $\qquad$ F $-C-C-$ $\quad$ Cl $\;\mid\;\mid$ $\qquad$ Br X_3X_4 $\quad$ (CN)			
Polydienes	Polybutadiene $-CH_2-CH=CH-CH_2-$	Polyisoprene $\quad CH_3$ $\quad\mid$ $-CH_2-C=CH-CH_2-$	$-CH_2-C=CH-CH_2-$ $\qquad\quad\mid$ $\qquad\quad R'$	

[1] Often also polyacrylonitrile and polymethacrylonitrile (−COOH replaced by −CN) are included in this family.

TABLE 2.3

Class of heterochain polymers

Main Polymer Families	Smallest basic unit (often obtained by Ring-opening Polymerization)	Bi-composed basic unit (obtained by Condensation Polymerization)
Polyoxides / ethers / acetals	$-[O]-R''-$	$-[O]-R_1''-[O]-R_2''-$
Polysulphides / thioesters	$-[S]-R''-$	$-[S]-R_1''-[S]-R_2''-$
Polyesters	$-[O-\overset{\parallel}{\underset{O}{C}}]-R''-$ Poly-lactones	$-O-R_1''-[O-\overset{\parallel}{\underset{O}{C}}]-R_2''-\overset{\parallel}{\underset{O}{C}}-$
Polyamides	$-[NH-\overset{\parallel}{\underset{O}{C}}]-R''-$ Poly-lactams	$-NH-R_1''-[NH-\overset{\parallel}{\underset{O}{C}}]-R_2''-\overset{\parallel}{\underset{O}{C}}-$
Polyurethanes	$-[NH-\overset{\parallel}{\underset{O}{C}}-O]-R''-$	$-O-R_1''-[O-\overset{\parallel}{\underset{O}{C}}-NH]-R_2''-NH-\overset{\parallel}{\underset{O}{C}}-$
Polyureas	$-[NH-\overset{\parallel}{\underset{O}{C}}-NH]-R''-$	$-NH-R_1''-[NH-\overset{\parallel}{\underset{O}{C}}-NH]-R_2''-NH-\overset{\parallel}{\underset{O}{C}}-$
Polyimides	$-R'''\left[\overset{\overset{O}{\parallel}}{\underset{\underset{O}{\parallel}}{\underset{C}{C}}}\right]N-$	$-R_1''-N\left[\overset{\overset{O}{\parallel}}{\underset{\underset{O}{\parallel}}{\underset{C}{C}}}\right]R_2''\left[\overset{\overset{O}{\parallel}}{\underset{\underset{O}{\parallel}}{\underset{C}{C}}}\right]N-$
Polyanhydrides	$-[\overset{\parallel}{\underset{O}{C}}-O-\overset{\parallel}{\underset{O}{C}}]-R''-$	$-\overset{\parallel}{\underset{O}{C}}-R_1''-[\overset{\parallel}{\underset{O}{C}}-O-\overset{\parallel}{\underset{O}{C}}]-R_2''-\overset{\parallel}{\underset{O}{C}}-O-$
Polycarbonates	$-[O-\overset{\parallel}{\underset{O}{C}}-O]-R''-$	$-O-R_1''-[O-\overset{\parallel}{\underset{O}{C}}-O]-R_2''-O-\overset{\parallel}{\underset{O}{C}}-$
Polyimines	$-[\underset{R'}{N}]-R''-$	$-[\underset{R'}{N}]-R_1''-[\underset{R'}{N}]-R_2''-$
Polysiloxanes	$-[\underset{R'}{\overset{R'}{Si}}-O]-$	$-[\underset{R_2'}{\overset{R_1'}{Si}}-O-\underset{R_2'}{\overset{R_1'}{Si}}]-R''-$

16

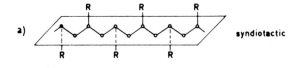

a) syndiotactic

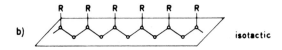

b) isotactic

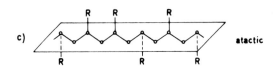

c) atactic

Fig. 2.1. Configurations in vinyl polymers. (The main carbon-homochain is depicted in the fully extended planar zigzag conformation. For clarity, hydrogen atoms are omitted.)

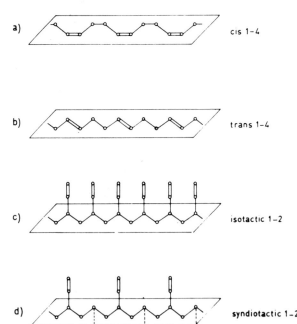

a) cis 1–4

b) trans 1–4

c) isotactic 1–2

d) syndiotactic 1–2

Fig. 2.2. Configurations involving a carbon--carbon double bond.

Branched polymers

Polymers obtained by condensation polymerization of purely bifunctional monomers must be linear. The chains produced in addition polymerizations may have a number of short or long branches attached at random along their axes. Especially in radical polymerization, branching is probable and cannot be easily controlled. Branching affects the properties of a polymer in the molten state and in solution. Viscometric, nuclear magnetic resonance and infrared absorption studies provide the most promising methods for the measuring of branching.

Network polymers

Network polymers are formed if trifunctional or even tetrafunctional monomers are present during the polymerization reaction.

A widely used type of network polymers are the formaldehyde resins, in which the following groupings are frequent:

$$\begin{array}{ccc} \diagdown & & \diagup \\ CH_2 & & CH_2 \\ \diagdown & \diagup & \\ & R''' & \\ & | & \\ & CH_2 & \\ & | & \end{array}$$

Other network polymers are the so-called unsaturated polyester resins, epoxy resins, polyurethane foams and vulcanized rubbers.

B. MOLECULAR WEIGHT AND DISTRIBUTION OF MOLECULAR WEIGHTS

Normally a polymeric product will contain molecules having many different chain lengths. These lengths are distributed according to a probability function which is governed by the mechanism of the polymerization reaction and by the conditions under which it was carried out.

In the last few years it has become clear that the processing behaviour and many end-use properties of polymers are influenced not only by the *average molecular weight* but also by the width and the shape of the *molecular weight distribution* (MWD). The basic reason is that some properties, including tensile and impact strength, are specifically governed by the short molecules; for other properties, like solution viscosity and low shear melt flow, the influence of the middle class of the chains is predominant; yet other properties, such as melt elasticity, are highly dependent on the amount of the longest chains present.

A MWD is reasonably characterized when *at least three* different molecular weights, the *number average* $\overline{M}_n$, the *weight average* $\overline{M}_w$ and the *z-average* $\overline{M}_z$, are known. These averages are defined as follows:

$$\overline{M}_n = \frac{\Sigma N_i M_i}{\Sigma N_i} = \frac{W}{N}$$

$$\bar{M}_w = \frac{\Sigma N_i M_i^2}{\Sigma N_i M_i} = \Sigma w_i M_i$$

$$\bar{M}_z = \frac{\Sigma N_i M_i^3}{\Sigma N_i M_i^2} = \frac{\Sigma w_i M_i^2}{\Sigma w_i M_i}$$

where N_i = number of molecules of molecular weight M_i

N = total number of molecules

w_i = weight fraction of molecules of molecular weight M_i

W = total weight

Fig. 2.3 shows a molecular weight distribution curve. Characteristic ratios are

$$Q = \frac{\bar{M}_w}{\bar{M}_n} \quad \text{and } Q' = \frac{\bar{M}_z}{\bar{M}_w} .$$

$Q = Q' = 1$ would correspond to a perfectly uniform or *monodisperse* polymer. A high Q-ratio points to a low-molecular-weight tail, whereas a high Q'-ratio indicates the presence of very high-molecular-weight material. Q may range from 1.5–2.0 to 20–50 in practice (the lower values for condensation polymers, the higher values for radical-chain addition polymers).

Most of the *thermodynamical properties* are dependent on the *number-average molecular weight*. Many of these properties can be described by an equation of the type:

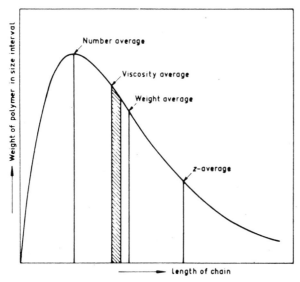

Fig. 2.3. Distribution of molecular weights in a typical polymer (after McGrew, 1958).

$$X = X_\infty - \frac{A}{\overline{M}_n} \qquad (2.1)$$

where X is the property considered, X_∞ is its asymptotic value at very high molecular weights, and A is a constant.

For a number of properties in this group, including density, specific heat capacity, refractive index, etc., X attains its limiting value X_∞ already at molecular weights below the real macromolecular range. For these properties the configuration of the structural unit alone is the preponderant factor determining the property.

Typical *mechanical properties,* such as tensile strength, vary significantly with molecular weight within the range of the real macromolecules. As formula (2.1) applies to these properties (*number-average molecular weight* being important), it indicates that the number of chain ends is a preponderant factor.

Bulk properties connected with *large deformations,* such as melt and solution viscosity, are largely determined by the weight-average molecular weight, i.e. by the mass to be transferred. Branching and cross-linking have a very pronounced effect in this case.

Typical viscoelastic properties, such as melt elasticity, depend on the *z-average molecular weight.*

Table 2.4 gives a summary of the most important methods for the determination of molecular weight averages.

For a description of the different methods we refer to the textbooks.

The three molecular weight averages *characterize* the distribution, but do not reveal further details. The full distribution curve may be obtained by *gel permeation chromatography* (GPC).

GPC is a technique which separates the molecules according to their dimensions. The separation method involves column chromatography in which the stationary phase is a heteroporous, solvent-swollen polymer gel varying in permeability over many orders of magnitude. As the liquid phase, which contains the polymer, passes through the gel, the polymer molecules diffuse into all parts of the gel not mechanically barred to them. The

TABLE 2.4.

Determination of average molecular weight of polymers

Method	Average M determined
Analytical determination of end groups	$\overline{M}_n$
Osmotic pressure	$\overline{M}_n$
Vapour pressure lowering	$\overline{M}_n$
Ebulliometry or cryoscopy	$\overline{M}_n$
Light scattering	$\overline{M}_w$
Ultra centrifugation	$\overline{M}_w$
	$\overline{M}_z$
Solution viscosity	$\overline{M}_v \approx \overline{M}_w$
Gel permeation chromatography	$\left.\begin{array}{l}\overline{M}_n\\\overline{M}_w\\\overline{M}_z\end{array}\right\}$ (Complete M-distribution)

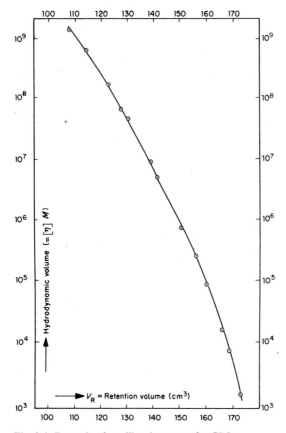

Fig. 2.4. Example of a calibration curve for GPC.

smaller molecules permeate more completely and spend more time in the pores than the larger molecules which pass through the column more rapidly. The instrument has to be calibrated by means of narrow fractions of known molecular weight (determined by some absolute method).

Fig. 2.4 gives an example of a calibration curve where the hydrodynamic volume (a quantity directly related to the molecular weight) is plotted versus the retention volume (the retention volume is the volume of liquid passed through the column from the middle of the sample injection to the peak maximum, as measured by a suitable detector, e.g. a differential refractometer).

C. PHASE TRANSITIONS IN POLYMERS

Simple molecules may occur in three states, the solid, the liquid and the gaseous state. The transitions between these phases are sharp and associated with a thermodynamic equilibrium. Under these conditions, phase changes are typical *first-order transitions,* in which a *primary* thermodynamic function, such as volume or enthalpy, shows a sudden jump.

In the case of polymer molecules the situation is much more complex. Polymers cannot be evaporated since they decompose before boiling. In the solid state a polymer is only exceptionally purely crystalline (so-called single crystals), but generally it is partially or totally amorphous. Furthermore the liquid state is characterized by a very high viscosity.

It is impossible to understand the properties of polymers without a knowledge of the types of transition that occur in such materials. Nearly all the properties of polymers are determined primarily by these transitions and the temperatures at which they occur.

The only "normal" phase state for polymers, known from the physics of small molecules, is the liquid state, though even here polymers show special properties, like viscoelasticity. The typical states of polymers are the *glassy,* the *rubbery* and the *semicrystalline* states, all of which are thermodynamically metastable.

An interesting classification of phase states is that based on two parameters: the degree of order (long- and short-range) and the time-dependence of stiffness (long- and short-time). Each state can be characterized by a matrix of the following form:

Short-Range Order SRO	Long-Range Order LRO
Short-Time Stiffness STS	Long-Time Stiffness LTS

If + means present and — means absent, we get the picture shown in fig. 2.5 for the possible phase states; ± means a transition case.

None of the phase states of polymers shows perfect long-range order. The basic difference of a glass and a (supercooled) liquid is the presence of short- and long-time stiffness (and therefore absence of the short-time fluidity) in the glass. The rubbery state, on the other hand, has all the properties of the liquid, except the short-time fluidity.

Fig. 2.5 holds for non-oriented polymers. Orientation in semicrystalline polymers gives the material a long-range order, which is important for many product properties.

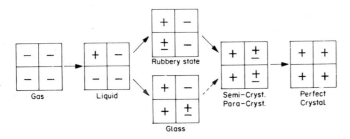

Fig. 2.5. Characterization of phase states.

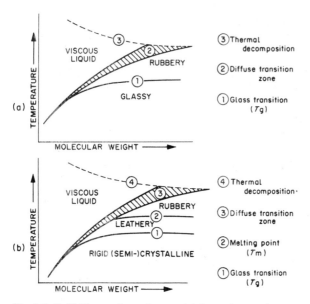

Fig. 2.6. *T–M* Diagram for polymers. (a) Amorphous polymers; (b) (semi)crystalline polymers.

Linear thermoplastic amorphous polymers

The situation for amorphous linear polymers is sketched in fig. 2.6a. If a polymeric glass is heated, it will begin to soften in the neighbourhood of the *glass–rubber transition* temperature (T_g) [1] and become quite rubbery. On further heating the elastic behaviour diminishes, but it is only at temperatures more than 50° above the glass–rubber transition temperature that a shear stress will cause viscous flow to predominate over elastic deformation.

If the molecular weight is sufficiently high, the glass–rubber transition temperature is almost independent of the molecular weight. On the other hand, the very *diffuse rubbery–liquid transition* heavily depends on the molecular weight, whilst the decomposition temperature tends to decrease slightly with increasing molecular weight.

As is well known, the glass–rubber transition is of considerable importance technologically. The glass transition temperature (T_g) determines the lower use limit of a rubber and the upper use limit of an amorphous thermoplastic material. With increasing molecular weight the ease of "forming" (shaping) diminishes.

Below the glass–rubber transition temperature glassy polymers also show other, *sec-*

---

[1] The glass–rubber transition temperature, commonly known as glass transition temperature (T_g), is a phase change *reminiscent* of a thermodynamic *second-order transition.* In the case of a second-order transition a plot of a primary quantity shows an abrupt change in slope, while a plot of a *secondary* quantity (such as expansion coefficient and specific heat) then shows a sudden jump.

In fact T_g is *not* a thermodynamic second-order transition, but is kinetically controlled. The exact position of T_g is determined by the rate of cooling; the slower the cooling process, the lower T_g. Yet, for practical purposes one can say that every polymer is characterized by its own T_g.

ondary transitions. Their effects are smaller and often less obvious, although they are important to the mechanical behaviour (to diminish brittleness). Secondary transitions can be detected by studies of mechanical damping, by nuclear magnetic resonance or by electric loss measurements over a range of temperatures.

While the main glass transition occurs as soon as large segments of the polymer backbone chain are free to move, secondary transitions occur at temperatures where subgroups, side chains etc., can freely move or oscillate.

Linear thermoplastic semicrystalline polymers

Many polymers show regions of high order and may be considered (semi)crystalline. The major factor determining whether a polymer can crystallize is the occurrence of successive units in the chain in a configuration of high geometrical regularity. If the chain elements are small, simple and equal, as in linear polyethylene, crystallinity is highly developed. If, however, the chain elements are complex, containing bulky (side) groups, as in polystyrene, the material can crystallize only if these substituent groups are arranged in an ordered or tactic configuration.

In these cases it is possible to identify a *melting temperature* (T_m). Above this melting temperature the polymer may be liquid, viscoelastic or rubbery according to its molecular weight, but below it, at least in the high molecular weight range, it will tend to be leathery and tough down to the glass transition temperature. (The lower-molecular-weight grades will tend to be rather brittle waxes in this zone).

The crystalline melting point, T_m, is (theoretically) the highest temperature at which polymer crystallites can exist. Normally, crystallites in a polymer melt in a certain temperature range.

Secondary crystalline transitions (below T_m) occur if the material transforms from one type of crystal to another. These transitions are, like the melting point, thermodynamic first-order transitions.

Suitable methods for studying the transitions in the crystalline state are X-ray diffraction measurements, differential thermal analysis and optical (birefringence) measurements.

The situation for crystalline linear polymers is sketched in fig. 2.6b.

Though in crystalline polymers T_m rather than T_g determines the upper service temperature of plastics and the lower service temperature of rubbers, T_g is still very important. The reason is that between T_g and T_m the polymer is likely to be tough; the best use region of the polymer may therefore be expected at the lower end of the leathery range [1]. Below the glass transition temperature many polymers tend to be brittle, especially if the molecular weight is not very high. Secondary transitions may be responsible if a rigid material is tough rather than brittle.

Fig. 2.7 gives a schematic survey of the influence of the main transition points on some important physical quantities.

---

[1] This, however, is an oversimplification, since in these polymers other (secondary) transitions occur which may override T_g in importance.

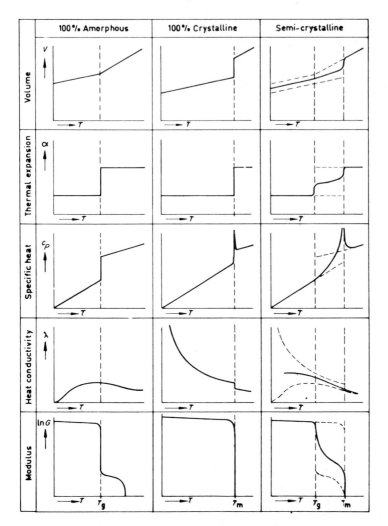

Fig. 2.7. Behaviour of some polymer properties at transition temperatures.

Linear non-thermoplastic polymers

Some polymers, such as cellulose, although linear in structure, have such a strong molecular interaction, mostly due to hydrogen bridges and polar groups, that they do not soften or melt. Consequently, the transition temperatures as such are less important to this class of polymers. Normally they are highly crystalline, with a crystalline melting point (far) above the decomposition temperature.

Their physical behaviour — except for the melting — is that of crystalline polymers. Therefore they are suitable raw materials for fibres (via solution spinning).

Many of these polymers are "plasticized" by water, due to the strong influence of water on the molecular interaction. The polymers can therefore be called "*hydroplastics*" in contradistinction to thermoplastics. Moisture may cause a tremendous depression of the glass transition temperature.

TABLE 2.5

Classification of polymers on the basis of mechanical behaviour (Nomenclature according to Leuchs, 1968)

Polymer class	General properties	Range of use temperatures	Degree of crystallinity	Degree of cross-linking	Example
I Molliplasts	elasto-viscous liquids	$T > T_g$	0	0	Polyisobutylene
II Mollielasts (Elastomers)	soft and flexible rubbery solids	$T > T_g$	0	low	Polybutadiene
III Fibroplasts	tough, leathery-to-hornlike solids	$T < T_m$ $(T > T_g)$	20–50	0	Polyamide
IV Fibroelasts	tough and flexible leathery solids	$T > T_g$ $(T < T_m)$	0	intermediate	Cross-linked polyethylene
V Duroplasts	hard and stiff solids	$T < T_g$	0	0	Polystyrene
	hard and tough, stiff solids	$T < T_m$	intermediate to high	0	Poly(4-methyl-pentene-1)
VI Duroelasts	hard solids	$T < T_g$	0	intermediate to high	Phenolic resin

Cross-linked polymers

If an amorphous polymer is cross-linked, the basic properties are fundamentally changed. In some respects the behaviour at a high degree of cross-linking is similar to that at a high degree of crystallinity. (Crystallization can be considered as a physical form of cross-linking). The influence of the glass transition temperature becomes less and less pronounced as cross-linking progresses.

Classification of polymers on the basis of their mechanical behaviour

On the basis of the general behaviour described in the preceding sections it is possible to develop a classification of polymers for practical use. This is given in table 2.5. The nomenclature is in agreement with a proposal by Leuchs (1968).

D. MORPHOLOGY OF SOLID POLYMERS

As discussed earlier, solid polymers can be distinguished into the amorphous and the semicrystalline categories.

Amorphous solid polymers are either in the glassy state, or -- with chain cross-linking

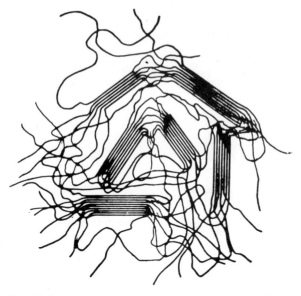

Fig. 2.8. Diagrammatic representation of the fringed micelle model.

— in the rubbery state. The usual model of the macromolecule in the amorphous state is the "random coil" [1].

The traditional model used to explain the properties of the (partly) crystalline polymers is the "*fringed micelle model*" of Hermann et al. (1930). While the coexistence of small crystallites and amorphous regions in this model is assumed to be such that polymer chains are perfectly ordered over distances corresponding to the dimensions of the crystallites, the same polymer chains include also disordered segments belonging to the amorphous regions, which leads to a composite single-phase structure (fig. 2.8).

The fringed micelle model gives an extremely simple interpretation of the "degree of crystallinity" in terms of fractions of well-defined crystalline and amorphous regions. Many excellent correlations have evolved from this model through the years, so that it has long been popular.

Recent events have made it necessary to re-examine the concept of the polymeric solid state. The most important of these events was the discovery and exploration of polymer single crystals (Schlesinger and Leeper, 1953; Keller, 1957). It had long been believed that single crystals could not be produced from polymer solutions because of the molecular entanglements of the chains. Since 1953 the existence of single crystals has been reported for so many polymers that the phenomenon appears to be quite general. These single crystals are platelets (lamellar structures), about 100 Å thick, in which perfect

---

[1] Also in polymer melts the "random coil" is the usual model. The fact, however, that melts of semi-crystalline molecules – although very viscous – show rapid crystallization when cooled, might be an indication that the conformation of a polymer molecule in such a melt is more nearly an irregularly folded molecule than it is a completely random coil.

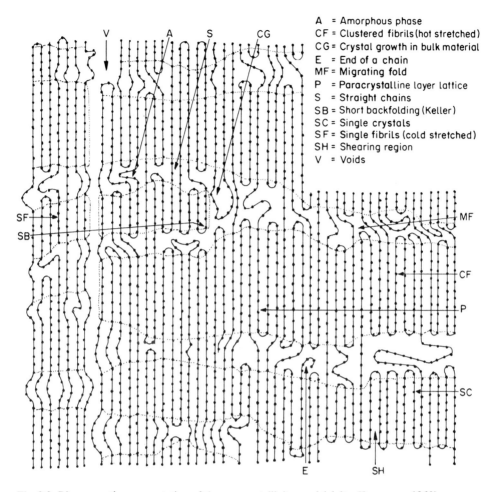

A = Amorphous phase
CF = Clustered fibrils (hot stretched)
CG = Crystal growth in bulk material
E = End of a chain
MF = Migrating fold
P = Paracrystalline layer lattice
S = Straight chains
SB = Short backfolding (Keller)
SC = Single crystals
SF = Single fibrils (cold stretched)
SH = Shearing region
V = Voids

Fig. 2.9. Diagrammatic representation of the paracrystallinity model (after Hosemann, 1962).

order exists, as has been shown by electron diffraction patterns. On the other hand, dislocations exactly analogous to those in metals and low-molecular crystals have been found in these polymeric single crystals.

A second important event was the development by Hosemann (1950), of a theory by which the X-ray patterns are explained in a completely different way, namely, in terms of statistical disorder. In this concept, the *paracrystallinity model* (fig. 2.9), the so-called amorphous regions appear to be the same as small defect sites. A randomized amorphous phase is not required to explain polymer behaviour. Several phenomena, such as creep, recrystallization and fracture, are better explained by motions of dislocations (as in solid state physics) than by the traditional fringed micelle model.

These two new insights, viz. lamellar, perfectly ordered structures – composed of

28

folded chain molecules — and paracrystallinity, are of preponderant importance in the present concept of polymer morphology.

In most solid crystalline polymers spherical aggregates of crystalline material, called *spherulites,* are recognized by their characteristic appearance under the polarizing microscope. Electron microscopy of fracture surfaces in spherulites has shown that here, too, lamellar structures persist throughout the body of the spherulites. The latter seem to be the normal result of crystal growth, in which the spherulites originating from a nucleus (often a foreign particle) grow at the expense of the non-crystalline melt.

In the present concept of the structure of crystalline polymers there is only room for the fringed micelle model when polymers of low crystallinity are concerned. For polymers of intermediate degrees of crystallinity, a structure involving "paracrystals" and discrete amorphous regions seems probable. For highly crystalline polymers there is no experimental evidence whatever of the existence of discrete amorphous regions. Here the fringed micelle model has to be rejected, whereas the paracrystallinity model is acceptable.

It is now generally accepted that the morphology of a polymer depends on the contributions of three different macroconformations: (a) the random coil or irregularly folded molecule as found in the glassy state, (b) the folded chain, as found in lamellar structures, and (c) the extended chain. The fringed micelle (d) may be seen as mixture of (a), (b) and (c) (see fig. 2.10) with paracrystallinity as an extreme.

A few words have to be said about the present concept of the composite structure of fibrous material in the oriented state. The basic element in this concept (Peterlin, 1971) is the *microfibril,* a very long (some μm) and thin (10—20 nm) structure composed of alter-

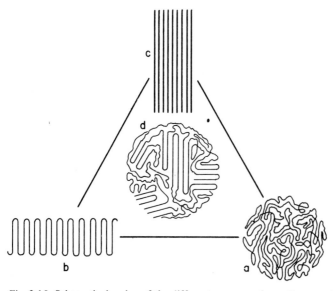

Fig. 2.10. Schematic drawing of the different macroconformations possible in solid linear macromolecules. a: Random, glassy; b: folded chain, lamellar; c: extended chain equilibrium; d: fringed micelle, mixture of a to c (after Wunderlich, 1970).

Fig. 2.11. Model concept of a polymeric fibre.

nating amorphous layers and crystalline blocks (see fig. 2.11). The microfibrils are formed during the orientation process (mainly in the "necking" zones); the stacked lamellae of the starting material are transformed into densely packed and aligned *bundles* of micro-fibrils, the *fibrils*. During the further phases of the drawing operation the fibrils may be sheared and axially displaced. The shearing of the fibrils displaces the microfibrils in the fibre direction and enormously extends the interfibrillar tie molecules by some chain un-folding without substantial change of the microfibrillar structure. The thus enhanced vol-ume fraction of *taut tie molecules* connecting the microfibrils is responsible for the strength and modulus of the fibrils, in the same way as the *intrafibrillar tie molecules* be-tween subsequent crystal blocks are responsible for the strength and modulus of the microfibril.

There is evidence that by a heat treatment both the crystalline and amorphous regions grow in length and in width, thus forming a definite two-phase system. On the other hand,

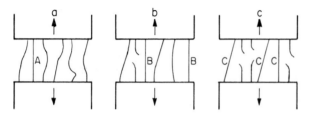

Fig. 2.12. Tie molecules in the "amorphous" layer between subsequent crystal blocks of the micro-fibril. At low strain (a) a single tie molecule (A), at medium strain (b) two tie molecules (B), and at the highest strain (c) three molecules (C) are stretched up to the rupture point (after Peterlin, 1971).

in cold drawing at high draw ratios the regions become very small and approach the para-crystalline concept.

This picture also illustrates the mechanical behaviour of semicrystalline polymers and the role of the small percentage of tie molecules (see fig. 2.12).

E. RELAXATION PHENOMENA

In all non-equilibrium systems relaxation phenomena can be observed. *Relaxation is the time-dependent return to equilibrium (or to a new equilibrium) after a disturbance.*

Relaxation processes are very universal. They are found in all branches of physics: mechanical relaxation (stress- and strain relaxation, creep), ultrasonic relaxation, dielectric relaxation, luminescence depolarization, electronic relaxation (fluorescence), etc. Also the chemical reaction might be classified under the relaxation phenomena. It will be readily understood that especially in polymer science this time-dependent behaviour is of particular importance.

The relaxation process is characterized by a driving force and by a rate constant. The driving force is always connected with the surplus of free energy in the non-equilibrium state. Sometimes the rate is directly proportional to the driving force; in this case the rate process is a first order process (cf. the first order chemical reaction). The reciprocal value of the rate constant is called *relaxation time* (Θ).

If P is the driving force, one gets:

$$-\frac{dP}{dt} = \frac{P}{\Theta} \tag{2.2}$$

which after integration gives:

$$\frac{P(t)}{P_0} = \exp\left(-\frac{t}{\Theta}\right) \tag{2.2a}$$

This equation shows that relaxation is strong if $t \geqslant \Theta$, whereas practically no relaxation takes place if $t \leqslant \Theta$. Θ is temperature-dependent; it is an exponential function of temperature:

$$\Theta \sim \exp(E_{act}/RT) \tag{2.3}$$

The ratio $\dfrac{\text{relaxation time}}{\text{observation time}} = \dfrac{\Theta}{t}$ is called *Deborah number*. It is zero for ideal fluids, infinite for ideal solids and unity at the glass transition temperature.

Frequently, however, relaxation is not a first order process. In that case

$$\frac{P(t)}{P_0} = f(t) \tag{2.2b}$$

Often $f(t)$ is approximated by the summation $\Sigma C_i \exp(-\dfrac{t}{\Theta_i})$ in which the combination of Θ_i-values is called the relaxation spectrum.

Sometimes the deviation from the equilibrium state is a periodic or cyclic process. If the latter is of the sinusoidal type,

$$P = P_0 \sin \omega t \tag{2.4}$$

where ω is the angular frequency, the response R [1] to the driving force P will be:

$$R = R_0 \sin(\omega t - \delta) \tag{2.5}$$

δ is the so-called phase angle, it is defined as the angle over which the response lags behind the driving force due to energy loss.

Using the "complex notation", this situation can be described by the equation:

$$P^* = P_0 \exp(i\omega t) \tag{2.4a}$$

$$R^* = R_0 \exp\{i(\omega t - \delta)\} \tag{2.5a}$$

So

$$\frac{P^*}{R^*} = \frac{P_0}{R_0} \exp(i\delta) = \frac{P_0}{R_0} \cos \delta + i\frac{P_0}{R_0} \sin \delta \tag{2.6}$$

If $P/R = S$, where S is the response coefficient [2]

$$S^* = S_0 \cos \delta + iS_0 \sin \delta = S' + iS'' \tag{2.7}$$

where S^* = the complex response coefficient
$\qquad S' = S_0 \cos \delta$ = the real component or *storage* component
$\qquad S'' = S_0 \sin \delta$ = the imaginary component or *loss* component
Furthermore it is obvious that:

$$\frac{S''}{S'} = \tan \delta \tag{2.8}$$

$$|S^*| = S_0 = [(S')^2 + (S'')^2]^{1/2} \tag{2.9}$$

---

[1] If P is a stress, the response R will be a strain; if P is an electric field strength, R will be the dielectric displacement, etc.
[2] S is a "modulus" in mechanical relaxations.

32

From the above equations one can derive that S'' shows a maximum when

$$\omega = 1/\Theta \tag{2.10}$$

Also tan δ shows a maximum, as a function of frequency, which practically coincides with that of S''.

Between the static (time-dependent) and the dynamic (frequency-dependent) behaviour the following correlation exists:

$$\tan \delta = \frac{S''}{S'} \approx \frac{\pi}{2}\left(\frac{d \ln R}{d \ln t}\right) \approx -\frac{\pi}{2}\left(\frac{d \ln P}{d \ln t}\right) \tag{2.11}$$

Very important phenomena in polymer behaviour, such as viscoelasticity, stress, strain, volume and enthalpy relaxation, ageing, etc., are characterized by time-dependence of the polymer properties.

F. MULTICOMPONENT POLYMER SYSTEMS

Polymeric materials consisting of more than one component are produced in ever larger quantities and their practical importance increases. By "multicomponent systems" polymer chemists mean polymer blends, copolymers and reinforced composites. These materials are often stronger and tougher than the one-component systems. Platzer (1971) presented a classification of these systems which is shown in fig. 2.13.

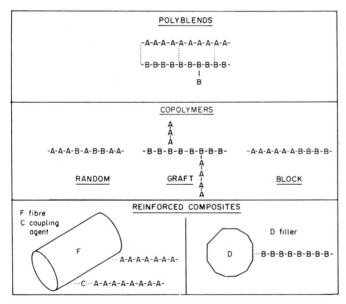

Fig. 2.13. Multicomponent polymer systems (after Platzer, 1971).

TABLE 2.6

Examples of copolymers

Type of copolymers	Examples of commercial systems
Random copolymers	Styrene–butadiene rubber Styrene–acrylonitrile rubber Ethylene–vinyl acetate copolymer
Graft copolymers	Rubber–styrene graft copolymers (high-impact polystyrene) Acrylonitrile–butadiene–styrene graft copolymer (ABS)
Block copolymers	Styrene–butadiene diblock copolymers Styrene–butadiene–styrene terblock copolymers Polyurethane multiblock copolymers (elastomeric yarns)

Poly-blends may be made from polymeric components by mixing and compounding them together on mill rolls, in extruders, or in other processing equipment. True compatibility of polymers is rare [1]. Incompatibility or partial compatibility is more frequent; heterogeneity prevails (Krause, 1972).

Heterogeneous poly-blending is widely used in the rubber industry. In the plastics industry heterogeneous blends find application in the production of impact-resistant materials (glassy polymers blended with elastomers).

While in poly-blends the components adhere together through secondary bond forces, in *copolymers* the components are linked by strong covalent bonds.

Random, graft and *block copolymers* can be distinguished. Random copolymers are obtained from two or more monomers which are present simultaneously in one polymerization reactor. In graft polymerization a homopolymer is prepared first and in a second step one or two monomers are grafted onto this polymer; the final product consists of a polymeric backbone with side branches. In block copolymerization one monomer is polymerized, after which another monomer is polymerized on to the living ends of the polymeric chains; the final block copolymer is a linear chain with a sequence of different segments.

All three types of copolymer have found industrial application. Some examples are shown in table 2.6.

In reinforced polymers (e.g. glass reinforced polyesters and epoxies, carbon black-reinforced elastomers) interfacial bonding is of primary importance. The economic importance of this class of materials is well known.

It is understandable that the properties of these multicomponent polymer systems are

---

[1] Examples of compatibility are the systems: poly(vinylidene fluoride) with poly(methyl methacrylate); poly(vinylidene fluoride) with poly(ethyl methacrylate); and poly(2,6-dimethylphenylene oxide) with polystyrene.

related to those of the homopolymers in a very complex way. In some cases, e.g. in random copolymers, additivity is found for certain properties.

BIBLIOGRAPHY, CHAPTER 2

General references

Billmeyer, F.W., "Textbook of Polymer Science", Interscience, New York, 1971.
Corradini, P., in "The Stereochemistry of Macromolecules" (A.D. Ketley, Ed.), Marcel Dekker, New York, Vol. 3, 1968.
Elias, H.G., "Makromoleküle", Hüthig & Wepf Verlag, Basel, 1971.
Flory, P.J., "Principles of Polymer Chemistry", Cornell University Press, Ithaca, N.Y., 1953.
Haward, R.N. (Ed.), "The Physics of Glassy Polymers", Applied Science Publ., London, 1973.
Hearle, J.W.S., in "Supramolecular Structures in Fibres" (P.H. Lindenmeyer, Ed.), Interscience, New York, 1967, pp. 215–251.
Holzmüller, W. and Altenburg, K., "Physik der Kunststoffe", Akademie Verlag, Berlin, 1961.
Jenkins, A.D. (Ed.), "Polymer Science", North Holland, Amsterdam, 1972.
Ke, B. (Ed.), "Newer Methods of Polymer Characterization", Interscience, New York, 1964.
Miller, M.L., "The Structure of Polymers", Reinhold, New York, 1966.
Rodriguez, F., "Principles of Polymer Systems", McGraw-Hill, New York, 1970.
Staudinger, H., "Die Hochmolekularen organischen Verbindungen", Springer, Berlin, 1932; "Arbeitserinnerungen", Hüttig Verlag, Heidelberg, 1961.
Wunderlich, B., "Macromolecular Physics", Academic Press, New York, 1973.

Special references

Becht, J. and Fischer, H., Kolloid-Z. 240 (1970) 766.
Bunn, C.W. and Alcock, T.C., Trans. Faraday Soc. 41 (1945) 317.
Fischer, E.W., Goddar, H. and Schmidt, G.F., Makromol. Chem. 119 (1968) 170.
Fischer, E.W. and Goddar, H., J. Polymer Sci. C 16 (1969) 4405.
Hermann, K., Gerngross, O. and Abitz, W., Z. physik. Chem. B 10 (1930) 371.
Hosemann, R., Z. Physik 128 (1950) 1, 465; Polymer 3 (1962) 349.
Hosemann, R. and Bonart, R., Kolloid-Z. 152 (1957) 53.
Huggins, M.L., Natta, G., Desreux, V. and Mark, H., J. Polymer Sci. 56 (1962) 153.
Keller, A., Phil. Mag. (8) 2 (1957) 1171.
Krause, S., J. Macromol. Sci. Rev. Macromol. Chem., C7 (1972) 251.
Leuchs, O., "The Classifying of High Polymers", Butterworth, London, 1968.
McGrew, F.C., J. Chem. Education 35 (1958) 178.
Natta, G. et al., J. Am. Chem. Soc. 77 (1955) 1708.
Natta, G. and Corradini, P., J. Polymer Sci. 20 (1956) 251; 39 (1959) 29.
Peterlin, A., J. Phys. Chem. 75 (1971) 3921; J. Polymer Sci. A-2, 7 (1969) 1151; IUPAC Symposium, Helsinki, 1972.
Platzer, N.A.J., "Multicomponent Polymer Systems", Advances in Chemistry Series No. 99, Am. Chem. Soc., Washington, 1971.
Schlesinger, W. and Leeper, H.M., J. Polymer Sci. 11 (1953) 203.
Sharples, A., in "Polymer Science" (A.D. Jenkins, Ed.), North Holland, Amsterdam, 1972, p. 277.
Statton, W.O., Polymer Sci. Symposium 32 (1970–71) 219.
Wunderlich, B., Ber. Bunsenges. 74 (1970) 772.

CHAPTER 3

TYPOLOGY OF NUMERICAL PROPERTIES

A. PHYSICAL QUANTITIES AND THEIR UNITS

A property can usually be expressed numerically by a physical quantity or by a combination or a function of physical quantities. The concept "physical quantity" was created by Maxwell (1873). Since then it has obtained a central position in the mathematical formalism of science and technology. In general one may write (Maxwell, 1873):

| physical quantity = numerical value × unit |

The unit of a physical quantity is in essence a reference quantity in which other quantities of the same kind can be expressed.

A well-organized system of units forms an essential part of the whole system of physical quantities and the equations by which they are interrelated. Until now different unit systems have been in use, which has given rise to much confusion and trouble. Here we confine ourselves to two of these unit systems.

Among scientists the so-called *dynamic or absolute system* of units is still widely used. It is founded on the three base quantities of mechanics: length, mass and time, with the corresponding units *centimetre, gram-mass* and *second.* The derived unit of force is called *dyne* $(= g \cdot cm/s^2)$ and the derived unit of energy is called *erg* $(= dyn \cdot cm \equiv g \cdot cm^2/s^2)$.

Physical and chemical thermodynamics required the introduction of two additional base quantities, viz. the temperature and the amount of substance; as corresponding base units the *degree Kelvin* (K) and the *gram-molecule* (mol) were introduced. Unfortunately, not the erg is normally used as a unit of energy in thermodynamics, but the *calorie,* which is 4.19×10^7 times as large as the erg. By this choise the coherence in the system of base units is broken, since now a conversion constant of a dimension cal/erg is introduced. Further complications arise if also the field of electricity is included in the unit system.

Among physicists, engineers and technologists the so-called practical unit system was increasingly gaining popularity. It is a really coherent system, which means that no multiplication factors are introduced in the definition of derived units as soon as the base units have been defined.

In 1969 this system was recommended by the International Organization for Standardization as *International System of Units* (SI = Système International d'Unités) and in 1973 it has been accepted as such, according to International Standard IS O 1000.

The International System of Units is founded on seven base quantities which cover the whole field of natural science. Again, the system of quantities and equations of mechanics rests on the three base quantities length, mass and time, for which the units *metre, kilogram* and *second* are now internationally accepted. The derived unit of force is the *newton* (N), being the force that gives the unit mass (kg) a unit acceleration (one metre per square second). The derived unit of energy is the *newton metre* (N · m).

Combination of the mechanical system with electric phenomena requires an additional base quantity of an electrical nature. As such the *ampere* has been chosen as basic unit. The derived unit of electrical energy, the *joule* (= volt · ampere · second = watt · second) is equal to and identical with the unit of mechanical energy, the N · m

$$1 \text{ N} \cdot \text{m} = 1 \text{ J} = 1 \text{ V} \cdot \text{A} \cdot \text{s} = 1 \text{ W} \cdot \text{s} (= 10^7 \text{ erg})$$

It is clear that with the definition of the ampere also the other electrical quantities are defined. Thermodynamics required the introduction of the base quantities temperature and amount of substance, with the *kelvin* and the *mol* as units. The unit of energy is the *joule,* so that no conversion factor is involved here either.

Finally in the field of light the base unit *candela* is introduced as unit of luminous intensity.

In the international system every physical quantity is represented by an appropriate symbol (which often is internationally agreed upon) printed in italics. The symbols of the units are printed in normal (straight) type.

B. CATEGORIES OF PHYSICAL QUANTITIES

Physical quantities may be divided into different categories, according to their nature. The following groups may be distinguished:

1. *Extensive quantities,* which are proportional to the extension of the system considered. Examples are: mass, volume, enthalpy, entropy, etc. When subsystems are combined, the values of the extensive quantities are summed up.

2. *Intensive quantities,* these are independent of the extension of the system, but, as the name suggests, determine an "intensity" or a "quality" of the system. Examples are: temperature, pressure, density, field strength, etc. When subsystems are combined, the intensive quantities are "averaged" in accordance with the composition. An intensive quantity may nearly always be regarded as the quotient of two extensive quantities.

$$\text{pressure} = \frac{\text{force}}{\text{area}}$$

$$\text{density} = \frac{\text{mass}}{\text{volume}}$$

$$\text{temperature} = \frac{\text{enthalpy difference}}{\text{entropy difference}}$$

3. *Specific quantities.* These, too, are independent of the extension of the system under consideration. They result from extensive quantities when these are related to the

unit of mass. So these quantities are also quotients of two extensive quantities and consequently have all the characteristics of intensive quantities. For mixtures the numerical value of these specific quantities is determined by the composition and averaged in accordance with it. Examples:

$$\text{specific volume} = \frac{\text{volume}}{\text{mass}}$$

$$\text{specific heat} = \frac{\text{heat capacity}}{\text{mass}}, \text{etc.}$$

Molar quantities are related to the specific quantities, but now numerically related to one gram-molecule as unit of amount of substance. These quantities are, inter alia, obtained by multiplication of the specific quantities (related to the unit of mass) by the molar weight. In particular the molar quantities will play an important role in the considerations that are to follow.

Extensive and intensive quantities are characterized in that together they can form parameter couples having the dimension of an energy. For instance:

Kind of energy	Parameter couple (product)	
	intensive quantity	extensive quantity
mechanical energy	pressure	volume
	tensile stress	elongation
	torque	torsion angle
	surface tension	area
electrical energy	potential	charge
magnetic energy	field strength	magnetization
thermal energy	temperature	entropy

C. DIMENSIONLESS GROUPS OF QUANTITIES

Dimensionless groups of quantities or *"numerics"* occupy a unique position in physics. The magnitude of a numeric is independent of the units in which its component physical properties are measured, provided only that these are measured in consistent units. The numerics form a distinct class of entities which, though being dimensionless, cannot be manipulated as pure numbers. They do not follow the usual rules of addition and multiplication since they have only a meaning if they are related to a specific phenomenon.

The laws of physics may all be expressed as relations between numerics and are in their simplest form when thus expressed. The use of dimensionless expressions is of particular value in dealing with phenomena too complicated for a complete treatment in terms of the fundamental transport equations of mass, energy and momentum. Most of the physical problems in the process industry are of this complicated nature and the combination of variables in the form of dimensionless groups can always be regarded as a safe start in the investigation of new problems.

A complete physical law expressed as an equation between numerics is independent of the size of the system. Therefore dimensionless expressions are of great importance in problems of change of scale. When two systems exhibit similarity, one of them, and usually the smaller system, can be regarded as the "model". Two systems are dynamically similar when the ratio of every pair of forces or rates in one system is the same as the corresponding ratio in the other. The ratio of any pair of forces or rates constitutes a dimensionless quantity. Corresponding dimensionless quantities must have the same numerical value if dynamical similarity holds.

The value of dimensionless groups has long been recognized. As early as 1873, Von Helmholtz derived groups now called the Reynolds and Froude "numbers", although Weber (1919) was the first to name these numerics.

The standardized notation of numerics is:

$$N_{Xy}$$

where the subscript Xy is a two-letter abbreviation of the name of the investigator after whom the numeric is named.

Categories of dimensionless groups

Engel (1954, 1958) has divided dimensionless groups into five categories:

1. Those that can be *derived from the fundamental equations of dynamics.* Engel calls these the groups that form the *model laws of dynamic similarity.* This is the most important category in engineering practice; we come back to it later.

Examples of numerics of this group are [1]:

$$N_{Re} = \frac{vL\rho}{\eta} \quad (\text{Re} = \text{Reynolds})$$

$$N_{Pe} = \frac{vLc_p\rho}{\lambda} \quad (\text{Pe} = \text{Péclet})$$

2. Dimensionless ways of *expressing an experimental result.* This category forming dependent variables, but not model laws, can be derived from the boundary conditions of the model laws.

Examples are:

$$N_{Nu} = \frac{hL}{\lambda} \qquad (\text{Nu} = \text{Nusselt})$$

$$N_{Sh} = \frac{k_m L}{D} \qquad (\text{Sh} = \text{Sherwood})$$

$$N_{Bm} = \frac{\tau L}{\eta v} \qquad (\text{Bm} = \text{Bingham})$$

3. Dimensionless combinations of quantities which describe the *properties of a material (intrinsic numerics)*

---

[1] For nomenclature see table 3.2.

Examples:

$$N_{Le} = \frac{\lambda}{c_p \rho D} \qquad \text{(Le = Lewis)}$$

$$N_{Sc} = \frac{\eta}{\rho D} \qquad \text{(Sc = Schmidt)}$$

$$N_{Pr} = \frac{c_p \eta}{\lambda} \qquad \text{(Pr = Prandtl)}$$

4. *Ratios* of two quantities with the same dimension.
These may be:

4a. *Reduced quantities*, i.e. ratios of quantities and chosen standard values:

$$N_{Ma} = \frac{v}{v_{sound}} \qquad \text{(Ma = Mach)}$$

Furthermore: T/T_g, T/T_m, etc.

4b. *Ratios of forces* (f):

$$\frac{\text{gravitational force}}{\text{pressure gradient}} = \frac{\rho g L}{\Delta p}$$

$$\frac{\text{gravitational force}}{\text{viscous force}} = \frac{\rho g L^2}{\eta v}$$

$$\frac{\text{viscous force}}{\text{surface tension}} = \frac{\eta v}{\gamma}$$

$$\frac{\text{shear force}}{\text{elastic force}} = \frac{\tau}{E} \quad \text{etc.}$$

4c. *Ratios of characteristic times*

$$\frac{\text{residence time (in reactor)}}{\text{characteristic reaction time}} = k_1 t_{res}$$

$$\frac{\text{residence time}}{\text{characteristic diffusion time}} = \frac{D t_{res}}{L^2}$$

$$\frac{\text{time of relaxation}}{\text{time of observation}} = \frac{\Theta}{t} = N_{De} \quad \text{(De = Deborah)}$$

$$\frac{\text{characteristic time of viscoelastic deformation}}{\text{reciprocal rate of deformation}} = \dot{\gamma}\Theta_0 = N_{Wg} \quad \text{(Wg = Weissenberg)}$$

4d. *"Intrinsic" ratios*. These are quantities such as:

$$\frac{T_m}{T_g}, \frac{\overline{M}_w}{\overline{M}_n}, \text{etc.}$$

TABLE 3.1

The three fundamental equations of conservation

EQUATION OF CONSERVATION OF:	I Local change		II Change by convection		III Change by diffusion		IV Change by production		V Boundary condition
MASS	$\dfrac{\partial c}{\partial t}$	+	$v\,\dfrac{\partial c}{\partial x}$	−	$D\,\dfrac{\partial^2 c}{\partial x^2}$	+	r	= 0	Mass transfer $= k_m \cdot \Delta c$
ENERGY	$c_p \rho\,\dfrac{\partial T}{\partial t}$	+	$c_p \rho v\,\dfrac{\partial T}{\partial x}$	−	$\lambda\,\dfrac{\partial^2 T}{\partial x^2}$	+	$\dot{q}$	= 0	Heat transfer $= h \cdot \Delta T$
MOMENTUM	$\rho\,\dfrac{\partial v}{\partial t}$	+	$\rho v\,\dfrac{\partial v}{\partial x}$	−	$\eta\,\dfrac{\partial^2 v}{\partial x^2}$	+	f	= 0	Shear force $= \tau \cdot a$ Surface tension force $= \gamma \cdot l$

CORRESPONDING QUANTITIES (per unit of volume)	Unit	Diffusive transport	Production	Boundary transfer
MASS	c	D	r	$k_m \Delta c$
ENERGY	$c_p \rho T$	λ	$\dot{q}$	$h \Delta T$
MOMENTUM	ρv	η	f	τ or γL^{-1}

Meaning of symbols
see Table 3.2

TABLE 3.2

System of dimensionless groups (numerics)

Ratio of terms in table 3.1	III : I	IV : I	V : I	II : III	IV : II	V : II	IV : III	V : III	IV : V
Mass	$\dfrac{Dt}{L^2}$	$\dfrac{rt}{c}$	$\dfrac{k_m t}{L}$	$\dfrac{vL}{D}$ $\boxed{\text{Bo}}$	$\dfrac{rL}{vc}$ $\boxed{\text{DaI}}$	$\dfrac{k_m}{v}$ $\boxed{\text{Me}}$	$\dfrac{rL^2}{Dc}$ $\boxed{\text{DaII}}$	$\dfrac{k_m L}{D}$ $\boxed{\text{Sh}}$	$\dfrac{rL}{k_m c}$
Energy	$\dfrac{\lambda t}{c_p \rho L^2}$ $\boxed{\text{Fo}}$	$\dfrac{\dot{q} t}{c_p \rho T}$	$\dfrac{h t}{c_p \rho L}$	$\dfrac{c_p \rho v L}{\lambda}$ $\boxed{\text{Pe}}$	$\dfrac{\dot{q} L}{c_p \rho T v}$ $\boxed{\text{DaIII}}$	$\dfrac{h}{c_p \rho v}$ $\boxed{\text{St}}$	$\dfrac{\dot{q} L^2}{\lambda T}$ $\boxed{\text{DaIV}}$	$\dfrac{h L}{\lambda}$ $\boxed{\text{Nu}}$	$\dfrac{\dot{q} L}{h T}$
Momentum	$\dfrac{\eta t}{\rho L^2}$	$\dfrac{f t}{\rho v}$	$\dfrac{\tau t}{\rho v L}$	$\dfrac{\rho v L}{\eta}$ $\boxed{\text{Re}}$	$\dfrac{f L}{\rho v^2}$ $\boxed{\text{We}}$	$\dfrac{\tau}{\rho v^2}$ $\boxed{\text{Fa}}$	$\dfrac{f L^2}{\eta v}$ $\boxed{\text{Po}}$	$\dfrac{\tau L}{\eta v}$ $\boxed{\text{Bm}}$	$\dfrac{f L}{\tau}$

NUMERICS (see Gen. Ref.)

Bm = Bingham
Bo = Bodenstein
Da = Damköhler
Fa = Fanning
Fo = Fourier
Me = Merkel
Nu = Nusselt
Pe = Péclet
Po = Poiseuille
Re = Reynolds
Sh = Sherwood
St = Stanton
We = Weber

MEANING OF SYMBOLS

a = surface per unit of volume
c = concentration
c_p = specific heat
D = diffusivity
e = electric charge
E = modulus of elasticity
f_{el} = electric field per unit of volume
g = gravitational acceleration
h = heat transfer coefficient
k = reaction rate constant
k_m = mass transfer coefficient
l = length per unit of volume
L = characteristic length
p = pressure
t = time
T = temperature
v = velocity
x = length coordinate

γ = surface tension
η = viscosity
λ = heat conductivity
ρ = density
τ = shear stress
ω = angular frequency

r = reaction rate per unit of volume
    first order $r = kc$
    second order $r = kc^2$ etc.
$\dot{q}$ = heat production rate per unit of volume
f = force per unit of volume
    gravitational $f = g\rho$
    centrifugal $f = \omega^2 L\rho$
    pressure gradient $f = \Delta p/L$
    elastic $f = E/L$
    surface tension $f = \gamma/L^2$
    electric $f = e f_{el}$

4e. *"Trivial" ratios.* These are only trivial in the sense that they are simple ratios of quantities with the same dimensions but their effects may be far from trivial. The most important representatives in this category are the *geometric shape factors* which are often of prime importance.

5. Derived groups which are simply combinations of the above.

Dimensionless groups derived from the equations of transport

The most important category of dimensionless groups is that of the numerics connected with transport (of mass, energy and momentum). Table 3.1 shows the three fundamental equations of conservation, written in their simplest form (i.e. one-dimensional). A complete system of numerics can be derived by forming "ratios" of the different terms of these three equations, as was suggested by Klinkenberg and Mooy (1943). This system is reproduced in table 3.2.

D. TYPES OF POLYMER PROPERTIES

Polymer properties may (from the molar viewpoint) be placed in three categories:

1. Colligative properties

Per gram-molecule of matter these properties have the same value, independent of the special constitution of the substance. The numerical value of the quantity measured experimentally therefore depends on the number of (gram-) molecules.

Real colligative properties are only found in ideal gases and ideal solutions. Examples are: osmotic pressure, vapour pressure reduction, boiling-point elevation, freezing-point depression, in other words: the osmotic properties.

2. Additive properties

Per gram-molecule these properties have a value which in the ideal case is equal to the sum of the values of the constituent atoms. Only the molar weight is strictly additive.

By approximation other quantities are additive as well, such as the molar volume, molar heat capacity, molar heat of combustion and formation, molar refraction, etc.

3. Constitutive properties

These properties are largely determined by the constitution of the molecule, without there being any question of additivity of colligativity. Typical constitutive properties are selective light absorption, magnetic resonance absorption, etc. Often these properties are the "fingerprints" of the substance.

Intramolecular and intermolecular interactions sometimes have a very great influence on colligativity and additivity, and often accentuate constitutive properties. *The coming considerations will deal in particular with the field of the additive properties* and the borderland between the additive and the constitutive properties.

E. ADDITIVE MOLAR FUNCTIONS

A powerful tool in the semi-empirical approach in the study of physical properties in general, and of polymer properties in particular, is the use of the *additivity principle*. This principle means that a large number of properties, when expressed per mole of a substance, may be calculated by summation of either atomic, group or bond contributions:

$$F = \sum_i n_i F_i \qquad (3.1)$$

where F is a molar property, n_i is the number of contributing components of the type i, and F_i is the numerical contribution of the component i. Due to their sequential structure, polymers are ideal materials for the application of the additivity principle. End groups play a minor part in general. *Therefore the molar quantities may be expressed per mole of the structural unit.*

The concept of additivity has proved extremely fruitful for studying the correlation between the chemical constitution of substances and their physical properties. Its usefulness applies both to individual compounds and to their mixtures, even if these mixtures are of considerable complexity such as mineral oils (Van Nes and Van Westen, 1951) or coals (Van Krevelen, 1961). Properties of homogeneous mixtures can be calculated very accurately by means of additive molar quantities.

Sometimes the discrepancies between numerical values calculated by means of the additivity principle and experimental values form an extremely important key to the disclosure of constitutional effects.

Methods for expressing the additivity within structural units

According to the nature of the structural elements used, three additive methods should be mentioned.

1. Use of *atomic contributions*. If the additivity is perfect, the property of a molecule may be calculated from the contributions of the atoms of which it is composed. This most simple system of additivity has at the same time a restricted value. Accurate comparison of molar properties of related compounds revealed that contributions of the same atoms should have somewhat different values according to the nature of their neighbour atoms. This has led to the introduction of

2. Use of *group contributions*. Here the small deviations of the atomic contributions caused by their surroundings are accounted for by combining the atoms into the most frequently used molecular groups. Finally there is a third approach, viz.

3. Use of *bond contributions*. It is possible to base the additivity principle on the different types of bonds between atoms. Also this method has been applied, but here, too, different values have to be used for the same bond, depending on the neighbouring bonds of the atoms involved.

For practical purposes the method of group contributions is to be preferred. The use of atomic contributions is too simplistic in general and the use of bond contributions leads to an impractically large number of different bond types.

Types of additive molar functions

The following types of additive molar functions in polymer science may be distinguished:

I The molar weight per structural unit **(M)**.

This is an additive function by definition.

II Molar intrinsic properties showing empirical and often theory-based additivity. Usually they are products of a specific quantity (e.g. specific heat) and molar weight **(M)**.

III More complicated additive molar functions, having a theoretical background (e.g. the electromagnetic theory of radiation). Usually they are products of the molar volume per structural unit **(V)** and of some function of an intensive numerical quantity.

IV Empirical additive functions; usually they are products of a function of a non-specific intrinsic quantity and either the molar weight **(M)** or the molar volume **(V)**. Until a theoretical background is developed they are just useful aids in calculations. They are chosen in such a way that a good additivity is obtained on the one hand and a nearby temperature-independence on the other.

Whereas the types I–III do not show correction-increments due to molecular interactions, this is often the case within type **IV**. Additive molar functions will be symbolized by bold face Latin capital letters.

Table 3.3 gives a survey of the most important additive molar functions and their symbols.

If a molar property can be calculated by means of the additivity principle, the relevant physical quantity can be calculated from the information on chemical structure only. For instance, surface tension follows from:

$$\gamma = \left(\frac{P_S}{V}\right)^4 \tag{3.2}$$

The accuracy of such a numerical value is limited, of course, since the additivity of a molar property is never exactly valid. Generally the accuracy is sufficient for practical use.

There are two ways to improve the accuracy of the calculation, viz. by using a "standard property" or by using a "standard substance". We shall explain what is meant by these terms.

1. *Method of Standard Properties.* Let us assume that the required physical property of a substance, e.g. its surface tension, is unknown, but that another property, e.g. its refractive index, has been measured with great accuracy. Then we can use the latter as a standard property and apply the formula

$$\gamma = \left(\frac{P_S}{R_{LL}} \frac{n^2 - 1}{n^2 + 2}\right)^4 \tag{3.3}$$

The attraction is twofold: first of all (3.3) has the advantage that the absolute value of the molar volume **V**, often the least reliable additive quantity, is not used; secondly, equation (3.3) can easily be transformed into a dimensionless group, viz.:

$$\frac{\gamma^{1/4}}{(n^2 - 1)/(n^2 + 2)} \frac{R_{LL}}{P_S} = 1 \tag{3.4}$$

TABLE 3.3

Survey of additive functions [1]

TYPE	Additive function	Symbol	Formula	Derived from, and useful for estimation of :	Introduced by:
I	Molar weight	**M**	ΣA	atomic weight (A)	Dalton (1801) Berzelius (1810)
II	Molar volume	**V**	$Mv = \dfrac{M}{\rho}$	specific volume (v) density (ρ)	Traube (1895) Kopp (1889)
	Molar heat capacity	$\mathbf{C}_\rho$	Mc_ρ	specific heat (c_ρ)	Kopp (1889) Satoh (1948)
	Molar entropy of fusion	$\Delta\mathbf{S}_m$	$M\Delta s_m$	specific entropy of fusion (Δs_m)	Bondi (1968)
	Molar cohesive energy	$\mathbf{E}_{coh}$	$\Delta H_{vap} - RT = Ve_{coh} = V\delta^2$	cohesive energy density (e_{coh}) solubility parameter (δ)	Bunn (1955)
	Molar magnetic susceptibility	**X**	$M\chi$	diamagnetic suscepti-bility (X)	Pascal (1923)
	Molar free enthalpy of formation	$\Delta\mathbf{G}_f^0$	$\Delta(\Delta G_f^0) = RT\ln K_{eq}$	equilibrium constant (K_{eq})	Franklin (1949) Van Krevelen–Chermin (1950)
III	Molar refraction	$\mathbf{R}_{LL}$	$\dfrac{M}{\rho} \cdot \dfrac{n^2-1}{n^2+2}$	refractive index (n)	Lorentz (1880) Lorenz (1880)
	do.	$\mathbf{R}_{GD}$	$\dfrac{M}{\rho}(n-1)$	do.	Gladstone–Dale (1858)
	Molar dielectric polarisation	**P**	$\dfrac{M}{\rho}\dfrac{\epsilon-1}{\epsilon+2}$	dielectric constant (ϵ)	Mosotti (1850) Clausius (1879) Debye (1912)
	Molar sound velocity function (Rao function)	**U**	$\dfrac{M}{\rho}\left(u_{long}\right)^{\frac{1}{3}}\left(\dfrac{1+\nu}{3(1-\nu)}\right)^{\frac{1}{6}}$	longitudinal sound velocity (u_{long}) Poisson modulus (ν)	Rao (1940) Schuyer (1958)
IV	Molar thermal expansion	**E**	$Me = \dfrac{M}{\rho}\alpha$	thermal expansivity (e) coefficient of thermal expansion (α)	This book
	Molar glass transi-tion function	**Yg**	MTg	glass transition temper-ature (Tg)	This book
	Molar melt transi-tion function	**Ym**	MT_m	crystalline melting temperature (T_m)	This book
	Molar attraction function	**F**	$\left(\dfrac{M}{\rho}E_{coh}\right)^{\frac{1}{2}} = \dfrac{M}{\rho}\delta$	solubility parameter (δ)	Small (1953)
	Molar parachor	$\mathbf{P}_S$	$\dfrac{M}{\rho}\gamma^{\frac{1}{4}}$	surface tension (γ)	Sugden (1924)
	Molar intrinsic viscosity function	**K**	$MK_\theta^{\frac{1}{2}} = M\left(\dfrac{[\eta]\theta}{\bar{M}^{\frac{1}{2}}}\right)^{\frac{1}{2}}$	intrinsic viscosity (η) average molecular weight $(\bar{M})$	Van Krevelen – Hoftyzer (1967)
	Molar refractive index (Vogel function)	$\mathbf{R}_V$	Mn	refractive index (n)	Vogel (1950)
	Molar viscosity-temperature function	$\mathbf{H}_\eta$	$ME_\eta^{\frac{1}{3}}(\infty)$	activation energy of viscous flow at high temp. $(E_\eta(\infty))$	Van Krevelen – Hoftyzer (1975)
	Molar char forma-tion tendency function	**CFT**	$M\dfrac{CR}{1200}$	char residu $(CR$ in wt-percentage$)$ on pyrolysis	Van Krevelen (1975)

[1] For polymers all molar functions are related to the structural unit.

with all the advantages of the dimensionless expressions.

2. *Method of Standard Substances.* This method may be applied if a physical property of the substance in question is unknown, but if the same property has been measured accurately in a related substance. In this case one may use the related substance as a "model" or a "standard" (symbol 0) and apply the rule:

$$\frac{\gamma}{\gamma_0} = \left(\frac{P_S}{P_{So}} \frac{V_0}{V}\right)^4 \tag{3.5}$$

Also this equation is dimensionless.

Especially by the possibility of these two refinements, the principle of additivity becomes even more useful for practice and permits us to estimate physical quantities with an accuracy which could hardly be expected.

The group additivity methods described in this chapter may be considered a special form of the more general method proposed by Huggins (1969, 1970). The latter method might be called an interaction additivity method. It assumes that a number of properties of a liquid (or a mixture) are equal to the sum of the contributions of every interaction between the groups present.

In its most general formulation this theory assumes that a property F may be calculated by

$$F = \sum_{i=1}^{n} \sum_{j=1}^{n} w_{ij} F_{ij} \tag{3.6}$$

where w_{ij} = a weight factor taking into account the relative importance of the contacts between groups i and j, F_{ij} = the contribution to property F, attributed to a contact between groups i and j, n = the number of groups present.

In the theory of Huggins, the weight factors w are supposed to be proportional to the area of contact between the groups i and j.

For a ditonic system, containing the groups A and B, equation (3.6) reduces to:

$$F = w_{aa} F_{aa} + w_{bb} F_{bb} + w_{ab} F_{ab} . \tag{3.7}$$

If the factors w are expressed in fractions of the numbers of moles n_A and n_B:

$$w_{aa} = \frac{n_A^2}{n_A + n_B}, \quad w_{bb} = \frac{n_B^2}{n_A + n_B}; \quad w_{ab} = \frac{2n_A n_B}{n_A + n_B}$$

and if it is assumed that:

$$F_{ab} = \tfrac{1}{2} F_{aa} + \tfrac{1}{2} F_{bb}$$

equation (3.7) reduces to:

$$F = n_A F_{aa} + n_B F_{bb} \tag{3.8}$$

which is the equation of a group additivity method for a ditonic system.

BIBLIOGRAPHY, CHAPTER 3

General references

Bondi, A., "Physical Properties of Molecular Crystals, Liquids and Glasses", Wiley, New York, 1968.
Bridgman, P.W., "Dimensional Analysis". Yale University Press, New Haven, 1931.
Catchpole, J.P. and Fulford, G., "Dimensionless Groups", Ind. and Eng. Chem. 58 (3) (1966) 46 and 60 (3) (1968) 71.
Exner, O., "Additive Physical Properties", Collection Czechoslov. Chem. Commun. Vol. 31 and 32.
Langhaar, H.L., "Dimensional Analysis and Theory of Models", Wiley, New York, 1951.

Special references

Bunn, C.W., J. Polymer Sci. 16 (1955) 323.
Clausius, R., "Die mechanische Wärmetheorie", Braunschweig, 1879, p. 62.
Debye, P., Phys. Z. 13 (1912) 97.
Engel, F.V.A., The Engineer 198 (1954) 637; 206 (1958) 479.
Franklin, J.L., Ind. Eng. Chem. 41 (1949) 1070.
Gladstone, J.H. and Dale, T.P., Trans. Roy. Soc. (London) A 148 (1858) 887; A 153 (1863) 317.
Huggins, M.L., J. Paint Technol. 41 (1969) 509; J. Phys. Chem. 74 (1970) 371.
Klinkenberg, A. and Mooy, H.H., Ned. T. Natuurk. 10 (1943) 29; Chem. Eng. Progr. 44 (1948) 17.
Lorentz, H.A., Wied. Ann. Phys. 9 (1880) 641.
Lorenz, L.V., Wied. Ann. Phys. 11 (1880) 70.
Maxwell, J.Cl., "A Treatise on Electricity and Magnetism", Oxford, 1873.
Mosotti, O.F., Mem. di mathem. e fisica Modina 24 II (1850) 49.
Pascal, P., Rev. Gen. Sci. 34 (1923) 388.
Rao, R., Indian J. Phys. 14 (1940) 109.
Satoh, S., J. Sci. Research Inst. (Tokyo) 43 (1948) 79.
Schuyer, J., Nature 181 (1958) 1394; J. Polymer Sci. 36 (1959) 1475.
Small, P.A., J. Appl. Chem. 3 (1953) 71.
Sugden, S., J. Chem. Soc. 125 (1924) 1177; "The Parachor and Valency", George Routledge, London, 1930.
Traube, J., Ber. dtsch. Chem. Ges. 28 (1895) 2722.
Van Krevelen, D.W., Polymer 16 (1975) 615.
Van Krevelen, D.W., "Coal", Elsevier, Amsterdam, 1961.
Van Krevelen, D.W. and Chermin, H.A.G., Ingenieur 38 (1950) Ch. T. 1; Chem. Eng. Sci. 1 (1951) 66.
Van Krevelen, D.W. and Hoftyzer, P.J., J. Appl. Polymer Sci. 11 (1967) 1409.
Van Krevelen, D.W. and Hoftyzer, P.J., Z. Angew. Makromol. Chem. (in press).
Van Nes, K. and Van Westen, H.A., "Aspects of the Constitution of Mineral Oils", Elsevier, Amsterdam, 1951.
Vogel, A., Chem. & Ind. (1950) 358; (1951) 376; (1952) 514; (1953) 19; (1954) 1045.
Von Helmholtz, H., Monatsber. königl. Preuss. Akad. Wiss. (1873) 501.
Weber, M., Jahrb. Schiffbautechn. Ges. 20 (1919) 355.

PART II

THERMOPHYSICAL PROPERTIES OF POLYMERS

CHAPTER 4

VOLUMETRIC PROPERTIES

The volumetric properties are extremely important for nearly every phenomenon or process. The main volumetric properties are:
(1) *specific* and *molar volumes* and the related reciprocals of specific volumes, the *densities;* these quantities are different for the glassy, rubbery and crystalline states;
(2) *specific* and *molar thermal expansivities,* again dependent on the physical state;
(3) *specific* and *molar melt expansion* for crystalline polymers.

It will be shown that the molar volumetric properties can be calculated with a remarkable accuracy from additive group contributions. Furthermore there exist interesting correlations with the Van der Waals volume.

A. VOLUME AND DENSITY

Specific volume — or its reciprocal: density — may be regarded as one of the most important polymer properties. This is obvious as far as the role of polymer density in practical applications is concerned. But also from a theoretical point of view the density of a polymer is an important property. For the calculation of a number of other properties (e.g. thermodynamical quantities) it is necessary to know the density. It is also used for the characterization of polymers; within a given family of polymers, for instance, density is closely related to the degree of crystallinity. Moreover, polymer density can easily be determined experimentally.

In this connection the lack of reliable and accurate data on polymer densities is surprising. There are only few literature surveys in this field. Therefore a method for estimating polymer density as a function of polymer structure is useful. Such a method has been proposed by Van Krevelen and Hoftyzer (1969). Comparable methods already existed for the prediction of the densities of organic liquids. These methods are based on the calculation of the molar volume by addition of group contributions for given structural units.

Definitions
1. *Specific volume* (= volume per unit weight)

$$v \equiv \frac{1}{\rho} \quad \text{(dimension: cm}^3/\text{g or m}^3/\text{kg).}$$

Normally densities at a certain specified temperature, e.g. 20°C or 25°C, are tabulated.
2. *Molar volume*

51

This is the product of specific volume and molar weight.

$$V \equiv Mv \equiv \frac{M}{\rho} \quad \text{(dimension: } cm^3/mol \text{ or } m^3/mol\text{)}$$

For polymers all molar functions are related to the structural unit. The following specified molar volumes are used:

2a) the molar volume at a certain standard temperature, e.g. room temperature: $V(298)$

2b) the *zero point molar volume*: $V^0(0)$ $(\equiv V_c(0))$

   This is the molar volume of the most stable condensed phase (crystal) at zero K.

2c) the *Van der Waals volume*: V_W

   This is the volume enclosed by the electron clouds of the molecules.

Molar volumes of organic liquids at room temperature

The molar volume at room temperature is one of the first physical quantities, for which group contribution methods have been proposed. Atomic contribution methods were derived by Traube (1895) and by Le Bas (1915). A characteristic difference between the two approaches was that Traube added to the sum of atomic contributions for a given compound an additional value called "residual volume" (Ω), so that

$$V_1(298) = \sum_i V_i(298) + \Omega \tag{4.1}$$

Ω is a constant with an average value of 24 cm^3/mol. The existence of a residual volume has been confirmed by a number of other investigators. As Le Bas disregarded this effect, his values for the atomic contributions are always larger than the corresponding values of Traube, and of little practical value. Nevertheless the method of Le Bas can still be found in a number of textbooks.

More recently, Davis and Gottlieb (1963) and Harrison (1965, 1966) improved the method of Traube. It appeared that the atomic contribution of a given element is not constant, but dependent on the nature of the surrounding atoms. This leads to a considerable increase of the number of "atomic" contribution values. For this reason group contributions are to be preferred to atomic contributions.

In the following sections, exclusively group contributions will be used. Literature data originally expressed in atomic contributions will be converted into group contribution values.

The best confirmations of the additivity of molar volume were obtained from the studies of homologous series. Studies of several series of compounds with increasing numbers of CH_2 groups have led to rather accurate values for the contribution of this group to the molar volume. Values found by several investigators are summarized in table 4.1. The mean value is 16.45 cm^3/mol with a standard deviation of 0.2 cm^3/mol.

For other groups, the contributions mentioned by different authors show larger variations. This appears from table 4.2, where published values of the contributions for a number of groups are compared. All the results are expressed in the form of bivalent groups. This has been done because a number of authors did not make a clear distinction between the contributions of monovalent end groups and the above mentioned residual volume.

The contributions of several hydrocarbon groups are rather accurately known and can be predicted with an accuracy of about 1 cm^3/mol. For other groups, variations range

TABLE 4.1. 53

Group contribution of CH_2 to molar volume

Investigators	CH_2 contribution to molar volume $(cm^3/mol = 10^{-6}\ m^3/mol)$
Traube (1895)	16.1
Kurtz and Lipkin (1941)	16.3
Van Nes and Van Westen (1951)	16.5
Simha and Hadden (1956)	16.5
Li et al. (1956)	16.5
Huggins (1958)	16.5
Tatevskii et al. (1961)	16.1
Davis and Gottlieb (1963)	16.6
Harrison (1965, 1966)	16.4
Exner (1967)	16.6
Rheineck and Lin (1968)	16.5

TABLE 4.2.

Group contributions to the molar volume of organic liquids at room temperature (cm^3/mol)

Groups	Investigators						
	Traube (1895)	Kurtz and Lipkin (1941)	Li et al. (1956)	Huggins (1954)	Davis and Gottlieb (1963)	Exner (1967)	Rheineck et al. (1968)
$-CH_2-$	16.1	16.3	16.5	16.5	16.6	16.6	16.5
$-CH(CH_3)-$	32.2	32.6			32.3	33.2	33.5
$-C(CH_3)_2-$	48.3	48.8		47.6	49.8	49.7	
$-CH=CH-$	24.3	26.4		26.5	25.0		
$-CH=C(CH_3)-$	40.4	42.6		40.3	40.6		
$-CH(CH=CH_2)-$	40.4	42.6	43.9		40.6	43.7	43.5
$-C_6H_{10}-$	77.2	78.9			78.5		
$-CH(C_6H_{11})-$	93.3	95.2	97.4		94.1	95.1	94.5
$-CH(C_5H_9)-$	77.2	82.0	82.6			80.3	
$-C_6H_4-$	58.6	60.3			61.8		
$-CH(C_6H_5)-$	74.7	76.6	78.8		77.4	75.8	74.5
$-CHF-$	18.5			17.8		16.3	
$-CHCl-$	26.2			26.6		24.1	23.5
$-CHBr-$	26.2			30.1		27.4	
$-CHI-$	26.2			37.3		34.1	
$-CH(CN)-$	24.4			27.2		23.8	
$-O-$	5.5				6.8	6.7	
$-CO-$	15.4					10.2	8.5
$-COO-$	20.9			23.9	15.5	19.5	16.5
$-CH(OH)-$	18.4		15.8	14.5		11.4	8.2
$-CH(CHO)-$	31.5			29.6	27.6	26.3	25.5
$-CH(COOH)-$	31.9		30.7	31.7	30.1	28.4	26.5
$-CH(NH_2)-$				21.8		18.8	18.5
$-CH(NO_2)-$				30.1		25.7	
$-CONH-$	20.0					17.5	
$-S-$	15.5				12.2	10.8	
$-CH(SH)-$	31.6		31.7	30.0		27.0	

Conversion factor: $1\ cm^3/mol = 10^{-6}\ m^3/mol$.

from 2 to 4 cm³/mol. It must be concluded that on the basis of these literature data the molar volume of an organic liquid can be predicted with an accuracy of, at best, some percent.

In a recent article Fedors (1974) proposed an extensive system of group contributions to the molecular volume of polymers at 25°C. These values, though not very accurate, can be used for a first orientation [1].

Molar volumes of rubbery amorphous polymers

The rubbery amorphous state of polymers has the greatest correspondence with the liquid state of organic compounds. So it may be expected that the molar volume per structural unit of polymers in this state can be predicted by using the values of the group contributions mentioned in table 4.2.

$$V_r(298) = \sum_i V_i(298) .$$ (4.1a)

Owing to the very high molecular weight, the residual volume Ω (equation (4.1)) may be neglected.

At room temperature, those amorphous polymers are in the rubbery state of which the glass transition temperature is lower than 25°C. The available literature data on the densities for this class of polymers are mentioned in table 4.3. For each polymer, the molar volume V_r has been calculated from the density. These values of V_r have been compared with values calculated with equation (4.1a), using group contributions mentioned in table 4.2. Although there was an obvious correspondence between the experimental and calculated values, the inaccuracy of this calculation was too large to provide a prediction of polymer densities that is of any practical value. Therefore new group contributions have been derived from the available data on rubbery amorphous polymers. These are mentioned in table 4.4. With the aid of these group contributions the calculated values of $V_r(298)$ in table 4.3 have been derived. The mean deviation between experimental and calculated values of V_r is 1.5%.

In table 4.4, the newly derived group contributions are compared with literature values from table 4.2. For reasons outlined above, the comparison has been limited to bivalent groups. The agreement between both series of values is quite reasonable, except for oxygen. Here the group contribution to V_r is much larger than the literature values. It proved necessary to use two different values for the contribution of a COO group. The lower value is used for an "acrylic" COO group, that is a COO group of which the carbon atom is directly attached to the main chain backbone.

For convenience, the combined bivalent groups of table 4.4 have been split up into a number of tetravalent, trivalent and monovalent groups. This subdivision, however, is rather arbitrary.

Molar volumes of glassy amorphous polymers

Those amorphous polymers for which the glass transition temperature is higher than

---

[1] In Chapter 7 these values are given (table 7.4), in combination with group contributions for the cohesive energy.

TABLE 4.3.

Molar volumes of rubbery amorphous polymers at 25°C

Polymer	ρ_r (g/cm^3)	V_r (cm^3/mol) experimental	calculated
polyethylene	0.855	32.8	32.9
polypropylene	0.85	49.5	49.1
polybutene	0.86	65.2	65.8
polypentene	0.85	82.5	82.0
polyhexene	0.86	97.9	98.5
polyisobutylene	0.84	66.8	66.8
poly(5-phenylpentene)	1.05	139.2	140.3
poly(vinylidene chloride)	1.66	58.4	58.0
poly(tetrafluoroethylene)	2.00	50.0	49.5
poly(isopropyl vinyl ether)	0.924	93.2	90.3
poly(butyl vinyl ether)	0.927	108.0	107.0
poly(sec.-butyl vinyl ether)	0.924	108.3	106.7
poly(isobutyl vinyl ether)	0.93	107.6	106.7
poly(pentyl vinyl ether)	0.918	124.4	123.4
poly(hexyl vinyl ether)	0.925	138.6	139.9
poly(octyl vinyl ether)	0.914	171.0	172.8
poly(2-ethylhexyl vinyl ether)	0.904	172.9	172.5
poly(decyl vinyl ether)	0.883	208.7	205.7
poly(dodecyl vinyl ether)	0.892	238.1	238.6
poly(vinyl propionate)	1.02	98.1	90.2
poly(vinyl methyl sulphide)	1.18	62.8	64.1
poly(vinyl butyl sulphide)	0.98	118.6	113.5
poly(methyl acrylate)	1.22	70.6	70.1
poly(ethyl acrylate)	1.12	89.4	86.6
poly(butyl methacrylate)	1.053	135.0	137.2
poly(hexyl methacrylate)	1.007	169.1	170.1
poly(2-ethylbutyl methacrylate)	1.040	163.8	169.8
poly(1-methylpentyl methacrylate)	1.013	168.1	169.8
poly(octyl methacrylate)	0.971	204.2	203.0
poly(dodecyl methacrylate)	0.929	273.8	268.8
polybutadiene	0.892	60.7	60.7
poly(2-methylbutadiene)	0.91	74.8	75.7
polypentadiene	0.89	76.5	76.9
poly(chlorobutadiene)	1.243	71.2	71.3
polyformaldehyde	1.25	24.0	25.0
poly(ethylene oxide)	1.13	38.9	41.4
poly(tetramethylene oxide)	0.98	73.5	74.3
polyacetaldehyde	1.071	41.2	41.2
poly(propylene oxide)	1.00	58.1	57.6
poly[3,3-bis(chloromethyl)oxacyclobutane]	1.386	111.8	115.9

Conversion factors: 1 g/cm^3 = 10^3 kg/m^3; 1 cm^3/mol = 10^{-6} m^3/mol.

TABLE 4.4.

Group contributions for V_r compared with those for V_1 (cm³/mol)

Groups		V_r	V_1
bivalent	$-CH_2-$	16.45	16.1–16.6
	$-CH(CH_3)-$	32.65	32.2–33.5
	$-C(CH_3)_2-$	50.35	47.6–49.8
	$-CH=CH-$	27.75	24.3–26.5
	$-CH=C(CH_3)-$	42.8	40.3–42.6
	$-C_6H_4-$	61.4	58.6–61.8
	$-CH(C_6H_5)-$	74.5	74.5–78.8
	$-CHF-$	19.85	16.3–18.5
	$-CHCl-$	28.25	23.5–26.6
	$-O-$	8.5	5.5– 6.8
	$-COO-$ (general)	24.6	15.5–23.9
	$-COO-$ (acrylic)	21.0	
	$-S-$	15.0	10.8–15.5
tetravalent	$-\overset{\mid}{\underset{\mid}{C}}-$	4.75	
trivalent	$-\overset{\mid}{CH}-$	9.85	
	$-CH=\overset{\mid}{C}-$	20.0	
monovalent	$-CH_3$	22.8	
	$-C_6H_5$	64.65	
	$-F$	10.0	
	$-Cl$	18.4	

Conversion factor: 1 cm³/mol = 10^{-6} m³/mol.

25°C are in the glassy state at room temperature. Table 4.5 gives a survey of all the available literature data on the densities of these polymers. For each polymer the molar volume per structural unit has been calculated from the density.

As was to be expected, the molar volumes of glassy polymers differ from the values calculated for the rubbery state with the group contributions mentioned in table 4.4. Therefore, special group contribution values for the glassy state have been calculated from the available literature data. In table 4.6 the group contributions to V_g are compared with those for V_r. Although both contribution values for the same group are always of about the same magnitude, there are significant differences. As for rubbery polymers, it was necessary to use a special value for the contribution of an "acrylic" COO group.

In table 4.5 the experimental values of V_g are compared with values calculated with the group contributions mentioned in table 4.6. The mean deviation between experimental and calculated values is 1.2%.

A disadvantage of the method presented for calculating V_r and V_g from group contributions is that these contributions are available for a limited number of groups only. For

TABLE 4.5.

Molar volumes of glassy amorphous polymers at 25°C

Polymer	ρ_g (g/cm^3)	V_g (cm^3/mol)	
		experimental	calculated
poly(4-methylpentene)	0.84	100.2	98.4
polystyrene	1.05	99.0	98.0
poly(α-methylstyrene)	1.065	111.0	117.1
poly(o-methylstyrene)	1.027	115.1	114.7
poly(p-methylstyrene)	1.04	113.7	114.7
poly(p-tert.-butylstyrene)	0.95	168.7	167.1
poly(m-trifluoromethylstyrene)	1.32	130.5	128.1
poly(4-fluoro-2-trifluoromethylstyrene)	1.43	132.9	133.0
poly(3-phenylpropene)	1.046	113.0	113.9
poly(vinyl chloride)	1.385	45.1	45.2
poly(chlorotrifluoroethylene)	1.92	60.7	61.8
poly(3,3,3-trifluoropropylene)	1.58	60.8	62.6
poly(vinylcyclohexane)	0.95	116.0	116.0
poly(vinyl alcohol)	1.26	35.0	35.0
poly(vinyl methyl ketone)	1.12	62.6	62.6
poly(vinyl acetate)	1.19	72.4	72.2
poly(vinyl chloroacetate)	1.45	83.1	84.1
poly(tert.-butyl acrylate)	1.00	128.2	119.9
poly(methyl methacrylate)	1.17	85.6	86.5
poly(ethyl methacrylate)	1.119	102.0	102.4
poly(propyl methacrylate)	1.08	118.7	118.2
poly(isopropyl methacrylate)	1.033	124.1	119.9
poly(sec.-butyl methacrylate)	1.052	135.2	135.7
poly(tert.-butyl methacrylate)	1.022	139.1	138.9
poly(isopentyl methacrylate) .	1.032	151.4	151.6
poly(1-methylbutyl methacrylate)	1.030	151.7	151.6
poly(neopentyl methacrylate)	0.993	157.3	154.8
poly(1,3-dimethylbutyl methacrylate)	1.005	169.5	169.1
poly(3,3-dimethylbutyl methacrylate)	1.001	170.1	170.6
poly(1,2,2-trimethylpropyl methacrylate)	0.991	171.9	172.3
poly(cyclohexyl methacrylate)	1.10	152.9	153.3
poly(p-cyclohexylphenyl methacrylate)	1.115	219.1	218.8
poly(phenyl methacrylate)	1.21	134.0	135.3
poly(benzyl methacrylate)	1.179	149.5	151.2
poly(1-phenylethyl methacrylate)	1.129	168.5	168.6
poly(diphenylmethyl methacrylate)	1.168	216.0	217.5
poly(1,2-diphenylethyl methacrylate)	1.147	232.2	233.3
poly(2-chloroethyl methacrylate)	1.32	112.6	114.2
poly(2,2,2-trifluoro-1-methylethyl methacrylate)	1.34	134.4	133.3
poly(1-o-chlorophenylethyl methacrylate)	1.269	177.1	181.4
poly(ethyl chloroacrylate)	1.39	96.8	98.4
poly(propyl chloroacrylate)	1.30	114.3	114.2
poly(isopropyl chloroacrylate)	1.27	117.0	115.9
poly(butyl chloroacrylate)	1.24	131.1	130.1
poly(sec.-butyl chloroacrylate)	1.24	131.1	131.7
poly(cyclohexyl chloroacrylate)	1.25	151.0	149.3

(Continued on p. 58)

TABLE 4.5. (continued)

Polymer	ρ_g (g/cm^3)	V_g (cm^3/mol)	
		experimental	calculated
polyacrylonitrile	1.184	44.8	44.8
polymethacrylonitrile	1.10	61.0	63.9
poly(methyl cyanoacrylate)	1.304	85.2	82.1
poly(dimethyl phenylene oxide)	1.07	112.3	114.1
poly(diphenyl phenylene oxide)	1.14	214.3	211.7
poly(glycolic acid)	1.60	36.3	38.9
polypivalolactone	1.097	91.2	91.3
poly(ethylene terephthalate)	1.33	144.5	143.2
poly(ethylene phthalate)	1.338	143.6	143.2
poly(ethylene isophthalate)	1.335	144.0	143.2
poly(tetramethylene isophthalate)	1.268	173.7	174.9
poly(cyclohexylenedimethylene terephthalate)	1.19	230.5	231.0
nylon 6	1.084	104.4	104.2
nylon 8	1.04	135.8	135.9
nylon 11	1.01	181.5	183.4
nylon 12	0.99	199.3	199.3
nylon 6,6	1.07	211.5	208.3
nylon 6,10	1.04	271.5	271.7
poly(4,4-methylenediphenylene carbonate)	1.24	182.4	178.3
poly(4,4-isopropylenediphenylene carbonate)	1.20	211.9	214.8
poly(thiodiphenylene carbonate)	1.355	180.2	180.2

Conversion factors: 1 g/cm^3 = 10^3 kg/m^3; 1 cm^3/mol = 10^{-6} m^3/mol.

polymers containing other structural groups, however, atomic contributions may still be used.

Molecular volumes of amorphous polymers, calculated with atomic contributions as mentioned by Traube, are generally too small. Therefore a set of improved atomic contributions to V_r and V_g, based on the group contributions of tables 4.4 and 4.6, have been calculated. They are shown in table 4.7, together with Traube's values.

A similar method has been proposed by Malone and Albert (1973). These authors start from the additive properties of the parachor P_S a quantity which will be discussed in Chapter 8. It is defined as

$$P_S = V\gamma^{1/4} \tag{4.2}$$

where γ = surface tension.

Although the surface tension of polymers varies from 19 to 46 mN/m, the variation in $\gamma^{1/4}$ is rather small, so that $\gamma^{1/4}$ may as a first approximation be assumed to be constant, the mean value being 2.47 (mN/m)$^{1/4}$. Thus

$$P_S \approx 2.47 \, V \qquad V = P_S/2.47 \tag{4.2a}$$

Therefore values of the atomic contributions to P_S as mentioned in the literature may be used to calculate approximate values of the atomic contributions to V. The values proposed by Malone and Albert are also mentioned in table 4.7. Although these values are quite different from those in the recommended set, they provide reasonably accurate molecular volumes for a number of polymers. An analogous method proposed by Sewell (1973) gives less accurate results.

TABLE 4.6

Group contributions for V_g compared with those for V_r (cm^3/mol)

Groups		V_g	V_r
bivalent	$-CH_2-$	15.85	16.45
	$-CH(CH_3)-$	33.35	32.65
	$-C(CH_3)_2-$	52.4	50.35
	$-C_6H_4-$	65.5	61.4
	$-CH(C_6H_5)-$	82.15	74.5
	$-C_6H_3(CH_3)-$	83.4	–
	$-C_6H_2(CH_3)_2-$	104.1	–
	$-C_6H_{10}-$	87.8	–
	$-CH(C_6H_{11})-$	100.15	–
	$-CHF-$	20.35	19.85
	$-CHCl-$	29.35	28.25
	$-CH(CN)-$	28.95	–
	$-O-$	10.0	8.5
	$-CO-$	13.4	–
	$-COO-$ (general)	23.0	24.6
	$-COO-$ (acrylic)	18.25	21.0
	$-O-CO-O-$	31.4	–
	$-CH(OH)-$	19.15	–
	$-CONH-$	24.9	–
	$-S-$	17.8	15.0
tetravalent	$-\overset{\mid}{\underset{\mid}{C}}-$	4.6	4.75
	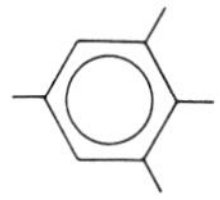 (benzene ring structure)	56.3	–
trivalent	$-\overset{\mid}{C}H-$	9.45	9.85
	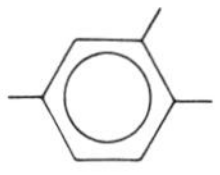 (benzene ring structure)	59.5	–
monovalent	$-CH_3$	23.9	22.8
	$-C_6H_5$	72.7	64.65
	$-C_6H_{11}$	90.7	–
	$-F$	10.9	10.0
	$-Cl$	19.9	18.4
	$-CN$	19.5	–
	$-OH$	9.7	–

Conversion factor: 1 cm^3/mol = 10^{-6} m^3/mol.

Volume relaxation

With respect to the values of V_g mentioned it should be noted that an amorphous polymer is not in thermodynamic equilibrium below its glass transition temperature T_g.

TABLE 4.7

Atomic contributions to molecular volume (cm^3/mol)

Element	Recommended values		Traube	Malone and Albert
	V_r	V_g		
C	10.0	10.0	9.9	3.65
H	3.2	3.3	3.1	6.3
double bond	0	–	(−1.7)	+7.2
ring	−13.2	−7.3	−13.2	+0.3
F	6.6	7.0	5.5	10.6
Cl	15.0	16.0	13.2	22.4
O (ether)	8.5	10.0	5.5	8.0
O (other)	6.4	5.4	5.5	11.1
N	–	6.0	1.5	7.1
S	15.0	17.8	15.5	19.9

Therefore glassy polymers show *volume relaxation*: the volume gradually changes with time. As amorphous glassy polymers are usually prepared by cooling at a certain rate to below T_g, this relaxation will usually be a contraction. It is a non-linear process which will continue for extremely long periods, except at temperatures in the immediate vicinity of T_g.

The values of V_g (20°C) should therefore be considered to represent practical conditions of polymer preparation, i.e. "normal" cooling rates. It is possible to prepare glassy polymers with varying molecular volumes by varying the thermal history.

Molar volume of semi-crystalline polymers

For a small number of polymers, the densities of both the purely amorphous and the purely crystalline states are known. These data have been collected in table 4.8. The ratio ρ_c/ρ_a shows a considerable variation; the mean value of this ratio is 1.13. The data are insufficient to make a distinction between rubbery and glassy amorphous polymers, but apparently

$$\rho_c/\rho_r > \rho_c/\rho_g$$

Tentatively a somewhat better approximation may be proposed:

$$\rho_c/\rho_r \approx 1.15 \text{ (to be used if } T_g < 298 \text{ K)}$$

$$\rho_c/\rho_g \approx 1.07 \text{ (to be used if } T_g > 298 \text{ K)}$$

For semi-crystalline polymers, the following very approximative relationship may be used

$$\frac{\rho_{sc}}{\rho_a} = \frac{V_a}{V_{sc}} \approx 1 + 0.13 x_c \tag{4.3}$$

where x_c = degree of crystallinity.

TABLE 4.8

Data of crystalline polymers

Polymer	ρ_c (g/cm^3)	ρ_a (g/cm^3)	ρ_c/ρ_a
polyethylene	1.00	0.85	1.18
polypropylene	0.95	0.85	1.12
polybutene	0.95	0.86	1.10
polyisobutylene	0.94	0.84	1.12
polypentene	0.92	0.85	1.08
polystyrene	1.13	1.05	1.08
poly(vinyl chloride)	1.52	1.39	1.10
poly(vinylidene fluoride)	2.00	1.74	1.15
poly(vinylidene chloride)	1.95	1.66	1.17
poly(trifluorochloroethylene)	2.19	1.92	1.14
poly(tetrafluoroethylene)	2.35	2.00	1.17
poly(vinyl alcohol)	1.35	1.26	1.07
poly(methyl methacrylate)	1.23	1.17	1.05
polybutadiene	1.01	0.89	1.14
polyisoprene (cis)	1.00	0.91	1.10
polyisoprene (trans)	1.05	0.90	1.16
polyacetylene	1.15	1.00	1.15
poly(methylene oxide)	1.54	1.25	1.25
poly(ethylene oxide)	1.33	1.12	1.19
poly(propylene oxide)	1.15	1.00	1.15
poly(tetramethylene oxide)	1.18	0.98	1.20
polypivalolactone	1.23	1.08	1.13
poly(ethylene terephthalate)	1.50	1.33	1.13
nylon 6	1.23	1.08	1.14
nylon 6,6	1.24	1.07	1.16
nylon 6,10	1.19	1.04	1.14
poly(bisphenol A carbonate)	1.31	1.20	1.09
Average			1.13

Conversion factor: 1 g/cm^3 = 10^3 kg/m^3.

Van der Waals volume

The Van der Waals volume of a molecule may be defined as the space occupied by this molecule, which is impenetrable to other molecules with normal thermal energies (i.e. corresponding with ordinary temperatures). For comparison with other quantities discussed in this chapter, the Van der Waals volume will be expressed in cm^3 per mole of unit structure.

For an approximate calculation, the Van der Waals volume is assumed to be bounded by the outer surface of a number of interpenetrating spheres. The radii of the spheres are assumed to be (constant) atomic radii for the elements involved and the distances between the centres of the spheres are the (constant) bond distances.

The contribution of a given atom with radius r_1 to the Van der Waals volume is then

TABLE 4.9

Van der Waals volume contributions (cm^3/mol)

Group	Bondi	Slonimskii et al.	Most probable value	$\dfrac{V_g}{V_W}$	$\dfrac{V_r}{V_W}$
$-CH_2-$	10.23	10.3	10.25	1.55	1.60
$-CH(CH_3)-$	20.45	20.8	20.5	1.63	1.59
$-C(CH_3)_2-$	30.67	31.3	31	1.69	1.62
$-CH=CH-$	16.94	18.1	17.5	–	1.59
$-CH=C(CH_3)-$	27.16	28.7	27.5	–	1.56
$-C_6H_{10}-$	53.34	54.5	54	1.63	–
$-CH(C_6H_{11})-$	63.58	64.8	64	1.56	–
$-C_6H_4-$	43.32	45.2	43.5	1.51	1.41
$-CH(C_6H_5)-$	52.62	55.7	53	1.55	1.41
$-CHF-$	13.0	13.4	13	1.57	1.53
$-CHCl-$	19.0	19.2	19	1.54	1.49
$-CF_2-$	15.3	16.6	16	1.65	1.55
$-CCl_2-$	27.8	28.2	28	1.59	1.48
$-CH(CN)-$	21.48	22.3	22	1.32	–
$-O-$	3.7	5.8	5.8	1.72	1.47
$-CO-$	11.7	11.2	11	1.22	–
$-COO-$	15.2	17.0	15	1.53	1.64
$-O-CO-O-$	18.9	23.0	19	1.65	–
$-CH(OH)-$	14.82	14.8	15	1.28	–
$-CONH-$	19.56	18.1	18	1.38	–
$-S-$	10.8	–	10	1.78	1.50

Conversion factor 1 cm^3/mol = 10^{-6} m^3/mol

given by

$$\Delta V_W = N_A \left[\frac{4}{3}\pi r_1^3 - \Sigma \pi h_i^2 \left(r_1 - \frac{h_i}{3} \right) \right]$$ (4.4)

$$h_i = r_1 - \frac{l_i}{2} - \frac{r_1^2}{2l_i} + \frac{r_i^2}{2l_i}$$

where N_A is Avogradro number, r_i is radius of atom i, l_i is bond distance between the atom considered and atom i.

According to this definition, the volume contribution ΔV_W of the atom considered is not an additive quantity, as its value depends on the nature of the surrounding atoms. It is possible to derive a set of truly additive quantities, if these are expressed as the contribution of a bivalent group surrounded by two CH_2 groups.

Table 4.9 gives a survey of a number of group contributions to V_W for bivalent groups, according to Bondi (1964, 1968) and Slonimskii et al. (1970). In general the values mentioned by the two authors show a good correspondence. The most important exception is the contribution of oxygen, for which Slonimskii et al. derived a much larger value than Bondi. Probably the value of Slonimskii et al. is more realistic.

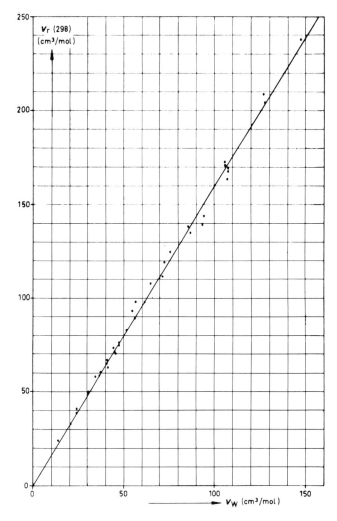

Fig. 4.1. Molar volume of rubbery amorphous polymers as a function of the Van der Waals volume.

Correlations between the various molar volumes and the Van der Waals volume

A certain parallelism between the Van der Waals volume and the real molar volume in a given state for various polymers is quite probable, as all these molar volumes obey analogous additivity rules. This is illustrated in figs. 4.1, 4.2 and 4.3, where V_r, V_g and V_c, respectively, have been plotted against V_W for all the available literature data.

In each figure, the points can be approximately represented by a straight line through the origin. Good correspondence is found between V_g and V_W and between V_r and V_W. It should be noted, however, that this parallelism does not hold for the separate group contributions. This may be seen in table 4.9, where the group contributions to V_g, V_r and V_W are compared. Obviously, the large variations in the group contribution ratios

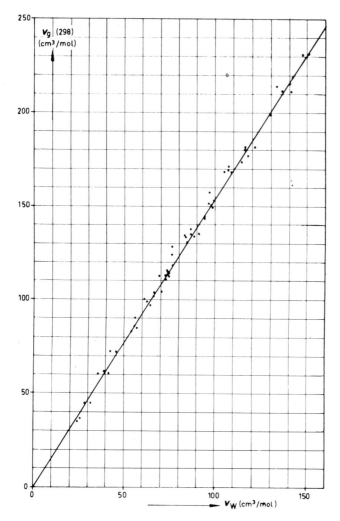

Fig. 4.2. Molar volume of glassy amorphous polymers as a function of the Van der Waals volume.

are partly compensated when the groups are combined in the structural unit of a polymer.

The following mean values for the molar volume ratios have been found:

$$\frac{V_r(298)}{V_W} = 1.60$$

$$\frac{V_g(298)}{V_W} = 1.55 \tag{4.5}$$

$$\frac{V_c(298)}{V_W} = 1.435$$

The value of 1.435, mentioned for the quotient $V_c(298)/V_W$, is based on data for the polymers mentioned in table 4.8. Fig. 4.3 includes all the available data on crystalline polymers collected by Lewis (1968). These data provide a mean value of $V_c(298)/V_W = 1.44$, but may include some semi-crystalline polymers.

Molar volumes calculated with the aid of the above-mentioned ratios show mean deviations of about 3% for V_r and V_g and of about 6% for V_c when compared with experimental values.

Zero point molar volume ($V^0(0)$)

Timmermans (1913) and Mathews (1916) introduced the concept of zero point density based on the extrapolation of densities of crystalline and liquid substances to 0 K. Sugden (1927) and Biltz (1934) developed an additive system for deriving values of $V^0(0)$ from chemical constitution. The zero point volume is closely related to the Van der Waals volume. According to Bondi (1968a) a good approximation is given by the following ex-

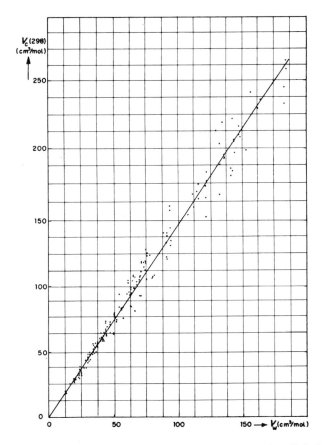

Fig. 4.3. Molar volume of crystalline polymers as a function of the Van der Waals volume.

pression:

$$\frac{V^0(0)}{V_W} = \frac{V_c(0)}{V_W} \approx 1.3.$$

(4.5a)

Example 4.1.

Estimate the densities of amorphous and crystalline poly(ethylene terephthalate).

Solution

The structural unit is

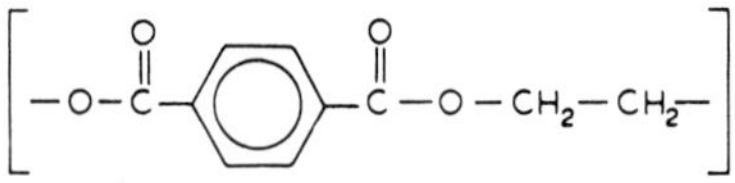

The molecular weight of this structural unit is 192.2. At room temperature, amorphous poly-(ethylene terephthalate) is in the glassy state. The following group contributions may be taken from tables 4.6 and 4.9:

groups	$V_g(298)$	V_W
$1\left(-\bigcirc-\right)$ 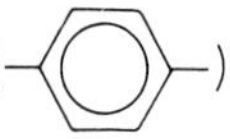	65.5	43.32
$2(-COO-)$	46.0	30.40
$2(-CH_2-)$	31.7	20.46
	143.2	94.18

So $\rho_g(298) = \dfrac{192.2}{143.2} = 1.34 \ g/cm^3$.

This is in good agreement with the experimental value

$\rho_g(298) = 1.33 \ g/cm^3$.

The ratio $\dfrac{V_g(298)}{V_W} = \dfrac{143.2}{94.18} = 1.52$

which is in good correspondence with eq. (4.5).

Application of eq. (4.3) leads to

$\rho_c(298) = 1.13\rho_g(298) = 1.52 \ g/cm^3$.

Experimental values of $\rho_c(298)$ range from 1.46 to 1.52 g/cm^3.

B. THERMAL EXPANSION

Definitions

A number of different but related notations are used to describe the thermal expansion of matter:

1. *the specific thermal expansivity:*

$$\left(\frac{\partial v}{\partial T}\right)_p \equiv e \qquad \text{(dimension: } cm^3/g \cdot K \text{ or } m^3/kg \cdot K)$$

2. *the temperature coefficient of density:*

$$\left(\frac{\partial \rho}{\partial T}\right)_p \equiv q \qquad \text{(dimension: } g/cm^3 \cdot K \text{ or } kg/m^3 \cdot K)$$

3. *the coefficient of thermal expansion:*

$$\frac{1}{v}\left(\frac{\partial v}{\partial T}\right)_p \equiv \alpha \qquad \text{(dimension: } K^{-1})$$

4. *the linear coefficient of thermal expansion:*

$$\frac{1}{L}\left(\frac{\partial L}{\partial T}\right)_p \equiv \beta \qquad \text{(dimension: } K^{-1})$$

5. *the molar thermal expansivity:*

$$\left(\frac{\partial V}{\partial T}\right)_p = E \qquad \text{(dimension: } cm^3/mol \cdot K \text{ or } m^3/mol \cdot K)$$

These quantities are interrelated in the following way:

$$e = -v^2 q \qquad e = \alpha v = \frac{\alpha}{\rho} \qquad \alpha = 3\beta$$

$$q = -e\rho^2 \qquad q = -\alpha\rho = -\frac{\alpha}{v} \qquad E = Me = \alpha V = \alpha\frac{M}{\rho}$$

(4.6)

Phenomenology

Experimental data available suggest that the thermal expansivity of a glass is of the same order as that of the crystal and that no great error is made by putting:

$$\alpha_g \approx \alpha_c \text{ or } e_g \approx e_c. \tag{4.7}$$

The expansivity of a solid polymer is not exactly independent of temperature, but generally shows a gradual increase with temperature (perceptible if the temperature range covered is large). However, it is convenient to ignore this gradual increase compared with the jump in expansivity on passing through the glass transition, and to represent the volume–temperature curve by two straight lines intersecting at the transition point.

It is common practice to report the expansivities immediately below (e_g) and above (e_l) the transition.

Empirically it has been found that often $q(= -\alpha\rho = -e\rho^2)$ is practically independent of temperature over a wide range (see Bondi, 1968c).

The expansivity of the rubbery or liquid polymer is always larger than that of the glassy or crystalline polymer.

TABLE 4.10

Some empirical rules

Rule	Proposed by	Formula No.
$\alpha_l - \alpha_g \approx 5 \times 10^{-4}$ K^{-1}	Tobolsky/Bueche (1960/1962)	(4.8)
$\alpha_l T_g \approx 0.16$	Boyer and Spencer (1944)	(4.9)
$\alpha_c T_m \approx 0.11$	Bondi (1968d)	(4.10)
$(\alpha_l - \alpha_g) T_g \approx 0.115$	Simha and Boyer (1962)	(4.11)

Empirical rules

A number of interesting rules are summarized in table 4.10.

Theory

The expansion of a material on heating is a phenomenon which depends on internal — mostly intermolecular — forces. Bond lengths between atoms are virtually independent of temperature. This also holds for bond lengths between segments of a polymer chain. Polymer systems, therefore, have lower expansivities than related low-molecular liquids.

Below the glass temperature the expansivity is reduced still further. When passing the glass transition point, the structural changes contributing to the expansion in liquids disappear.

The Simha–Boyer model

One of the most useful — though simplified — models to visualize thermal expansion phenomena is based on a concept of Simha and Boyer, and is reproduced in fig. 4.4. When a liquid is cooled below a potential crystalline melting temperature, two things may happen: it either crystallizes or becomes an undercooled liquid; the latter occurs when crystallization is impeded, e.g. by high viscosity and low molecular symmetry.

Undercooling of the liquid may occur until a temperature is reached at which the free volume of the molecules becomes so small that molecular movements of the whole molecule or of large chain segments are no longer possible: then the glassy state is reached. The temperature at which this occurs is the glass transition temperature.

It is assumed that the molar volumes of undercooled liquid and crystalline solid at 0 K are equal ($= V_c(0)$) and that eq. (4.7) holds, so that $\Delta V_g(0) = \Delta V_g$.

On the basis of fig. 4.4 some simple approximative relationships for the molar heat capacities may be derived. From fig. 4.4 it is obvious that

$$\frac{V_l(T) - V_c(0)}{T} = \frac{V_l(298) - V_c(0)}{298} = E_l \tag{4.12}$$

Likewise

$$E_g = \frac{V_g(T) - V_g(0)}{T} \approx \frac{V_c(T) - V_c(0)}{T} = \frac{V_c(298) - V_c(0)}{298} = E_c. \tag{4.13}$$

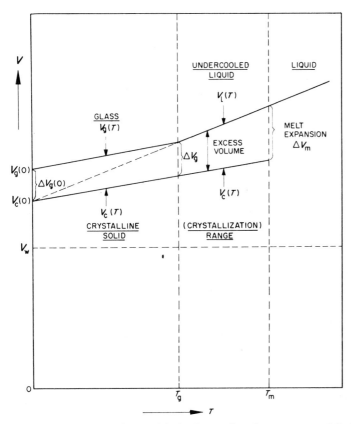

Fig. 4.4. Thermal expansion model of polymers (based on a concept of Simha and Boyer, 1962).

According to eq. (4.4), $V_l(298) = V_r(298) = 1.60\ V_W$ and $V_c(298) = 1.435\ V_W$. If it is further assumed (see Bondi, 1968a) that $V_c(0) = 1.3\ V_W$, we obtain

$$E_l \approx 10 \times 10^{-4}\ V_W \tag{4.12a}$$

$$E_g \approx 4.5 \times 10^{-4}\ V_W. \tag{4.13a}$$

These relationships may be compared with experimental data. In fig. 4.5 literature values of E_l and E_g are plotted against V_W. Although there is a considerable amount of scatter, the relationships between E_l, E_g and V_W may approximately be represented by two straight lines, corresponding to the following mean values for the coefficients.

$$E_l = 10.0 \times 10^{-4}\ V_W \tag{4.12b}$$

$$E_g = 4.5 \times 10^{-4}\ V_W. \tag{4.13b}$$

The correspondence between eqs. (4.12a) – (4.12b) and (4.13a) – (4.13b) is remarkable.

TABLE 4.11

Thermal expansivity of polymers

Polymer	M (g/mol)	V_W (cm³/mol)	e_g exp. (10^{-4} cm³/g · K)	e_l exp. (10^{-4} cm³/g · K)	E_g exp. (10^{-4} cm³/mol · K)
polyethylene	28.0	20.46	2.4/3.6	7.5/9.6	67/101
polypropylene	42.1	30.68	2.2	5.5/9.4	93
poly(1-butene)	56.1	40.91	3.8	8.8	214
poly(1-pentene)	70.1	51.14	–	9.2	–
polyisobutylene	56.1	40.90	1.6/2.0	5.6/6.9	90/112
poly(4-methyl-1-pentene)	84.2	61.36	3.85	7.6	324
polystyrene	104.1	62.85	1.7/2.7	4.3/6.8	177/281
poly(vinyl chloride)	62.5	29.23	1.4/2.1	4.2/5.2	88/131
poly(vinylidene fluoride)	64.0	25.56	1.2	2.1/4.6	77
poly(chlorotrifluoroethylene)	116.5	36.90	1.0/1.5	2.0/3.5	117/175
poly(vinyl alcohol)	44.0	25.05	3.0	–	132
poly(vinyl acetate)	86.1	45.88	1.8/2.3	5.0/6.0	155/198
poly(methyl acrylate)	86.1	45.88	1.8/2.7	4.6/5.6	155/232
poly(ethyl acrylate)	100.1	56.11	2.8	6.1	280
poly(isopropyl acrylate)	114.2	66.33	2.2/2.6	6.1/6.3	251/297
poly(butyl acrylate)	128.2	76.57	2.6	6.0	333
poly(sec.-butyl acrylate)	128.2	76.56	2.75	6.1	353
poly(2,2-dimethylpropyl acrylate)	142.2	86.78	2.0	6.5	284
poly(1-ethylpropyl acrylate)	142.2	86.79	3.3	5.9	469
poly(methyl methacrylate)	100.1	56.10	2.3	5.2/5.5	230
poly(ethyl methacrylate)	114.1	66.33	2.8	5.4/5.7	319
poly(propyl methacrylate)	128.2	76.56	3.15	5.8	404
poly(isopropyl methacrylate)	128.2	76.55	2.0/2.4	6.2	256/308
poly(butyl methacrylate)	142.2	86.79	–	5.9/6.3	–
poly(isobutyl methacrylate)	142.2	86.78	2.2/2.5	5.8/6.1	313/356
poly(sec.-butyl methacrylate)	142.2	86.78	3.4	6.3	483
poly(tert.-butyl methacrylate)	142.2	86.77	2.7	6.9	384
poly(hexyl methacrylate)	170.3	107.25	–	6.3/6.6	–
poly(2-ethylbutyl methacrylate)	170.3	107.24	–	5.8	–
poly(octyl methacrylate)	198.4	127.71	–	5.8	–
poly(dodecyl methacrylate)	254.4	168.63	3.8	6.8	967
poly(2-methoxyethyl methacrylate)	144.2	80.26	–	5.45	–
poly(2-propoxyethyl methacrylate)	172.2	100.72	–	6.1	–
poly(cyclohexyl methacrylate)	168.2	99.23	2.7	–	454
polybutadiene	54.1	37.40	2.0	6.4/7.7	108
polyisoprene	68.1	47.61	–	6.0/8.3	–
polychloroprene	88.5	45.56	–	4.2/5.0	–
polyformaldehyde	30.0	13.93	1.8	–	54
poly(ethylene oxide)	44.1	24.16	–	6.2/6.6	–
poly(tetramethylene oxide)	72.1	44.62	–	6.9	–
polyacetaldehyde	44.1	24.15	2.1	6.3	93
poly(propylene oxide)	58.1	34.38	–	7.0/7.3	–
polyepichlorohydrin	92.5	42.56	–	5.6	–
poly(ethylene terephthalate)	192.2	94.18	2.2/2.4	6.0/7.4	423/461

E_g calc. (10^{-4} cm^3/mol · K)	E_l exp. (10^{-4} cm^3/mol · K)	E_l calc. (10^{-4} cm^3/mol · K)	$e_l - e_g$ (10^{-4} cm^3/g · K)	T_g (K)	ρ (g/cm^3)	$(\alpha_l - \alpha_g)T_g$ ($\times 10^4$)
92	210/269	205	3.9/7.2	195	0.87	660/1220
138	232/396	307	3.3/7.2	263	0.85	740/1610
184	494	409	5.0	249	0.85	1060
230	645	511	–	–	–	–
184	314/388	409	3.6/5.3	198	0.87	620/910
276	640	614	3.75	302	0.84	950
283	448/708	629	2.6/5.1	373	1.06	1030/2020
132	262/325	292	2.1/3.8	358	1.38	1040/1880
115	134/294	256	0.9/3.4	235	1.74	370/1390
166	233/408	369	0.5/2.5	325	2.03	330/1650
113	–	251	–	–	–	–
206	413/517	459	2.7/4.2	303	1.19	970/1510
206	396/482	459	1.9/3.8	282	1.22	650/1310
252	611	561	3.3	252	1.12	930
298	697/719	663	3.5/4.1	270	1.08	1020/1190
345	769	766	3.4	224	1.08	820
345	782	766	3.35	256	1.05	900
391	924	868	4.5	295	1.04	1380
391	839	868	2.6	267	1.04	720
252	520/550	561	2.9/3.2	387	1.17	1310/1450
298	616/650	663	2.6/2.9	339	1.12	990/1100
345	744	766	2.65	310	1.08	890
345	795	766	3.8/4.2	354	1.04	1400/1540
391	839/896	868	–	–	–	–
391	825/867	868	3.3/3.9	320	1.04	1100/1300
391	896	868	2.9	333	1.04	1000
390	981	868	4.2	380	1.03	1640
483	1073/1124	1073	–	–	–	–
483	988	1072	–	–	–	–
575	1151	1277	–	–	–	–
759	1730	1686	3.0	218	0.93	610
361	786	803	–	–	–	–
453	1050	1007	–	–	–	–
447	–	992	–	–	–	–
168	346/417	374	4.4/5.7	171/259	0.89	670/1310
214	409/565	476	–	–	–	–
205	372/443	456	–	–	–	–
63	–	139	–	–	–	–
109	273/291	242	–	–	–	–
201	497	446	–	–	–	–
109	278	242	4.2	243	1.07	1090
155	407/424	344	–	–	–	–
192	518	426	–	–	–	–
424	1153/1422	942	3.6/5.2	342	1.33	1640/2360

(Continued on pp. 72/73)

TABLE 4.11. (continued)

Polymer	M (g/mol)	V_W (cm³/mol)	e_g exp. (10^{-4} cm³/g·K)	e_l exp. (10^{-4} cm³/g·K)	E_g exp. (10^{-4} cm³/mol·K)
poly(decamethylene terephthalate)	304.4	176.02	–	5.3	–
poly(ethylene phthalate)	192.2	94.18	1.7	5.9	327
poly(ethylene isophthalate)	192.2	94.18	2.0	3.8/5.3	384
poly[ethylene (2,6-naphthalate)]	242.2	119.86	–	4.9	–
poly[ethylene (2,7-naphthalate)]	242.2	119.86	–	5.0	–
nylon 6	113.2	70.71	–	5.6	–
nylon 7	127.2	80.94	3.5	–	445
nylon 8	141.2	91.17	3.1	–	438
nylon 9	155.2	101.40	3.6	–	559
nylon 10	169.3	111.63	3.5	–	593
nylon 11	183.3	121.86	3.6	–	660
nylon 12	197.3	132.09	3.8	–	750
nylon 10, 9	324.5	213.03	–	6.6	–
nylon 10, 10	338.5	223.26	–	6.7	–
poly(bisphenol carbonate)	254.3	136.21	2.4/2.9	4.8/5.9	610/737

mean value

Conversion factors: 1 g/mol = 10^{-3} kg/mol; 1 cm³/mol = 10^{-6} m³/mol; 1 cm³/g·K = 10^{-3} m³/kg·K; 1 cm³/mol·K = 10^{-6} m³/mol·K; 1 g/cm³ = 10^3 kg/m³.

In table 4.11 the literature values of E_1 and E_g are compared with values calculated with eqs. (4.12b) and (4.13b). The mean deviation is 8% for E_1 and 15% for E_g.

The simple model of fig. 4.4 may also be used to derive relationships equivalent with eqs. (4.8) to (4.11) mentioned above.

If $E_1 = 10.0 \times 10^{-4} V_W$, $E_g = 4.5 \times 10^{-4} V_W$; $V_r(298) = 1.60 V_W$ and $V_g(298) = 1.55 V_W$:

$$\alpha_1(298) \approx 10.0 \times 10^{-4}/1.60 \approx 6.25 \times 10^{-4},$$

$$\alpha_g(298) \approx 4.5 \times 10^{-4}/1.55 \approx 2.9 \times 10^{-4}$$

and

$$\alpha_1(298) - \alpha_g(298) \approx 3.4 \times 10^{-4} \text{ K}^{-1}. \tag{4.8a}$$

Eq. (4.8a) corresponds to the Tobolsky–Bueche equation, except for the much smaller coefficient.

The Simha–Boyer rule may be derived if it is assumed that the *fractional excess volume* ϕ_e at T_g is a universal constant for all polymers. In this case we have

$$V_1(T_g) = V_c(0) + E_1 T_g$$
$$V_g(T_g) = V_g(0) + E_g T_g.$$

E_g calc. $(10^{-4}$ cm³/mol · K)	E_l exp. $(10^{-4}$ cm³/mol · K)	E_l calc. $(10^{-4}$ cm³/mol · K)	$e_l - e_g$ $(10^{-4}$ cm³/g · K)	T_g (K)	ρ (g/cm³)	$(\alpha_1 - \alpha_g)T_g$ $(\times 10^4)$
792	1613	1760	–	–	–	–
424	1134	942	4.2	290	1.34	1630
424	730/1019	942	1.8/3.3	324	1.34	780/1430
539	1187	1199	–	–	–	–
539	1211	1199	–	–	–	–
318	634	707	–	–	–	–
364	–	809	–	–	–	–
410	–	912	–	–	–	–
456	–	1014	–	–	–	–
502	–	1116	–	–	–	–
548	–	1219	–	–	–	–
594	–	1321	–	–	–	–
959	2142	2130	–	–	–	–
1005	2268	2233	–	–	–	–
613	1220/1500	1362	1.9/3.5	423	1.20	960/1780
						1100

Since at T_g, $V_1 = V_g$, there results

$$(E_1 - E_g)T_g = V_g(0) - V_c(0) = \Delta V_g(0) = \Delta V_g$$

$$\frac{(E_1 - E_g)T_g}{V_g(T_g)} = \frac{E_1 T_g}{V_1(T_g)} - \frac{E_g T_g}{V_g(T_g)} = \frac{\Delta V_g}{V_g(T_g)} = \phi_e$$

so that

$$(\alpha_1 - \alpha_g)T_g = \phi_e = \text{constant.} \tag{4.11a}$$

In table 4.11 eq. (4.11a) is confronted with the available experimental data. The mean value of $\phi_e = 0.11$, with a mean deviation of 17%. This is in good correspondence with the value $\phi_e = 0.115$ proposed by Simha and Boyer.

Now eq. (4.11a) may be combined with the value derived above for the ratio $\alpha_1/\alpha_g = 2.17$. This leads to

$$\alpha_1 \left(1 - \frac{1}{2.17}\right) T_g = 0.11$$

$$\alpha_1 T_g = 0.20. \tag{4.9a}$$

Likewise $\alpha_c(2.17 - 1)T_g = 0.11$. If it is assumed that $T_m \approx 1.5\, T_g$

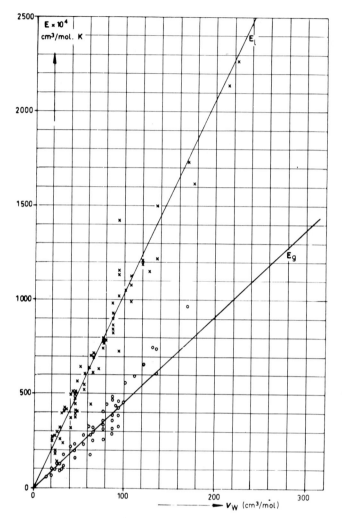

Fig. 4.5. E_l and E_g as a function of V_W.

$$\alpha_c T_m \approx 0.14. \tag{4.10a}$$

Eqs. (4.8a) – (4.11a) may be used for estimating values of α_l and α_g. Eqs. (4.12b) and (4.13b) are to be preferred, however, because they give smaller deviations from experimental values.

Expressions for the molar volume as a function of temperature

The following expressions for $V_r(T)$ $(= V_l(T))$, $V_g(T)$ and $V_c(T)$ may be generally used:

$$V_r(T) = V_1(T) = V_r(298) + E_1(T - 298)$$
$$\approx V_r(298)[1 + 0.625 \times 10^{-3}(T - 298)] = V_r(298)[0.81 + 0.625 \times 10^{-3}T]$$
$$\approx V_W[1.60 + 10^{-3}(T - 298)] = V_W[1.30 + 10^{-3}T]$$

$$V_g(T) = V_g(298) + E_g(T - 298) = V_g(298) + E_c(T - 298)$$
$$\approx V_g(298)[1 + 0.29 \times 10^{-3}(T - 298)] = V_g(298)[0.914 + 0.29 \times 10^{-3}T] \qquad (4.14)$$
$$\approx V_W[1.55 + 0.45 \times 10^{-3}(T - 298)] = V_W[1.415 + 0.45 \times 10^{-3}T]$$

$$V_c(T) = V_c(298) + E_c(T - 298)$$
$$\approx V_c(298)[1 + 0.29 \times 10^{-3}(T - 298)] = V_c(298)[0.914 + 0.29 \times 10^{-3}T]$$
$$\approx V_W[1.435 + 0.45 \times 10^{-3}(T - 298)] = V_W[1.30 + 0.45 \times 10^{-3}T]$$

Melting expansion

A quantity that is important both practically and theoretically is the increase in molar volume accompanying the melting process:

$$\Delta V_m = V_1(T_m) - V_c(T_m) . \qquad (4.15)$$

If it is assumed that fig. 4.4 is valid up to the melting point, ΔV_m can be calculated if ρ_a, ρ_c, E_1 and E_c are known. If one of these data is lacking, it can be estimated with the methods given in this chapter.

For $T_g < 298$ K

$$\Delta V_m = V_a(298) - V_c(298) + (T_m - 298)(E_1 - E_c) . \qquad (4.15a)$$

For $T_g > 298$ K

$$\Delta V_m = V_a(298) - V_c(298) + (T_m - T_g)(E_1 - E_c) . \qquad (4.15b)$$

Another method for estimating ΔV_m is also based on fig. 4.4. If it is assumed that

$$V_1(298) = 1.6 \, V_W \quad \text{and} \quad V_c(298) = 1.435 \, V_W$$

$$\Delta V_m = 0.165 \frac{T_m}{298} V_W . \qquad (4.16)$$

In table 4.12 values of ΔV_m, calculated according to both methods, are compared with published experimental values. The only conclusion which can be drawn is that the calculated values of ΔV_m are of the correct order of magnitude. The deviations between calculated and experimental values do not exceed the deviations between values mentioned by different investigators.

Example 4.2

Estimate the expansion coefficient of the poly(ethylene terephthalate) melt and its density at the extrusion temperature of 277°C (= 550 K).

TABLE 4.12

Calculated and experimental values of ΔV_m

Polymer	$\Delta V_m(cm^3/mol)$			References
	calc. (1) eq. (4.15)	calc. (2) eq. (4.16)	found	
polyethylene	6	4.7	3.1/5.9	Starkweather and Boyd (1960)/Robertson (1969)
polypropylene	8	7.7	9.6	Allen (1964)
polybutene	9	8.6	8.4	Allen (1964)
poly(4-methyl pentene)	16	17.4	9.8	Kirshenbaum (1965)
polyisobutylene	8	6.3	6.7	Allen (1964)
polystyrene	12	18.3	11.4	Allen (1964)
poly(tetrafluoroethylene)	11	10.4	7.3/14.5	Starkweather and Boyd (1960)/ Allen (1964)
polyformaldehyde	6	3.7	3.5/5.1	Starkweather and Boyd (1960)/Fortune and Malcolm (1960)
poly(ethylene oxide)	6	4.5	5.3	Allen (1964)
poly(ethylene terephthalate)	25	28.8	11.5	Allen (1964)
nylon 6, 6	44	42	24.8	Allen (1964)

Conversion factor: $1\ cm^3/mol = 10^{-6}\ m^3/mol$.

Solution

Application of eqs. (4.12b) and (4.13b) gives for the molar thermal expansivity:

$E_g = E_c = 4.5 \times 10^{-4}\ V_W = 4.5 \times 94.18 \times 10^{-4} = 4.2 \times 10^{-2}$

$E_l = 10.0 \times 10^{-4}\ V_W = 10.0 \times 94.18 \times 10^{-4} = 9.4 \times 10^{-2}$

So with $T_g = 343$ K the molar volume of the melt at 550 K will be:

$V_l(550) = V_g(298) + E_g(T_g - 298) + E_l(550 - T_g) =$

$= 143.2 + 4.2 \times 10^{-2} \times 45 + 9.4 \times 10^{-2} \times 207 = 164.3.$

This results in

$$\rho_l(550) = \frac{192.2}{164.3} = 1.17\ g/cm^3.$$

This is in excellent agreement with the experimental value of 1.16 (determination in the author's laboratory).

The thermal expansion coefficients follow from the definitions

specific thermal expansivity $\qquad e_l = \dfrac{E_l}{M} = \dfrac{9.4 \times 10^{-2}}{192.2} = 4.9 \times 10^{-4}\ cm^3/g \cdot K$

$$e_g = \frac{E_g}{M} = \frac{4.2 \times 10^{-2}}{192.2} = 2.2 \times 10^{-4}\ cm^3/g \cdot K.$$

The average literature values are 6×10^{-4} and 2.3×10^{-4} respectively, which is in very satisfactory agreement with the calculated values.

C. ISOTHERMAL COMPRESSION; VOLUME OF POLYMERS AT HIGH PRESSURE

One of the most suitable expressions to represent the pVT behaviour of liquids, including polymeric liquids, is the Tait-relation:

$$\frac{V(p=1) - V(p)}{V(p=1)} = C \ln\left(1 + \frac{p}{B'}\right) \tag{4.17}$$

where p is the pressure in bar, C is a dimensionless constant ($C \approx 0.1$) and B' is a temperature dependent constant with the same basic dimension as pressure. Simha et al. (1973) have shown that C is indeed almost constant ($C = 0.0894$) and that the constant B' can be expressed by

$$B' = b_1 \exp(-b_2 T') \tag{4.18}$$

where b_1 and b_2 are empirical constants and T' is the temperature in °C. Substituting (4.18) into (4.17) gives:

$$\frac{V(p=1) - V(p)}{V(p=1)} = C \times 2.3 \log\left\{1 + \frac{p}{b_1} \exp(b_2 T')\right\} \tag{4.19}$$

Quach and Simha (1971), Simha et al. (1973) and Beret and Prausnitz (1975) measured the relative volumes for a number of polymers, from which data of C, b_1 and b_2 can be derived. Table 4.13 exhibits these data. Constant b_2 has a value in the neighbourhood of 5×10^{-3} $(°C)^{-1}$ whereas b_1 is obviously dependent on the nature of the polymer. Further analysis showed that b_1 is proportional to the bulk modulus (B) at room temperature (the latter will be treated in Chapter 13); roughly $b_1 \approx 0.06\ B$ (in consistent units). So if no data for the constants are known, one may apply the approximative formula:

$$\frac{V(p=1) - V(p)}{V(p=1)} \approx 0.23 \log\left\{1 + \frac{p(\text{bar}) \times 10^5}{0.06\ B} \exp(5 \times 10^{-3}\ T')\right\} \tag{4.20}$$

where B is expressed in N/m^2.

TABLE 4.13

Constants of the Tait-equation for polymer melts

Polymer	$C \times 10^2$	b_1 (10^3 bar)	b_2 ($10^{-3}(°C)^{-1}$)
polyethylene (ld)	9.70	1.99	5.10
polyisobutylene	8.71	1.91	4.15
polystyrene	(8.94)	2.44	4.14
poly(vinyl chloride)	(8.94)	3.52	5.65
poly(methyl methacrylate)	(8.94)	3.85	6.72
poly(vinyl acetate)	10.46	2.23	3.43
poly(dimethyl siloxane)	10.09	1.04	5.85

Simha et al. (1973) showed that the Tait relation is also valid for polymers in the glassy state. In this case the value of b_1 is about the same as for polymer melts, but b_2 is smaller ($b_2 \approx 3 \times 10^{-3}$).

Example 4.3

Estimate the isothermal compression of polyethylene ($\rho = 0.92$) at a temperature of 200°C and a pressure of 1000 bar.

Solution

a. According to equation (4.19) and the data in table 4.13 we find:

$$\frac{\mathbf{V}(p = 1) - \mathbf{V}(p = 1000)}{\mathbf{V}(p = 1)} = 9.70 \times 10^{-2} \times 2.3 \log \left\{ 1 + \frac{1000}{1990} \exp(5.10 \times 10^{-3} \times 200) \right\}$$

$$= 0.223 \log \{1 + 0.503 \times 2.77\} = 0.085$$

b. According to equation (4.20) and the B-value of polyethylene ($B = 3.4 \times 10^9$ N/m^2; see table 13.5 in chapter 13) we get:

$$\frac{\mathbf{V}(p = 1) - \mathbf{V}(p = 1000)}{\mathbf{V}(p = 1)} = 0.23 \log \{1 + 0.49 \times 2.72\} = 0.085$$

The experimental value, according to Beret and Prausnitz (1975) is 0.085.

BIBLIOGRAPHY, CHAPTER 4

General references

Bondi, A., "Physical Properties of Molecular Crystals, Liquids and Glasses", Wiley, New York, 1968.
Brandrup, J. and Immergut, E.H. (Eds.), "Polymer Handbook", Interscience, New York, 1st ed. 1966; 2nd ed., 1975.
Bueche, F., "Physical Properties of Polymers", Interscience, New York, 1962.
Lewis, O. Griffin, "Physical Constants of Linear Homopolymers", Springer, Berlin, New York, 1968.
Tobolsky, A.V., "Properties and Structure of Polymers", Wiley, New York, 1960.

Special references

Allen, G., J. Appl. Chem. 14 (1964) 1.
Beret, S. and Prausnitz, J.M., Macromolecules 8 (1975) 536.
Biltz, W., "Raumchemie der festen Stoffe", Voss, Leipzig, 1934.
Bondi, A., J. Phys. Chem. 68 (1964) 441.
Bondi, A., See General references. (1968a): Chapters 3 and 4; (1968b): Chapter 14; (1968c): p. 236; (1968d): p. 50.
Boyer, R.F. and Spencer, R.S., J. Appl. Phys. 15 (1944) 398.
Bueche, F., see General references (1962): Chapter 4.
Davis, H.G. and Gottlieb, S., Fuel 42 (1963) 37.
Exner, O., Collection Czech. Chem. Comm. 32 (1967) 1.
Fedors, R.F., Polymer Eng. Sci. 14 (1974) 147, 472.
Fortune, L.R. and Malcolm, G.N., J. Phys. Chem. 64 (1960) 934.
Harrison, E.K., Fuel 44 (1965) 339; 45 (1966) 397.
Huggins, M.L., J. Am. Chem. Soc. 76 (1954) 843; "Physical Chemistry of High Polymers", Wiley, New York, 1958.

Kirshenbaum, I., J. Polymer Sci. A3 (1965) 1869.

Krause, S., Gormley, J.J., Roman, N., Shetter, J.A. and Watanabe, W.H., J. Polymer Sci. A3 (1965) 3573.

Kurtz, S.S. and Lipkin, M.R., Ind. Eng. Chem. 33 (1941) 779.

Le Bas, G., "Molecular Volumes of Liquid Chemical Compounds", Longmans, New York, 1915.

Li, K., Arnett, R.L., Epstein, M.B., Ries, R.B., Bitler, L.P., Lynch, J.M. and Rossini, F.D., J. Phys. Chem. 60 (1956) 1400.

Malone, W.M. and Albert, R., J. Appl. Polymer Sci. 17 (1973) 2457.

Mathews, A.P., J. Phys. Chem. 20 (1916) 554.

Quach, A. and Simha, R., J. Appl. Phys. 42 (1971) 4592.

Rheineck, A.E. and Lin, K.F., J. Paint Technol. 40 (1968) 611.

Robertson, R.E., Macromolecules 2 (1969) 250.

Sewell, J.H., J. Appl. Polymer Sci. 17 (1973) 1741.

Simha, R. and Boyer, R.F., J. Chem. Phys. 37 (1962) 1003.

Simha, R. and Hadden, S.T., J. Chem. Phys. 25 (1956) 702.

Simha, R., Wilson, P.S. and Olabisi, O., Kolloid-Z. 251 (1973) 402.

Slonimskii, G.L., Askadskii, A.A. and Kitaigorodskii, A.I., Visokomolekuliarnie Soedinenia 12 (1970) 494.

Starkweather, H.W. and Boyd, B.H., J. Phys. Chem. 64 (1960) 410.

Sugden, S., J. Chem. Soc. (1927) 1780 and 1786.

Timmermans, J., Bull. Soc. Chim. Belg. 26 (1913) 205.

Tatevskii, V.M., Benderskii, V.A. and Yarovoi, S.S., "Rules and Methods for Calculating the Physico-chemical Properties of Paraffinic Hydrocarbons", Pergamon Press, London, 1961.

Tobolsky, A.V., (1960), see General references, p. 85.

Traube, J., Ber. dtsch. Chem. Ges. 28 (1895) 2722.

Van Krevelen, D.W. and Hoftyzer, P.J., J. Appl. Polymer Sci. 13 (1969) 871.

Van Nes, K. and Van Westen, H.A., "Aspects of the Constitution of Mineral Oils", Elsevier, Amsterdam, 1951.

Wilson, Ph.S. and Simha, R., Macromolecules 6 (1973) 902.

CHAPTER 5

CALORIMETRIC PROPERTIES

The following properties belong to the calorimetric category: (1) *specific and molar heat capacities*, (2) *latent heats of crystallization or fusion.* It will be shown that both groups of properties can be calculated as additive molar quantities. Furthermore, starting from these properties the molar *entropy* and *enthalpy* of polymers can be estimated.

A. HEAT CAPACITY

Definitions

The specific heat capacity is the heat which must be added per kg of a substance to raise the temperature by one degree. The molar heat capacity is the specific heat multiplied by the molar weight (the molar weight of a structural unit in the case of polymers). Specific and molar heat capacity may be defined at constant volume or at constant pressure. The heat added causes a change in the internal energy (U) and in the enthalpy (heat content, H) of the substance.

The following notations can be formulated:

1. *Specific heat capacity at constant volume*

$$c_v = \left(\frac{\partial U}{\partial T}\right)_v \qquad \text{(dimension: J/kg} \cdot \text{K)}$$

2. *Specific heat capacity at constant pressure*

$$c_p = \left(\frac{\partial (U + pV)}{\partial T}\right)_p = \left(\frac{\partial H}{\partial T}\right)_p \qquad \text{(dimension: J/kg} \cdot \text{K)}$$

3. *Molar heat capacity at constant volume*

$$C_v = Mc_v \qquad \text{(dimension: J/mol} \cdot \text{K)}$$

4. *Molar heat capacity at constant pressure*

$$C_p = Mc_p = \left(\frac{\partial H}{\partial T}\right)_p \qquad \text{(dimension: J/mol} \cdot \text{K)}$$

where H is the enthalpy (heat content) per mol.

81

Molar heat capacity of solid and liquid polymers at 25°C

Reliable values for the molar heat capacity in the solid and the liquid state are available for a limited number of polymers only. This emphasizes the importance of correlations between $C_p^s(298)$ and $C_p^l(298)$ and the structure of polymers.

For compounds of low molecular weight such correlations are available. Satoh (1948) proposed a method for the prediction of C_p^s at 200 K, 300 K and 400 K by the addition of group contributions. The same method was used by Shaw (1969) for $C_p^l(298)$ and by Johnson and Huang (1955) for $C_p^l(293)$. The question was whether these increments are applicable to polymers.

A survey of the group contributions to $C_p^s(300)$ by Satoh and to $C_p^l(298)$ by Shaw is given in table 5.1. Satoh does not mention values for some important groups: $-COO-$, $-CONH-$, $-SO_2-$, $-F$, while Shaw omits values for $-Cl$, $-F$ and $-CONH-$. The most probable values for these groups, according to the available experimental data, are mentioned in parentheses in table 5.1. The value for the contribution of $-CONH-$ to C_p^s is still dubious.

In table 5.2 the available experimental values for $C_p^s(298)$, $C_p^s(200)$ and $C_p^l(298)$ are compared with values predicted by the methods of Satoh and Shaw. In general, the correspondence between experimental and calculated values is quite satisfactory. The mean deviation between experimental and calculated values is 2% for $C_p^s(298)$ and 3.5% for $C_p^l(298)$. Values for C_p^l, calculated with Johnson's method show greater deviations from the experimental values than those according to Shaw. For the temperature region of 50 to 240 K, Wunderlich and Jones (1969) published group contributions for the calculation of C_p^s. If the uncertainty in the extrapolation of these data to 300 K is taken into account, these group contributions correspond with those of Satoh.

Example 5.1.

Calculate the heat capacity of polypropylene with a degree of crystallinity of 30% at 25°C.

Solution

$C_p^s(298)$ and $C_p^l(298)$ may be calculated by the addition of group contributions (table 5.1):

	$C_p^s(298)$	$C_p^l(298)$
$(-CH_2-)$	25.35	30.4
$(-CH-)$	15.6	20.95
$(-CH_3)$	30.9	36.9
	71.9	88.3

It is assumed that the semicrystalline polymer consists of an amorphous fraction with heat capacity C_p^l and a crystalline fraction with heat capacity C_p^s. For a polymer with 30% crystallinity the estimated molar heat capacity is $C_p(298) = 0.3 \times 71.9 + 0.7 \times 88.3 = 83.3$ J/mol · K. The specific heat capacity is $C_p/M = 83.3/0.042 = 1980$ J/kg · K.

Specific heat as a function of temperature

The complete course of the specific heat capacity as a function of temperature has been published for a limited number of polymers only. As an example, fig. 5.1 shows

TABLE 5.1

Group contributions to the molar heat at 25°C (J/mol · K)

Group	C_p^s (Satoh)	C_p^l (Shaw)	C_p^s/R per atom	C_p^l/R per atom
$-CH_3$	30.9	36.9	0.92	1.10
$-CH_2-$	25.35	30.4	1.01	1.21
$-CH-$	15.6	20.95	0.93	1.25
$-C-$	6.2	7.4	0.74	0.88
$=CH_2$	22.6	21.8	0.90	0.87
$=CH-$	18.65	21.4	1.11	1.28
$=C-$	10.5	15.9	1.25	1.90
$-CH_2-$ (5 ring)	19.9	26.4	0.79	1.05
$-CH_2-$ (6 ring)	18.0	26.4	0.71	1.03
CH_{ar}	15.4	22.2	0.92	1.33
$C_{ar}-$	8.55	12.2	1.02	1.45
(benzene ring)	85.6	123.2	0.94	1.35
(para-disubstituted ring)	78.8	113.1	0.95	1.36
(trisubstituted ring)	65.0	93.0	0.98	1.40
$-F$	(21.4)	(21.0)	2.55	2.50
$-Cl$	27.1	(39.8)	3.23	4.75
$-Br$	26.3	–	3.14	–
$-I$	22.4	–	2.67	–
$-CN$	(25)	–	1.50	–
$-OH$	17.0	44.8	1.01	2.68
$-O-$	16.8	35.6	2.01	<4.25
$-CO-$	23.05	52.8	1.38	3.15
$-COOH$	(50)	98.9	1.50	2.95
$-COO-$	(46)	65.0	1.83	2.58
$-NH_2$	20.95	–	0.83	–
$-NH-$	14.25	(31.8)	0.85	1.90
$N-$	17.1	(44.0)	2.04	5.25
$-NO_2$	41.9	–	1.67	–
$-CONH-$	(38–54)	(90.1)	1.12–1.63	2.68
$-S-$	24.05	44.8	2.37	5.35
$-SH$	46.8	52.4	2.78	3.12
$-SO_2-$	(50)	–	2.00	–

TABLE 5.2

Experimental and calculated heat capacities of polymers

Polymer	Solid				
	$c_p^S(298)$ exp. (J/kg · K)	$C_p^S(298)$ exp. (J/mol · K)	$C_p^S(298)$ Satoh (J/mol · K)	$C_p^S(200)$ exp. (J/mol · K)	$C_p^S(200)$ Satoh (J/mol · K)
polyethylene	1550/1760	44/49	51	34	33
polypropylene	1630/1760	69	72	48	46
polybutene	1550/1760	>87	97	69	62
poly(4-methylpentene)	1680	141	144	100	91
polyisobutylene	1680	94	93	65	58
polystyrene	1220	128	127	84	81
poly(vinyl chloride)	960/1090	60/68	68	42/49	47
poly(vinylidene chloride)	–	–	86	70	60
poly(tetrafluoroethylene)	~960	96	(98)	69	–
poly(chlorotrifluoroethylene)	920	105	(104)	–	–
poly(vinyl alcohol)	1300	57	58	39	37
poly(vinyl acetate)	~1470	~127	(118)	88	–
poly(methyl acrylate)	1340	115	(118)	–	–
poly(ethyl acrylate)	1450	145	(143)	–	–
poly(butyl acrylate)	1640	210	(194)	–	–
poly(methyl methacrylate)	1380	138	(139)	~101	–
poly(ethyl methacrylate)	1450	166	(165)	–	–
poly(butyl methacrylate)	1680	239	(215)	–	–
polyacrylonitrile	1260	67	(66)	48	–
polybutadiene	1630	88	88	~63	58
polyisoprene	1590	108	111	~78	75
polychloroprene	–	–	107	–	75
poly(methylene oxide)	1420	43	42	29	29
poly(ethylene oxide)	~1260	<70	68	42	46
poly(tetramethylene oxide)	~1590	~118	118	84/88	79
poly(propylene oxide)	~1420	~83	89	65	58
poly(2,6-dimethylphenylene oxide)	1260	148	144	108	92
poly(propylene sulphone)	1170	123	(122)	91	–
poly(butylene sulphone)	1220	147	(148)	108	–
poly(hexene sulphone)	1380	205	(198)	148	–
poly(ethylene sebacate)	–	–	(346)	–	–
poly(ethylene terephthalate)	1130	218	(222)	159	–
nylon 6	1470	164	(164)	117	–
nylon 6, 6	1470	331	(329)	–	–
nylon 6, 10	~1590	~448	(430)	–	–
poly(bisphenol-A carbonate)	1170	303	(289)	207	–
diamond	–	6	6	2	–
graphite	–	9	6	5	–
sulphur	–	24	24	–	–
silicon	–	21	–	–	–

Conversion factors: 1 J/kg · K = 0.24 × 10^{-3} cal/g · K; 1 J/mol · K = 0.24 cal/mol · K.

Liquid			$C_p^l(298)$	T_m(K)	$C_p^s(T_m)$ (J/mol · K)	$C_p^l(T_m)$ (J/mol · K)	$C_p^l(T_m)$
$c_p^l(298)$ exp. (J/kg · K)	$C_p^l(298)$ exp. (J/mol · K)	$C_p^l(298)$ Shaw (J/mol · K)	$C_p^s(298)$				$C_p^s(T_m)$
2260	63	61	1.28/1.46	410	65	71	1.09
2140	91	88	1.31	450	100	107	1.07
2140	120	119	–	400	127	134	1.06
–	–	176	(1.26)	500/520	–	–	–
1970	111	112	1.18	320	100	114	1.14
1720	178	175	1.40	513	211	223	1.06
1220	76	(91)	–	–	–	–	–
–	–	(117)	(1.37)	463	–	–	–
960	96	(99)	~1.00	300	96	96	1.00
–	–	(117)	(1.12)	490	165	159?	–
1930	~166	153	~1.31	–	–	–	–
1800	155	153	1.35	–	–	–	–
1820	182	184	1.26	–	–	–	–
1790	230	245	1.10	320	224	236	1.05
~1800	~182	177	~1.32	433	194	212	1.09
–	–	207	–	–	–	–	–
1860	264	268	1.10	–	–	–	–
–	–	–	–	590	–	–	–
1890	102	104	1.16	370	107	111	1.04
1930	131	135	1.22	309/340	122	132	1.08
–	–	(138)	(1.29)	343	–	–	–
~2100	63	66	~1.47	460	64	75	1.17
2050	91	96	>1.30	340	79	95	1.20
2100	150	157	~1.27	310	122	152	1.25
1930	111	124	~1.35	350	96	118	1.23
~1760	~212	202	~1.43	530	251	271	1.08
–	–	–	–	570	–	–	–
–	–	–	–	–	–	–	–
~1930	~442	434	(1.28)	345	–	–	–
~1550	298	304	1.36	540	376	385	1.02
2140/2470	242	(242)	1.48	496	261	299	1.15
–	–	(484)	(1.47)	–	–	–	–
2180	616	(606)	~1.37	496	714	762	1.07
1590	410	(408)	1.35	500	487	508	1.05
–	–	–					
–	–	–					
–	–	–					
–	–	–					

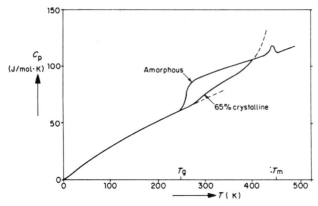

Fig. 5.1. Molar heat capacity of polypropylene.

some experimental data for polypropylene, according to Dainton et al. (1962) and Passaglia and Kevorkian (1963). Recent measurements by Gee and Melia (1970) allowed extrapolation to purely amorphous and purely crystalline material, leading to the schematic course of molar heat capacity as a function of temperature shown in fig. 5.2.

According to this figure a crystalline polymer follows the curve for the solid state to the melting point. At T_m the value of C_p increases to that of the liquid polymer. *The molar heat capacity of an amorphous polymer follows the same curve for the solid up to the glass transition temperature, where the value increases to that of the liquid (rubbery) material.*

In general a polymer sample is neither completely crystalline nor completely amorphous. Therefore, in the temperature region between T_g and T_m, the molar heat capacity follows some course between the curves for solid and liquid (as shown in fig. 5.1 for 65% crystalline polypropylene). This means that published single data for the specific heat capacity of polymers should be regarded with some suspicion. Reliable values can only be

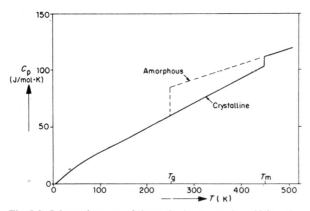

Fig. 5.2. Schematic curve of the molar heat capacity of isotactic polypropylene.

derived from the course of the specific heat capacity as a function of temperature for a number of samples.

Examination of the available literature data showed that, for all the polymers investigated, the curves for the molar heat capacity of solid and liquid may be approximated by straight lines, except for the solid below 150 K. So if the slopes of these lines are known, the heat capacity at an arbitrary temperature may be calculated approximately from its value at 298 K. For a number of polymers the slopes of the heat capacity curves, related to the heat capacity at 298 K, are mentioned in table 5.3.

The slopes of the heat capacity lines for solid polymers show a mean value

$$\frac{1}{C_p^s(298)} \frac{dC_p^s}{dT} = 3 \times 10^{-3}$$

with a mean deviation of 5%.

For liquid polymers, an analogous expression may be used, but much larger deviations occur. In this case

$$\frac{1}{C_p^l(298)} \frac{dC_p^l}{dT} = 1.2 \times 10^{-3}$$

with a mean deviation of 30%. Nevertheless, if experimental data are lacking, the temperature function of the heat capacity may be approximated with these mean values, so that:

$$C_p^s(T) = C_p^s(298)[1 + 3 \times 10^{-3}(T - 298)] = C_p^s(298)[0.106 + 3 \times 10^{-3}T] \quad (5.1)$$

$$C_p^l(T) = C_p^l(298)[1 + 1.2 \times 10^{-3}(T - 298)] = C_p^l(298)[0.64 + 1.2 \times 10^{-3}T] \quad (5.2)$$

With the aid of eqs. (5.1) and (5.2) the specific heat capacity in the solid and the liquid state at temperatures of practical interest may be predicted approximately from their values at room temperature.

As can be seen from table 5.2, the ratio $r = C_p^l(298)/C_p^s(298)$ shows a mean deviation of 7% from the mean value $r = 1.32$. This ratio will decrease, however, with increasing temperature, as the slope of C_p^s is steeper than that of C_p^l. The linear approximations of the curves for C_p^s and C_p^l as a function of temperature (eqs. (5.1) and (5.2)) may be used for estimating C_p^l and C_p^s at the melting point. The ratio C_p^l/C_p^s at the melting point shows a mean deviation of 6% from the mean value $r = 1.12$. This can also be seen from table 5.2.

Theoretical background

Our discussion of the specific heat capacity of polymers on the preceding pages has been quite empirical. There are, in fact, few fundamental rules that can be used for the prediction of specific heat capacity. At very low temperatures, the equations of Debye and Einstein may be used.

On the basis of the equipartition of the energy content of a molecule over the degrees

TABLE 5.3

Temperature function of the molar heat capacity (K^{-1})

Polymer	$\dfrac{1}{C_p^s(298)}\dfrac{dC_p^s}{dT}$	$\dfrac{1}{C_p^l(298)}\dfrac{dC_p^l}{dT}$
polyethylene	3.0×10^{-3}	1.0×10^{-3}
polybutene	3.1×10^{-3}	1.4×10^{-3}
poly(4-methylpentene)	3.0×10^{-3}	$-$
polyisobutylene	3.3×10^{-3}	2.2×10^{-3}
polystyrene	3.4×10^{-3}	1.2×10^{-3}
poly(vinyl chloride)	2.8×10^{-3}	$-$
poly(vinyl acetate)	2.9×10^{-3}	$-$
poly(methyl acrylate)	2.6×10^{-3}	1.1×10^{-3}
poly(ethyl acrylate)	2.7×10^{-3}	1.5×10^{-3}
poly(butyl acrylate)	3.0×10^{-3}	1.5×10^{-3}
poly(methyl methacrylate)	3.0×10^{-3}	1.5×10^{-3}
poly(ethyl methacrylate)	3.0×10^{-3}	$-$
poly(butyl methacrylate)	3.2×10^{-3}	1.9×10^{-3}
polybutadiene	3.1×10^{-3}	$-$
polyisoprene	3.0×10^{-3}	1.8×10^{-3}
poly(ethylene oxide)	2.6×10^{-3}	0.5×10^{-3}
poly(tetramethylene oxide)	2.9×10^{-3}	1.0×10^{-3}
poly(propylene oxide)	2.9×10^{-3}	1.4×10^{-3}
poly(phenylene oxide)	2.7×10^{-3}	0.9×10^{-3}
poly(ethylene sebacate)	$-$	1.2×10^{-3}
poly(hexamethylene adipamide)	3.0×10^{-3}	0.5×10^{-3}
poly(bisphenol-A carbonate)	3.2×10^{-3}	1.4×10^{-3}

of freedom, the maximum value of the molar heat would correspond to $3 R$ per atom. In reality, part of the degrees of freedom are always frozen in, which results in a lower value of the molar heat capacity. The increase of the specific heat capacity with temperature depends on an increase of the vibrational degrees of freedom.

Empirically it has been found that for polymers at room temperature the molar heat capacity is of the order of R per atom. This may be seen from table 5.1, where the value of C_p/R per atom has been calculated for the group contributions to the molar heat. For hydrocarbon groups C_p^s/R per atom is somewhat lower than unity; the mean value of C_p^l/R is about unity. Groups containing other elements show higher values for C_p/R.

It is interesting to note that for some groups C_p/R per atom is greater than the maximum value of 3, which corresponds to all vibrational degrees of freedom of the group. This means that the presence of these groups influences the degrees of freedom of adjacent groups. This is one of the reasons why linear additivity rules do not hold exactly for these groups.

On the basis of the hole theory of liquids, Wunderlich (1960) concluded that the difference $C_p^l - C_p^s$ at the glass transition temperature should be constant per structural group in the polymer. A structural group in this sense is defined as the smallest section of the molecule that can move as unit in internal rotation.

Eqs. (5.1) and (5.2) allow the calculation of approximate values for $C_p^l(T_g)$ and $C_p^s(T_g)$ for a number of polymers. The difference in C_p per group calculated in this way shows a variation from 8.0–13.0 J/mol · K, which corresponds reasonably well to the value of 11.3 J/mol · K mentioned by Wunderlich.

C_p/C_v relationships

So far only c_p and C_p, the specific and the molar heat capacity at constant pressure, have been discussed. Obviously, these quantities are always dealt with in normal measurements.

For the calculation of the specific heat capacity at constant volume, c_v, some relationships are available. An exact thermodynamic derivation leads to the equation:

$$c_v = c_p - Tv\frac{\alpha^2}{\kappa} \tag{5.3}$$

where v = specific volume, α = expansion coefficient, κ = compressibility.

Approximative relationships for polymers were derived by Warfield et al. (1969); their results are shown in figs. 5.3 and 5.4.

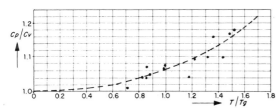

Fig. 5.3. Corresponding state relationship between C_p/C_v and T/T_g for amorphous polymers (after Warfield et al., 1969).

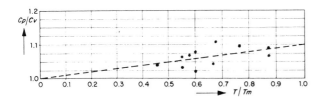

Fig. 5.4. Corresponding state relationship between C_p/C_v and T/T_m for semicrystalline and crystalline polymers (after Warfield et al., 1969).

B. LATENT HEAT OF CRYSTALLIZATION AND FUSION

The latent heat of fusion (crystallization) or the enthalpy difference

$$H_l(T_m) - H_c(T_m) = \Delta H_m(T_m) \tag{5.4}$$

is an important quantity for the calculation of other thermodynamic functions. Furthermore, a knowledge of ΔH_m is necessary for the design of a number of polymer processing apparatus.

Experimental values for ΔH_m are available, however, for a limited number of polymers only. This is probably due to difficulties arising in the experimental determination of ΔH_m. In a direct determination, the degree of crystallinity of the sample has to be taken into account, while indirect determination (e.g. from solution properties) is dependent on the validity of the thermodynamic formulae used. In this connection, a large scatter in published values for ΔH_m may be observed. As a general rule, the highest value of ΔH_m mentioned for a given polymer is the most probable one.

Table 5.4 gives a survey of the available literature data for ΔH_m. In view of the small number of polymers for which ΔH_m has been determined, the development of a method for the prediction of ΔH_m is very desirable. The data of table 5.4, however, are not nearly sufficient for the derivation of a reliable correlation with polymer structure. Nevertheless, table 5.5 mentions a number of group contributions to ΔH_m, that are in reasonable agreement with the data of table 5.4. Values of ΔH_m, calculated in this way, should be considered a very rough first approximation.

It is very improbable that a method can be derived for the calculation of accurate values of ΔH_m by a simple addition of group contributions. Even for compounds of low molecular weight for which a large number of experimental values of ΔH_m are available, such a method could not be derived (Bondi, 1968).

This is in agreement with the experience acquired in another field of thermodynamics. Redlich et al. (1959) tried to calculate the interaction energy between non-electrolyte molecules in a solution as the sum of contributions of the constitutional groups. Instead of attributing a certain contribution to each group present, they had to add contributions corresponding with each pair of interacting groups. This might be called a second-order additivity rule and is the only way to account for the heat of solution.

Application of this method to the heat content of homologous series of organic compounds in the liquid state would result in a nonlinear course of the heat content as a function of the number of methylene groups. This is exactly what is found experimentally for the heat of fusion as a function of the number of methylene groups. A second order additivity rule, however, is too complicated for practical application if a large number of structural groups is involved. It would require the compilation of innumerable group pair contributions.

As was stated by Bondi (1968), the entropy of fusion, ΔS_m, shows a much more regular relation with structure than the enthalpy of fusion. At the melting point T_m, the entropy of fusion may be calculated as:

$$\Delta S_m = \frac{\Delta H_m}{T_m} \tag{5.5}$$

The available experimental values of ΔH_m for a number of polymers, mentioned in table 5.4, permit the calculation of ΔS_m for these polymers. The data mentioned for 3 polyoxides, 6 polyesters, 4 polyterephthalates and 4 polyamides show that ΔS_m for these polymers may be represented by the equation:

$$\Delta S_m = \sum n_i \Delta S_i \tag{5.6}$$

TABLE 5.4

Enthalpy and entropy of fusion for some polymers

Polymer	ΔH_m (J/mol)		T_m(K)	ΔS_m (J/mol · K)
	literature	predicted (table 5.5)		
polyethylene	7500–8400	7600	414	18.0–20.1
polypropylene	8800–10900	10100	456	19.3–23.9
polystyrene	8400–10100	–	513	16.3–19.7
poly(vinyl chloride)	11300	–	558	20.1
poly(vinyl fluoride)	7500	–	473	15.9
poly(tetrafluoroethylene)	5900	–	600	9.6
poly(chlorotrifluoroethylene)	5000–8800	–	491	10.1–17.9
poly(vinyl alcohol)	6900	–	531	13.0
polyacrylonitrile	5000	–	590	8.4
polybutadiene	9200–10100	9700	421	21.8–23.9
polyisoprene	12600	12200	309–347	36.0–40.6
polychloroprene	8400	–	316	26.4
polyformaldehyde	7100	5500	460	15.5
poly(ethylene oxide)	8400–9200	9300	340	24.7–27.2
poly(tetramethylene oxide)	12600	16900	310	40.6
poly(propylene oxide)	8400	11800	348	23.9
polyester 2, 6	15900	14400	320	49.9
polyester 2, 10	25600–29000	29600	345	74.2–84.1
polyester 10, 6	42700	44800	343	124.9
polyester 9, 9	43200	52400	338	127.8
polyester 10, 9	41900	56200	340	123.2
polyester 10, 10	50300	60000	344	146.2
poly(ethylene terephthalate)	22600–24300	21400	543	41.5–44.8
poly(tetramethylene terephthalate)	31800	29000	505	62.9
poly(hexamethylene terephthalate)	34800–35200	36600	434	80.0
poly(decamethylene terephthalate)	43600–48600	51800	411	106.1–118.2
poly(tetramethylene isophthalate)	42300	–	426	99.3
polyamide 6	21800–23500	21900	496	44.0–47.3
polyamide 11	41500	40900	463	89.7
polyamide 6, 6	44400–46100	43800	538	82.5–85.5
polyamide 6, 10	54500–56600	59000	496	109.8–114.0
poly(2,2-dimethylamide-3)	13000	–	546	23.9
poly(bisphenol-Λ carbonate)	36900	–	540	68.3

Conversion factors: 1 J/mol = 0.24 cal/mol; 1 J/mol · K = 0.24 cal/mol · K.

where n_i = number of groups of type i, ΔS_i = entropy contribution per group i. Table 5.6 shows the values of ΔS_i.

Obviously, ester groups and amide groups do not contribute to the entropy of fusion. The contribution of a methylene group in these linear polymers, 8.4 J/mol · K, is

TABLE 5.5

Approximate values of group contribution to the heat of fusion of polymers (ΔH_m)

Group	Group contribution (J/mol)
$-CH_2-$	3800
$-CH(CH_3)-$	6300
$-CH=CH-$	2100
$-CH=C(CH_3)-$	4600
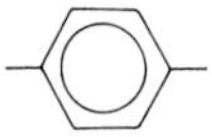	22200
$-O-$	1700
$-COO-$	-4200
$-CONH-$	2900

Conversion factor: 1 J/mol = 0.24 cal/mol

much smaller than the corresponding value for polyethylene, 9.8 J/mol · K. The latter value, again, differs from the high values for methylene group contributions – about 11.1 – observed in homologous series of low-molecular-weight compounds (Bondi, 1968). For some series of low-molecular-weight compounds, however, a contribution for the methylene group of about 9.8 was found.

An analogous effect was observed many years ago for the heat of fusion of homologous series of low-molecular-weight compounds (King and Garner, 1934). It was found that long methylene chains could crystallize into two distinct crystal structures, with quite different values for the heat of fusion.

These facts lead to the conclusion that experimental data for low-molecular-weight compounds should not be used for predicting the heat of fusion of polymers. Further-

TABLE 5.6

Group contributions to the entropy of fusion (ΔS_m)

Group	ΔS_i (J/mol · K)
$-CH_2-$	8.4
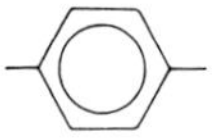	29.3
$-O-$	7.5
$-COO-$	0.0
$-CONH-$	0.0

Conversion factor: 1 J/mol · K = 0.24 cal/mol · K.

more, the group contribution to thermodynamic quantities of methylene in polyethylene is obviously different from the group contribution of methylene in series of linear polymers containing non-hydrocarbon groups.

On the basis of the equation for ΔS_m, given above, the heat of fusion can be calculated for linear polymers containing methylene, paraphenylene, oxygen, ester and amide groups, provided the melting temperatures are known.

C. ENTHALPY AND ENTROPY

In determining the course of enthalpy and entropy of a substance with temperature it is usual to start from very accurate specific heat measurements. Enthalpy and entropy may then be calculated by integration:

$$H(T) = H(0) + \int_0^T C_p \, dT + \sum \Delta H_i \tag{5.7}$$

$$S(T) = S(0) + \int_0^T \frac{C_p}{T} \, dT + \sum \Delta S_i \tag{5.8}$$

where $H(0)$ and $S(0)$ are the enthalpy and entropy at 0 K and ΔH_i and ΔS_i are the enthalpy and entropy changes at first order phase transitions.

If this method is applied to thermodynamic data of polymers, the same difficulty arises as mentioned in 5A for the determination of the specific heat: most polymer samples are partly crystalline. The thermodynamic quantities have values somewhere between those for the purely crystalline and the purely amorphous polymer. A large number of measurements are needed to derive the data for these two idealized states. Only for a limited number of polymers have data of this kind been published.

As an example, in figs. 5.5 and 5.6 enthalpy and entropy as a function of temperature are plotted for polypropylene, according to the data of Gee and Melia (1970), Dainton et al. (1962) and Passaglia and Kevorkian (1963).

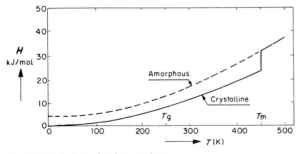

Fig. 5.5. Enthalpy of polypropylene.

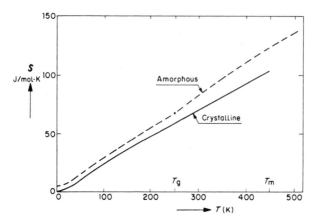

Fig. 5.6. Entropy of polypropylene.

The corresponding data for some other polymers may be found in a series of articles by Dainton et al. (1962).

As appears from fig. 5.5, the enthalphy curves for crystalline and amorphous polypropylene run parallel up to the glass transition temperature. The distance between these curves is called $\Delta H(0)$ = the enthalpy of the amorphous polymer at 0 K. From the glass transition temperature the curve for the amorphous polymer gradually approaches the curve for the melt, while the curve for the crystalline polymer shows a discontinuity at the melting point. The distance between the curves for crystal and liquid at the melting point is the latent heat of fusion, ΔH_m.

The curves for the entropy of crystalline and amorphous polymer in fig. 5.6 show an analogous course.

Application of eq. (5.7) to crystalline and liquid (or rubbery amorphous) polymers leads to:

$$H_c(T) = H_c(0) + \int_0^T C_p^s dT \qquad (T < T_m) \tag{5.9}$$

$$H_l(T) = H_c(0) + \int_0^{T_m} C_p^s dT + \int_{T_m}^T C_p^l dT + \Delta H_m \tag{5.10}$$

According to fig. 5.5, $H_l(T_g) = H_c(T_g) + \Delta H(0)$. Combination of these equations and substitution of eqs. (5.1) and (5.2) gives:

$$\Delta H_m - \Delta H(0) = \{0.64 C_p^l(298) - 0.107 C_p^s(298)\}(T_m - T_g)$$
$$+ \{0.0006 C_p^l(298) - 0.0015 C_p^s(298)\}(T_m^2 - T_g^2). \tag{5.11}$$

Although eqs. (5.1) and (5.2) are certainly not valid at very low temperatures, the de-

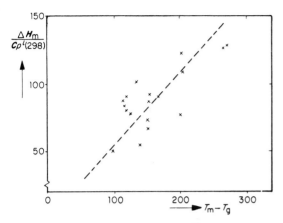

Fig. 5.7. Approximate correlation for ΔH_m.

viations cancel out for the greater part, because the curves for H_l and H_s run parallel at low temperatures.

Application of eq. (5.11) to a number of polymers gave the correct order of magnitude for $\Delta H_m - \Delta H(0)$. The equation cannot be used for an accurate prediction of ΔH_m, however, because of lack of data for $\Delta H(0)$ and the approximate character of eqs. (5.1) and (5.2). But eq. (5.11) suggests that ΔH_m will increase with increasing values of $C_p^l(298)$ and $(T_m - T_g)$. This is proved in fig. 5.7, where the ratio $\Delta H_m/C_p^l(298)$ is plotted against $(T_m - T_g)$ for a number of polymers, for which values of ΔH_m have been published. As a first approximation

$$\frac{\Delta H_m}{C_p^l(298)} = 0.55(T_m - T_g) \tag{5.12}$$

(standard deviation about 25%).

An equation analogous to (5.11) can be derived for the entropy:

$$\Delta S_m - \Delta S(0) = \{0.64 C_p^l(298) - 0.107 C_p^s(298)\}\ln(T_m/T_g)$$
$$+ \{0.0012 C_p^l(298) - 0.003 C_p^s(298)\}(T_m - T_g) . \tag{5.13}$$

This equation can be checked more accurately than eq. (5.11) because the order of magnitude of $\Delta S(0)$ can be estimated. The data given by Bestul and Chang (1964) correspond to a contribution to $\Delta S(0)$ of about 2.9 J/mol · K per chain atom. With these values for $\Delta S(0)$, ΔS_m may be calculated according to eq. (5.13). Fig. 5.8 shows calculated values of ΔS_m for a number of polymers plotted against experimental values of ΔS_m. Considering the inaccuracy of the data used, the result is satisfactory.

Finally, reference is made to a series of articles by Griskey et al. (1966, 1967) mentioning values for enthalpy and entropy as a function of temperature and pressure for a number of commercial plastics.

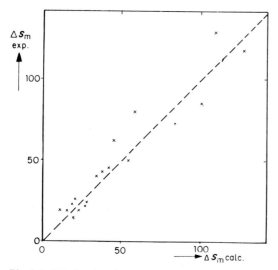

Fig. 5.8. Calculated and experimental values of ΔS_m.

Example 5.2

Estimate the following properties of poly(ethylene terephthalate):
a. the specific heat of the solid polymer at 25°C (= 298 K)
b. the specific heat of the liquid polymer at spinning temperature (277°C = 550 K)
c. the heat of fusion at the melting point.
d. the enthalpy difference between the solid and the rubbery form at the glass transition temperature.

Solution

With the data of tables 5.1 and 5.5 we find:

Group	$C_p^s(298)$	$C_p^l(298)$	ΔH_m
$\bigcirc = \begin{cases} 4\ CH_{ar} \\ 2\ C_{ar} \end{cases}$	61.7 17.1	88.8 24.4	22200
$2\ -CH_2-$	50.7	60.8	7600
$2\ -COO-$	92	130.0	−8400
	221.5	304.0	21400

Ad a) The specific heat of the solid polymer at 25°C will be:

$$c_p^s(298) = \frac{221.5}{192.2} \times 10^3 = 1152\ \text{J/kg} \cdot \text{K}$$

in excellent agreement with the experimental value 1130.
Ad b) According to eq. (5.2) the molar heat capacity of the liquid is:

$$C_p^l(550) = C_p^l(298)\{0.64 + 0.0012T\} = 304.0(0.64 + 0.66) = 395.2$$

The specific heat will be:

$$c_p^l(550) = \frac{395.2}{192.2} \times 10^3 = 2056 \qquad \text{(experimental value 2010)}.$$

Ad c) The heat of fusion at the melting point is 21400 J/mol, in reasonable agreement with the experimental value 22600.

Ad d) According to eq. (5.11) we have

$$\Delta H(T_g) = \Delta H(0) = \Delta H_m - \{0.64C_p^l(298) - 0.107C_p^s(298)\}(T_m - T_g)$$
$$- \{0.0006C_p^l(298) - 0.0015C_p^s(298)\}(T_m^2 - T_g^2)$$

or

$$\Delta H(T_g) = 21400 - (0.64 \times 304.0 - 0.107 \times 221.5)(543 - 343)$$
$$- (0.0006 \times 304.0 - 0.0015 \times 221.5)(543^2 - 343^2)$$
$$= 21400 - 34400 + 26800 = 13800 \text{ J/mol}.$$

The corresponding eq. (5.13) for $\Delta S(T_g)$ leads to

$$\Delta S(T_g) = \Delta S_m - \{0.64C_p^l(298) - 0.107C_p^s(298)\} \ln(T_m/T_g)$$
$$- \{0.0012C_p^l(298) - 0.003C_p^s(298)\}(T_m - T_g)$$
$$\Delta S_m = \frac{\Delta H_m}{T_m} = \frac{21400}{543} = 39.4 \text{ J/mol} \cdot \text{K}.$$

Addition of the group contributions of table 5.6 gives

$$\Delta S_m = 2 \times 8.4 + 29.3 = 46.1 \text{ J/mol} \cdot \text{K}.$$

With the former value of ΔS_m we obtain:

$$\Delta S(T_g) = 39.4 - (0.64 \times 304.0 - 0.107 \times 221.5) \ln(543/343)$$
$$- (0.0012 \times 304.0 - 0.003 \times 221.5)(543 - 343)$$
$$= 39.4 - 78.5 + 60.0 = 20.9 \text{ J/mol} \cdot \text{K}.$$

Note that $\Delta S(T_g) < \Delta H(T_g)/T_g$, as solid and liquid are not in equilibrium at T_g.

BIBLIOGRAPHY, CHAPTER 5

General references

Bondi, A., "Physical Properties of Molecular Crystals, Liquids and Glasses", Wiley, New York, 1968.
Reid, R.C. and Sherwood, Th.K., "The Properties of Gases and Liquids", McGraw-Hill, New York, 1st ed., 1958, 2nd ed., 1966.

Special references

Bestul, A.B. and Chang, S.S., J. Chem. Phys. 40 (1964) 3731.
Dainton, F.S., Evans, D.M., Hoare, F.E. and Melia, T.P., Polymer 3 (1962) 286.
Gee, D.R. and Melia, T.P., Makromol. Chem. 132 (1970) 195.
Griskey, R.G. et al., several articles in Modern Plastics 43 (1966); 44 (1967).
Johnson, A.J. and Huang, C.J., Can. J. Technol. 33 (1955) 421.

King, A.M. and Garner, W.E., J. Chem. Soc. (1934) 1449.
Passaglia, E. and Kevorkian, R., J. Appl. Phys. 34 (1963) 90.
Redlich, O., Derr, E.L. and Pierotti, G.J., J. Am. Chem. Soc. 81 (1959) 2283.
Satoh, S., J. Sci. Research Inst. (Tokyo) 43 (1948) 79.
Shaw, R., J. Chem. Eng. Data 14 (1969) 461.
Warfield, R.W., Pastine, D.J. and Petree, M.C., U.S. Naval Ordnance Lab., RPT NOLTR 69-98, 1969.
Wunderlich, B., J. Phys. Chem. 64 (1960) 1052.
Wunderlich, B. and Jones, L.D., J. Macromol. Sci. Phys. B3 (1969) 67.

CHAPTER 6

TRANSITION TEMPERATURES

In this chapter it will be demonstrated that the two main transition temperatures, viz. the glass–rubber transition temperature and the crystalline melting
temperature can be correlated with the chemical structure by means of a method
based on group contributions. The correlations have a purely empirical character.

Introduction

As was stated in Chapter 2, it is impossible to understand the properties of polymers if
the transitions that occur in such materials and specifically the temperatures at which
these occur are not known. The main transitions are the glass–rubber transition and the
crystalline melting point. These two will be discussed in this chapter.

However, several other transitions of secondary importance may often be observed. As
to the denomination of these transitions there is a complete lack of uniformity. Usually
the symbols T_α, T_β, etc., are used, but different authors use different symbols for the
same transition.

There may be at least three transitions in the glassy state below T_g, viz. at $0.5\ T_g$ –
$0.8\ T_g$, at $0.35\ T_g$ – $0.5\ T_g$ and at very low temperatures (4–40 K). Between T_g and T_m,
transitions may be observed in the rubbery amorphous state and in the crystalline state.

A. THE GLASS TRANSITION TEMPERATURE

Several authors have proposed correlations between the chemical structure and the
glass transition temperature of polymers. Their methods are usually based on the assumption that the structural groups in the repeating units provide weighed additive contributions to the T_g. In the case of ideal additivity the contribution of a given group is independent of the nature of adjacent groups. Although this ideal case is seldom encountered
in practice, additivity can often be approximated by a proper choice of structural groups.
We will revert to this point later.

The general form of the correlations for T_g is

$$T_g \sum_i s_i = \sum_i s_i T_{gi} \tag{6.1}$$

so that

$$T_g = \frac{\sum_i s_i T_{gi}}{\sum_i s_i} \tag{6.2}$$

where T_{gi} is the specific contribution to T_g of a given structural group, and s_i is a weight factor attributed to a given structural group.

Hayes (1961) assumed $\Sigma_i s_i T_{gi}$ to be identical with the molar cohesive energy and derived from this a number of rules for calculating the individual s_i-values. Barton and Lee (1968) suggested that s_i is identical with the weight or mole fraction of structural groups and calculated values of the characteristic constant T_{gi} for the groups involved.

In a more recent article Lee (1970) compared four methods of counting s_i for a small selected group of polymers. A good correlation could be obtained by assuming that the T_{gi}-value of a given structural group was dependent on the nature of adjacent groups. This, however, leads to a very large number of T_{gi}-values. The correlation obtained with independent T_{gi}-values was far less good.

Weyland et al. (1970) also examined different methods for counting s_i and found that the quality of the correlation obtained is rather insensitive to the rules adapted for calculating s_i. A good fit was obtained by putting s_i equal to *the number of atom distances in the main chain of the repeating unit* (i.e. equal to the number of atoms Z_i along the main chain that constitute the backbone of the repeating unit). On this basis, T_{gi}-values could be calculated for a number of important structural groups. This method was also applied in the first edition of this book.

A quite different method for calculating T_g was proposed by Marcinčin and Romanov (1975). They developed the formula

$$T_g = \frac{V}{V_s} 10^{k E_{coh}/\rho V_s} \tag{6.3}$$

where V = molar volume of polymer unit
$\quad\quad\quad k$ = constant
$\quad\quad\quad E_{coh}$ = cohesive energy
$\quad\quad\quad \rho$ = density
$\quad\quad\quad V_s$ = parameter with additive properties

The authors applied eq. (6.3) to a limited number of polymers; rather large deviations were found.

Recent work of Van Krevelen and Hoftyzer (1975) has shown that in applying eq. (6.2) the use of weight fractions for s_i instead of numbers of chain atoms offers some advantages. Also for reasons of uniformity with the other additive quantities it was decided to introduce the following additive quantity:

$$Y_g = \sum_i Y_{gi} = T_g \cdot M \tag{6.4}$$

so that

$$\boxed{T_g = \frac{Y_g}{M} = \frac{\sum_i Y_{gi}}{M}} \tag{6.5}$$

The function $\mathbf{Y}_g$ is called *molar glass transition function* (K · g/mol).

Equation (6.4) has been applied to all available literature data on T_g's of polymers, in all nearly 600; from this study correlation rules for $\mathbf{Y}_g$ have been derived.

As was stated above, the principle of ideal additivity, i.e. $\mathbf{Y}_{gi}$-values independent of the nature of other groups present in the structural unit, does not hold properly. The group contributions and structural corrections obtained are summarized in tables 6.1 and 6.2. We shall discuss these data step by step.

1. The unbranched polymethylene chain

Considerable confusion exists in the literature concerning the real glass transition temperature of polymethylene, i.e. of ideal linear polyethylene. Values between 140 K and 340 K have been reported (see Boyer, 1973, 1975). In agreement with Boyer we are convinced, for a variety of reasons (see Boyer, 1973), that the correct T_g of amorphous polymethylene is 195 ± 10 K. This gives for the basic contribution of $-CH_2-$ to $\mathbf{Y}_g$:

$$\mathbf{Y}_g(-CH_2-) = 195 \times 14.03 = 2736 \pm 140 \text{ K · g/mol}$$

We shall apply a round value of 2700.

2. Linear unbranched alipathic condensation polymers

In this class a fair number of data are available for polyoxides, polysulphides, polyesters and polyamides. In these polymers a bivalent polar group is "embedded" in a chain of flexible CH_2 groups. If $\mathbf{Y}_g$ for a homologous series of polymers, containing no hydrogen bonds, is plotted versus n_{CH_2} (number of methylene groups per structural unit), the slope tends towards a value of 2700 for long methylene chains per structural unit (see fig. 6.1, curve a for polyesters). In shorter structural units we see a marked deviation due to interactions between the polar groups. In polyamides this interaction tends to be predominant, due to the formation of a network of hydrogen bonds. This even gives the impression that the contribution per CH_2 group is markedly higher in polyamides than in other polymers (see fig. 6.1, curve b for polyamides). We have found that the interaction of polar groups can be formulated by means of an *interaction factor* I_x, which is a kind of "linear concentration" of polar groups within a flexible chain of methylene beads. I_x is defined as the number of main chain atoms in the polar group (X) divided by the number of chain atoms of this group plus those of the directly connected methylene chains. For the configuration

$$-(CH_2)_{n_1} -X-(CH_2)_{n_2} -$$

in which the characteristic group X contains n_x chain atoms, the formula of I_x is:

$$I_x = \frac{n_x}{n_x + n_1 + n_2} \tag{6.6}$$

In this way it has been possible to describe the T_g's of polyesters, polycarbonates and polyamides by the following general formula:

$$\mathbf{Y}_g = \sum_i \mathbf{Y}_{gi} + \sum (\text{corrections}), \text{ or}$$

TABLE 6.1

Group contributions to Y_g (K · g/mol)

Group	Y_{gi}	Group	Y_{gi}	Group	Y_{gi}	$Y_g(I_x)$
$-CH_2-$	2,700	(benzene, 1,4-disubstituted)	32,000	$-O-$	4,000	—
$-CH(CH_3)-$	8,000	(benzene with Cl)	51,000	$O=C<$	27,000	—
$-CH(C_2H_5)-$	10,500	(benzene with CH_3)	35,000	$-\overset{\displaystyle O}{\overset{\|}{C}}-O-$	8,000	12,000 I
$-CH(C_3H_7)-$	13,100	(benzene with CH_3)	35,000	$-O-\overset{\displaystyle O}{\overset{\|}{C}}-O-$	16,000	10,000 I
$-CH(C_6H_5)-$	35,000	(benzene with two CH_3)	(55,000)	$-S-$	(20,000)	?
$-CH(C_6H_4CH_3)-$	42,000	(benzene, monosubstituted)	28,000	$O=S<$	7,500	—
$-CH(OCH_3)-$	11,900	(benzene with CH_3)	30,000	$O=S=O$	(58,000)	?
$-CH(COOCH_3)-$	21,300	(benzene, ortho)	7,000	$O=S-O$	(31,000)	?
$-C(CH_3)_2-$	8,400[1] / 15,000	(naphthalene)	58,000	$-\overset{\displaystyle O}{\overset{\|}{C}}-NH-$	12,000	$1{,}800\,I^{-1} + 2 \times 10^{6}\dfrac{n_\phi}{M}$
$-C(CH_3)(C_2H_5)-$	17,700	(cyclohexane, trans)	31,000	$-O-\overset{\displaystyle O}{\overset{\|}{C}}-NH-$	(25,000)	?
$-C(CH_3)(C_6H_5)-$	(50,000)			$-NH-\overset{\displaystyle O}{\overset{\|}{C}}-NH-$	20,000	2,100 I^{-1}
$-C(CH_3)(COOCH_3)-$	35,100			$-\overset{CH_3}{\underset{CH_3}{Si}}-$	8,000	—
$-CH(OH)-$	13,000					
$-CHF-$	11,000					
$-CHCl-$	20,000					
$-CF_2-$	13,000					
$-CCl_2-$	25,000					
$-CFCl-$	23,000					

$$Y_g = \sum_i Y_{gi} + \sum Y_g(I_{xi})$$

(6.7)

Table 6.1 gives the numerical values of Y_{gi} and $Y_g(I_{xi})$.

The contributions derived for the ester and the amide group in aliphatic polymers are (table 6.1):

$$Y_g(-COO-) = 8,000 + 12,000\,I$$

$$Y_g(-CONH-) = 12,000 + 1,800\,I^{-1}$$

The functional influence of I_x in polyamides is markedly different from that in poly-esters. In polyesters the contribution of I_x becomes smaller as the polar group is "em-bedded" in a medium of more methylene groups. In polyamides, on the contrary, the in-fluence per individual amide group becomes more and more pronounced with increasing "dilution"; here it is the hydrogen bond network that determines the T_g, its asymptote being about 300 K. Even a very tenuous network exerts a profound influence on the rheological behaviour, i.e. on T_g. Fig. 6.1 shows how well Y_g is described by the given ex-pression (drawn lines).

3. Linear unbranched condensation polymers containing CH_2 groups and aromatic rings

Single aromatic rings in the structural unit have the following contributions to Y_g for

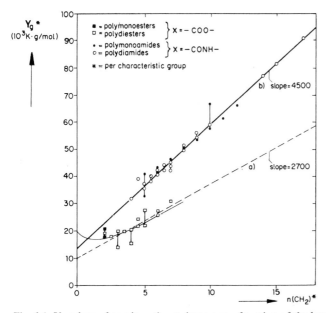

Fig. 6.1. Y_g values of condensation polymers as a function of the length of the methylene chain per structural unit.

polymers without hydrogen bonds:

32,000

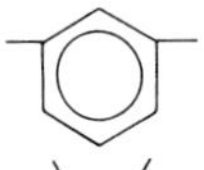

28,000

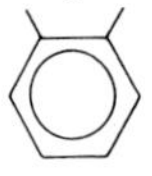

7,000

In polyamides and related compounds the hydrogen bond networks are influenced by the aromatic rings in such a way that the −CONH− contribution is modified to:

$$Y_g(-CONH-) = 12,000 + 1,800\, I^{-1} + 2 \times 10^6 \, \frac{n_\phi}{M}$$

where n_ϕ is the number of phenylene groups per structural unit of molar weight M.

4. Aromatic condensation polymers with special structures

By means of table 6.1 the T_g's of all common condensation polymers can be estimated fairly accurately. Deviations are found, however, in aromatic polymers of special structures, e.g. if phenylene groups are directly linked to each other or connected by an ether bond, in fully aromatic polymers, etc. For these classes a number of special rules were derived (table 6.2):

a. If two phenylene groups are directly connected, this causes a structural Y_g correction (+ 13,000 for p-phenylene groups, + 47,000 for o-phenylene groups).

b. If two single p-phenylene groups are connected by −O−, this causes a depression of − 5,000.

c. If the grouping −(CH₂)ₗ−is present in an asymmetrical way within the structural unit, it causes a depressing effect of − 10,000.

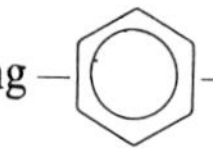

d. If a linear aromatic condensation polymer contains no methylene groups at all, there is a structural effect increasing Y_g by 10,000 to 20,000.

5. Linear polymers containing "small" side groups

The main representative polymer family of this class are the simplest vinyl polymers. Their group contributions (substituted −CH₂− groups) are given in table 6.1.

6. Linear polymers containing "long" side chains ("Comb polymers")

The main representatives are the vinyl polymers, viz. of the type

$$(-CH_2-Y-)_n$$
$$(CH_2)_N$$
$$CH_3$$

where Y stands for a trivalent structural group; the polymer with N = 0 is called the basic

TABLE 6.2

Structural corrections in more complicated aromatic polymers

Case	Group	Correction term	Integral contribution of composed groups
I. Flexible chains containing $-CH_2-$ group segments	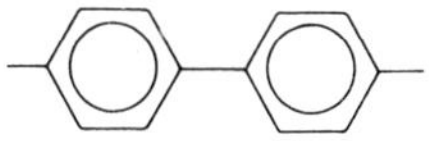 (para-phenylene)–(para-phenylene)	13,000	77,000
	(fused ring pair)	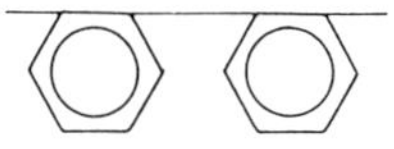 47,000	61,000
	(phenylene)–O–(phenylene)	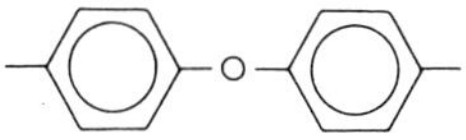 −5,000	63,000
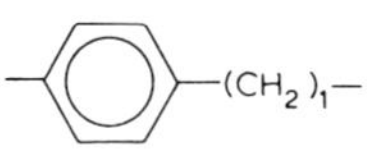	(phenylene)–$(CH_2)_1$– symmetrical	0	34,700
	asymmetrical	−10,000	25,000
II. Rigid polyester and polyamide chains containing *no* $-CH_2-$ group segments	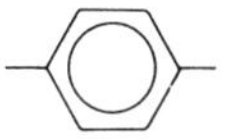 (phenylene) ⎫ in polyamides only	10,000	42,000
	(phenylene) ⎭	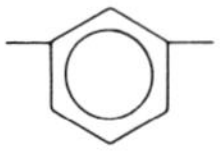 10,000	38,000
	(phenylene)–(phenylene)	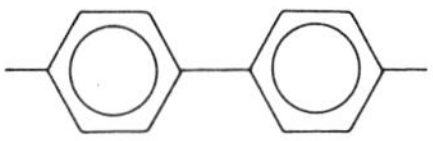 10,000	87,000
	(fused ring pair)	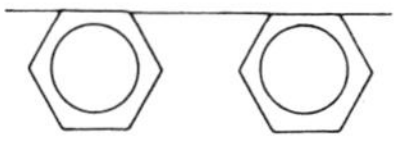 10,000	71,000
	(phenylene)–CH(phenyl)–(phenylene)	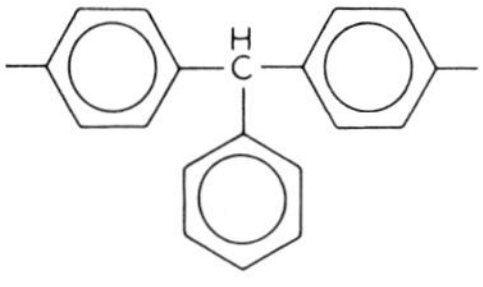 10,000	109,000
	(phenylene)–C(CH_3)(CH_3)–(phenylene)	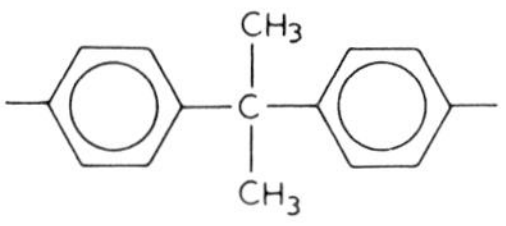 20,000	99,000
	(phenylene)–O–(phenylene)	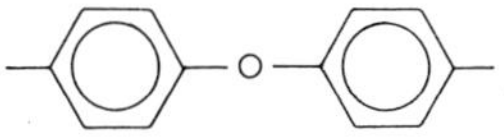 20,000	83,000

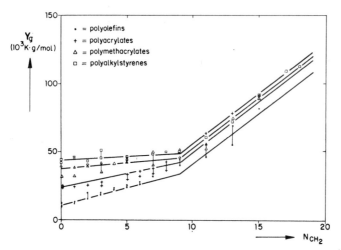

Fig. 6.2. Y_g values of vinyl polymers with side chains.

polymer. With increasing length of the methylene chain, T_g at first decreases, passes through a minimum and then increases. This behaviour may be approximately described by starting from the fact that for each series a minimum value of $T_g \approx 200$ K is reached at $N = 9$ (see fig. 6.2). It was found that T_g may be predicted with the aid of the equations

$$
\begin{array}{ll}
N = 9 & Y_g = 200 \, M \; (= Y_{g9}) \\
N < 9 & Y_g = Y_{g0} + \dfrac{N}{9}(Y_{g9} - Y_{g0}) \\
N > 9 & Y_g = Y_{g9} + 7500(N - 9)
\end{array}
\tag{6.8}
$$

Table 6.3 mentions values of Y_{g0} and Y_{g9} for some series of vinyl polymers.

Comparison between calculated and experimental values
    Table 6.4 gives a comparison of experimental and calculated values for a selection of polymers. The agreement is satisfactory.
    The method of estimation described made it possible to calculate the T_g values of the 600 polymers whose T_g values were measured. About 80% of the T_g values calculated differed less than 20 K from the experimental values. A certain percentage of the literature values is probably unreliable. So as a whole the result may be considered very satisfactory.

Example 6.1
    Estimate the glass transition temperature of poly(ethylene terephthalate). Structural formula:

TABLE 6.3

Basic data for vinyl polymers with longer side chains

Series	Basic polymer	Trivalent group Y	Y_{g0}	Y_{g9}
polyolefins	polypropylene	$-\overset{\overset{\text{H}}{\mid}}{\underset{\mid}{\text{C}}}-$ H	10,700	33,600
polyalkylstyrenes	poly(p-methylstyrene)	$-\overset{\overset{\text{H}}{\mid}}{\text{C}}-$  ⬡	44,700	48,800
polyvinyl ethers	poly(vinyl methyl ether)	$-\overset{\overset{\text{H}}{\mid}}{\text{C}}-$ O	14,600	36,800
polyvinyl esters	poly(vinyl acetate)	$-\overset{\overset{\text{H}}{\mid}}{\text{C}}-$ O C=O	26,000	42,400
polyacrylates	poly(methyl acrylate)	$-\overset{\overset{\text{H}}{\mid}}{\text{C}}-$ C=O O	24,000	42,400
polymethacrylates	poly(methyl methacrylate)	$-\overset{\overset{\text{CH}_3}{\mid}}{\text{C}}-$ C=O O	37,800	45,200

Solution

For the ester groups, the interaction factor is $I = 2/(2 + 2) = 0.5$. So according to table 6.1 the group contributions to Y_g are:

	Y_{gi}
$2 -CH_2-$	5,400
 ⬡	32,000
$2 -COO- 2(8,000 + 0.5 \times 12,000) =$	28,000
$Y_g =$	65,400

TABLE 6.4

Experimental and calculated values of T_g for a number of polymers (K)

Polymer	T_g exp.	T_g calc.
poly(methylene oxide)	188/243	223
poly(ethylene oxide)	206/246	214
poly(trimethylene oxide)	195/228	209
poly(tetramethylene oxide)	185/194	206
poly(paraxylylene disulphide)	296	312
poly(decamethylene tetrasulphide)	197	212
poly(ethylene adipate)	203/233	222
poly(ethylene dodecate)	202	202
poly(decamethylene adipate)	217	200
poly(ethylene terephthalate)	342/350	341
poly(decamethylene terephthalate)	268/298	260
poly(diethyleneglycol malonate)	244	248
poly(diethyleneglycol octadecanedioate)	205	198
poly(metaphenylene isophthalate)	411/428	400
poly(4,4'-methylene diphenylene carbonate)	393/420	410
poly(4,4'-isopropylidene diphenylene carbonate)	414/423	413
poly(4,4'-tetramethylene dibenzoic anhydride)	319	339
poly(4,4'-methylenedioxy dibenzoic anhydride)	357	351
poly(hexamethylene adipamide)	318/330	321
poly(decamethylene sebacamide)	319/333	320
poly(heptamethylene terephthalamide)	383/396	410
poly(paraphenylene diethylene sebacamide)	378	370
poly(tetramethylene hexamethylene diurethane)	215/332	298
poly(phenylene dimethylene hexamethylene diurethane)	329	339
poly(hexamethylene dodecamethylene diurea)	322	349
poly[methylene bis(oxydiparaphenylene)sulphone]	453	451
poly[oxy bis(oxydiparaphenylene)ketone]	423	413
poly(isopropylidene diparaphenylene metaphenylene disulphonate)	385/388	393
poly(dimethyl siloxane)	146/150	162
polyethylene	143/250	193
polypropylene	238/299	255
polyisobutylene	198/243	316
polystyrene	353/380	200
poly(vinyl fluoride)	253/314	298
poly(vinylidene fluoride)	238/286	245
poly(1,2-difluoroethylene)	323/371	344
poly(vinyl chloride)	247/354	360
poly(vinylidene chloride)	255/288	286
poly(trifluorochloroethylene)	318/373	310
poly(vinyl alcohol)	343/372	357
poly(1-butene)	228/249	238
poly(1-pentene)	221/287	227
poly(1-octene)	208/228	210
poly(1-octadecene)	328	312
poly(p-methylstyrene)	366/379	379
poly(p-ethylstyrene)	300/351	342

TABLE 6.4 (continued)

Polymer	T_g exp.	T_g calc.
poly(p-hexylstyrene)	246	250
poly(p-decylstyrene)	208	200
poly(p-nonadecylstyrene)	305	314
poly(vinyl methyl ether)	242/260	252
poly(vinyl ethyl ether)	231/254	237
poly(vinyl hexyl ether)	196/223	210
poly(vinyl decyl ether)	215	200
poly(methyl acrylate)	279/282	279
poly(ethyl acrylate)	249/252	260
poly(hexyl acrylate)	213/216	219
poly(nonyl acrylate)	184/215	204
poly(hexadecyl acrylate)	308	295
poly(methyl methacrylate)	266/399	378
poly(ethyl methacrylate)	281/338	339
poly(hexyl methacrylate)	256/268	247
poly(decyl methacrylate)	203/218	200
poly(hexadecyl methacrylate)	288	290

$M = 192$, so $T_g = \dfrac{65,400}{192} = 341$ K

Experimental values range from 342 to 350 K.

Example 6.2

Estimate the glass transition temperature of poly(hexadecyl methacrylate). Structural formula:

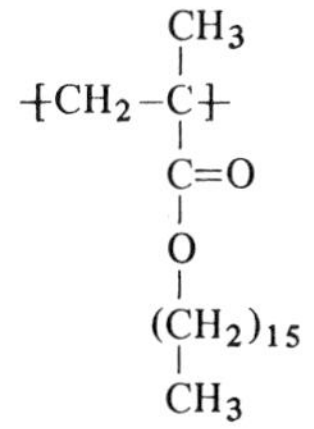

$$
\begin{array}{c}
\quad\quad CH_3 \\
\quad\quad | \\
+CH_2-C+ \\
\quad\quad | \\
\quad\quad C=O \\
\quad\quad | \\
\quad\quad O \\
\quad\quad | \\
\quad\quad (CH_2)_{15} \\
\quad\quad | \\
\quad\quad CH_3
\end{array}
$$

Solution

For this polymer $N = 15$, $Y_{g9} = 45,200$ and $M = 311$. With equation (6.8)

$Y_g = Y_{g9} + 7500 (N - 9) = 45,200 + 7500 \times 6 = 90,200$

$T_g = \dfrac{Y_g}{M} = \dfrac{90,200}{311} = 290$ K

The literature value is $T_g = 288$ K.

Example 6.3

Estimate the limiting value of T_g for polylactams (aliphatic polyamides) at increasing number of CH_2 groups in the chain.

Solution
    The structural formula of polylactams is:

$$[-(CH_2)_n-CONH-]$$

so

$$I = \frac{2}{2 + 2n}$$

since $-(CH_2)_n-$ is found on both sides of $-CONH-$

therefore

$$Y_g = 2700n + 12,000 + 1800\left(\frac{2 + 2n}{2}\right)$$

and

$$T_g = \frac{13,800 + 4500n}{43 + 14n} \approx \frac{4500}{14} = 321 \text{ (if } n \to \infty).$$

This is in good agreement with the experimental values (for dry polylactams).

The influence of molecular weight on the glass transition temperature

The influence of molecular weight on T_g can be approximately described by an equation of the type (2.1):

$$T_g = T_g(\infty) - \frac{A}{\bar{M}_n}$$

where $T_g(\infty)$ is the value of T_g for very high molecular weights.

According to Cowie (1975), however, T_g shows no further increase if the molecular weight is above a certain critical value. This value corresponds roughly with the critical molecular weight found in melt viscosity experiments, which will be discussed in Chapter 15.

The influence of tacticity on the glass transition temperature

Karasz and Mac Knight (1968) collected the available data for glass transition temperatures of vinyl polymers of the general formula

$$\left(-CH_2-\underset{\underset{Q}{|}}{\overset{\overset{P}{|}}{C}}-\right)_x$$

They observed that steric configuration affects T_g only if $P \neq Q$ and neither P nor Q is hydrogen.

A theoretical derivation based on the Gibbs−Di Marzio (1958) theory of the glass transition leads to the conclusion that for the series of polyalkyl methacrylates

$$T_g(\text{syndiotactic}) - T_g(\text{isotactic}) = \text{constant} \approx 112°$$

TABLE 6.5

T_g of stereoregular polyalkyl methacrylates (K)

Polymer	T_g syndio	T_g iso
poly(methyl methacrylate)	433	316
poly(ethyl methacrylate)	393	281
poly(isopropyl methacrylate)	412	300
poly(butyl methacrylate)	361	249
poly(isobutyl methacrylate)	393	281
poly(cyclohexyl methacrylate)	436	324

Values of T_g for purely syndiotactic and isotactic polyalkyl methacrylates, as mentioned by Karasz and Mac Knight, are given in table 6.5.

Thermodynamics of the glass–rubber transition

In contradiction to the melting point, the glass–rubber transition temperature is not a real thermodynamic transition point. It shows some resemblance, however, to a second order transition. If T_g were a real second-order transition, the following relationship would hold:

$$\frac{dT_g}{dp} = \frac{T_g V(T_g) \Delta\alpha}{\Delta C_p} = \frac{\Delta\kappa}{\Delta\alpha} \tag{6.9}$$

or

$$\Delta C_p \Delta\kappa = T_g V(T_g)(\Delta\alpha)^2 \tag{6.10}$$

where

T_g = glass transition temperature
p = pressure
$V(T_g)$ = molar volume at T_g
$\Delta\alpha$ = $\alpha_1 - \alpha_g$ = difference in thermal expansion coefficient at T_g
ΔC_p = $C_p^1(T_g) - C_p^s(T_g)$ = difference in molar heat capacity at T_g
$\Delta\kappa$ = $\kappa_1 - \kappa_g$ = difference in compressibility at T_g.

Staverman (1966) and Breuer and Rehage (1967) extensively discussed the thermodynamics of the glass–rubber transition. They concluded that it is not a real second-order transition, mainly because the glassy state is not completely defined by the normal state variables p, V, T.

It would be interesting to test the validity of eqs. (6.9) and (6.10) against experimental data. Unfortunately, the available data show large deviations, so that the calculations merely lead to the correct order of magnitude. The only accurate data are those for polystyrene determined by Breuer and Rehage. They lead to the following results:

$\Delta\alpha = 3.3 \times 10^{-4}$ K^{-1}

$\Delta\kappa = 1.65 \times 10^{-10} \text{ m}^2/\text{N}$

$\Delta C_p = 26.8 \text{ J} \cdot \text{mol}^{-1} \cdot \text{K}^{-1}$

$\dfrac{dT_g}{dp} = 2.5 \times 10^{-7} \text{ m}^2 \cdot \text{K/N}$

$T_g = 375 \text{ K}$

$V(T_g) = 1.00 \times 10^{-4} \text{ m}^3/\text{mol}$

$$\frac{\dfrac{dT_g}{dp}\Delta C_p}{T_g V(T_g)\Delta\alpha} = \frac{2.5 \times 10^{-7} \times 26.8}{375 \times 10^{-4} \times 3.3 \times 10^{-4}} = 0.54$$

$$\frac{\dfrac{dT_g}{dp}\Delta\alpha}{\Delta\kappa} = \frac{2.5 \times 10^{-7} \times 3.3 \times 10^{-4}}{1.65 \times 10^{-10}} = 0.50$$

$$\frac{\Delta C_p \Delta\kappa}{T_g V(T_g)(\Delta\alpha)^2} = 1.08.$$

Obviously, eqs. (6.9) and (6.10) are valid within the limits of accuracy of the available data.

These values are slightly different from those published earlier by Gee (1966).

The data on polyisobutylene, poly(vinyl acetate), poly(vinyl chloride) and poly(methyl methacrylate) mentioned by Bianchi (1965) and Kovacs (1963) show effects of the same order of magnitude.

Eqs. (6.9) and (6.10) may therefore be used to estimate the order of magnitude of one of the quantities involved, if the other quantities are known.

B. THE CRYSTALLINE MELTING POINT

It is remarkable that practically no T_m–structure relationships have been proposed in the literature, although there are more experimental data available for T_m than for T_g.

Many years ago a certain correspondence was already observed between T_g and T_m for the same polymer, which suggests that a treatment analogous to that proposed for T_g could also be used for the prediction of T_m. This leads to a formula equivalent to eq. (6.1):

$$T_m \sum_i s_i = \sum_i s_i T_{mi} \tag{6.11}$$

There is a fundamental difference between T_g and T_m, however, in that the melting point is a real first-order transition point, at which the free energies of both phases in equilibrium are equal. Thus:

$$T_m \Delta S_m = \Delta H_m \tag{6.12}$$

where ΔS_m is entropy of fusion, ΔH_m is enthalpy of fusion.

Equation (6.12) suggests that a method for predicting T_m could be based on calculation of both ΔH_m and ΔS_m by group contribution methods. As was stated in Chapter 5, however, the lack of data for ΔH_m makes this method impracticable.

In view of this the correlation for T_m to be presented in this section will be based on eq. (6.11). The value of $\sum_i s_i$ will be put equal to the molar weight of the structural unit, in the same way as was done for the T_g-correlation. *It should be emphasized that this results in a purely empirical correlation method*, so that no physical significance should be attributed to the *absolute* values of the group contributions. Thus a formula equivalent to (6.4) will be used:

$$Y_m = \sum_i Y_{mi} = T_m \cdot M \tag{6.13}$$

or

$$\boxed{T_m = \frac{Y_m}{M} = \frac{\sum_i Y_{mi}}{M}} \tag{6.14}$$

The function Y_m will be called *molar melt transition function* (K · g/mol). Equation (6.13) has been applied to all available literature data on crystalline melting points of polymers, totalling nearly 800; from this the correlation rules for Y_m have been derived.

The quantity Y_m (like Y_g) does not show pure linear additivity. It is necessary to introduce a number of correction terms for interactions between different groups. These interactions, of course, become more complicated as more different structural groups are present. The group contributions and their structural corrections are summarized in tables 6.6–6.8. We shall again discuss these data step by step.

1. The unbranched polymethylene chain

It is known from the literature that the melting point of pure polymethylene is 409 K. This gives for the contribution of $-CH_2-$ to Y_m:

$$Y_m(-CH_2-) = 409 \times 14.03 = 5738 \text{ K} \cdot \text{g/mol}.$$

We shall apply a round value of 5700.

2. Linear unbranched aliphatic condensation polymers

The most reliable data are those of polyesters and of polyamides. From fig. 6.3 it is obvious that with polyesters the slope of Y_m versus n_{CH_2} approaches 5700 if the methylene chain contains more than 10 CH_2 groups. The same is true of polyamides if the methylene chain contains more than 15 CH_2 groups. The deviation for polymers with shorter methylene chains can be adequately described by means of the interaction function I (see formula 6.6) on the one hand and by an odd–even effect on the other (like low-molecular crystals of organic acids and diacids, semicrystalline polymers show an

114

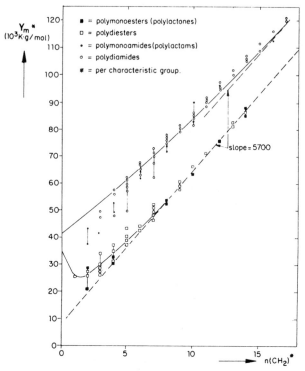

Fig. 6.3. Y_m values of condensation polymers as a function of the length of the methylene chain per structural unit.

odd–even fluctuation of their melting points as a function of the length of their methylene chains in the structural unit).

In formula:

$$Y_m = \sum_i Y_{mi} + \sum (\text{structural corrections}) \tag{6.15}$$

where the last term consists of two contributions:

the interaction contribution, equal to $\sum Y_m(I_x)$

the odd-even correction (negative), equal to $\sum Y_m(\text{ODD})$

Here

$Y_m(I_x)$ = interaction correction per group X

$Y_m(\text{ODD})$ = correction (reduction) per odd methylene chain adjacent to X.

So the final formula for simple linear condensation polymers becomes:

$$Y_m = \sum_i Y_{mi} + \sum Y_m(I_x) + \sum Y_m(\text{ODD}) \tag{6.16}$$

TABLE 6.6

Group contributions to Y_m (K · g/mol)

Group	Y_{mi}	Group (aromatic/cyclic structures)	Y_{mi}	Group	Y_{mi}	$Y_m(I_x)$	$Y_m(ODD)$
$-CH_2-$	5,700	*p*-phenylene ring	50,000	$-O-$	$-3,300$	$33,000\,I^1$	-300
$-CH(CH_3)-$ { symm. / asymm. }	13,000 / $-7,000$	dimethyl-benzene ring (CH_3, CH_3)	35,000	$O{=}C{<}$	?		
$-CH(C_6H_5)-$	48,000	ring ($\varnothing$, $\varnothing$)	153,000	$-C{-}O-$, $O{=}C{-}O-$	5,000	$30,000\,I$	$-1,500$
$-CH(OCH_3)-$	19,000	benzene ring	25,000	$-O{-}C{-}O-$ ($O{=}$)	7,000	$30,000\,I$	$(-1,500)$
$-CH(COOCH_3)-$	—	*o*-benzene ring	13,000	$O{=}C{-}O{-}C{=}O$	14,000	$36,000\,I$	$-1,500$
$-C(CH_3)_2-$	12,000	cyclohexane ring { trans / cis }	50,000 / 26,000	$-S{-}S-$	1,700	$60,000\,I^1$	$-1,000$
$-C(CH_3)(COOCH_3)-$	(37,500)			$O{=}S{=}O$	5,000	$60,000\,I^1$	$-1,000$
$-CH(OH)-$	18,000			$O{=}S{=}O$	?		
$-CHF-$	14,700			$O{=}C{-}NH-$	48,000	$-6,000\,I^{-1/2}$	$-2,500$
$-CHCl-$	23,700			$-O{-}C{-}NH-$ ($O{=}$)	42,000	$-6,000\,I^{-1/2}$	$-2,500$
$-CF_2-$	23,700			$-NH{-}C{-}NH-$	55,000	$-6,000\,I^{-1/2}$	$-2,500$
$-CCl_2-$	41,700						
$-CFCl-$	32,700						

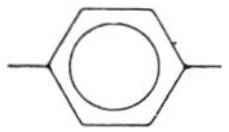

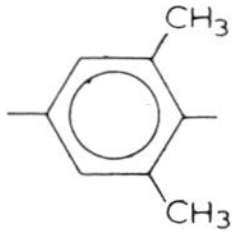

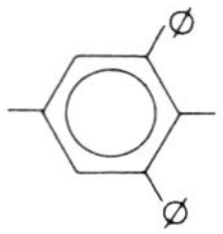

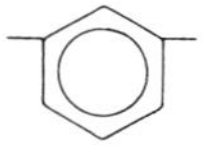

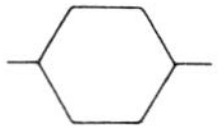

[1] Not valid at $I_x = 1$.

Table 6.6 (last three columns) summarizes the different terms for various polar groups; fig. 6.3 shows how well equation (6.16) (drawn lines, with the given values for group and correction terms) describes the actual data. It is understandable that for polyamides, polyurethanes and polyureas, with their strong hydrogen bonding, the form of the $Y_m(I_x)$ correction differs from that of polymers without hydrogen bonding.

3. Linear, unbranched condensation polymers containing $-CH_2-$ groups and aromatic rings

This group of polymers generally follows the rules given in table 6.6. A number of aromatic polymers show deviations (see 4).

4. Linear condensation polymers with special structures

By means of table 6.6 the melting points of the majority of the condensation polymers can be estimated. Like the glass transition temperatures, also the melting points of the more complicated and asymmetrical polymers show deviations. For a number of polymers the following estimation methods have been derived.

a. Linear unbranched aliphatic condensation polymers containing several types of polar groups in the same structural unit

In polymers of mixed type, such as polyether/esters, polyether/amides, polysulphide/esters, polysulphide/amides, it has been found that the presence of more than one type of polar group per structural unit has a depressing effect on Y_m. Table 6.7 gives some data.

b. Aromatic polymers containing symmetrical, composed groups

The correction terms to be applied are found in table 6.8. For normal use it is easier to handle these groups as entities with their own Y_{mi}.

c. Aromatic polymers containing asymmetrical groups
If the combinations

TABLE 6.7

Correction terms for "mixed" condensation polymers

Type of polymer	1 O atom per 2 characteristic groups	1 O atom per characteristic group	S
polyether/esters	−18,000	−12,500	−15,000
polyether/anhydrides	−	−16,000	−12,000
polyether/amides } polyether/urethanes	−12,000	−9,000	−8,000

TABLE 6.8

Contributions to Y_m of some special group combinations

Combination			Correction	Y_{mi}
$-CH_2-\langle C_6H_4\rangle-CH_2-$	p-xylylene	in	8,500	69,900
	polyamides		0	61,400
	polyurethanes, polyureas		−5,000	56,400
	polyesters		−20,000	41,500
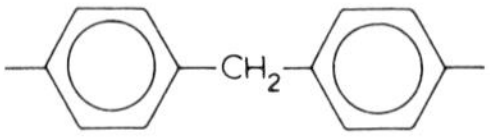 $-\langle C_6H_4\rangle-CH_2-\langle C_6H_4\rangle-$			−16,000	90,000
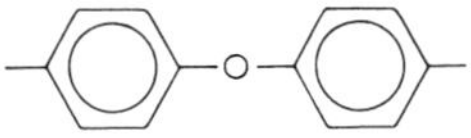 $-\langle C_6H_4\rangle-O-\langle C_6H_4\rangle-$			(−50,000)	80,000
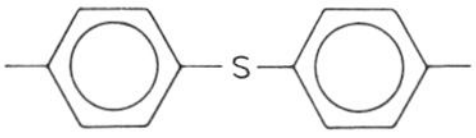 $-\langle C_6H_4\rangle-S-\langle C_6H_4\rangle-$			(−70,000)	90,000
$-\langle C_6H_4\rangle-SO_2-\langle C_6H_4\rangle-$			?	120,000
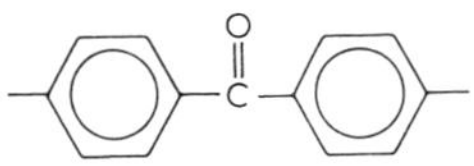 $-\langle C_6H_4\rangle-CO-\langle C_6H_4\rangle-$			?	90,000

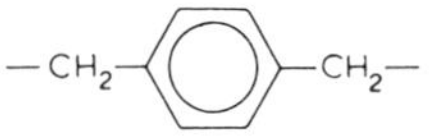

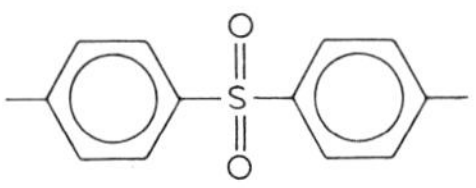

are present in such a way that the structural unit of the polymer is asymmetrical, this has a depressing effect: Y_m decreases by 10,000.

5. Linear polymers containing "short" side groups (e.g. vinyl polymers)

Table 6.6 gives the basic data. It is interesting to note that substitution of H by halogen atoms shows a marked regularity in Y_m. Substitution of H by F causes an increase of 9000, that of H by Cl an increase of 18,000 per substituted H.

6. Linear polymers containing "long" side chains ("comb polymers")

Vinyl polymers with longer methylene side chains have the general formula:

$$\pm CH_2-Y \pm$$
$$|$$
$$(CH_2)_N$$
$$|$$
$$CH_3$$

in which Y stands for a number of different trivalent structural groups. The polymer with N = 0 is called the basic polymer. The melting point first decreases with increasing N, to reach a minimum value at about N = 5. If N increases further, the value of T_m also increases (similar but not equal to the behaviour of T_g). It was found that this behaviour can be approximately described by some simple rules (see fig. 6.4):

    a. for each series, a minimum value of T_m = 235 K is reached at N = 5.

    b. for N < 5, Y_m is a linear function of N determined by the values at N = 0 (basic polymer) and N = 5

    c. for N > 5, Y_m increases by 5700 for each methylene group added.

In formula:

$$
\begin{array}{ll}
N = 5 & Y_m = 235\, M\ (= Y_{m5}) \\[2mm]
N < 5 & Y_m = Y_{m0} + \dfrac{N}{5}(Y_{m5} - Y_{m0}) \\[2mm]
N > 5 & Y_m = Y_{m5} + 5700(N - 5)
\end{array}
\qquad (6.17)
$$

In table 6.9 values of Y_{m0} and Y_{m5} are given for the most important vinyl polymers.

TABLE 6.9

Basic data for vinyl polymers with longer side chains

Series	Basic polymers	Y	Y_{m0}	Y_{m5}
polyolefins	polypropylene	$\begin{array}{c} H \\ \mid \\ -C- \\ \mid \\ H \end{array}$	18,700	26,300
polyvinyl ethers	poly(vinyl methyl ether)	$\begin{array}{c} H \\ \mid \\ -C- \\ \mid \\ O \end{array}$	24,400	30,100
polyacrylates	poly(methyl acrylate)	$\begin{array}{c} H \\ \mid \\ -C- \\ \mid \\ C{=}O \\ \mid \\ O \end{array}$	48,000 [1]	36,700
polyvinyl esters	poly(vinyl acetate)	$\begin{array}{c} H \\ \mid \\ -C- \\ \mid \\ O \\ \mid \\ C{=}O \end{array}$	–	36,700
polymethacrylates	poly(methyl methacrylate)	$\begin{array}{c} CH_3 \\ \mid \\ -C- \\ \mid \\ C{=}O \\ \mid \\ O \end{array}$	43,300	40,000

[1] By extrapolation.

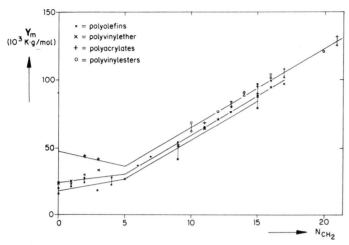

Fig. 6.4. Y_m values of vinyl polymers with side chains.

TABLE 6.10

Experimental and calculated values of T_m for a number of polymers (K)

Polymer	T_m exp.	T_m calc.
poly(methylene oxide)	333/473	426
poly(ethylene oxide)	335/349	334
poly(trimethylene oxide)	308	309
poly(tetramethylene oxide)	308/333	322
poly(tetramethylene acetal)	296	317
poly(decamethylene acetal)	330	328
poly(ethylene sulphide)	418/483	418
poly(decamethylene sulphide)	351/365	358
poly(ethylene disulphide)	386/418	396
poly(decamethylene disulphide)	318/332	331
poly(ethylene adipate)	320/338	344
poly(decamethylene adipate)	343/355	344
poly(decamethylene sebacate)	344/358	349
poly(ethylene terephthalate)	538/557	528
poly(decamethylene terephthalate)	396/411	418
poly(paraphenylene dimethylene adipate)	343/354	357
poly(tetramethylene anhydride)	350/371	364
poly(hexadecamethylene anhydride)	368	366
poly(tetramethylene carbonate)	332	320
poly(decamethylene carbonate)	328/378	345
polyethylene	410 (368/414)	407
polyethylidene	463	464
polypropylene	385/481	445
polyisobutylene	275/317	316
polystyrene	498/523	516

(Continued on p. 120)

TABLE 6.10 (continued)

Polymer	T_m exp.	T_m calc.
poly(vinyl fluoride)	473	443
poly(vinylidene fluoride)	410/511	459
poly(tetrafluoroethylene)	292/672	474
poly(vinyl chloride)	485/583	470
poly(vinylidene chloride)	463/483	489
poly(trifluorochloroethylene)	483/533	486
poly(fluorostyrene)	523/543	547
poly(hexamethylene adipamide)	523/545	547
poly(decamethylene sebacamide)	467/489	474
poly(6-aminocaproic acid)	487/506	503
poly(11-aminoundecanoic acid)	455/493	465
poly(nonamethylene azelamide)	438/462	455
poly(ethylene terephthalamide)	728	739
poly(hexamethylene terephthalamide)	623/644	635
poly(octadecamethylene terephthalamide)	528	507
poly(paraphenylene dimethylene adipamide)	606/613	621
poly(hexamethylene-4,4'-oxydibutyramide)	460	444
poly(tetramethylene hexamethylene diurethane)	446/462	450
poly(decamethylene hexadecamethylene diurethane)	401	403
poly(paraphenylene dimethylene tetramethylene diurethane)	500	499
poly(hexamethylene octamethylene diurea)	498/526	517
poly(paraphenylene dimethylene hexamethylene diurea)	579	588
polybutene	379/415	361
polyoctene	235	235
polyoctadecene	314/383	331
poly(vinyl methyl ether)	417/423	421
poly(vinyl ethyl ether)	359	355
poly(vinyl heptadecyl ether)	333	328
poly(propyl acrylate)	388/435	381
poly(butyl acrylate)	320	322
poly(docosyl acrylate)	329/345	336
poly(vinyl dodecanoate)	274/302	288
poly(methyl methacrylate)	433/473	433
poly(docosyl methacrylate)	328/334	332

Comparison between calculated and experimental values

Table 6.10 gives a comparison of experimental and calculated values for a random selection of polymers. The agreement is good.

Of the nearly 800 polymers whose melting points are reported about 75% gave calculated values which differed less than 20° from the experimental ones. Part of the experimental values of the other 25% is not fully reliable. The result may be considered satisfactory for the method presented.

We shall now illustrate the method again by some typical examples.

Example 6.4

Calculate the melting point of the polyester of ethylene glycol and 11-(p-carboxy-phenoxy)undecanoic acid. Structural formula:

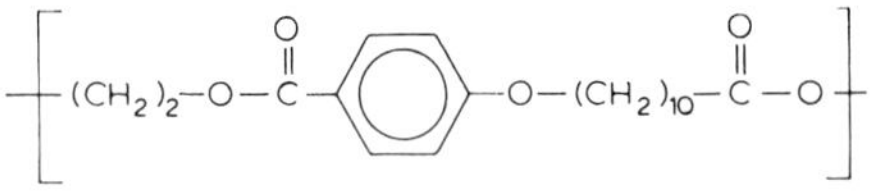

Solution

The polymer structural unit contains the combination ―⟨○⟩―O― , which makes the unit asymmetrical. The two ester groups have different surroundings. The interaction factors are:

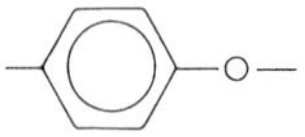

$I(-COO-)_1 = 2/(2 + 2) = 0.5$

$I(-COO-)_2 = 2/(2 + 2 + 10) = 0.143$

$I(-O-) = 1/(1 + 10) = 0.091$

There are no odd methylene chain segments, so $Y_m(ODD) = 0$.

The following contributions to $\sum_1 Y_m$ are read in the tables 6.6 and 6.7:

(from table 6.6)

		Y_{mi}
$\left\{\begin{array}{l} 12 \times -CH_2- \end{array}\right.$		68,400
―⟨○⟩―		50,000
$(COO)_1$	$\left\{\begin{array}{l} Y_{mi} \\ Y_I(0.5 \times 30,000) \\ Y(ODD) \end{array}\right.$	5,000 15,000 0
$(COO)_2$	$\left\{\begin{array}{l} Y_{mi} \\ Y_I(0.143 \times 30,000) \\ Y(ODD) \end{array}\right.$	5,000 4,300 0
$-O-$	$\left\{\begin{array}{l} Y_{mi} \\ Y_I(0.091 \times 33,000) \\ Y(ODD) \end{array}\right.$	−3,300 3,000 0

(from table 6.7)

COO–O– interaction	−18,000
asymmetry correction	−10,000
	= 119,400

The molecular weight of the structural unit, M = 348, so

$$T_m = \frac{119,400}{348} = 343 \text{ K.}$$

The literature value is T_m = 338 K.

Example 6.5
Estimate the melting point of poly(vinyl 1-decyl ether). Structural formula

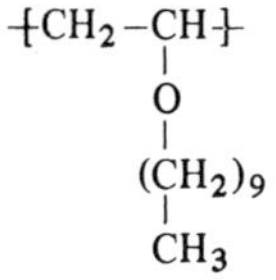

$$\begin{array}{c} +CH_2-CH+ \\ | \\ O \\ | \\ (CH_2)_9 \\ | \\ CH_3 \end{array}$$

Solution
Equation 6.17 for N > 5 gives

$$Y_m = Y_{m5} + 5700(N - 5) = 30,100 + 5700 \times 4 = 52,900$$

$$T_m = \frac{Y_m}{M} = \frac{52,900}{184} = 288 \text{ K}$$

The literature value is T_m = 280 K.

C. RELATIONSHIP BETWEEN GLASS TRANSITION TEMPERATURE AND MELTING POINT OF POLYMERS

It has been observed that the ratio of glass transition temperature to melting point (both expressed in K) has about the same value for many polymers: $T_g/T_m \approx 2/3$. This feature was first reported by Boyer (1952) and, independently, by Beaman (1953) and Bunn (1953). In later work Boyer (1954, 1963) discussed the subject more fully and gave the following rules:

$$\frac{T_g}{T_m} = \begin{cases} \frac{1}{2} \text{ for symmetrical polymers} \\ \frac{2}{3} \text{ for unsymmetrical polymers} \end{cases}$$

(Unsymmetrical polymers were defined as those containing a main-chain atom which does not have two identical substituents. Other polymers are regarded as symmetrical.) Since then many workers have used this relationship as a rule of thumb.

In an extensive study Lee and Knight (1970) investigated the relationship for 138 polymers and found the ratio to vary widely.

In fig. 6.5 their results are graphically represented. The integral distribution curves show the number N of polymers, for which T_g/T_m is smaller than or equal to a given value, as a function of the value of T_g/T_m. About 80% of both symmetrical and unsymmetrical polymers have values in the range 0.5 to 0.8 with a maximum number centred around 0.66, while 20% of the polymers have ratios outside this range. According to these authors there is no real basis for distinguishing between symmetrical and unsymmetrical polymers. They also argue that it is unlikely, from a thermodynamical point of view, that a simple relationship between T_g and T_m can be formulated; the molecular mechanisms of the two phenomena differ fundamentally.

The truth probably lies between these two opinions: the two phenomena show both points of correspondence and points of difference. Thus a constant T_g/T_m ratio may be considered as a general rule with a number of exceptions, to be attributed to structural details of the polymers. This is in agreement with the fact that the methods for predicting T_m and T_g, described in this chapter, show many points of correspondence, but differ in details.

In conformity with these considerations, the following general rules for the T_g/T_m ratio may be formulated:

1. Polymers with T_g/T_m ratios below 0.5 are highly symmetrical and have short repeating units consisting of one or two main-chain atoms each, carrying substituents consisting of only a single atom (polymethylene, polyethylene, polytetrafluoroethylene, polymethylene oxide). They are markedly crystalline.

2. Polymers with T_g/T_m ratios above 0.76 are unsymmetrical. They can also be highly crystalline if they have long sequences of methylene groups or are highly stereoregular; all have a much more complex structure than the polymers with ratios below 0.5.

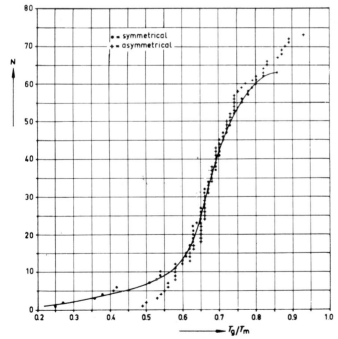

Fig. 6.5. Integral distribution curves of T_g/T_m.

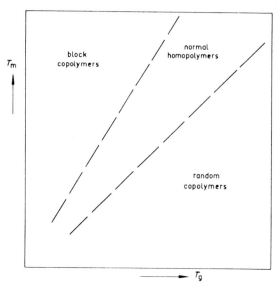

Fig. 6.6. A schematic plot of T_m versus T_g for some types of polymers (from Alfrey and Gurnee, 1967).

3. The majority of the polymers have T_g/T_m ratios between 0.56 and 0.76 with a maximum number centred around 2/3; both symmetrical and unsymmetrical polymers belong to this group.

These rules may be considered as a modification of Boyer's rules and are useful in practical estimations.

In some cases quite different values for the T_g/T_m ratio may be observed in copolymers In this connection, random copolymers and block copolymers should be distinguished . Owing to the irregularity of the structure, crystallization is more difficult in random copolymers than in each of the pure homopolymers. Therefore the melting point is depressed, while the glass transition temperature may have a normal value between those for the homopolymers. This results in a high value for the T_g/T_m ratio.

In block copolymers, on the other hand, long sequences of equal structural units may crystallize in the same way as in the homopolymer. In some cases, a block copolymer may be obtained that combines a high crystalline melting point (corresponding with the value of one component as a homopolymer) with a low glass transition temperature (corresponding with the other pure homopolymer). This results in a low T_g/T_m ratio. A schematic plot is given in fig. 6.6.

D. RELATIONSHIP BETWEEN T_g, T_m AND OTHER TRANSITION TEMPERATURES

In a recent paper Boyer (1975) discusses some other transition temperatures which are often encountered in polymers, and the relationships between these transitions and the

TABLE 6.11

Transition temperatures and their ratios for a number of polymers

Polymer	degree of crystallinity	$T < T_g$	$T_g(L)$	$T_g(U)$	$T_{\alpha c}$	T_m	$\dfrac{T<T_g}{T_g}$	$\dfrac{T_g(U)}{T_g(L)}$	$\dfrac{T_g(L)}{T_m}$	$\dfrac{T_g(U)}{T_m}$	$\dfrac{T_{\alpha c}}{T_m}$
Polyethylene	(0); 0.3; 0.5; 0.7	145	195; 200; 203; 206	(243); 220; 235; 253	378	410	0.75	(1.25); 1.10; 1.16; 1.23	0.475	0.60	0.42
Polyoxymethylene		(178)	(235)	(295)	408; 433	471	(0.75)	(1.25)	(0.50)	(0.63)	0.88; 0.92
Poly(ethylene oxide)	(c)	(140)	(173)	(215)	323	342	(0.80)	(1.25)	(0.51)	0.72	0.94
Polypropylene (iso)		212	258	300	391	445	0.82	1.18	0.58	0.675	0.89
Polybutene	0.75		236	278	343; 323	370; 407		1.29	0.64	0.75	0.925; 0.79
Polypentene	(c)		221	263; 291				1.19; 1.26			
Poly(4-methylpentene)	0.05		291; 302	403	443; 463	522; 551		1.36	0.555	0.775	0.88
Polybutadiene (trans)			253	308							
Polyisoprene (gutta-percha) (trans)											
Polyisoprene (cis)	0.2–0.25		210; 202	265; 233	423	490		1.26; 1.15			0.86
Poly(vinyl fluoride)		236	340								
Poly(vinyl chloride)		253	(353)		433	493	(0.71)		0.72		0.88
Poly(trifluorochloroethylene)	0.77										
Poly(vinylidene fluoride)		176	221	286	363; 373	443	0.78	1.29	0.51	0.65	0.82; 0.85
Poly(vinylidene chloride)			288	353	400?	470?		1.23			
Poly(tetrafluoroethylene)		160	220	(300)	403; 473	505; 538	0.73				0.80; 0.75
Poly(vinyl alcohol)			353	393	473			1.11			
Nylon 6		(140)	323; 353	(405); 398	473	498		1.13	0.65	(0.81)	0.945
Polysulphide (iso)	(c)		363	433				1.18			
Polyacrylonitrile			378	413				(1.09)			
Poly(ethylene tereph. halate)	0.7		339	388				1.14			

two main transitions: glass transition and melting point:

1. The local mode relaxation ($T < T_g$ in Boyer's notation)
This relaxation involves a very short section of a polymer chain. It is often called the β-relaxation. As a general rule

$$T(< T_g) \approx 0.75 \, T_g \qquad \text{(at 100 Hz)}.$$

It is found in both glassy amorphous and semicrystalline polymers.

2. A liquid–liquid relaxation above T_g ($T_{1.1}$)
This relaxation has been discovered fairly recently in some unvulcanized amorphous polymers and copolymers. It tends to fall at $(1.1 - 1.2)T_g$

3. A second glass transition in semicrystalline polymers
In some semicrystalline polymers, two glass transitions can be distinguished: a lower glass transition ($T_g(L)$) and an upper glass transition ($T_g(U)$). It may be assumed that $T_g(L)$ arises from purely amorphous material, while $T_g(U)$ arises from amorphous material which is under restraint due to the vicinity of crystallites. Frequently $T_g(U)$ increases with the degree of crystallization. Some general rules are:

$$T_g(U) \approx (1.1 - 1.3)T_g(L)$$
$$T_g(L) \approx (0.5 - 0.65)T_m$$
$$T_g(U) \approx (0.6 - 0.8)T_m$$

4. A premelting transition ($T_{\alpha c}$)
Some semicrystalline polymers show a mechanical loss peak just below T_m. This $T_{\alpha c}$ is the temperature at which hindered rotation of polymer chains inside the folded crystals can occur. As a general rule

$$T_{\alpha c} \approx 0.9 \, T_m$$

Table 6.11 gives a survey of these transitions and their ratios for a number of polymers.

BIBLIOGRAPHY, CHAPTER 6

General references
Alfrey, T. and Gurnee, E.F., "Organic Polymers", Ch. 3, Prentice-Hall, Englewood Cliffs, N.J., 1967.
Boyer, R.F., "The Relation of Transition Temperatures to Chemical Structure in High Polymers", Rubber Chem. Technol. 36 (1963) 1303.
Boyer, R.F., (Ed.), "Transitions and Relaxations in Polymers", Interscience, New York, 1967.
Brandrup, J. and Immergut, E.H. (Eds.), "Polymer Handbook", Wiley, New York, 1st ed., 1966; 2nd ed., 1975.
Bueche, F., "Physical Properties of Polymers", Ch. 4, 5, 11, Interscience, New York, 1962.
Bunn, C.W., "Melting and Second Order Phenomena", Ch. 12, in "Fibres from Synthetic Polymers" (R. Hill, Ed.), Elsevier, Amsterdam, 1953.

McCrum, N.G., Read, B.E. and Williams, G., "Anelastic and Dielectric Effects in Polymeric Solids", Wiley, New York, 1967.
Meares, P., "Polymers: Structure and Bulk Properties", Van Nostrand, Princeton, 1965.
Shen, M.C. and Eisenberg, A., "Glass Transitions in Polymers", Rubber Chem. Technol. 43 (1970) 95.

Special references

Barton, J.M. and Lee, W.A., Polymer 9 (1968) 602.
Beaman, R.G., J. Polymer Sci. 9 (1953) 472.
Bianchi, U., J. Phys. Chem. 69 (1965) 1497.
Boyer, R.F., 2nd Int. Conf. Phys. Chem., Paris, June 6, 1952.
Boyer, R.F., J. Appl. Phys. 25 (1954) 825.
Boyer, R.F., Am. Chem. Soc. Preprints 30 (1970) nr. 2.
Boyer, R.F., Macromolecules 6 (1973) 288.
Boyer, R.F., J. Polymer Sci., Symposium No. 50 (1975) 189.
Breuer, H. and Rehage, G., Kolloid-Z. 216/217 (1967) 159.
Cowie, J.M.G., Europ. Polymer J. 11 (1975) 297.
Gee, G., Polymer 7 (1966) 177.
Gibbs, J.H. and Di Marzio, E.A., J. Chem. Phys. 28 (1958) 373.
Hayes, R.A., J. Appl. Polymer Sci. 5 (1961) 318.
Karasz, F.E. and Mac Knight, W.J., Macromolecules 1 (1968) 537.
Kovacs, A.J., Fortschr. Hochpol. Forsch. 3 (1963) 394.
Lee, W.A. and Knight, G.J., Brit. Polymer J. 2 (1970) 73.
Lee, W.A., J. Polymer Sci. A-2,8 (1970) 555.
Marcinčin, K. and Romanov, A., Polymer 16 (1975) 173, 177.
Staverman, A.J., Rheologica Acta 5 (1966) 283.
Van Krevelen, D.W. and Hoftyzer, P.J., (1975) unpublished.
Weyland, H.G., Hoftyzer, P.J. and Van Krevelen, D.W., Polymer 11 (1970) 79.

CHAPTER 7

COHESIVE PROPERTIES AND SOLUBILITY

A quantitative measure of the cohesive properties of a substance is the *cohesive energy*. The cohesive energy per unit of volume is called *cohesive energy density*. The latter is closely related to the *internal pressure*, a quantity appearing in the equation of state.

The square root of cohesive energy density is called *solubility parameter*. It is widely used for correlating polymer solvent interactions. As a refinement, three solubility parameter components can be distinguished, representing dispersion, polar, and hydrogen bond interactions.

Although rigorous additivity rules are not applicable in this case, a fair estimation of the cohesive energy and the solubility parameter of polymers can be made by group contribution methods.

Introduction

The cohesive properties of a polymer find direct expression in its solubility in organic liquids. The cohesive properties of a substance are expressed quantitatively in the cohesive energy. This quantity is closely related to the internal pressure, a parameter appearing in the equation of state of the substance.

As early as 1916 Hildebrand pointed out that the order of solubility of a given solute in a series of solvents is determined by the internal pressures of the solvents. Later Scatchard (1931) introduced the concept of "cohesive energy density" into Hildebrands theories, identifying this quantity with the cohesive energy per unit volume. Finally Hildebrand (1936) gave a comprehensive treatment of this concept and proposed the square root of the cohesive energy density as a parameter identifying the behaviour of specific solvents. In 1949 he proposed the term solubility parameter and the symbol δ.

The solubility of a given polymer in various solvents is largely determined by its chemical structure. As a general rule, structural similarity favours solubility. In terms of the above-mentioned quantities this means that the solubility of a given polymer in a given solvent is favoured if the solubility parameters of polymer and solvent are equal. The solubility parameter of the polymer is always defined as the square root of the cohesive energy density in the amorphous state at room temperature. The greater part of this chapter will be devoted to the cohesive energy and the solubility parameter, and to the correlation of these quantities with chemical structure.

Besides the chemical structure, also the physical state of a polymer is important for its solubility properties. Crystalline polymers are relatively insoluble and often dissolve only at temperatures slightly below their crystalline melting points.

129

130

As a general rule, the solubility decreases as the molecular weight of the solute increases. This property can be used to fractionate polymers according to molecular weight.

A. COHESIVE ENERGY

Definitions

The cohesive energy $\mathbf{E}_{coh}$ of a substance in a condensed state is defined as the increase in internal energy U per mole of substance if all the intermolecular forces are eliminated:

the cohesive energy $\equiv \mathbf{E}_{coh} = \Delta U$ (dimension: J/mol)

Directly related to the cohesive energy are the quantities

cohesive energy density: $e_{coh} \equiv \dfrac{\mathbf{E}_{coh}}{V}$ (at 298 K)   (dimension: J/cm^3)

solubility parameter $\delta = \left(\dfrac{\mathbf{E}_{coh}}{V}\right)^{1/2} \equiv e_{coh}^{1/2}$ (at 298 K)   (dimension: J$^{1/2}$/cm$^{3/2}$)

Determination of $\mathbf{E}_{coh}$

For liquids of low molecular weight, the cohesive energy is closely related to the molar heat of evaporation $\Delta \mathbf{H}_{vap}$ (at a given temperature):

$$\mathbf{E}_{coh} = \Delta U_{vap} = \Delta \mathbf{H}_{vap} - p\Delta V \approx \Delta \mathbf{H}_{vap} - RT \tag{7.1}$$

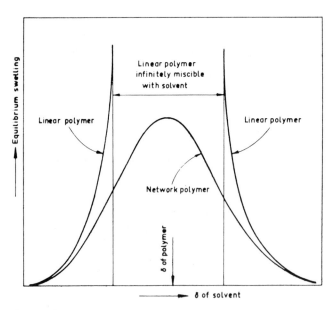

Fig. 7.1. Equilibrium swelling as a function of the solubility parameter of the solvent for linear and cross-linked polystyrene.

Therefore, for low-molecular-weight substances E_{coh} can easily be calculated from the heat of evaporation or from the course of the vapour pressure as a function of temperature. As polymers cannot be evaporated, indirect methods have to be used for the determination of their cohesive energy, e.g. comparative swelling or dissolution experiments in liquids of known cohesive energy density. This method is illustrated in fig. 7.1.

For a prediction of the cohesive energy of substances some group additivity methods have been developed.

For substances of low molecular weight, E_{coh} was considered as an additive property many years ago by Dunkel (1928), who derived group contributions for the cohesive energy of liquids at room temperature. Rheineck and Lin (1968), however, found that for homologous series of low-molecular-weight liquids, the contribution to the cohesive energy of a methylene group was not constant, but depended on the value of other structural groups in the molecule.

Hayes (1961), Di Benedetto (1963), Hoftyzer and Van Krevelen (1970) and Fedors (1974) have applied Dunkel's original method to polymers.

Bunn (1955) dealt with the cohesive energy at the boiling point, while Bondi (1964, 1968) investigated the cohesive energy properties at 0 K (H_o^o).

Table 7.1 gives a survey of the contributions of the most important structural groups to E_{coh}. (Values between brackets are not given as such in the literature but have been calculated by addition and subtraction) [1]

The values given by the different authors show a rough correspondence. Since the cohesive energy will decrease with increasing temperature, the following rule is obeyed in general, as could be expected:

$$H_o^o > E_{coh}(298) > E_{coh}(T_b).$$

When applied to low-molecular substances, the values of Bunn proved to give by far the best prediction of the cohesive energy. But they can only be applied to substances at the boiling point, so that these values have no direct significance for the cohesive energy of polymers. A good correlation is obtained by the method of Rheineck and Lin, but the disadvantage of their system is that many corrections due to vicinal groups, have to be applied. The systems of Di Benedetto and Hayes have the restriction that only values for a limited number of groups are given by these authors.

Although the work of Rheineck and Lin showed that the additivity principle does not apply exactly to the cohesive energy at room temperature, a reasonably good prediction of the cohesive energy of polymers can nevertheless be obtained by this method. The values to be used for the group contributions need not be identical, however, with those for low-molecular-weight compounds. Hoftyzer and Van Krevelen (1970) showed that from the available E_{coh}-data on polymers a new set of group contribution values could be obtained that gives the best possible correlation with all available data. Updated values are mentioned in table 7.1.

---

[1] The values in the literature are normally based on the calorie as unit of energy; here (as a matter of system) the joule is used as unit of energy.

TABLE 7.1

Group contributions to E_{coh} (J/mol)

| Group | H_0° Bondi | $E_{coh}(298)$ | | | | | $E_{coh}(T_b)$ Bunn | $E_{coh}(298)$ Hoftyzer and Van Krevelen |
		Rheineck and Lin	Dunkel	Di Benedetto	Hayes	Fedors		
$-CH_3$	10560	4150	7460	–	–	4710	7120	9640
$-CH_2-$	6350	5150	4150	3600	4150	4940	2850	4190
$-\overset{H}{\underset{\,}{C}}-$	(–270)	4060	–1590	–	–	3430	(–1840)	420
$-C-$	(–8000)	–	(–7340)	–	–	1470	(–6280)	–5580
$-CH(CH_3)-$	(10290)	(8210)	(5870)	–	7120	(8140)	5700	(10060)
$-C(CH_3)_2-$	(13120)	–	7580	10390	11900	(10890)	7960	(13700)
$\overset{H\;\;H}{-C=C-}$	–	–	8300	7210	7500	(8620)	7120	10200
$\overset{H}{-C=C-}$	–	–	(2560)	–	–	(8620)	(2940)	4860
$-C(CH_3)=CH-$	–	–	10020	10900	11480	(13330)	10060	(14500)
cyclopentyl	33770	–	–	–	–	(24240)	–	–
cyclohexyl	38210	29500	–	–	–	(29180)	–	–
phenyl	41060	31220	30920	–	–	31940	22630	31000
p-phenylene	35950	–	–	–	23880	31940	16340	25140

TABLE 7.1 (continued)

Group	H°_c Bondi	$E_{coh}(298)$ Rheineck and Lin	Dunkel	Di Benedetto	Hayes	Fedors	$E_{coh}(T_b)$ Bunn	$E_{coh}(298)$ Hoftyzer and Van Krevelen
—F	—	—	8630	—	—	4190	(4730)	4470
—Cl	—	11690	14250	—	—	11550	11730	12990
—Br	—	—	—	—	—	15490	12990	15500
—I	—	—	—	—	—	19050	17600	—
—CN	—	—	—	—	—	25530	—	25000
—CHCN—	—	—	—	—	24130	28960	24300	25420
—OH	—	32810	30380	—	—	29800	4190	—
—O—	—	—	6830	—	6830	3350	11150	6290
—CO—	—	—	17890	—	—	17370	23460	—
—COOH	—	32810	37580	—	—	27630	—	—
—COO—	—	(19530)	(16010)	—	14160	18000	12150	13410
$-O-\overset{\overset{O}{\|}}{C}-O-$	—	—	—	—	—	17580	—	—
$\overset{\overset{O}{\|}}{C}-O-\overset{\overset{O}{\|}}{C}$	—	—	—	—	—	—	—	—
$-\overset{\overset{O}{\|}}{C}-O-C-\overset{H}{}$	—	—	67880	—	—	30560	16340	—
$-\overset{\overset{O}{\|}}{C}-N-\overset{H}{}$	—	—	—	—	44750	33490	35620	60760
$-O-\overset{\overset{O}{\|}}{C}-N-\overset{H}{}$	—	—	—	—	26310	26370	36620	—
—S—	—	—	—	—	—	14150	9220	8800

Earlier, Small (1953) had demonstrated that the combination $(\mathbf{E}_{coh}V(298))^{\frac{1}{2}} = \mathbf{F}$, the *molar attraction constant,* is a useful additive quantity for low-molecular as well as for high-molecular substances. His set of values is very frequently applied. More recently, Hoy (1970) proposed group contributions to $\mathbf{F}$, slightly different from those of Small.

TABLE 7.2

Group contributions to $\mathbf{F}$

Group	Small	Van Krevelen	Hoy
$-CH_3$	438	420	303.4
$-CH_2-$	272	280	269.0
$-\overset{\text{H}}{\underset{\text{\textbar}}{C}}-$	57	140	176.0
$-\overset{\text{\textbar}}{\underset{\text{\textbar}}{C}}-$	−190	0	65.5
$-CH(CH_3)-$	495	560	(479.4)
$-C(CH_3)_2-$	686	840	(672.3)
$\overset{\text{H H}}{-C=C-}$	454	444	497.4
$\overset{\text{H}}{-C=C-}$	266	304	421.5
$-C(CH_3)=CH-$	(704)	724	(724.9)
cyclopentyl	–	1384	1295.1
cyclohexyl	–	1664	1473.3
phenyl	1504	1517	1398.4
p-phenylene	1346	1377	1442.2
$-F$	(250)	164	84.5
$-Cl$	552	471	419.6
$-Br$	696	614	527.7
$-I$	870	–	–
$-CN$	839	982	725.5
$-CHCN-$	(896)	1122	(901.5)
$-OH$	–	754	462.0
$-O-$	143	256	235.3
$-CO-$	563	685	538.1
$-COOH$	–	652	(1000.1)
$-COO-$	634	512	668.2
$-O-\overset{O}{\overset{\|}{C}}-O-$	–	767	(903.5)
$-\overset{O}{\overset{\|}{C}}-O-\overset{O}{\overset{\|}{C}}-$	–	767	1160.7
$-\overset{O}{\overset{\|}{C}}-\overset{H}{\underset{}{N}}-$	–	1228	(906.4)
$-O-\overset{O}{\overset{\|}{C}}-\overset{H}{\underset{}{N}}-$	–	1483	(1036.5)
$-S-$	460	460	428.4

Van Krevelen (1965) derived a set of atomic contributions to calculate F. Via F it is possible to derive in an indirect way the value of E_{coh} for polymers. The group contributions to F, proposed by Small, Hoy and Van Krevelen, are mentioned in table 7.2.

Table 7.3 gives the values of E_{coh} for a series of 41 polymers, calculated by different methods, in comparison with the experimental data.

The experimental data of E_{coh} for some polymers show large variations and the predicted values according to each of the methods mentioned in table 7.3 fall within the experimental limits of accuracy. There is some evidence, however, that the lower limits of the experimental values are often more reliable. If this effect is taken into account, the methods of Hayes, Small, Hoy, and Hoftyzer and Van Krevelen are superior to the other methods and each of them predicts the cohesive energy with a mean accuracy of about 10%.

The system of group contributions published by Fedors (1974) gives a less accurate prediction of E_{coh}. As Fedors calculated contributions to E_{coh} for a great number of structural groups, however, these data together with Fedors' group contributions to the molecular volume V are reproduced in table 7.4.

Example 7.1
Estimate the cohesive energy of poly(butyl methacrylate).

$$\begin{array}{c} CH_3 \\ | \\ [-CH_2-C-] \\ | \\ C=O \\ | \\ O \\ | \\ (CH_2)_3 \\ | \\ CH_3 \end{array}$$

a. with the aid of the group contributions proposed in this chapter (H. and V.Kr.).
b. according to Small's method.

Solution
Addition of group contributions to be found in tables 7.1 and 7.2 gives the following result:

groups	ΣE_i	ΣF_i	ΣV_i (table 4.4)
$4-CH_2-$	16760	1088	65.80
$2-CH_3$	19280	876	
1 $\diagdown_{\diagup}C\diagup_{\diagdown}$	-5580	-190	50.35
1 $-COO-$	13410	634	21.00
	$E_{coh} = 43870$	$F = 2408$	$V = 137.15$

a. the direct method gives $E_{coh} = 43870$ J/mol unit,
b. Small's method leads to:

$$E_{coh} = \frac{F^2}{V} = 42300 \text{ J/mol.}$$

Experimental values of the solubility parameter δ range from 17.8 to 18.4. This corresponds to values of $E_{coh} = \delta^2 V$ from 43500 to 46500 J/mol.

TABLE 7.3

Cohesive energy of polymers

Polymer	δ ($J^{1/2}/cm^{3/2}$)		V (cm^3/mol)	E_{coh} (from δ) (J/mol)	
	from	to		from	to
Polyethylene	15.8	17.1	32.9	8200	9
Polypropylene	16.8	18.8	49.1	13900	1
Polyisobutylene	16.0	16.6	66.8	17100	1
Polystyrene	17.4	19.0	98.0	29700	3
Poly(vinyl chloride)	19.2	22.1	45.2	16700	2
Poly(vinyl bromide)	19.4	–	48.6	18300	
Poly(vinylidene chloride)	20.3	25.0	58.0	23900	3
Poly(tetrafluoroethylene)	12.7	–	49.5	8000	
Poly(chlorotrifluoroethylene)	14.7	16.2	61.8	13400	1
Poly(vinyl alcohol)	25.8	29.1	35.0	23300	2
Poly(vinyl acetate)	19.1	22.6	72.2	26300	3
Poly(vinyl propionate)	18.0	–	90.2	29200	
Poly(methyl acrylate)	19.9	21.3	70.1	27800	3
Poly(ethyl acrylate)	18.8	19.2	86.6	30600	3
Poly(propyl acrylate)	18.5	–	103.1	35300	
Poly(butyl acrylate)	18.0	18.6	119.5	38700	4
Poly(isobutyl acrylate)	17.8	22.5	119.3	37800	6
Poly(2,2,3,3,4,4,4-heptafluorobutyl acrylate)	13.7	–	148.0	27800	
Poly(methyl methacrylate)	18.6	26.2	86.5	29900	5
Poly(ethyl methacrylate)	18.2	18.7	102.4	33900	3
Poly(butyl methacrylate)	17.8	18.4	137.2	43500	4
Poly(isobutyl methacrylate)	16.8	21.5	135.7	38300	6
Poly(tert.-butyl methacrylate)	17.0	–	138.9	40100	
Poly(benzyl methacrylate)	20.1	20.5	151.2	61100	6
Poly(ethoxyethyl methacrylate)	18.4	20.3	145.6	49300	6
Polyacrylonitrile	25.6	31.5	44.8	29400	4
Polymethacrylonitrile	21.9	–	63.9	30600	
Poly(α-cyanomethyl acrylate)	28.7	29.7	82.1	67600	7
Polybutadiene	16.6	17.6	60.7	16700	1
Polyisoprene	16.2	20.5	75.7	19900	3
Polychloroprene	16.8	18.9	71.3	20100	2
Polyformaldehyde	20.9	22.5	25.0	10900	1
Poly(tetramethylene oxide)	17.0	17.5	74.3	21500	2
Poly(propylene oxide)	15.4	20.3	57.6	13700	2
Polyepichlorohydrin	19.2	–	69.7	25700	
Poly(ethylene sulphide)	18.4	19.2	47.9	16200	1
Poly(styrene sulphide)	19.0	–	115.8	41800	
Poly(ethylene terephthalate)	19.9	21.9	143.2	56700	6
Poly(8-aminocaprylic acid)	26.0	–	135.9	91900	
Poly(hexamethylene adipamide)	27.8	–	208.3	161000	

Conversion factors: 1 $J^{1/2}/cm^{3/2}$ = 0.49 $cal^{1/2}/cm^{3/2}$; 1 cm^3/mol = 10^{-6} m^3/mol; 1 J/mol = 0.24 cal/mol.

(calculated)
ol)

el	Di Benedetto	Hayes	Fedors	Small	Van Krevelen	Hoy	Hoftyzer and Van Krevelen
J	7200	8300	9880	9000	9500	8800	8380
0	–	11270	13080	12000	14400	11400	14250
J	13990	16050	15830	13700	18800	13300	17890
0	41060	34270	40310	34300	38300	34700	35610
0	16930	21660	19920	17200	17600	16500	17600
–	–	–	23860	21600	22000	19500	20110
0	–	15460	25670	24300	25700	23800	24590
0	–	9640	17180	7800	8700	4400	6720
0	–	–	23250	13800	15000	10500	15240
0	–	–	38170	–	39400	23500	–
0	28990	25430	31080	27200	25300	27800	27660
0	32590	29580	36020	31000	29500	31500	31850
0	28990	25430	31080	28000	26100	28600	27660
0	32590	29580	36020	32300	30800	32800	31850
0	36190	33730	40960	36700	35500	37000	36040
0	39790	37880	45900	41100	40200	41400	40230
0	–	36700	44160	39400	40300	39300	41910
0	–	–	56860	39400	37600	31800	36760
0	–	30210	33830	29300	30800	29900	31300
0	–	34360	38770	33900	35700	34500	35490
0	–	42660	48650	42300	44500	42600	43870
0	–	41480	46910	41000	45000	41000	45550
0	–	42110	44720	37400	44000	37500	45000
0	–	–	66000	56500	59600	58200	56850
0	–	49490	52000	44700	51100	48300	50160
–	–	28280	33900	30500	43900	30600	29610
–	–	–	36650	28900	44300	29100	33250
–	–	–	54650	48400	58600	50300	46660
0	14410	15800	18500	16400	16600	17700	18580
0	18100	19780	23210	20600	21800	21100	22880
0	20950	20910	30050	26600	25000	26700	26230
0	–	10980	8290	6900	11500	10200	10480
0	–	23430	23110	20400	25500	23100	23050
0	–	18110	16430	14400	20900	16800	20540
–	–	–	28210	24100	29200	26900	28080
–	–	–	24030	21000	21700	19500	17180
–	–	–	54460	45400	49600	44600	44410
–	–	60500	77820	69600	61200	76800	60340
0	–	73800	68070	–	74800	57100	90090
0	–	131000	116380	–	132600	97300	163420

TABLE 7.4

Group contributions to E_{coh} and V according to Fedors

Group	E_{coh} (J/mol)	V (cm³/mol)
$-CH_3$	4710	33.5
$-CH_2-$	4940	16.1
$\backslash$CH$-$ /	3430	−1.0
$\backslash$ / C / $\backslash$	1470	−19.2
$H_2C=$	4310	28.5
$-CH=$	4310	13.5
$\backslash$C= /	4310	−5.5
HC≡	3850	27.4
$-C≡$	7070	6.5
Phenyl	31940	71.4
Phenylene (o, m, p)	31940	52.4
Phenyl (trisubstituted)	31940	33.4
Phenyl (tetrasubstituted)	31940	14.4
Phenyl (pentasubstituted)	31940	−4.6
Phenyl (hexasubstituted)	31940	−23.6
Ring closure 5 or more atoms	1050	16
Ring closure 3 or 4 atoms	3140	18
Conjugation in ring for each double bond	1670	−2.2
Halogen attached to carbon atom with double bond	−20% of E_{coh} of halogen	4.0
$-F$	4190	18.0
$-F$ (disubstituted)	3560	20.0
$-F$ (trisubstituted)	2300	22.0
$-CF_2-$ (for perfluoro compounds)	4270	23.0
$-CF_3$ (for perfluoro compounds)	4270	57.5
$-Cl$	11550	24.0
$-Cl$ (disubstituted)	9630	26.0
$-Cl$ (trisubstituted)	7530	27.3
$-Br$	15490	30.0
$-Br$ (disubstituted)	12350	31.0
$-Br$ (trisubstituted)	10670	32.4
$-I$	19050	31.5
$-I$ (disubstituted)	16740	33.5
$-I$ (trisubstituted)	16330	37.0
$-CN$	25530	24.0
$-OH$	29800	10.0
$-OH$ (disubstituted or on adjacent C atoms)	21850	13.0
$-O-$	3350	3.8
$-CHO$ (aldehyde)	21350	22.3
$-CO-$	17370	10.8
$-COOH$	27630	28.5
$-CO_2-$	18000	18.0
$-CO_3-$ (carbonate)	17580	22.0
$-C_2O_3-$ (anhydride)	30560	30.0

TABLE 7.4 (continued)

Group	E_{coh} (J/mol)	V (cm³/mol)
HCOO– (formate)	18000	32.5
–CO_2CO_2– (oxalate)	26790	37.3
–HCO_3	12560	18.0
–COF	13400	29.0
–COCl	17580	38.1
–COBr	24150	41.6
–COI	29300	48.7
–NH_2	12560	19.2
–NH–	8370	4.5
–N$\backslash^{/}$	4190	–9.0
–N=	11720	5.0
–$NHNH_2$	21980	–
–NNH_2	16740	16
–NHNH–	16740	16
–N_2 (diazo)	8370	23
–N=N–	4190	–
$\backslash$C=N–N=C$^{/}$	20090	0
–N=C=N–	11470	–
–NC	18840	23.1
–NF_2	7660	33.1
–NF–	5070	24.5
–$CONH_2$	41860	17.5
–CONH–	33490	9.5
–CON$^{/}$	29510	–7.7
HCON$^{/}$	27630	11.3
HCONH–	43950	27.0
–NHCOO–	26370	18.5
–NHCONH–	50230	–
–NHCON$^{/}$	41860	–
$\backslash$NCON$^{/}$	20930	–14.5
NH_2COO–	37000	–
–NCO	28460	35.0
–ONH_2	19050	20.0
$\backslash$C=NOH	25120	11.3
–CH=NOH	25120	24.0
–NO_2 (aliphatic)	29300	24.0
–NO_2 (aromatic)	15360	32.0
–NO_3	20930	33.5
–NO_2 (nitrite)	11720	33.5
–$NHNO_2$	39770	28.7

(Continued on p. 140)

TABLE 7.4 (continued)

Group	E_{coh} (J/mol)	V (cm^3/mol)
−NNO−	27210	10
−SH	14440	28.0
−S−	14150	12
−S$_2$−	23860	23.0
−S$_3$−	13400	47.2
$>$SO	39140	−
SO$_3$	18840	27.6
SO$_4$	28460	31.6
−SO$_2$Cl	37070	43.5
−SCN	20090	37.0
−NCS	25120	40.0
P	9420	−1.0
PO$_3$	14230	22.7
PO$_4$	20930	28.0
PO$_3$(OH)	31810	32.2
Si	3390	0
SiO$_4$	21770	20.0
B	13810	−2.0
BO$_3$	0	20.4
Al	13810	−2.0
Ga	13810	−2.0
In	13810	−2.0
Tl	13810	−2.0
Ge	8080	−1.5
Sn	11300	1.5
Pb	17160	2.5
As	12980	7.0
Sb	16330	8.9
Bi	21350	9.5
Se	17160	16.0
Te	20090	17.4
Zn	14480	2.5
Cd	17790	6.5
Hg	22810	7.5

The cohesive energy is an important quantity for characterizing the physical state of a given polymer. It is related to other polymer properties for which cohesive forces are important, as will be discussed in other chapters.

The cohesive energy has found its most important applications, however, in the interactions between polymers and solvents. For this purpose the solubility parameter δ is generally used. Therefore the greater part of this chapter will be devoted to properties and applications of the solubility parameter.

B. SOLUBILITY

The solubility parameter

At first sight it is rather unpractical to use a quantity δ with dimensions $J^{1/2}/cm^{3/2}$ instead of the cohesive energy. The definition of δ is based, however, on thermodynamic considerations, as will be discussed below. In the course of time the values of δ, expressed in $cal^{1/2}/cm^{3/2}$, have become familiar quantities for many investigators. In this connection the change to SI units has some disadvantages. Conversion of $cal^{1/2}/cm^{3/2}$ into $J^{1/2}/cm^{3/2}$ is simple, however, as it only requires multiplication by a factor of 2 (2.046 to be exact).

The thermodynamic criteria of solubility are based on the free energy of mixing ΔG_M. Two substances are mutually soluble if ΔG_M is negative. By definition,

$$\Delta G_M = \Delta H_M - T \Delta S_M \tag{7.2}$$

where
ΔH_M = enthalpy of mixing
ΔS_M = entropy of mixing.
As ΔS_M is generally positive, there is a certain limiting positive value of ΔH_M below which dissolution is possible.

As early as 1916 Hildebrand tried to correlate solubility with the cohesive properties of the solvents. In 1949 he proposed the term solubility parameter and the symbol δ, as defined in the beginning of this chapter.

According to Hildebrand, the enthalpy of mixing can be calculated by

$$\Delta h_M = \phi_1 \phi_2 (\delta_1 - \delta_2)^2 \tag{7.3}$$

where
Δh_M = enthalpy of mixing per unit volume
ϕ_1 and ϕ_2 = volume fractions of components 1 and 2
δ_1 and δ_2 = solubility parameters of components 1 and 2.
Eq. (7.3) predicts that $\Delta H_M = 0$ if $\delta_1 = \delta_2$, so that two substances with equal solubility parameters should be mutually soluble due to the negative entropy factor. This is in accordance with the general rule that chemical and structural similarity favours solubility. As the difference between δ_1 and δ_2 increases, the tendency towards dissolution decreases.

We may conclude that as a requirement for the solubility of a polymer P in a solvent S, the quantity

$$(\delta_P - \delta_S)^2$$

has to be small, as small as possible [1].

---

[1] This quantity plays a part in an expression for the thermodynamic interaction parameter χ:
$$\chi \approx 0.34 + \frac{V_S}{RT}(\delta_P - \delta_S)^2.$$

The solubility parameter of a given material can be calculated either from the cohesive energy, or from the molar attraction constant $\mathbf{F}$, as $\delta = \mathbf{F}/\mathbf{V}$.

In the derivation of eq. (7.3) it was assumed that no specific forces are active between the structural units of the substances involved. Therefore it does not hold for crystalline polymers.

Also if one of the substances involved contains strongly polar groups or hydrogen bridges, ΔH_M may become higher than predicted by eq. (7.3), so that ΔG_M becomes positive even for $\delta_1 = \delta_2$ and dissolution does not occur. Conversely, if both substances contain polar groups or hydrogen bridges, solubility may be promoted.

For these reasons a more refined treatment of the solubility parameter concept is often necessary, especially for interactions between polymers and solvents. Nevertheless, the solubility parameters of polymers and solvents are important quantities in all phenomena involving interactions between polymers and solvents.

Table 7.5 gives δ-values for some polymers (experimental and calculated) and Table VI, Part VII, gives solubility parameter values for a number of solvents.

Evidently, the most important application of the solubility parameters to be discussed in this chapter is the prediction of the solubility of polymers in various solvents. A first requirement of mutual solubility is that the solubility parameter of the polymer δ_P and that of the solvent δ_S do not differ too much.

This requirement, however, is not sufficient. There are combinations of polymer and solvent for which $\delta_P \approx \delta_S$, but yet do not show mutual solubility. Mutual solubility only occurs if the degree of hydrogen bonding is about equal. This led Burrell (1955) towards a division of solvents into three classes, viz. poorly, moderately and strongly hydrogen-bonded. In combination with the total solubility parameter δ a considerably improved classification of solvents is obtained. The system of Burrell is represented in table 7.6.

Refinements of the solubility parameter concept

In the derivation of eq. (7.3) by Hildebrand only dispersion forces between structural units have been taken into account. For many liquids and amorphous polymers, however, the cohesive energy is also dependent on the interaction between polar groups and on hydrogen bonding. In these cases the solubility parameter as defined corresponds with the total cohesive energy.

Formally, the cohesive energy may be divided into three parts, corresponding with the three types of interaction forces

$$\mathbf{E}_{coh} = E_d + E_p + E_h \tag{7.4}$$

where
E_d = contribution of dispersion forces
E_p = contribution of polar forces
E_h = contribution of hydrogen bonding

The corresponding equation for the solubility parameter is

$$\delta^2 = \delta_d^2 + \delta_p^2 + \delta_h^2 \tag{7.5}$$

The equivalent of eq. (7.3) becomes

$$\Delta h_M = \phi_1 \phi_2 [(\delta_{d1} - \delta_{d2})^2 + (\delta_{p1} - \delta_{p2})^2 + (\delta_{h1} - \delta_{h2})^2] \tag{7.6}$$

TABLE 7.5

Experimental and calculated values of δ for some polymers

Polymer	δ exp. $(J^{1/2}/cm^{3/2})$		δ calc. (H. + v.K.) $(J^{1/2}/cm^{3/2})$
	from	to	
Polyethylene	15.8	17.1	16.0
Polypropylene	16.8	18.8	17.0
Polyisobutylene	16.0	16.6	16.4
Polystyrene	17.4	19.0	19.1
Poly(vinyl chloride)	19.2	22.1	19.7
Poly(vinyl bromide)	19.4	–	20.3
Poly(vinylidene chloride)	20.3	25.0	20.6
Poly(tetrafluoroethylene)	12.7	–	11.7
Poly(chlorotrifluoroethylene)	14.7	16.2	15.7
Poly(vinyl alcohol)	25.8	29.1	–
Poly(vinyl acetate)	19.1	22.6	19.6
Poly(vinyl propionate)	18.0	–	18.8
Poly(methyl acrylate)	19.9	21.3	19.9
Poly(ethyl acrylate)	18.8	19.2	19.2
Poly(propyl acrylate)	18.5	–	18.7
Poly(butyl acrylate)	18.0	18.6	18.3
Poly(isobutyl acrylate)	17.8	22.5	18.7
Poly(2,2,3,3,4,4,4-heptafluorobutyl acrylate)	13.7	–	15.8
Poly(methyl methacrylate)	18.6	26.2	19.0
Poly(ethyl methacrylate)	18.2	18.7	18.6
Poly(butyl methacrylate)	17.8	18.4	17.9
Poly(isobutyl methacrylate)	16.8	21.5	18.3
Poly(tert.-butyl methacrylate)	17.0	–	18.0
Poly(benzyl methacrylate)	20.1	20.5	19.3
Poly(ethoxyethyl methacrylate)	18.4	20.3	18.6
Polyacrylonitrile	25.6	31.5	25.7
Polymethacrylonitrile	21.9	–	22.8
Poly(α-cyanomethyl acrylate)	28.7	29.7	23.8
Polybutadiene	16.6	17.6	17.5
Polyisoprene	16.2	20.5	17.4
Polychloroprene	16.8	18.9	19.2
Polyformaldehyde	20.9	22.5	20.5
Poly(tetramethylene oxide)	17.0	17.5	17.6
Poly(propylene oxide)	15.4	20.3	18.9
Polyepichlorohydrin	19.2	–	20.1
Poly(ethylene sulphide)	18.4	19.2	18.9
Poly(styrene sulphide)	19.0	–	19.6
Poly(ethylene terephthalate)	19.9	21.9	20.5
Poly(8-aminocaprylic acid)	26.0	–	25.7
Poly(hexamethylene adipamide)	27.8	–	28.0

Unfortunately, values of δ_d, δ_p and δ_h cannot be determined directly.

There are, in principle, two ways for a more intricate use of the solubility parameter

TABLE 7.6

Hydrogen-bonding tendency of solvents

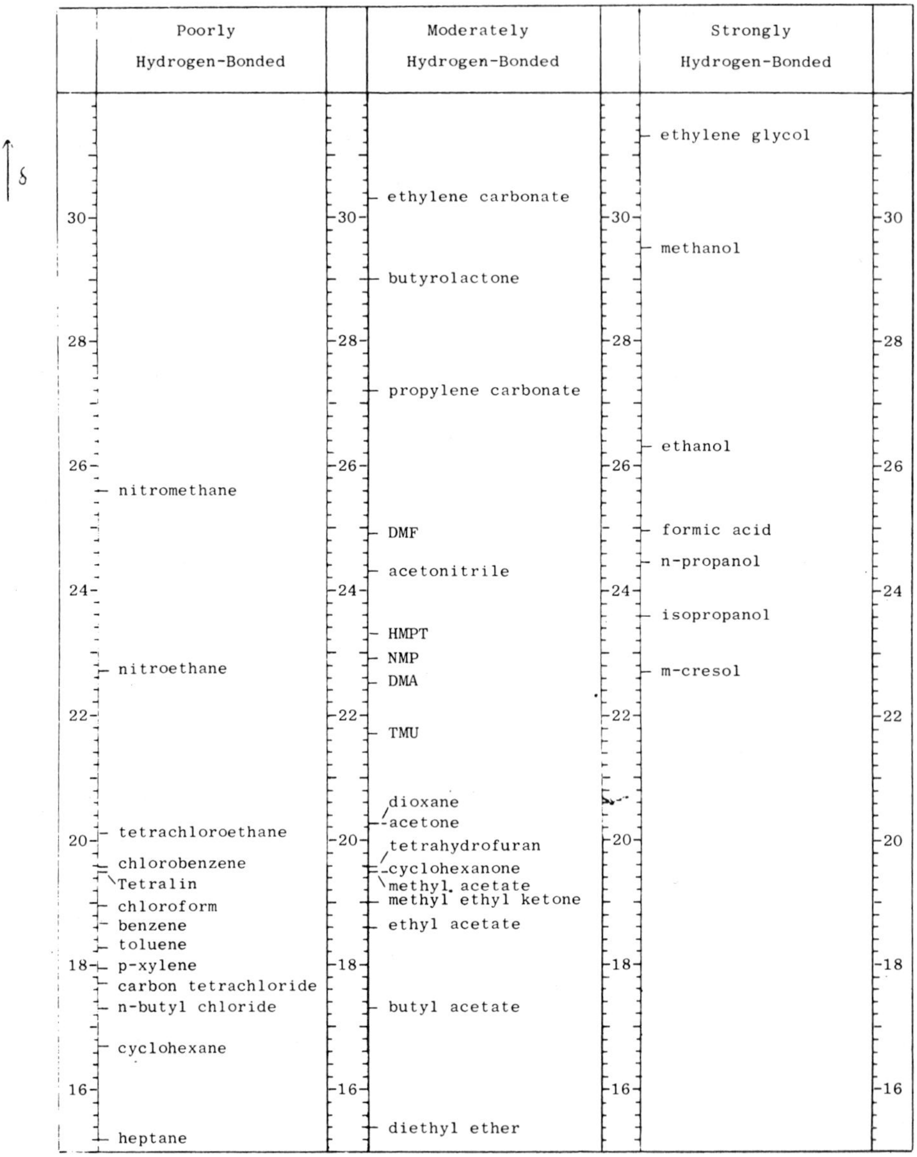

	Poorly Hydrogen-Bonded	Moderately Hydrogen-Bonded	Strongly Hydrogen-Bonded	

$\uparrow \delta$

	Poorly	Moderately	Strongly	
			— ethylene glycol	
		— ethylene carbonate		
30	30		30 — methanol	30
		— butyrolactone		
28	28		28	28
		— propylene carbonate		
			— ethanol	
26	26		26	26
	— nitromethane	— DMF	— formic acid	
		— acetonitrile	— n-propanol	
24	24		24	24
		— HMPT	— isopropanol	
	— nitroethane	— NMP	— m-cresol	
		— DMA		
22	22		22	22
		— TMU		
		/dioxane		
20	— tetrachloroethane	20 — acetone / tetrahydrofuran	20	20
	— chlorobenzene	— cyclohexanone		
	— Tetralin	— methyl acetate		
	— chloroform	— methyl ethyl ketone		
	— benzene	— ethyl acetate		
	— toluene			
18	— p-xylene	18	18	18
	— carbon tetrachloride			
	— n-butyl chloride	— butyl acetate		
	— cyclohexane			
16	16	16	16	16
	— heptane	— diethyl ether		

DMA   —   dimethylacetamide
DMF   —   dimethylformamide
HMPT —   hexamethylphosphoramide
NMP   —   N-methylpyrrolidone
TMU   —   tetramethylurea

concept:
a. the use of other measurable physical quantities besides the solubility parameter for expressing the solvent properties of a liquid;
b. indirect determination of the solubility parameter components δ_d, δ_p and δ_h.

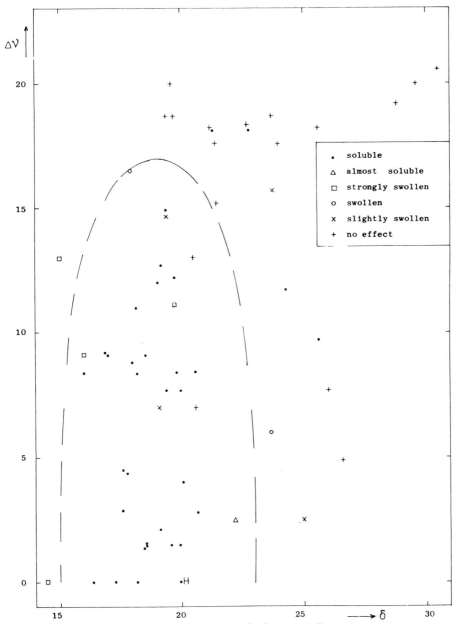

Fig. 7.2. Solubility of polystyrene in various solvents in the $\Delta\nu - \delta$ diagram.

The first method was used by Beerbower et al. (1967), who expressed the amount of hydrogen bonding energy by the hydrogen bonding number $\Delta\nu$. This quantity was defined by Gordy and Stanford (1939–1941) as the shift of the infrared absorption band in the 4 μm range occurring when a given liquid is added to a solution of deuterated methanol in benzene.

Beerbower et al. plotted the data for various solvents in a diagram with the solubility parameter δ along the horizontal axis and the hydrogen bonding number $\Delta\nu$ along the vertical axis. All the solvents in which a given polymer is soluble fall within a certain region. As an example, fig. 7.2 shows such a diagram for polystyrene.

Crowley et al. (1966, 1967) used an extension of this method by including the dipole moment of the solvent in the characterization. However, as this involves a comparison of a number of solvents in a three-dimensional system, the method is unpractical.

The second method was developed by Hansen (1967, 1969). Hansen presumed the applicability of eqs. (7.5) and (7.6) and developed a method for the determination of δ_d, δ_p and δ_h for a number of solvents. The value of δ_d of a given solvent was assumed to be equal to that of a non-polar substance (e.g. hydrocarbon) of about the same chemical structure. This permitted the calculation of $\delta_p^2 + \delta_h^2 = \delta^2 - \delta_d^2$.

Now Hansen determined experimentally the solubility of a number of polymers in a series of solvents. All the solvents were characterized by a point in a three-dimensional structure, in which δ_d, δ_p and δ_h could be plotted on three mutually perpendicular axes. The values of δ_p and δ_h for the various solvents were shifted until all the solvents in which a given polymer was soluble were close together in space.

Values of δ_d, δ_p and δ_h for a number of solvents determined in this way can be found in Table VI (Part VII). For comparison also values of the dipole moment μ and the hydrogen bonding number $\Delta\nu$ are mentioned.

Hansen also determined δ_d, δ_p and δ_h of the polymers involved, being the coordinates of the centre of the solvents region in his three-dimensional structure. Table 7.7 shows his parameters for some polymers [1].

TABLE 7.7

Hansen's specified solubility parameters for some polymers

Polymer	δ	δ_d	δ_p	δ_h
Polyisobutylene	17.6	16.0	2.0	7.2
Polystyrene	20.1	17.6	6.1	4.1
Poly(vinyl chloride)	22.5	19.2	9.2	7.2
Poly(vinyl acetate)	23.1	19.0	10.2	8.2
Poly(methyl methacrylate)	23.1	18.8	10.2	8.6
Poly(ethyl methacrylate)	22.1	18.8	10.8	4.3
Polybutadiene	18.8	18.0	5.1	2.5
Polyisoprene	18.0	17.4	3.1	3.1

---

[1] A number of these values, however, seem to be rather doubtful (see, e.g., the δ_h values of polyisobutylene and polystyrene and the δ_p value of polybutadiene).

The method of Hansen has the disadvantage that three-dimensional structures are necessary for a graphical representation of the interaction between polymers and solvents. For practical applications a two-dimensional method is to be preferred.

Thermodynamic considerations led Bagley et al. (1971) to the conclusion that the effects of δ_d and δ_p show close similarity, while the effect of δ_h is of a quite different nature. Accordingly, they introduced the parameter $\delta_v = \sqrt{(\delta_d^2 + \delta_p^2)}$. This leads to a diagram in which δ_v and δ_h are plotted on the axes.

Such a diagram is shown in fig. 7.3 for the interaction between polystyrene and a number of solvents. The majority of the points for good solvents indeed fall in a single region of fig 7.3. This region can approximately be delimitated by a circle the centre of which is indicated by the symbol *. (This location differs from that proposed by Hansen, according to the data of table 7.7, and indicated by the symbol H.) Obviously, fig. 7.3 is superior to fig. 7.2 in demarcating a solubility region.

A method of representation very similar to that of fig. 7.3 was proposed by Chen (1971). He introduced a quantity

$$\chi_H = \frac{V_S}{RT}[(\delta_{dS} - \delta_{dP})^2 + (\delta_{pS} - \delta_{pP})^2] \tag{7.7}$$

where the subscripts S and P denote solvent and polymer, respectively. The solubility data are then plotted in a $\delta_h - \chi_H$-diagram. A disadvantage of this method is that the characteristics of the polymer should be estimated beforehand.

Other two-dimensional methods for the representation of solubility data are the $\delta_p - \delta_h$-diagram proposed by Henry (1974) and the $\delta - \delta_h$-diagram proposed by Hoernschemeyer (1974).

At the moment the $\delta_v - \delta_h$-diagram seems to be the most efficient way to represent polymer–solvent interactions.

Solubility of polymers in solvents

In the $\delta_h - \delta_v$-diagram the degree of solubility (volume of polymer per volume of solvent) can be indicated by a number. This is shown in fig. 7.4 for the data of Kambour et al. (1973) on the solubility of polystyrene in a number of solvents.

The solubility region can approximately be delimitated by a circle with a radius of about 5 δ-units. The centre of this circle is indicated by the symbol *; it has the coordinate values: $\delta_v = 18; \delta_h = 5$. It can be seen that the solubility increases approximately as the distance from the centre decreases.

As a general rule, polystyrene is soluble in solvents for which

$$|\sqrt{(\delta_v - 18)^2 + (\delta_h - 5)^2}| < 5 \tag{7.8}$$

The literature mentions analogous data for a number of other polymers, which will not be discussed here. When plotted in a $\delta_h - \delta_v$-diagram, they generally show the same type of picture. The reader should be warned, however, of the limited accuracy of this method. The diagrams give only an indication of solubility relationships and always show a number of deviating points.

The solubility limits of a given polymer are closely related to the Flory-temperatures of the polymer in various solvents.

The *Flory-temperature* (Θ_F) is defined as the temperature where the *partial molar free energy* due to polymer-solvent interactions *is zero*, so that the polymer-solvent systems show ideal solution behaviour. If $T = \Theta_F$ the molecules can interpenetrate one another freely with no net interactions. At $T < \Theta_F$ the molecules attract one another. If the temperature is much below Θ_F, precipitation occurs.

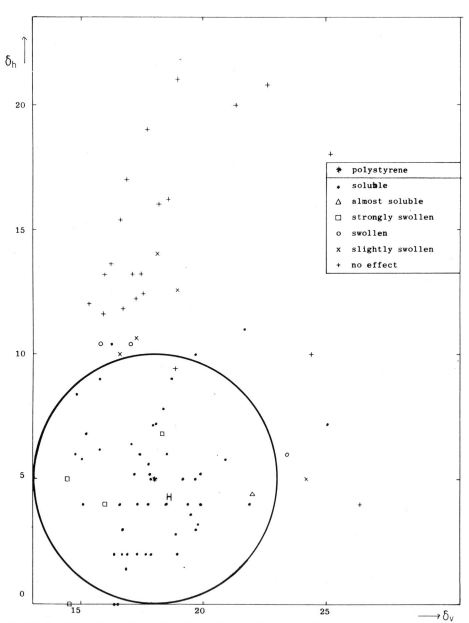

Fig. 7.3. Solubility of polystyrene in various solvents in the $\delta_v - \delta_h$ diagram.

Thermodynamical considerations have led to the following equation for the temperature at which phase separation of polymer solutions begins:

$$T_{cr} \approx \frac{\Theta_F}{1 + \dfrac{C}{M^{1/2}}}$$ (7.9)

where C is a constant for the polymer–solvent system.

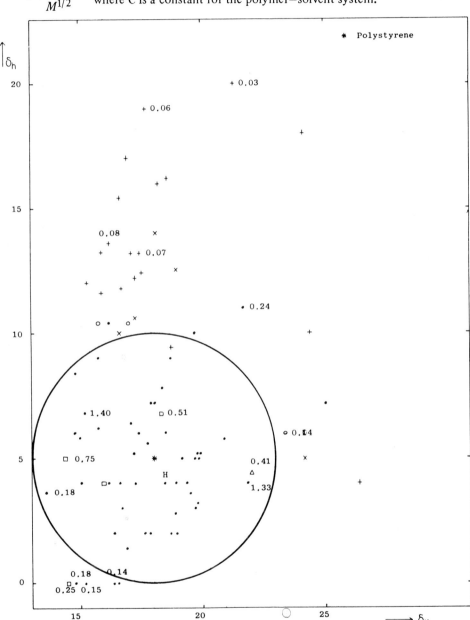

Fig. 7.4. Solubility of polystyrene in various solvents (numbers: vol. styrene/vol. solvent).

150

It is clear that the *Flory-temperature is the critical miscibility temperature in the limit of infinite molecular weight.*

Fox (1962) succeeded in correlating Θ_F-temperatures of polymer—solvent systems with the solubility parameter δ_S of the solvent. Plots of δ_S as a function of Θ_F are shown in fig. 7.5.

At a given temperature, a solvent for the polymer should have a δ-value approximately between the limits, indicated by the two straight lines in the figure.

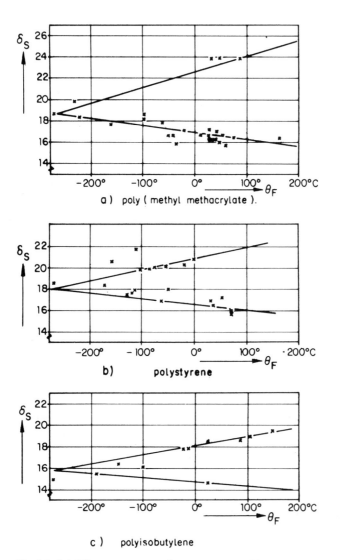

a) poly (methyl methacrylate).

b) polystyrene

c) polyisobutylene

Fig. 7.5. Solubility parameters and Θ-temperatures (Van Krevelen and Hoftyzer, 1967).

An even better correlation of Flory-temperatures with solubility parameters can be given in a $\delta_h - \delta_v$-diagram. This is shown in fig. 7.6 for polystyrene. The circle drawn in fig. 7.6 corresponds again with eq. (7.8).

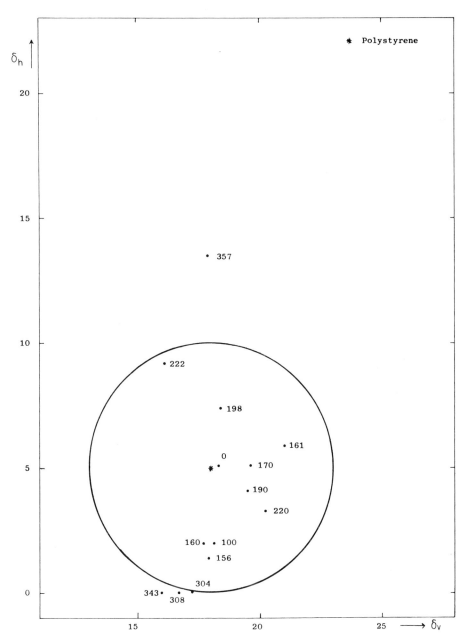

Fig. 7.6. Flory-temperatures of polystyrene in various solvents.

Other applications of solubility parameter diagrams

Solubility parameter diagrams, e.g. $\delta_h - \delta_v$-diagrams, may be useful for the correlation of some phenomena attended with polymer–solvent interaction. These phenomena will only be mentioned here.

a. Characteristic parameters of dilute polymer solutions (see Chapter 9), e.g.:

    (1) the Mark–Houwink exponent *a*

    (2) the composition of solvent mixtures forming Θ-solutions with a given polymer

    (3) partial density of polymers in solution

b. Deterioration of polymers by solvents (see Chapter 21), e.g.:

    (1) swelling of polymers by solvents

    (2) solvent crazing and cracking

    (3) decrease of mechanical properties, e.g. tensile strength

c. Shrinkage of polymer fibres, immersed in solvents

d. Crystallization of polymers induced by solvents.

All these applications may lead to better and more consistent values of the parameter components.

Prediction of solubility parameter components

The solubility parameter components δ_d, δ_p and δ_h (and their combinations $\delta_a = \sqrt{\delta_p^2 + \delta_h^2}$ and $\delta_v = \sqrt{\delta_d^2 + \delta_p^2}$) are known for a limited number of solvents only. Therefore a method for predicting these quantities will be valuable.

It is to be expected that the polar component δ_p is correlated with the dipole moment μ and that the hydrogen bonding component δ_h is correlated with the hydrogen bonding number $\Delta\nu$. This is not of much use, however, as also μ and $\Delta\nu$ are only known for a limited number of solvents. A useful prediction method must be based on the molecular structure of the solvent.

The available experimental data prove, however, that it is impossible to derive a simple system for an accurate prediction of solubility parameter components from the chemical structure. Especially the interaction of different structural groups in producing overall polar and hydrogen-bonding properties is so complicated that it does not obey simple rules.

If nevertheless such a prediction method is presented here, it does not pretend to give more than rather rough estimates. Yet this may sometimes be preferable to a complete lack of data.

The solubility parameter components may be predicted from group contributions, using the following equations:

$$\delta_d = \frac{\sum F_{di}}{V} \tag{7.10}$$

$$\delta_p = \frac{\sqrt{\sum F_{pi}^2}}{V} \tag{7.11}$$

$$\delta_h = \sqrt{\frac{\sum E_{hi}}{V}} \tag{7.12}$$

This means that for the prediction of δ_d the same type of formula is used as Small proposed for the prediction of the total solubility parameter δ. The group contributions F_{di} to the dispersion component F_d of the molar attraction constant can simply be added.

The same method holds for δ_p as long as only one polar group is present. To correct for the interaction of polar groups, the form of equation (7.11) has been chosen.

The polar component is still further reduced, if two identical polar groups are present in a symmetrical position. To take this effect into account, the value of δ_p, calculated with eq. (7.11) must be multiplied by a symmetry factor of:

0.5 for one plane of symmetry
0.25 for two planes of symmetry
0 for more planes of symmetry

The F-method is not applicable to the calculation of δ_h. It has already been stated by Hansen that the hydrogen bonding energy E_{hi} per structural group is approximately constant. This leads to the form of equation (7.12). For molecules with several planes of symmetry, $\delta_h = 0$.

The group contributions F_{di}, F_{pi} and E_{hi} for a number of structural groups are given in table 7.8.

Example 7.2
Estimate the solubility parameter components of diacetone alcohol

$$H_3C-\underset{\underset{O}{\|}}{C}-CH_2-\underset{\underset{CH_3}{|}}{\overset{\overset{OH}{|}}{C}}-CH_3$$

Solution
The molar volume $V = 123.8$ cm^3/mol. Addition of the group contributions gives

	F_{di}	F_{pi}^2	E_{hi}
3 $-CH_3$	1260	0	0
$-CH_2-$	270	0	0
$\diagdown C \diagup$	-70	0	0
$-CO-$	290	593000	2000
$-OH$	210	250000	20000
	1960	843000	22000

According to equations (7.10) to (7.12)

$$\delta_d = \frac{\sum F_{di}}{V} = \frac{1960}{123.8} = 15.8 \ J^{1/2}/cm^{3/2}$$

$$\delta_p = \frac{\sqrt{\sum F_{pi}^2}}{V} = \frac{\sqrt{843000}}{123.8} = 7.4 \ J^{1/2}/cm^{3/2}$$

$$\delta_h = \sqrt{\frac{\sum E_{hi}}{V}} = \sqrt{\frac{22000}{123.8}} = 13.3 \ J^{1/2}/cm^{3/2}$$

TABLE 7.8

Solubility parameter component group contributions

Structural group	F_{di} $(J^{1/2} \cdot cm^{3/2} \cdot mol^{-1})$	F_{pi} $(J^{1/2} \cdot cm^{3/2} \cdot mol^{-1})$	E_{hi} (J/mol)
$-CH_3$	420	0	0
$-CH_2-$	270	0	0
$-CH-$	80	0	0
$-C-$	−70	0	0
$=CH_2$	400	0	0
$=CH-$	200	0	0
$=C\Big\langle$	70	0	0
⬡ (cyclohexyl)	1620	0	0
⬡ (phenyl)	1430	110	0
⬡ (o, m, p)	1270	110	0
$-F$	(220)	−	−
$-Cl$	450	550	400
$-Br$	(550)	−	−
$-CN$	430	1100	2500
$-OH$	210	500	20000
$-O-$	100	400	3000
$-COH$	470	800	4500
$-CO-$	290	770	2000
$-COOH$	530	420	10000
$-COO-$	390	490	7000
$HCOO-$	530	−	−
$-NH_2$	280	−	8400
$-NH-$	160	210	3100
$-N\Big\langle$	20	800	5000
$-NO_2$	500	1070	1500
$-S-$	440	−	−
$=PO_4-$	740	1890	13000
ring	190	−	−
one plane of symmetry	−	0.50x	−
two planes of symmetry	−	0.25x	−
more planes of symmetry	−	0x	0x

The literature values are δ_d = 15.7

$\qquad\qquad \delta_p$ = 8.2

$\qquad\qquad \delta_h$ = 10.9

From the calculated components an overall value of the solubility parameter is found:

$$\delta = \sqrt{\delta_d^2 + \delta_p^2 + \delta_h^2} = 21.9 \text{ J}^{1/2}/\text{cm}^{3/2}$$

The experimental values for δ vary from 18.8 to 20.8 J$^{1/2}$/cm$^{3/2}$.

Influence of crystallinity

It was pointed out from the beginning that the concept of the solubility parameter was applicable only to amorphous polymers.

In order to adapt the method to highly crystalline polymers some way must be found to deal with the heat of fusion (ΔH_m) in the free enthalpy equation:

$$\Delta G_M = \{\Delta H_M + \Delta H_m\} - T\{\Delta S_M + \Delta S_m\} \qquad (7.13)$$

Highly crystalline polymers such as polyethylene and poly(tetrafluoroethylene) are insoluble in all solvents at room temperature. These polymers, however, obey the solubility parameter rules at

$$T \geqslant 0.9 T_m .$$

For instance, polyethylene becomes soluble above 80°C. Furthermore, crystalline polymers do obey the rules even at room temperature in so far as swelling behaviour is concerned. This again is a demonstration that crystalline regions serve as apparent (physical) cross-links.

Some crystalline polymers with strong hydrogen bonding groups can be made to dissolve at room temperature. But in these cases a very specific interaction between polymer and solvent must occur. For example, cellulose is soluble in 70% sulphuric acid and in aqueous ammonium thiocyanate; nylon 6,6 is soluble in phenol and in a 15% calcium chloride solution in methanol.

C. INTERNAL PRESSURE

Spencer and Gilmore (1950) showed that the $p-v-T$ behaviour of polymer melts can be represented reasonably well by the following modified Van der Waals equation of state [1]:

$$(v - \omega)(p + \pi) = \frac{RT}{M_u} \qquad (7.14)$$

where p is the applied pressure, v is the specific volume of the polymer and M_u the molecular weight of an "interacting unit". π and ω are constants which must be determined ex-

---

[1] A comparison between some empirical equations of state for polymers with regard to their standard deviations was made by Kamal and Levan (1973).

perimentally, just as the interaction unit $M_u \cdot \pi$ in this equation is the *internal pressure*, which is independent of specific volume and, therefore, of temperature and pressure. It is obvious that the internal pressure will be related to the cohesive energy density (both have the dimension $J/cm^3 \equiv N/cm^2$).

Spencer and Gilmore evaluated the constants π and M_u from a series of $p-v$-measurements at fixed temperatures. In synthetic linear polymers M_u could be identified with the molecular weight of the structural unit. In this case $(M_u \omega = V(0))$ the equation of state becomes:

$$(V - V(0))(p + \pi) = RT \tag{7.15}$$

At atmospheric conditions the internal pressure π is much greater than the external pressure p, so that for the liquid polymer:

$$\pi = \frac{RT}{V(T) - V(0)} \approx \frac{R}{E_1} \tag{7.16}$$

The same result is obtained by differentiation of the equation of state:

$$\left(\frac{\partial v}{\partial T}\right)_p = \frac{R}{M_u \pi}$$

or

$$\pi = \frac{R}{M_u \left(\frac{\partial v}{\partial T}\right)_p} = \frac{R}{M_u e_1} = \frac{R}{E_1}$$

In table 7.9 the results calculated by means of eq. (7.16) are compared with the experimental data. The figures obtained are of the right order of magnitude.

TABLE 7.9

Equation of state constants [1]

Polymer	π (bar)		ω (cm^3/g)	
	exp.	calc. $\pi = R/E_1$	exp.	calc. $\omega = V(0)/M$ $= 1.3 V_W/M$
polyethylene	3290	3470	0.88	0.95
polypropylene	2470	2650	0.83	0.95
poly(1-butene)	1850	2030	0.91	0.95
poly(4-methylpentene)	1050	1360	0.83	0.95
polystyrene	1870	1460	0.82	0.79
poly(methyl methacrylate)	2180	1730	0.73	0.73
poly(caproamide) (nylon 6)	1110	1180	0.62	0.815
poly(hexamethylene sebacamide)(nylon 6,8)	540	515	0.77	0.75
polycarbonate	460	610	0.56	0.695

[1] Experimental data from Spencer and Gilmore (1950) and Sagalaev et al. (1974).
Conversion factors: 1 bar = 10^5 N/m^2 = 0.987 atm; 1 cm^3/g = 10^{-3} m^3/kg.

Smith (1970) derived an equation of state for liquid polymers based on the hole theory of liquids. For higher temperatures, this equation can be reduced to a form equivalent to that of eq. (7.14).

It should be remarked that for cellulose derivatives (cellulose acetate, butyrate and ethylcellulose) the values of M_u were found to be much smaller than the molecular weight of the structural units.

By means of eq. (7.15) a good impression of the $p-v-T$ behaviour of a polymer melt can be obtained if no data are available at all. Since $V(0) \approx 1.3\ V_W$ and $E_1 \approx 10.3 \times 10^{-4}\ V_W$, V_W only has to be calculated from group contributions in this case.

Example 7.3

Estimate the specific volume of molten polypropylene
(a) at 200°C, 1 atm
(b) at 250°C, 1 atm
(c) at 200°C, 600 atm

Solution

We can calculate v with the aid of a modification of eq. (7.14):

$$v = \omega + \frac{RT}{M_u(p + \pi)}$$

The following data may be used:

$R \quad = 83.14\ \text{cm}^3 \cdot \text{bar} \cdot \text{mol}^{-1} \cdot \text{K}^{-1}$

$M_u \quad = 42.1\ \text{g/mol} = M$

$\omega \quad = \dfrac{1.3 V_W}{M} = \dfrac{1.3 \times 30.68}{42.1} = 0.947\ \text{cm}^3/\text{g}$

$V_W \quad = 30.68\ \text{cm}^3/\text{mol}$ (table 4.11)

$\pi \quad = \dfrac{R}{E_1} = \dfrac{83.14}{0.0396} = 2100\ \text{bar}$

$E_1 \quad = 0.0396\ \text{cm}^3 \cdot \text{mol}^{-1} \cdot \text{K}^{-1}$

Calculation leads to the following results:

T	p	v_{calc}	v_{exp}
°C	bar	cm³/g	cm³/g
200	1	1.39	1.34
250	1	1.44	1.39
200	600	1.29	1.28

The experimental data were determined by Foster, et al. (1966).

From the equation of state, equations for the *thermal expansion coefficient* (α) and for the *compressibility* (κ) can be obtained. Rearrangement of eq. (7.15) gives

$$V = V(0) + \frac{RT}{p + \pi} \qquad (7.17)$$

from which the following partial derivatives are obtained:

$$\left(\frac{\partial V}{\partial T}\right)_p = \frac{R}{p + \pi} \qquad \text{and} \qquad \left(\frac{\partial V}{\partial p}\right)_T = -\frac{RT}{(p + \pi)^2} \tag{7.18}$$

Substitution gives:

$$\alpha = \frac{1}{V}\left(\frac{\partial V}{\partial T}\right)_p = \frac{1}{T + \dfrac{V(0)}{R}(p + \pi)} \tag{7.19}$$

$$\kappa = -\frac{1}{V}\left(\frac{\partial V}{\partial p}\right)_T = \frac{1}{(p + \pi) + \dfrac{V(0)}{RT}(p + \pi)^2} \tag{7.20}$$

The compressibility κ is the reciprocal of the compression modulus or bulk modulus of the material. This important property will be discussed in Chapter 13 (Mechanical properties of isotropic solid polymers).

The application of eq. (7.15) is restricted to polymer melts. For amorphous polymers below the melting point, the internal pressure π may be defined as well:

$$\pi = \left(\frac{\partial U}{\partial V}\right)_T = T\left(\frac{\partial p}{\partial T}\right)_v - p \tag{7.21}$$

where U is the internal energy per mole, but here π is dependent on T and p.

Values of the internal pressure for some polymers at room temperature have been mentioned by Allen et al. (1960). They appeared to be of the same order of magnitude as the cohesive energy density e_{coh}. A theoretical derivation by Voeks (1964) resulted in:

$$\pi \approx 1.3\, e_{coh} \tag{7.22}$$

Values of π and e_{coh} for a number of polymers are compared in table 7.10, which shows eq. (7.22) to be valid as a first approximation.

TABLE 7.10

Comparison of π and e_{coh} at $20°C$

Polymer	π (bar)	e_{coh} (bar)
polyethylene	3200	2500/2900
polyisobutylene	3300	2500/2700
polystyrene	4600	3000/3600
poly(chlorotrifluoroethylene)	3700	2200/2600
poly(vinyl acetate)	4300	3600/5100
poly(ethyl acrylate)	4400	3500/3700
poly(methyl methacrylate)	3800	3400/6900
poly(propylene oxide)	3700	2300/4200
poly(dimethyl siloxane)	2400	2200/2400

Conversion factor: 1 bar = 10^5 N/m^2 = 0.987 atm.

BIBLIOGRAPHY, CHAPTER 7

General references

Hildebrand, J.H. and Scott, R.L., "The Solubility of Non-Electrolytes", Reinhold, New York, 2nd ed., 1936; 3rd ed., 1949.

Flory, P.J., "Principles of Polymer Chemistry", Cornell University Press, Ithaca, N.Y., 1953.

Tanford, C., "Physical Chemistry of Macromolecules", Wiley, New York, 1961.

Tompa, H., "Polymer Solutions", Academic Press, New York, 1956.

Weiss, Ph. (Ed.), "Adhesion and Cohesion", Elsevier, Amsterdam, 1962.

Special references

Allen, G., Gee, G., Mangaraj, D., Sims, D. and Wilson, G.J., Polymer 1 (1960) 467.

Bagley, E.B., Nelson, T.P. and Scigliano, J.M., J. Paint Technol. 43 (1971) 35.

Beerbower, A., Kaye, L.A. and Pattison, D.A., Chem. Eng., Dec. 18, 1967, p. 118.

Blanks, R.F. and Prausnitz, J.M., Ind. Eng. Chem. Fundamentals 3 (1964) 1.

Bondi, A., J. Chem. Eng. Data 8 (1963) 371; J. Polymer Sci. A2 (1964) 3159; "Physical Properties of Molecular Crystals, Liquids and Glasses", Wiley, New York, 1968.

Bunn, C.W., J. Polymer Sci. 16 (1955) 323.

Burrell, H., Official Digest 27, Nr. 369 (1955) 726; 29, Nr. 394 (1957) 1069 and 1159.

Burrell, H., in "Polymer Handbook" (J. Brandrup and E.H. Immergut, Eds.), Part IV, p. 337, Interscience, New York, 2nd ed., 1975.

Chen, S.-A., J. Appl. Polymer Sci. 15 (1971) 1247.

Crowley, J.D., Teague, G.S. and Lowe, J.W., J. Paint Technol. 38 (1966) 269; 39 (1967) 19.

Di Benedetto, A.T., J. Polymer Sci. A1 (1963) 3459.

Dunkel, M., Z. physik. Chem. A138 (1928) 42.

Fedors, R.F., Polymer Eng. Sci. 14 (1974) 147.

Foster, G.N., Waldman, N. and Griskey, R.G., Polymer Eng. Sci. 6 (1966) 131.

Fox, T.G., Polymer 3 (1962) 111.

Gordy, W. and Stanford, S.C., J. Chem. Phys. 7 (1939) 93; 8 (1940) 170; 9 (1941) 204.

Hansen, C.M., Thesis, Copenhagen, 1967.

Hansen, C.M., J. Paint Technol. 39 (1967) 104 and 511.

Hansen, C.M., Ind. Eng. Chem. Prod. Res. Dev. 8 (1969) 2.

Hayes, R.A., J. Appl. Polymer Sci. 5 (1961) 318.

Henry, L.F., Polymer Eng. Sci. 14 (1974) 167.

Hildebrand, J.H., J. Am. Chem. Soc. 38 (1916) 1452.

Hoernschemeyer, D., J. Appl. Polymer Sci. 18 (1974) 61.

Hoftyzer, P.J. and Van Krevelen, D.W., Paper (Nr. IIIa-15) presented at the International Symposium on Macromolecules of IUPAC, Leyden (1970).

Hoy, K.L., J. Paint Technol. 42 (1970) 76.

Kamal, M.R. and Levan, N.T., Polymer Eng. Sci. 13 (1973) 131.

Kambour, R.P., Gruner, C.L. and Romagosa, E.E., J. Polymer Sci., Polymer Phys. 11 (1973) 1879.

Koehnen, D.M. and Smolders, C.A., J. Appl. Polymer Sci. 19 (1975) 1163.

Rheineck, A.E. and Lin, K.F., J. Paint Technol. 40 (1968) 611.

Sagalaev, G.V., Ismailow, T.M., Ragimow, A.M., Makhmudov, A.A. and Svyatodukhov, B.P., Int. Polymer Sci. Technol. 1 (1974) 76 (Russian).

Scatchard, G., Chem. Revs. 8 (1931) 321.

Small, P.A., J. Appl. Chem. 3 (1953) 71.

Smith, R.P., J. Polymer Sci. A2, 8 (1970) 1337.

Spencer, R.S. and Gilmore, G.D., J. Appl. Phys. 21 (1950) 523.

Van Krevelen, D.W., Fuel 44 (1965) 236.

Van Krevelen, D.W. and Hoftyzer, P.J., J. Appl. Polymer Sci. 11 (1967) 2189.

Voeks, J.F., J. Polymer Sci. A2 (1964) 5319.

CHAPTER 8

INTERFACIAL ENERGY PROPERTIES

The specific surface energy of a polymer can be estimated by means of an additive quantity, the *Parachor*. Alternatively, it may be calculated from the molar cohesive energy (which is also additive). Rules are given for the estimation of the interfacial tension and the contact angle of a liquid on a solid.

Introduction

Surface energy is a direct manifestation of intermolecular forces. The molecules at the surface of a liquid or a solid are influenced by unbalanced molecular forces and therefore possess additional energy, in contrast with the molecules inside the liquid or solid.

In liquids the surface energy manifests itself as an internal force which tends to reduce the surface area to a minimum. It is measured in units of force per unit length, or in units of energy per unit area.

The surface of a solid, like that of a liquid, possesses additional free energy, but owing to the lack of mobility at the surface of solids this free energy is not directly observable, it must be measured by indirect methods.

The additional free energy at the interface between two condensed phases is known as *interfacial energy*.

Surface and interfacial energy are important because of their controlling influence on such practical applications as spinning, polymer adhesion, stability of dispersions and wetting of solids by liquids.

Definitions

The specific *free surface energy* of a material is the excess energy per unit area due to the existence of the free surface; it is also the thermodynamic work to be done per unit area of surface extension.

In liquids the specific free surface energy is also called *surface tension,* since it is equivalent to a line tension acting in all directions parallel to the surface.

The *specific interfacial energy* or *interfacial tension* is the excess energy per unit area due to the formation of an interface (solid/liquid; solid/vapour).

The surface or interfacial tension is expressed in J/m^2 ($\equiv N/m$) or more often in mJ/m^2 ($\equiv mN/m$). The latter expression is identical with erg/cm^2 ($\equiv dyn/cm$) in the c.g.s. unit system.

The notation is the following:

γ_1 surface tension of liquid

γ_s surface tension of solid
γ_{sl} interfacial tension between liquid and solid
γ_{sv} surface tension of the solid in equilibrium with the saturated vapour pressure of the liquid
$\pi_{eq} \equiv (\gamma_s - \gamma_{sv})$ equilibrium spreading pressure

A. SURFACE ENERGY OF LIQUIDS AND MELTS

Methods for determining the surface tension of liquids

There are a number of independent methods for determining the surface tension of liquids. First of all there are direct methods measuring the force required to pull, for instance, a metal disk or a metal ring out of a liquid. One of the most popular quasi-static methods is that of capillary rise. Also the dropweight and the bubble-pressure methods are two related methods for measuring the surface tension which depend essentially on the excess pressure under curved surfaces.

Finally there are dynamic methods, measuring the wavelength of ripples produced on a surface by a source of known frequency or measuring the period of oscillation of vibrating drops.

Estimation of surface tension of liquids from related properties

Since the surface tension is a manifestation of intermolecular forces, it may be expected to be related to other properties derived from intermolecular forces, such as internal pressure, compressibility and cohesion energy density. This is found to be so indeed. In the first place there exists a relationship between compressibility and surface tension. According to McGowan (1967) the correlation is:

$$\kappa \gamma^{3/2} = 1.33 \times 10^{-8} \text{ (cgs units)} \tag{8.1}$$

Another interesting empirical relationship, viz. between surface tension and solubility parameter, was found by Hildebrand and Scott (1949):

$$\delta = 4.1(\gamma/V^{1/3})^{0.43} \text{(cgs units)} \tag{8.2}$$

This relationship was recently examined by Lee (1970) with 129 non-polar and polar liquids. Lee proved that 65% of liquids obey the equation; the major discrepancy being caused by the molar volume term in the case of hydrogen bonded liquids.

Eq. (8.2) indicates a relationship between surface tension, cohesive energy and molar volume. A quantitative and dimensionally correct relationship between these quantities has been derived by Grunberg and Nissan (1949). For compounds of low molecular weight they defined a quantity W_{coh}, called work of cohesion.

$$W_{coh} = 2\gamma N_A^{1/3} V^{2/3} \tag{8.3}$$

where N_A is the Avogadro number. The ratio E_{coh}/W_{coh} is a characteristic constant of the liquid considered. Its value is about 3.5 for non-polar liquids and between 4 and 8 for hydrogen-bonded liquids.

Calculation of surface tension from an additive function; the Parachor

The molar parachor is a useful means of estimating surface tensions. It is the following additive quantity:

$$P_S = \gamma^{1/4}\frac{M}{\rho} = \gamma^{1/4}V. \tag{8.4}$$

The parachor was introduced by Sugden (1924), who gave a list of atomic constants. Later the atomic and group contributions were slightly modified and improved by Mumford and Phillips (1929) and by Quayle (1953).

The conventional numerical values of the parachor and of its group contributions are expressed in $(cm^3/mol) \times (erg/cm^2)^{1/4}$, which is equivalent to $(cm^3/mol) \times (m\ J/m^2)^{1/4}$.

For obvious reasons we shall keep these numerical values unchanged, although an expression in $(m^3/mol) \times (J/m^2)^{1/4}$ would be more consistent.

The group contributions to the parachor as presented by different investigators are given in table 8.1. If the group contributions of P_S and V are known, γ results from the expression:

$$\boxed{\gamma = \left(\frac{P_S}{V}\right)^4} \tag{8.5}$$

TABLE 8.1

Atomic and structural contributions to the parachor

Unit	Values assigned by		
	Sugden	Mumford and Phillips	Quayle
CH$_2$	39.0	40.0	40.0
C	4.8	9.2	9.0
H	17.1	15.4	15.5
O	20.0	20.0	19.8
O$_2$ (in esters)	60.0	60.0	54.8
N	12.5	17.5	17.5
S	48.2	50.0	49.1
F	25.7	25.5	26.1
Cl	54.3	55.0	55.2
Br	68.0	69.0	68.0
I	91.0	90.0	90.3
Double bond	23.2	19.0	16.3–19.1
Triple bond	46.4	38.0	40.6
Three-membered ring	16.7	12.5	12.5
Four-membered ring	11.6	6.0	6.0
Five-membered ring	8.5	3.0	3.0
Six-membered ring	6.1	0.8	0.8
Seven-membered ring		−4.0	4.0

Since the parachor (P_S) is practically independent of temperature, expression (8.5) can also be used to calculate the temperature-dependence of the surface tension (γ).

Interfacial tension between a solid and a liquid

In fig. 8.1, S represents a solid surface in contact with faces of liquids; the situations are supposed to continue to the left. The liquid L_1 wets the solid and tends to spread right over the surface. The *contact angle* ϑ is zero. In the second case (liquid L_2) the tendency to spread over the surface is less marked and the contact angle lies between 0 and $\pi/2$. The third instance (liquid L_3) is one where the liquid does not wet the surface and where the contact angle is greater than $\pi/2$, the liquid tending to shrink away from the solid.

Equilibrium contact angles of liquids on solids are usually discussed in terms of *Young's equation*:

$$\gamma_1 \cos \vartheta = (\gamma_s - \gamma_{sl}) - (\gamma_s - \gamma_{sv}) = (\gamma_s - \gamma_{sl}) - \pi_{eq} \approx \gamma_s - \gamma_{sl} \tag{8.6}$$

The assumption $\pi_{eq} \approx 0$ is allowed for normal polymeric surfaces. $\gamma_1 \cos \vartheta$ is called the *adhesion tension.* Complete wetting occurs when $\cos \vartheta = 1$ or $\vartheta = 0°$.

It is evident that wetting is favoured by relatively low interfacial free energy, high solid surface energy and low liquid surface free energy (surface tension). Unfortunately, only γ_1 and ϑ are eligible for direct experimental determination. In order to understand adhesion phenomena, however, it is essential to know γ_s and γ_{sl}. Fox and Zisman (1952) made an important approach to this problem. They found that for homologous series of liquids on a given solid a plot of $\cos \vartheta$ versus γ_1 is generally a straight line. Zisman (1962, 1963) introduced the concept of *critical surface tension of wetting* (γ_{cr}), which is defined as the value of γ_1 at the intercept of the $\cos \vartheta - \gamma_1$-plot with the horizontal line $\cos \vartheta = 1$. A liquid of γ_1 less than γ_{cr} will spread on the surface. Numerically, γ_{cr} is nearly equal to γ_s.

Another approach is that of Girifalco and Good (1957–60) who derived the following

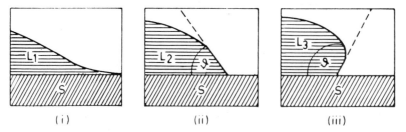

(i)   (ii)   (iii)

Fig. 8.1. Contact angle of different liquids on a solid.

important relationship between γ_s, γ_l and γ_{sl}:

$$\gamma_{sl} = \gamma_s + \gamma_l - 2\Phi(\gamma_s\gamma_l)^{1/2} \tag{8.7}$$

where

$$\Phi \approx \frac{4(V_sV_l)^{1/3}}{(V_s^{1/3} + V_l^{1/3})^2} . \tag{8.8}$$

Combining eqs. (8.6) and (8.7) results in:

$$\gamma_s = \frac{[\gamma_1(1 + \cos \vartheta) + \pi_{eq}]^2}{4\Phi^2\gamma_1} \approx \gamma_1\frac{(1 + \cos \vartheta)^2}{4\Phi^2} \tag{8.9}$$

$$\cos \vartheta = 2\Phi\left(\frac{\gamma_s}{\gamma_1}\right)^{1/2} - 1 - \frac{\pi_{eq}}{\gamma_1} \approx 2\Phi\left(\frac{\gamma_s}{\gamma_1}\right)^{1/2} - 1 \tag{8.10}$$

By means of eq. (8.9) the surface tension of the solid can be calculated from measurements of the contact angle. If γ_s is known, eq. (8.7) provides the possibility of calculating the interfacial tension γ_{sl}. The contact angle can be predicted for solid–liquid systems by means of eq. (8.10).

B. SURFACE ENERGY OF SOLID POLYMERS

Methods to determine surface tension of solids
　　Three ways are available for the estimation of γ_s, the surface tension of the solid. The first is the method measuring the contact angle between the solid and different liquids and applying eq. (8.9).
　　The second is the determination of γ_{cr} according to Zisman (1964), with the assumption that $\gamma_s \approx \gamma_{cr}$.
　　The third way is the extrapolation of surface tension data of polymer melts to room temperature (Roe, 1965; Wu, 1969–71).

Estimation of surface tensions of solid polymers from the parachor
　　Due to the fact that the extrapolation of surface tensions of melts to room temperature leads to reliable values for the solid polymer, the surface tension of solid polymers may be calculated from the parachor per structural unit by applying eq. (8.5). The molar volume of the *amorphous* state has to be used. We have found that the original group contributions given by Sugden show the best correspondence with experimental values for polymers.

TABLE 8.2

Experimental [1] and calculated values of surface tension of polymers [2]

Polymer	γ_s observed			γ_s calculated	
	extrapolation of γ_{melt}	from contact angle	from γ_{cr}	from $\gamma = (P_S/V)^4$ (8.5)	from $\gamma = 0.75\ e_{coh}^{2/3}$ (8.11)
polyethylene	35.7	33.2	31	31.5	30
polypropylene	29.6		29	32.5	33
polyisobutylene	33.6		27	30.5	31
polystyrene	40.7	42	33–36	43	38
poly(2-chlorostyrene)			42	46	40
poly(vinyl fluoride)		36.7	28	32.5	30
poly(vinyl chloride)		41.5	39	42	40
poly(vinylidene fluoride)		32.7	25	28	26
poly(vinylidene chloride)		39.9	40	47	42
poly(trifluoroethylene)		23.9	22	29	24
poly(trifluorochloroethylene)	30.8		31	27	30
poly(tetrafluoroethylene)		19.0	18.5	26	20
poly(hexafluoropropylene)			16–17	26	20
poly(vinyl alcohol)			37	59	
poly(methyl vinyl ether)			29	32	
poly(vinyl acetate)	36.5		37	40	39
poly(methyl acrylate)			41	45	40
poly(ethyl acrylate)			35	42	38
poly(methyl methacrylate)	41.1	40.2	39	42	38
poly(ethyl methacrylate)			33	42	37
polyacrylonitrile			44	61	57
polybutadiene (cis)			32	32.5	34
polyisoprene (cis)			31	35	34
polychloroprene	43.6		38	43	39
poly(methylene oxide)			36	38.5	43
poly(ethylene oxide)	43		43	42	39
poly(tetramethylene oxide)	31.9			31.5	35
poly(propylene oxide)	32		32	32.5	38
poly(ethylene terephthalate)		43	40–43	49	42
nylon 6		40–47	42	47	64
nylon 11		31.0	33–42	42.5	51
nylon 6,6		39.3	42–46	47.5	63
nylon 10,10		28.5	32	43	53
poly(bisphenol carbonate)			45	42.5	
poly(dimethyl siloxane)	19.8		24	21.5	

[1] See: Dann (1970); Fowkes (1964, 1965, 1969); Lee (1967, 1970); Panzer (1973); Roe (1965); Schoenhorn (1966); Wu (1971); Zisman (1962, 1963, 1964).
[2] Expressed in $mJ/m^2 = mN/m = erg/cm^2 = dyn/cm$.

Numerical values and comparison of the different methods

Table 8.2 compares the experimental values of the surface tension of polymers (obtained by different methods) and the calculated values, the latter being obtained by means of the parachor.

The discrepancies between the different experimental values are reasonably small. The calculated values are, with a few exceptions, in reasonable agreement with the experimental values.

If no experimental data are available, calculation by means of the group contributions to the parachor gives a reliable approximation. A still higher accuracy can be reached if the methods of "standard properties" or "standard substances", discussed in Chapter 3, are applied.

From what has been said about the surface tensions of liquids it may be expected that a relation also exists between the surface tension and the cohesive energy density of solid polymers. This proves to be so; with γ expressed in mJ/m^2 and e_{coh} in MJ/m^3, the following empirical expression may be used:

$$\gamma \approx 0.75 \, e_{coh}^{2/3} \tag{8.11}$$

Table 8.2 also shows γ-values calculated by means of this formula. Only the polymers with strong hydrogen bonding show rather large deviations.

Example 8.1

Estimate the surface tension of solid poly(methyl methacrylate) and its contact angle with methylene iodide ($\gamma = 50.8$).

Solution

The polymeric unit is:

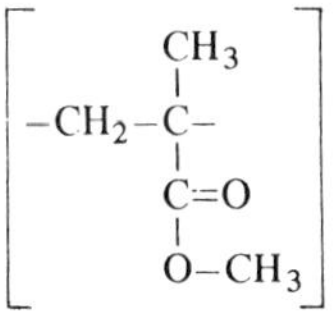

$$\left[\begin{array}{c} CH_3 \\ | \\ -CH_2-C- \\ | \\ C=O \\ | \\ O-CH_3 \end{array} \right]$$

From tables 8.1 and 4.6 we obtain the following group contributions to parachor and molar volume:

	P_{Si}	$V_i(cm^3)$
1(−CH₂−)	39.0	15.85
1(−C−)	4.8	4.6
2(−CH₃)	112.2	47.8
1(−COO−)	64.8	18.25
	220.8	86.5

So $\gamma = \left(\dfrac{P_S}{V}\right)^4 = \left(\dfrac{220.8}{86.5}\right)^4 = 2.55^4 = 42.5.$

According to eqs. (8.10) and (8.8)

$$\cos \vartheta \approx 2\Phi \left(\frac{\gamma_s}{\gamma_l}\right)^{1/2} - 1$$

$$\Phi = \frac{4(V_s V_l)^{1/3}}{(V_s^{1/3} + V_l^{1/3})^2}.$$

As calculated above, V_s = 86.5. For methylene iodide, M = 267.9 and ρ = 3.33, so that V_1 = 80.6. With these values for V_s and V_1, Φ = 1.00. For the contact angle with methylene iodide we find:

$$\cos \vartheta \approx 2\left(\frac{\gamma_s}{\gamma_1}\right)^{1/2} - 1 \approx 2\left(\frac{42.5}{50.8}\right)^{1/2} - 1 = 0.83$$

so that $\vartheta \approx 34°$. The adhesion tension of methylene iodide on poly(methyl methacrylate) will be:

$$\gamma_1 \cos \vartheta = 50.8 \times 0.83 \approx 42 \text{ mJ/cm}^2$$

An experimental value of ϑ = 41° has been published by Jarvis et al. (1964). Application of eq. (8.9) gives γ_s = 39 mJ/cm^2, which is in good correspondence with experimental values of γ_{cr}.

GENERAL EXPRESSION FOR THE INTERFACIAL TENSION

Expression (8.7) may be generalized to read:

$$\gamma_{12} = \gamma_1 + \gamma_2 - 2\Phi(\gamma_1\gamma_2)^{1/2} \tag{8.12}$$

or

$$\gamma_{12} \approx (\gamma_1^{1/2} - \gamma_2^{1/2})^2 \tag{8.12a}$$

since $\Phi \approx 1$. This equation, however, is only valid for substances without hydrogen bonds, as was demonstrated by Fowkes (1964).

Fowkes, in a theoretical consideration of attractive forces at interfaces, has suggested that the total free energy at a surface is the sum of contributions from the different intermolecular forces at the surface. Thus the surface free energy may be written:

$$\gamma = \gamma^d + \gamma^h \tag{8.13}$$

where the superscripts d and h refer to dispersion and hydrogen bonding force components. Following this suggestion, Owens and Wendt (1969) proposed the following general form of the expression for the interfacial tension:

$$\gamma_{12} = \gamma_1 + \gamma_2 - 2(\gamma_1^d\gamma_2^d)^{1/2} - 2(\gamma_1^h\gamma_2^h)^{1/2} \tag{8.14}$$

or

$$\boxed{\gamma_{12} = [(\gamma_1^d)^{1/2} - (\gamma_2^d)^{1/2}]^2 + [(\gamma_1^h)^{1/2} - (\gamma_2^h)^{1/2}]^2} \tag{8.14a}$$

Substances 1 and 2 may either be liquids, or solids, or they may be a combination of a solid and a liquid.

If 1 and 2 are immiscible liquids of which γ_1 and γ_2 are known, and of which one is apolar (γ^h = 0), the γ-components of both liquids may be derived in the following way: the interfacial tension γ_{12} is measured by one of the available methods and the equations (8.14) and (8.13) are solved. In this way several liquids have been investigated; the values of γ_1, γ_1^d and γ_1^h are given in table 8.3.

TABLE 8.3

Force components of surface tension of several liquids (after Fowkes (1964) and Owens and Wendt (1969)) (γ in mJ/m^2)

Liquid	γ_l	γ_l^d	γ_l^h
n-hexane	18.4	18.4	0
dimethyl siloxane	19.0	16.9	2.1
cyclohexane	25.5	25.5	0
decalin	29.9	29.9	0
bromobenzene	36.3	36.0	≈ 0
tricresyl phosphate	40.9	39.2 ± 4	≈ 1
aniline	42.9	24.2	18.7
α-bromonaphthalene	44.6	47 ± 7	≈ 0
trichlorobiphenyl	45.3	44 ± 6	≈ 1.3
glycol	48.0	33.8	14.2
methylene iodide	50.8	49.5 ± 1	≈ 1.3
formamide	58.2	39.5 ± 7	≈ 19
glycerol	63.4	37.0 ± 4	≈ 26
water	72.8	21.8 ± 0.7	51

Example 8.2

Estimate γ^d and γ^h of water if the following data are given:

   a. $\gamma_{H_2O} = 72.8$ mJ/m^2 (at 20°C)
   b. the interfacial tension cyclohexane/water is 50.2 (at 20°C)
   c. $\gamma_{cyclohexane} = 25.5$

Solution

For cyclohexane $\gamma_{ch}^h = 0$, so that $\gamma_{ch}^d = \gamma_{ch} = 25.5$. From eq. (8.14) we get:

$$\gamma_{12} = \gamma_{H_2O,ch} = 50.2 = 25.5 + 72.8 - 2(25.5\gamma_{H_2O}^d)^{1/2}$$

from which $\gamma_{H_2O}^d = 22.7$, so that $\gamma_{H_2O}^h = 72.8 - 22.7 = 50.1$ which is in fair agreement with the most reliable values $\gamma_{H_2O}^d = 21.8$ and $\gamma_{H_2O}^h = 51.0$

Owens and Wendt also gave a more general expression for (8.10), viz.:

$$1 + \cos \vartheta \approx 2\left[\frac{(\gamma_s^d)^{1/2}(\gamma_l^d)^{1/2}}{\gamma_1} + \frac{(\gamma_s^h)^{1/2}(\gamma_l^h)^{1/2}}{\gamma_1}\right]. \tag{8.15}$$

This equation permits the derivation of γ_s^d and γ_s^h via measurements of the contact angles ϑ of two liquids if γ_1 and γ_l^d and γ_l^h of both liquids are known.

Example 8.3

Estimate γ_s and its components γ_s^d and γ_s^h for poly(vinyl chloride) if the following data are known:

a. for water: $\gamma_{H_2O} = 72.8$; $\gamma_{H_2O}^d = 21.8$; $\gamma_{H_2O}^h = 51.0$

b. for methylene iodide: $\gamma_{mi} = 50.8$; $\gamma_{mi}^d = 49.5$; $\gamma_{mi}^h = 1.3$

c. for the contact angles on PVC: $\vartheta_{H_2O} = 87°$; $\vartheta_{mi} = 36°$

Solution

Substitution of the data in eq. (8.15) gives:

TABLE 8.4

Components of surface energy for various solid polymers (Owens and Wendt, 1969) (γ in mJ/m^2)

Polymer	γ_s^d	γ_s^h	γ_s	γ_{cr}
polyethylene (l.d.)	33.2	0.0	33.2	31
polystyrene	41.4	0.6	42.0	43
poly(vinyl chloride)	40.0	1.5	41.5	39
poly(vinylidene chloride)	42.0	3.0	45.0	40
poly(vinyl fluoride)	31.3	5.4	36.7	28
poly(vinylidene fluoride)	23.2	7.1	30.3	25
poly(trifluoroethylene)	19.9	4.0	23.9	22
poly(tetrafluoroethylene)	18.6	0.5	19.1	18.5
poly(methyl methacrylate)	35.9	4.3	40.2	39
poly(ethylene terephthalate)	43.2	4.1	47.3	43
nylon 6,6	40.8	6.2	47.0	46

for water:

$$1 + 0.052 = 2\left[\frac{(\gamma_s^d)^{1/2}21.8^{1/2}}{72.8} + \frac{(\gamma_s^h)^{1/2}51.0^{1/2}}{72.8}\right]$$

for methylene iodide:

$$1 + 0.809 = 2\left[\frac{(\gamma_s^d)^{1/2}49.5^{1/2}}{50.8} + \frac{(\gamma_s^h)^{1/2}1.3^{1/2}}{50.8}\right]$$

Solution of these simultaneous equations gives:

$\gamma_s^d = 40.0$; $\gamma_s^h = 1.5$; $\gamma_s = 41.5$.

Owens and Wendt determined in this way the free surface energy and its components of a number of solid polymers. The values are given in table 8.4.

POLYMER ADHESION

A measure of the attraction of two solids S_1 and S_2 across an interface is the reversible work of adhesion W_{adh}. This quantity is given by the *relationship of Dupré*

$$W_{adh} = \gamma_{s_1} + \gamma_{s_2} - \gamma_{s_1 s_2} \approx 2\left[(\gamma_{s_1}^d \gamma_{s_2}^d)^{1/2} + (\gamma_{s_1}^h \gamma_{s_2}^h)^{1/2}\right] \tag{8.16}$$

W_{adh} is the work required to separate S_1 and S_2, thereby creating unit areas of S_1 and S_2 surface at the expense of a unit area of $S_1 - S_2$ interface.

In practice it is important to know whether an adhesive joint is stable towards liquids. In this case the work of adhesion is

$$W_{adh} = \gamma_{s_1 1} + \gamma_{s_2 1} - \gamma_{s_1 s_2}. \tag{8.17}$$

If an interface $S_1 - S_2$ is immersed in a liquid L and the work of adhesion W_{adh} according to (8.17) is negative, separation of S_1 and S_2 is favoured and will occur spontaneously, since the free energy of the system is reduced by the separation. The condition for spontaneous separation is:

$$\gamma_{s_1 s_2} > \gamma_{s_1 1} + \gamma_{s_2 1}. \tag{8.18}$$

All interfacial tensions may be calculated by means of eq. (8.14).

Example 8.4 (after Owens (1970))

Estimate if separation occurs between coating and substrate in the case where flame-treated polypropylene film, coated with vinylidene chloride/methyl acrylate copolymer is immersed in a solution of sodium n-dodecyl sulphate (concentration 0.5%). The data of polymer, coating and liquid are the following (determined in separate experiments):

	γ^d	γ^h	γ
Flame-treated polypropylene	33.5	4.1	37.6
Copolymer	38.9	14.7	53.6
Sodium n-dodecyl sulphate solution	29.0	8.2	37.2

Solution

We first calculate the interfacial tensions (γ_{12}) i.e. $\gamma_{s_1 s_2}$, $\gamma_{s_1 1}$ and $\gamma_{s_2 1}$ by application of eq. (8.14). In this way we obtain:

$$\gamma_{s_1 s_2} = 37.6 + 53.6 - 2(33.5 \times 38.9)^{1/2} - 2(4.1 \times 14.7)^{1/2} = 3.5$$

$$\gamma_{s_1 1} = 37.6 + 37.2 - 2(33.5 \times 29.0)^{1/2} - 2(4.1 \times 8.2)^{1/2} = 0.9$$

$$\gamma_{s_2 1} = 53.6 + 37.2 - 2(38.9 \times 29.0)^{1/2} - 2(14.7 \times 8.2)^{1/2} = 1.7$$

Applying the rule (8.17) we get:

$$W_{adh} = 1.6 + 0.9 - 3.4 = -0.9.$$

Since W_{adh} is negative, separation will occur.

It must be emphasized that polymer adhesion is a complex phenomenon. The effectivity of an adhesive is only partly determined by interfacial properties. Cassidy et al. (1972) found that effects on the glass transition temperature of the adhesive may be more important than interfacial properties. An additive which lowers T_g from a point above the test temperature to below it causes a decrease in the strength of the system with cohesive failure within the adhesive.

BIBLIOGRAPHY, CHAPTER 8

General references

Blake, T.D. and Haynes, J.M., "Contact-angle Hysteresis", in "Progress in Surface and Membrane Science" (J.F. Danielli, M.D. Rosenberg and D.A. Cadenhead, Eds.), Academic Press, New York, 1973, Vol. 6, pp. 125–138.

Elliot, G.E.P. and Riddiford, A.C., "Contact Angles", in "Recent Progress in Surface Science" (J.F. Danielli, K.G.A. Pankhurst and A.C. Riddiford, Eds.), Academic Press, New York, 1964, Vol. 2, pp. 111–128.

Fowkes, F.M., in "Contact Angle, Wettability and Adhesion", Adv. Chem. Ser. 43, Am. Chem. Soc., 1964, pp. 108–110.

Fowkes, F.M., in "Chemistry and Physics of Interfaces", Am. Chem. Soc., 1965, pp. 1–12.

Fowkes, F.M. (Ed.), "Hydrophobic Surfaces", Academic Press, New York, 1969.

Hildebrand, J.H. and Scott, R.L., "The Solubility of Nonelectrolytes", Reinhold Publishing Comp., New York, 1949.

Johnson, R.E. and Dettre, R.H., "Wettability and Contact Angles", in "Surface and Colloid Science" (E. Matijević, Ed.), Interscience, New York, 1969, Vol. II, pp. 85–153.

Kaelble, D.H., "Physical Chemistry of Adhesion", Interscience, New York, 1971.

Lee, L.H., in "Interaction of Liquids at Solid Substrates" (R.F. Gould, Ed.), Adv. in Chem. Ser. 87, Am. Chem. Soc., 1968, pp. 106–123.

Padday, J.F., "Surface Tension", in "Surface and Colloid Science" (E. Matijević, Ed.), Interscience, New York, 1969, Vol. I, pp. 39–251.

Quayle, O.R., Chem. Revs. 53 (1953) 439.

Sugden, S., "The Parachor and Valency", George Routledge, London, 1930.

Wu, S., J. Macromol. Sci., Rev. Macromol. Chem. 10 (1974) 1.

Zisman, W.A., in "Contact Angle, Wettability and Adhesion", Adv. in Chem. Ser. 43, Am. Chem. Soc., 1964, pp. 1–51; in "Adhesion and Cohesion" (P. Weiss, Ed.), Elsevier, Amsterdam, 1962, pp. 176–208.

Special references

Cassidy, P.E., Johnson, J.M. and Locke, C.E., J. Adhesion 4 (1972) 183.

Dann, J.R., J. Colloid Interface Sci. 32 (1970) 302.

Fowkes, F.M., Ind. Eng. Chem. 56 (1964) 40.

Fox, H.W. and Zisman, W.A., J. Colloid Sci. 7 (1952) 109 and 428.

Girifalco, L.A. and Good, R.J., J. Phys. Chem. 61 (1957) 904; 62 (1958) 1418 and 64 (1960) 561.

Grunberg, L. and Nissan, A.H., Trans. Faraday Soc. 45 (1949) 125.

Jarvis, N.L., Fox, R.B. and Zisman, W.A., Advances in Chem. 43 (1964) 317.

Lee, L.H., J. Polymer Sci. A-2,5 (1967) 1103.

Lee, L.H., J. Paint Techn. 42 (1970) 365.

McGowan, J.C., Polymer 8 (1967) 57.

Mumford, S.A. and Phillips, J.W.C., J. Chem. Soc. 130 (1929) 2112.

Owens, D.K., J. Appl. Polymer Sci. 14 (1970) 1725.

Owens, D.K. and Wendt, R.C., J. Appl. Polymer Sci. 13 (1969) 1741.

Panzer, J., J. Colloid Interface Sci. 44 (1973) 142.

Roe, R.-J., J. Phys. Chem. 69 (1965) 2809.

Schoenhorn, H., Ryan, F.W. and Sharpe, L.H., J. Polymer Sci. A-2,4 (1966) 538.

Sugden, S., J. Chem. Soc. 125 (1924) 1177.

Wu, S., J. Colloid Interface Sci. 31 (1969) 153; J. Phys. Chem. 74 (1970) 632; J. Polymer Sci. C 34 (1971) 19.

Zisman, W.A., Ind. Eng. Chem. 55 (1963) 19.

CHAPTER 9

LIMITING VISCOSITY NUMBER (INTRINSIC VISCOSITY) AND RELATED PROPERTIES OF VERY DILUTE SOLUTIONS

The properties of very dilute polymer solutions are determined by the conformational states of the separate polymer molecules.

The conformational state may be expressed in molecular dimensions (e.g. the mean square end-to-end distance of a polymer molecule) or in the *limiting viscosity number* (intrinsic viscosity).

If the interaction forces between polymer and solvent molecules can be neglected (the so-called Θ-solution) the polymer molecule is in an unperturbed conformational state. In this situation, the molecular dimensions and the limiting viscosity number can be predicted rather accurately. For a normal dilute polymer solution, however, only approximate values of these quantities can be estimated.

Introduction

This chapter deals exclusively with the properties of very dilute polymer solutions. It is under these conditions only that isolated linear polymer molecules can be studied.

An isolated linear macromolecule generally tends to assume a random coil configuration. Only in exceptional cases a rodlike configuration is assumed. Several types of measurements can be used to determine the dimensions of the random coil configuration. Conversely, if the appropriate relationships have been established, the same measurements can be used to determine the mean molecular weight of a given polymer.

The principal types of measurements on very dilute polymer solutions are:

1. Viscosity measurements.

    The results can be expressed in the limiting viscosity number (intrinsic viscosity) $[\eta]$. This quantity will be discussed furtheron in this chapter.

2. Light scattering measurements.

    This phenomenon will be treated in Chapter 10.

3. Small angle X-ray scattering.

4. Osmotic pressure measurements.

    The second virial coefficient A_2 in the osmotic pressure equations can also be used to determine random coil dimensions (see Chapter 10).

A. MOLECULAR DIMENSIONS OF THE CONFORMATIONAL STATE

1. Random coil statistics. Definitions of end-to-end distance

Initiated principally by Flory (1953), an extensive literature on the statistical description of macromolecular coil conformations has developed. An extensive survey has been written by Kurata and Stockmayer (1963). Detailed conformational calculations can be found in a monograph of Flory (1969). Here only some headlines can be mentioned.

In the *absence of any type of interaction,* except for the covalent binding forces which fix the length of the chain links, thus assuming completely free internal rotations, a long chain molecule obeys Gaussian or *random-flight* statistics. In such a configuration the mean square value of the end-to-end distance of the chain is given by:

$$\langle h^2 \rangle_{oo} = nl^2 \tag{9.1}$$

where n is the number of bonds and l the bond length. The double zero subscript denotes the lack of short-range as well as long-range interactions.

Short-range interactions, i.e. those interactions between atoms or groups separated by only a small number of valence bonds, result in an effective constancy of bond angles and in torques hindering internal rotations.

A theoretical type of conformation, often referred to, is the *free-rotation model with fixed bond angles.* Then the mean square end-to-end distance is

$$\langle h^2 \rangle_{or} = b \langle h^2 \rangle_{oo} = bnl^2 \approx nl^2 \frac{1 + \cos \vartheta}{1 - \cos \vartheta} \tag{9.2}$$

where b = bond angle factor

ϑ = *supplement* of bond angle.

For a polymethylene chain, the bond angle is about $110°$, so that $\cos \vartheta \approx 1/3$ and

$$\langle h^2 \rangle_{or} \approx 2\, nl^2$$

For fixed bond angles and rotations restricted by short-range interactions the polymer molecule assumes a so-called *"unperturbed state"* and the effective end-to-end distance becomes

$$\langle h^2 \rangle_{o} = \sigma^2 \langle h^2 \rangle_{or} = b\sigma^2 \langle h^2 \rangle_{oo} = s \langle h^2 \rangle_{oo} = snl^2 \tag{9.3}$$

where σ = stiffness factor

s = skeletal factor

Both σ and s are used to characterize the flexibility of a chain molecule.

Long-range interactions are those between non-bonded groups which are separated in the basic chain structure by many valence bonds. These interactions cause the molecule to pervade a larger volume:

$$\langle h^2 \rangle = \alpha^2 \langle h^2 \rangle_{o} = \alpha^2 s \langle h^2 \rangle_{oo} = \alpha^2 snl^2 \tag{9.4}$$

where α is the so-called *expansion coefficient.*

Only in the so-called theta solvents, or more precisely under theta conditions, the volume expansion can be offset. A *theta solvent* is a specially selected poor solvent at a particular temperature, called *theta temperature*. In these Θ-conditions the macromolecule pervades the volume of the unperturbed state. Therefore the concept of a linear macromolecule under Θ-conditions is of paramount importance in treating the properties of the macromolecule *per se*. Owing to thermal — or Brownian — motion the configuration of a macromolecule is constantly changing.

2. Conformational models

The methods of conformational statistics, discussed so far, had as starting point *the real polymer chain*. The aim was to relate the dimensions of the coiled polymer molecule statistically to the mutual displaceability of the chain atoms. Nearly exact relationships are obtained for a large number of freely jointed or freely rotating elements. Under conditions of restricted movability, however, the statistical equations can generally not be solved and empirical factors like s, σ and α are introduced.

To avoid the difficulty of unsolvable statistical equations, some *models of a polymer chain* have been developed. The most widely used is the *random-walk necklace model*, proposed by Kuhn (1934). It defines as a statistical element not a single chain atom but a short section of the polymer chain containing several chain atoms. The length of the section A is chosen so that both its ends may be regarded as completely free joints in the chain. Now equation (9.1) applies again for a sufficiently large number of elements, but at the cost of introducing a new empirical factor A.

Quite the opposite method has been used by Porod and Kratky (1949) in developing the *wormlike chain model*. Here the chain with a finite bond length and a discontinuity at every chain atom is replaced by a chain divided in elements that are so small, that the orientation becomes continuous. Also in this case an empirical factor has to be introduced, viz. the so-called persistence length a. This is defined as the average projection of an infinitely long chain on the initial tangent of the chain.

These polymer chain models find their application not so much in the calculation of chain dimensions as in the application of calculated chain conformations for the prediction of other properties of polymer solutions, of which the solution viscosity is the most important. There is a very extensive literature in this field, with which the names of Rouse (1953) and Zimm (1956) are closely connected. A recent review has been published by Williams (1975).

Up to now, however, it has not been possible to calculate the limiting viscosity number under arbitrary conditions from basic material properties. Therefore these statistical calculations on polymer chain models will not further be discussed here.

3. Quantitative relationships

We shall now consider the quantitative relationships of the isolated macromolecule and of the macromolecule in very dilute solutions.

The extended linear macromolecule

If a polymer is fully extended, its end-to-end distance is:

$$h_{max} = nl \cos\left(\tfrac{1}{2}\vartheta\right) \tag{9.5}$$

For a polyethylene chain, $\vartheta \approx 70°$ and

$$h_{max} \approx 0.83 \; nl = 0.83 \; l\left(\frac{M}{M}\right)Z \tag{9.6}$$

For polymer chains containing other structural elements, a somewhat different value is calculated for the coefficient in eq. (9.6).

The "unperturbed" random-coil macromolecule
Equation (9.3) may be written as:

$$\langle h^2\rangle_0^{1/2} = s^{1/2}n^{1/2}l = s^{1/2}l\left(\frac{M}{M}\right)^{1/2} Z^{1/2} \tag{9.7}$$

$\langle h^2\rangle_0^{1/2}$ is the root-mean-square unperturbed end-to-end distance. The skeletal factor s has a value between 4 and 16 for most polymers. For polymethylene, $s \approx 6.5$. The maximum extension ratio Λ_{max} of an isolated unperturbed polymethylene molecule is therefore:

$$\Lambda_{max} = \frac{h_{max}}{\langle h^2\rangle_0^{1/2}} \approx \frac{0.83}{6.5^{1/2}}\left(\frac{M}{M}\right)^{1/2}Z^{1/2} \approx 0.33\left(\frac{M}{M}\right)^{1/2}Z^{1/2} \tag{9.8}$$

This means that a polymer coil with $Z = 2$ and a degree of polymerization M/M of 10^4 can be extended about 50-fold. This deformability of the isolated molecule is closely related to the reversible deformability of elastomeric polymers in the bulk state.

The "normal" macromolecule in solution
The real polymer coil has a larger end-to-end distance than the unperturbed one, due to the molecular interactions with its surroundings:

$$\boxed{\langle h^2\rangle^{1/2} = \alpha\langle h^2\rangle_0^{1/2} = \alpha s^{1/2}l\left(\frac{M}{M}\right)^{1/2} Z^{1/2}} \tag{9.9}$$

The expansion factor α is a ratio varying from 1 to ≈ 2; α is *dependent on the chain length* (molecular weight). An empirical approximation is the following:

$$\langle h^2\rangle^{1/2} = K_h M^b \tag{9.10}$$

4. Other characteristic quantities of the macromolecular coil
The above-mentioned quantity $\langle h^2\rangle^{1/2}$ is closely related to the so-called radius of gyration R_G, which is the root-mean-square average of the distances of the molecular segments from the centre of gravity of the coil, $\langle S^2\rangle^{1/2}$. The interrelation of these quantities is:

$$R_G \equiv \langle S^2\rangle^{1/2} = \left(\frac{\langle h^2\rangle}{6}\right)^{1/2} \tag{9.11}$$

For the Θ-conditions we have:

$$\boxed{R_{Go} = \langle S^2\rangle_0^{1/2} = \left(\frac{\langle h^2\rangle_0}{6}\right)^{1/2}} \tag{9.12}$$

Numerical values of these quantities can be obtained from measurements of light scattering (see Chapter 10) and of the limiting viscosity number of polymer solutions, especially in Θ-conditions. From (9.9) it follows that:

$$R_G = \alpha R_{G_0} \tag{9.13}$$

B. THE LIMITING VISCOSITY NUMBER (INTRINSIC VISCOSITY)

1. Definitions

The viscosity of a dilute polymer solution depends on the nature of polymer and solvent, the concentration of the polymer, its average molecular weight and molecular weight distribution, the temperature and the rate of deformation. In the following exposition it is assumed that the rate of deformation is so low, that its influence can be neglected.

The most important characteristic quantity in very dilute solutions is the *limiting viscosity number,* which is defined as:

$$[\eta] = \lim_{c \to 0} \frac{\eta - \eta_S}{\eta_S c} = \lim_{c \to 0} \frac{\eta_{sp}}{c} \tag{9.14}$$

where η is the viscosity of the solution, η_S that of the pure solvent, c the polymer concentration and η_{sp} the so-called *specific viscosity* (see nomenclature in table 9.1). $[\eta]$ has the dimensions of a reciprocal concentration or a reciprocal density, for which cm^3/g is used here. Many literature data of $[\eta]$ are expressed in dl/g, which is no longer allowed in the system of S.I. units.

TABLE 9.1

Nomenclature of solution viscosity

Common name	Name recommended by the International Union of Pure and Applied Chemistry	Symbol and defining equation
Relative viscosity	Viscosity ratio	$\eta_{rel} = \dfrac{\eta}{\eta_S} \approx \dfrac{t}{t_S}$
Specific viscosity		$\eta_{sp} = \eta_{rel} - 1 = \dfrac{\eta - \eta_S}{\eta_S} \approx \dfrac{t - t_S}{t_S}$
Reduced viscosity	Viscosity number	$\eta_{red} = \dfrac{\eta_{sp}}{c}$
Inherent viscosity	Logarithmic viscosity number	$\eta_{inh} = \dfrac{\ln \eta_{rel}}{c}$
Intrinsic viscosity	Limiting viscosity number (Staudinger index)	$[\eta] = \left(\dfrac{\eta_{sp}}{c}\right)_{c=0} = \left(\dfrac{\ln \eta_{rel}}{c}\right)_{c=0}$

2. Interrelationships of the limiting viscosity number

The limiting viscosity number is connected with the dimension of the isolated polymer molecule: In the first place there is the well-known empirical expression first proposed by Mark (1938) and Houwink (1940)

$$\boxed{[\eta] = KM^a}$$

(9.15)

Furthermore there is a theoretical approach which leads to

$$[\eta] = \Phi \frac{\langle h^2 \rangle_h^{3/2}}{M}$$

(9.16)

where $\langle h^2 \rangle_h$ = hydrodynamic equivalent mean-square end-to-end distance of the polymer molecule

Φ = proportionality constant.

Equation (9.16) can be derived from the Einstein equation for suspensions of solid spheres:

$$\frac{\eta - \eta_S}{\eta_S} = 2.5 \, \phi = 2.5 \, \frac{n_p v_h}{V}$$

(9.17)

where ϕ is the volume concentration of the suspended particles, v_h the (hydrodynamic) volume per particle, n_p the number of particles and V the volume of the suspension. Assuming that a polymer coil behaves as a particle, and applying the material balance:

$$V \cdot c = n_p \frac{M}{N_A} \qquad \text{or} \qquad \frac{n_p}{V} = \frac{cN_A}{M}$$

(9.18)

one gets by substitution of (9.18) into (9.17):

$$\eta_{sp} = 2.5 \, N_A c \frac{v_h}{M}$$

or

$$\lim_{c \to 0} \left(\frac{\eta_{sp}}{c} \right) = [\eta] = 2.5 \, N_A \frac{v_h}{M}$$

(9.19)

Taking $k \langle h^2 \rangle_h^{3/2}$ as a measure for the hydrodynamic volume of the coil (with k as a proportionality constant), we get:

$$[\eta] = 2.5 \, N_A \frac{v_h}{M} = \underbrace{2.5 \, N_A k}_{\Phi} \frac{\langle h^2 \rangle_h^{3/2}}{M}$$

The hydrodynamic equivalent molecular dimensions can be related to the unperturbed dimensions by the introduction of a hydrodynamic expansion factor α_h. Then equation (9.9) reads

$$\langle h^2 \rangle_h^{1/2} = \alpha_h \langle h^2 \rangle_0^{1/2} = \alpha_h s^{1/2} l \left(\frac{M}{M} \right)^{1/2} Z^{1/2}$$

(9.20)

α_h appears to increase with increasing molecular weight.

Substitution of (9.20) into (9.16) gives

$$\boxed{[\eta] = \Phi_{\text{o}} \frac{\langle h^2 \rangle_{\text{o}}^{3/2}}{M} \alpha_{\text{h}}^3 = [\eta]_{\Theta} \alpha_{\text{h}}^3} \tag{9.21}$$

A relation between (9.15) and (9.21) can be derived, if it is assumed that

$$\alpha_{\text{h}} = C_1 M^{\epsilon/2} \tag{9.22}$$

where C_1 = constant. Then

$$\langle h^2 \rangle_{\text{h}}^{1/2} = C_2 M^{(1+\epsilon)/2} \tag{9.23}$$

where C_2 = constant.
   Substitution into eq. (9.16) gives

$$[\eta] = KM^{(1+3\epsilon)/2} = KM^a \tag{9.24}$$

   This is the Mark–Houwink equation. For polydisperse polymers, M is replaced by $\bar{M}_{\text{v}}$, the so-called viscosity-average molecular weight, so that

$$[\eta] = K\bar{M}_{\text{v}}^a \tag{9.25}$$

   Under theta conditions (unperturbed random coil), $\epsilon = 0$, so $a = 0.5$:

$$\boxed{[\eta]_{\Theta} = K_{\Theta} \bar{M}_{\text{v}}^{1/2}} \tag{9.26}$$

Combination of (9.21) and (9.26) gives

$$\boxed{[\eta] = \alpha_{\text{h}}^3 [\eta]_{\Theta} = \alpha_{\text{h}}^3 K_{\Theta} \bar{M}_{\text{v}}^{1/2}} \tag{9.27}$$

   For rod-like molecules, $\epsilon = 1$, so $a = 2$:

$$[\eta]_{\text{rod}} = K_{\text{rod}} \bar{M}_{\text{v}}^2 \tag{9.28}$$

   Besides the simple experimental relationship between α_{h} and M (9.22), quite a number of other equations have been proposed. They always contain a parameter which expresses the interaction between polymer and solvent. For a detailed discussion the reader is referred to the literature. A simple equation between α_{h} and M has been proposed by Stockmayer and Fixman (1963), which can be written as

$$\alpha_{\text{h}}^3 = 1 + BM^{1/2}/K_{\Theta} \tag{9.29}$$

in which B is an interaction parameter. Combination of eqs. (9.29) and (9.27) gives

$$\boxed{[\eta] = K_{\Theta} M^{1/2} + BM} \tag{9.30}$$

the well-known *Stockmayer–Fixman equation*.
   In its converted form

$$\frac{[\eta]}{M^{1/2}} = K_{\Theta} + BM^{1/2} \tag{9.31}$$

this equation is often used for the determination of K_Θ from viscosity measurements on an arbitrary polymer–solvent system.

It is interesting to note, that an analogous equation has been proposed by Krigbaum (1955). His equation reads

$$[\eta] = K_\Theta M^{1/2} + 0.5\, A_2 M \tag{9.32}$$

in which A_2 is the second virial coefficient for the polymer–solvent system considered. Values of A_2 may be determined by various experimental techniques, e.g. light scattering or osmometry.

Although there exists a large scatter in the experimental values of both B and A_2, a global correspondence cannot be denied. In general, the value of the quotient B/A_2 varies between 0.25 and 0.5. This relationship is too inaccurate, however, to be used for a prediction of the limiting viscosity number from A_2 values

3. Prediction of the limiting viscosity number under Θ-conditions

Under Θ-conditions eq. (9.21) reads

$$[\eta]_\Theta = K_\Theta M^{1/2} = \Phi_0 \frac{\langle h^2 \rangle_0^{3/2}}{M} \tag{9.33}$$

where Φ_0 is a universal constant; $\Phi_0 \approx 2.5 \times 10^{23}\ \text{mol}^{-1}$.

Equation (9.33) may be used to calculate the limiting viscosity number of a theta solution, if the unperturbed dimensions of the macromolecule have been determined by some other method.

Another method for the estimation of $[\eta]_\Theta$ was proposed by Van Krevelen and Hoftyzer (1967). It makes use of eq. (9.26)

$$K_\Theta = \frac{[\eta]_\Theta}{\overline{M}_v^{1/2}} = \Phi_0 \left(\frac{\langle h^2 \rangle_0^{1/2}}{\overline{M}_v^{1/2}} \right)^3 \tag{9.34}$$

It was found that K_Θ can be estimated by means of additive group contributions.

A somewhat modified version of this method is given here [1]. A *molar limiting viscosity number function* or *molar stiffness function* K is defined as:

$$\mathbf{K} = M K_\Theta^{1/2} \tag{9.35}$$

K proves an additive quantity according to the formula

$$\mathbf{K} = \sum_i n_i \mathbf{K}_i + 4.2\, Z \tag{9.36}$$

where $\mathbf{K}_i$ are contributions of specific groups

Z = number of backbone atoms per structural unit [2].

---

[1] The advantage of the new version is that the numerical value of a group contribution in either backbone or side chain is equal.

[2] By chain backbone is understood the polymer chain proper without side groups and branches. For instance, all vinyl polymers have two atoms per structural unit in the chain backbone. If an aromatic ring is part of the backbone, Z is counted as follows: o-phenylene, $Z = 2$; m-phenylene, $Z = 3$; p-phenylene, $Z = 4$. For alicyclic rings the same rule is applied.

TABLE 9.2

Group contributions to the molar limiting viscosity number function

Structural group	K_i	Structural group	K_i	Structural group	K_i
$-CH_3$	3.55	$-Cl$	12.25	$-CONH_2$	(23)
$-CH_2-$	2.35	$-Br$	(11)	$-CONH-$	12.6
$\diagdown CH-$	1.15	$-CN$	(15)	$-CON\diagup$	(8)
$\diagdown C \diagup$	0	$-OH$	(8)	$-OCONH-$	(25)
$-CH=CH-$	0.5	$-O-$	0.1	$-SO_2-$	(12)
$-CH=C\diagup$	−0.65	$-COOH$	8.0	$-SO_2OH$	(18)
⬡	10.0	$-COO-$ $-COO-$ (acrylic)	9.0 6.4	$\diagdown Si \diagup$	(5)
⬡—	8.0	$-OCOO-$	(27.5)	−pyridine	(18)
⬡ (naphthyl)	18.25			−pyrrolidone	(18)
—⬡—	16.3			−carbazole	(41)

Table 9.2 mentions the group contributions K_i.

As the dimensions of K_Θ are $cm^3 \cdot mol^{1/2}/g^{3/2}$, K is expressed in $g^{1/4} \cdot cm^{3/2}/mol^{3/4}$.

Values of K_Θ calculated from these group contributions generally fall within the limits of accuracy of the available literature data. A comparison between experimental and calculated K_Θ values is made in table 9.3.

4. Prediction of the limiting viscosity number under non-Θ-conditions

An abundance of data on the limiting viscosity number of polymer solutions can be found in the literature. This is because this quantity is generally used for the determination of the molecular weight of polymers. Often the molecular weight is not calculated at all and the limiting viscosity number is used to characterize the polymer.

Unfortunately these experimental data show large variations, if limiting viscosity numbers determined by different investigators on the same polymer are compared. This is due to the use of different experimental methods and different ways of interpretation of the data. This means that an exact prediction of the limiting viscosity number of a given polymer solution is out of the question. If, conversely, a limiting viscosity number determination is to be used to calculate the molecular weight of a sample, the method has to be

182

TABLE 9.3

Experimental and calculated values of K_Θ (cm$^3 \cdot$ mol$^{1/2}$/g$^{3/2}$)

Polymer	M	Z	ΣK_i	K_Θ calc.	K_Θ literature	
					from	to
polyethylene	28	2	4.7	0.219	0.20	0.26
polypropylene	42	2	7.05	0.135	0.12	0.18
polybutene	56	2	9.4	0.101	0.11	0.13
polyisobutylene	56	2	9.45	0.102	0.085	0.115
polystyrene	104	2	21.75	0.084	0.07	0.09
poly(α-methylstyrene)	118	2	24.15	0.076	0.064	0.084
poly(vinyl chloride)	62.5	2	15.75	0.149	0.095	0.335
poly(vinyl alcohol)	44	2	11.5	0.205	0.16	0.30
poly(vinyl acetate)	86	2	16.05	0.081	0.077	0.103
poly(methyl acrylate)	86	2	13.45	0.065	0.054	0.081
poly(methyl methacrylate)	100	2	15.85	0.059	0.043	0.090
polyacrylonitrile	53	2	18.5	0.258	0.20	0.25
polymethacrylonitrile	67	2	20.9	0.191	0.22	–
polybutadiene	54	4	5.2	0.166	0.13	0.185
polyisoprene	68	4	7.6	0.129	0.11	0.15
polychloroprene	88.5	4	16.3	0.140	0.095	0.135
poly(methylene oxide)	30	2	2.45	0.131	0.132	0.38
poly(ethylene oxide)	44	3	4.8	0.156	0.100	0.23
poly(tetramethylene oxide)	72	5	9.5	0.179	0.18	0.33
poly(propylene oxide)	58	3	7.15	0.116	0.105	0.125
poly(hexamethylene succinate)	200	12	36.8	0.190	0.145	0.185
poly(hexamethylene sebacate)	284	18	50.9	0.198	0.155	0.275
poly(ethylene terephthalate)	192	10	39.0	0.178	0.15	0.20
nylon 6	113	7	24.35	0.226	0.19	0.23
polycarbonate	254	12	67.2	0.214	0.16	0.28

standardized on samples of known molecular weight.

So a prediction method for the limiting viscosity number can at best give the order of magnitude of this quantity. Such a method will be described on the following pages. The method is based on the empirical relationship between $[\eta]$ and M: the Mark–Houwink equation (9.24). In principle, the Stockmayer–Fixman equation (9.30) could be used as well, but the majority of the literature data has been expressed in the constant K and the exponent a of the Mark–Houwink equation.

Prediction of $[\eta]$ therefore means: prediction of a and K.

Prediction of the exponent a from solvent properties

Obviously the value a is dependent on the nature of the polymer–solvent interaction: in theta solvents $a = 0.5$, while in "good" solvents $a \approx 0.8$. Therefore some relationship between a and the solubility parameter of the solvent, δ_S, may be expected.

The most sophisticated correlation method would make use of the solubility parameter components, discussed in Chapter 7. This would mean, however, a correlation of a with six parameters:

δ_{dP} dispersion force component for the polymer
δ_{pP} polar component for the polymer
δ_{hP} hydrogen bonding component for the polymer
δ_{dS} dispersion force component for the solvent
δ_{pS} polar component for the solvent
δ_{hS} hydrogen bonding component for the solvent

The available experimental data prove to be insufficient for such a correlation.

The next possibility is the use of four parameters: $\delta_{vP} = \sqrt{\delta_{dP}^2 + \delta_{pP}^2}, \delta_{hP}, \delta_{vS} = \sqrt{\delta_{dS}^2 + \delta_{pS}^2}$ and δ_{hS}. This four-parameter method was used in Chapter 7 to correlate solubilities of polymers in solvents. As an example, some values of a are indicated in fig. 9.1 in a δ_{vS} vs. δ_{hS} diagram for poly(methyl methacrylate). The approximate limit of the solubility region is indicated by a circle. The highest values of a are indeed found near the centre.

This method is not suited, however, for an accurate prediction of a from solubility parameter values. This may be caused by the inaccuracy of the parameter values available. For most other polymers even less data can be found in the literature. Therefore these data do not justify the use of solubility parameter components for a prediction of a.

The next logical step is to look for a correlation between a and the total solubility parameters δ_P and δ_S. In figure 9.2 literature values of a are plotted against $\delta_S - \delta_P$. The values of δ_S have been taken from Table VI (Part VII), while δ_P values have been calculated from E_{coh} in table 7.2, calculated in its turn from group contributions.

Although fig. 9.2 shows a considerable amount of scatter, there is a broad correlation, which may be approximated by

$$
\begin{array}{|ll|}
\hline
a \approx 0.8 - 0.1 \ |(\delta_S - \delta_P)| & \\
\quad\quad\quad\quad \text{if } |(\delta_S - \delta_P)| \leqslant 3 & \\
a = 0.5 \quad\quad \text{if } |(\delta_S - \delta_P)| > 3 & \\
\hline
\end{array}
\qquad (9.37)
$$

Large deviations from eq. (9.37) may be found for highly crystalline polymers, such as polyethylene, and if the solvent has a much higher hydrogen bonding activity than the polymer.

In table 9.4, calculated values of the Mark–Houwink exponent a are compared with literature values. There is a reasonable agreement, except if the solvent has hydrogen bonding properties considerably different from that of the polymer.

Prediction of K

Van Krevelen and Hoftyzer (1966, 1967) demonstrated the existence of a relationship between K and a. This could be approximated by

$$
-\log \frac{K}{K_\Theta} = C(a - \tfrac{1}{2}) \qquad (9.38)
$$

where C is a constant, with a numerical value of 3.7 ± 0.7. This is illustrated in fig. 9.3 where the available literature data on limiting viscosity numbers of polystyrene solutions are plotted as $(\log K_\Theta/K)$ against a. Although eq. (9.38) is a fair first approximation, a more accurate equation is desirable, since the mean difference between experimental and estimated *K*-values is about 30%. For this purpose the Mark–Houwink equation will be transformed into a dimensionless form. As the reference value of *M* the critical molecular weight M_{cr} is chosen. This is the molecular weight above which molecular entanglements are assumed to play a part in the flow of a molten polymer. This quantity is discussed in

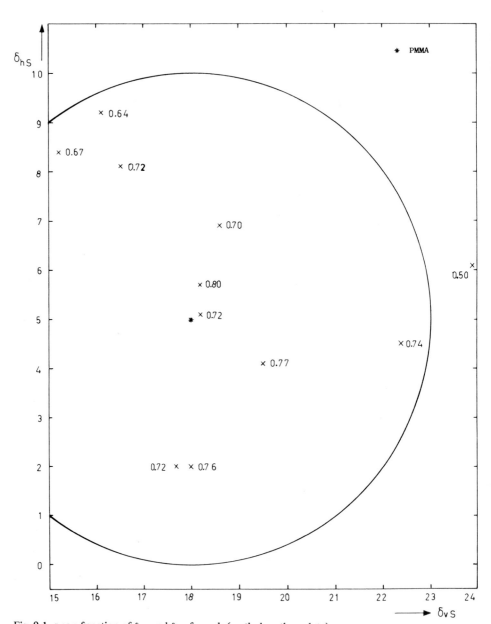

Fig. 9.1. *a* as a function of δ_{vS} and δ_{hS} for poly(methyl methacrylate).

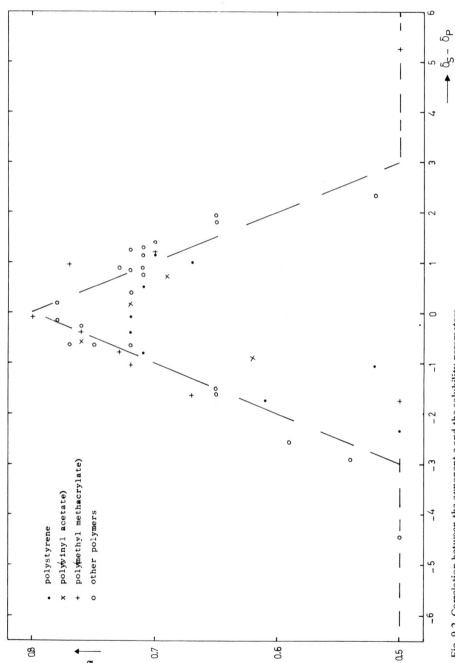

Fig. 9.2. Correlation between the exponent *a* and the solubility parameters.

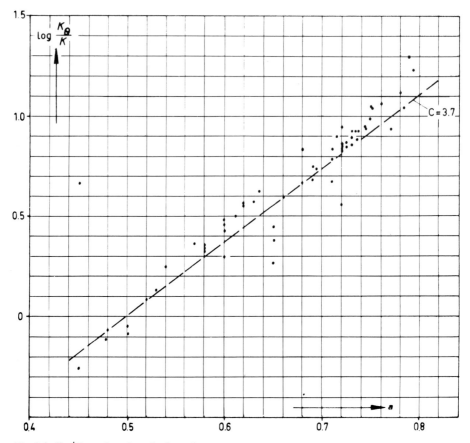

Fig. 9.3. K_Θ/K as a function of a for polystyrene.

Chapter 15, where an empirical relationship between M_{cr} and K_Θ is mentioned:

$$K_\Theta M_{cr}^{1/2} \approx 13 \qquad (cm^3/g) \tag{9.39}$$

If the limiting viscosity number at the critical molecular weight is called $[\eta]_{cr}$, the Mark—Houwink equation may be written as

$$\frac{[\eta]}{[\eta]_{cr}} = \left(\frac{M}{M_{cr}}\right)^a \tag{9.40}$$

Eq. (9.40) has not yet the desired general form, as $[\eta]_{cr}$ is still dependent on the nature of the polymer—solvent system. As a reference value of the limiting viscosity number the quantity

$$[\eta]_R = [\eta]_{cr,\Theta} = K_\Theta M_{cr}^{1/2} \tag{9.41}$$

TABLE 9.4

Comparison of calculated and literature data on the limiting viscosity number

Polymer	log M_{cr}	log K_Θ	δ_P	Solvent	δ_S	log K literature	a literature	a calc.	log [η] for M = 2.5 × 10⁵ literature	calc.
polypropylene	3.96	−0.87	17.0	cyclohexane	16.7	−1.68 to −1.80	0.76−0.80	0.77	2.42−2.52	2.49
				toluene	18.25	−1.66	0.725	0.675	2.26	2.18
				benzene	18.65	−1.57 to −1.47	0.67−0.71	0.635	2.15−2.26	2.08
polyisobutylene	4.20	−0.99	16.35	cyclohexane	16.7	−1.58 to −1.40	0.69−0.72	0.765	2.15−2.49	2.27
				carbon tetrachloride	17.7	−1.54	0.68	0.665	2.13	1.98
				toluene	18.25	−1.70 to −1.06	0.56−0.67	0.61	1.92−1.96	1.87
				benzene	18.65	−1.21 to −0.97	0.50−0.56	0.57	1.73−1.81	1.80
polystyrene	4.37	−1.07	19.05	cyclohexane	16.7	−1.07 to −0.97	0.48−0.50	0.565	1.62−1.63	1.69
				butyl chloride	17.3	−1.82	0.66	0.625	1.74	1.87
				ethylbenzene	17.95	−1.75	0.68	0.69	1.92	1.91
				decalin	18.0	−1.17	0.52	0.695	1.64	1.92
				toluene	18.25	−2.38 to −1.36	0.65−0.79	0.72	1.88−2.15	2.11
				benzene	18.65	−2.20 to −1.38	0.60−0.78	0.76	1.86−2.25	2.12
				chloroform	18.95	−2.31 to −1.95	0.73−0.795	0.79	1.96−1.99	2.26[1]
				butanone	19.0	−1.52 to −1.41	0.58−0.60	0.795	1.72	2.29[1]
				chlorobenzene	19.55	−2.13	0.75	0.75	1.91	2.08
				dioxane	20.2	−1.82	0.695	0.685	1.93	1.90
poly(vinyl acetate)	4.40	−1.09	19.55	methyl isobutyl ketone	17.35	−1.35	0.60	0.58	1.89	1.66
				toluene	18.25	−0.97	0.53	0.67	1.89	1.79
				3-heptanone	18.5	−1.09 to −1.03	0.50	0.695	1.61−1.67	1.86
				benzene	18.65	−1.66 to −1.25	0.62−0.65	0.71	1.85−2.10	1.88
				chloroform	18.95	−1.80 to −1.69	0.72−0.74	0.74	2.20	1.96
				butanone	19.0	−1.97 to −1.38	0.62−0.71	0.745	1.86−1.97	1.97
				ethyl formate	19.4	−1.50	0.65	0.785	2.01	2.16[1]
				chlorobenzene	19.55	−1.03	0.56	0.80	1.99	2.22
				dioxane	20.2	−1.94	0.74	0.735	2.06	1.94
				acetone	20.25	−2.07 to −1.61	0.68−0.74	0.73	1.90−2.05	1.93

(Continued on p. 188)

TABLE 9.4 (continued)

Polymer	log M_{cr}	log K_Θ	δ_P	Solvent	δ_S	log K literature	a literature	a calc.	log $[\eta]$ for $M = 2.5 \times 10^5$ literature	calc.
poly(vinyl acetate) (continued)	4.40	−1.09	19.55	acetonitrile	24.3	−1.79 to −1.38	0.62−0.71	0.50	1.97−2.04	1.56
				methanol	29.45	−1.50 to −1.42	0.59−0.60	0.50	1.80−1.77	1.56
poly(methyl methacrylate)	4.70	−1.26	19.05	butyl chloride	17.3	−1.30	0.50	0.625	1.40	1.55
				methyl isobutyrate	17.4	−2.00	0.67	0.635	1.62	1.56
				methyl methacrylate	18.0	−2.17	0.72	0.695	1.72	1.64
				toluene	18.25	−2.15 to −2.09	0.71−0.73	0.72	1.80−2.21	1.72
				heptanone	18.5	−1.23 to −1.20	0.48−0.50	0.745	1.36−1.50	1.78
				ethyl acetate	18.6	−1.68	0.64	0.755	1.78	1.81
				benzene	18.65	−2.42 to −1.08	0.52−0.79	0.76	1.73−1.96	1.83
				chloroform	18.95	−2.47 to −2.02	0.78−0.83	0.79	2.00−2.19	1.97
				butanone	19.0	−2.17 to −2.03	0.68−0.72	0.795	1.64−1.74	1.99
				dichloroethane	20.0	−2.28 to −1.77	0.68−0.77	0.705	1.78	1.81
				tetrachloroethane	20.05	−1.89	0.73	0.70	2.05	1.67
				acetone	20.25	−2.61 to −2.02	0.69−0.80	0.68	1.66−1.71	1.63
				nitroethane	22.7	−2.24	0.74	0.50	1.76	1.43
				acetonitrile	24.3	−1.41	0.50	0.50	1.29−1.53	1.43
polyacrylonitrile	3.40	−0.59	25.7	dimethyl acetamide	22.45	−1.51	0.76	0.50	2.60	2.11
				dimethyl formamide	24.9	−1.81 to −1.24	0.73−0.81	0.72	2.37−2.70	2.68
				dimethyl sulfoxide	26.6	−1.49	0.75	0.71	2.56	2.64
				butyrolactone	28.95	−1.47 to −1.24	0.67−0.73	0.50	2.31−2.48	2.11
polybutadiene	3.78	−0.78	17.5	cyclohexane	16.7	−1.95	0.75	0.72	2.10	2.41
				isobutyl acetate	17.1	−0.73	0.50	0.76	1.97	2.57[1]
				toluene	18.25	−1.52 to −1.47	0.69−0.725	0.725	2.25−2.40	2.43
				benzene	18.65	−2.07 to −1.47	0.715−0.78	0.685	2.14−2.39	2.31
polyisoprene	4.00	−0.89	17.4	hexane	14.85	−1.17	0.58	0.545	1.96	1.86
				isooctane	15.8	−1.65	0.685	0.64	2.04	2.04
				toluene	18.25	−1.70 to −1.30	0.67−0.73	0.715	2.23−2.30	2.24
				benzene	18.65	−1.73	0.74	0.675	2.27	2.13

TABLE 9.4 (continued)

Polymer	log M_{cr}	log K_Θ	δ_p	Solvent	δS	log K literature	a literature	a calc.	log [η] for M = 2.5 × 10^5 literature	calc.
poly(ethylene oxide)	3.83	−0.80	19.3	cyclohexane	16.7	−1.46	0.69	0.54	2.27	1.95
				carbon tetrachloride	17.7	−1.16	0.61	0.64	2.13	2.16
				benzene	18.65	−1.32 to −0.89	0.50– 0.68	0.735	1.81–2.35	2.43
				chloroform	18.95	−0.69	0.50	0.765	2.01	2.56
				dioxane	20.2	−1.46 to −0.86	0.50–0.71	0.71	1.84–2.37	2.34
				acetone	20.25	−0.81	0.50	0.705	1.89	2.33 [1]
				dimethyl formamide	24.9	−1.62	0.73	0.50	2.32	1.89 [1]
				methanol	29.45	−1.48	0.72	0.50	2.41	1.89 [1]
poly(propylene oxide)	4.09	−0.94	18.9	toluene	18.25	−1.95	0.75	0.735	2.16	2.22
				benzene	18.65	−1.89	0.77	0.775	2.21	2.50

[1] High δ_{hS} (as compared with δ_{hP}).

is introduced. $[\eta]_R$ is the limiting viscosity number of a theta solution of a polymer with $M = M_{cr}$. If eq. (9.39) holds, $[\eta]_R \approx 13$ cm^3/g.

According to eq. (9.21),

$$[\eta]_{cr} = \alpha_{h,cr}^3 [\eta]_R \tag{9.42}$$

so that

$$\boxed{\frac{[\eta]}{[\eta]_R} = \alpha_{h,cr}^3 \left(\frac{M}{M_{cr}}\right)^a} \tag{9.43}$$

where $\alpha_{h,cr}$ = hydrodynamic expansion factor at $M = M_{cr}$. This is the reduced Mark–Houwink equation, which still contains two parameters: a and α_h. Its relation to the original Mark–Houwink equation is given by:

$$K = \frac{[\eta]_R \alpha_{h,cr}^3}{M_{cr}^a} \tag{9.44}$$

Combination of eqs. (9.41) and (9.44) leads to

$$\boxed{- \log \frac{K}{K_\Theta} = (a - \tfrac{1}{2}) \log M_{cr} - \log \alpha_{h,cr}^3} \tag{9.45}$$

Eq. (9.45) may be considered as a corrected form of eq. (9.38), the correction factor being $\alpha_{h,cr}^3$.

For a number of selected, reliable literature data on different polymer–solvent combinations, $\alpha_{h,cr}^3$ was calculated with the aid of eq. (9.44). It appears that the quantity $\alpha_{h,cr}^3$ is correlated with a. This is shown in fig. 9.4. By definition $\alpha_{h,cr}^3 = 1$ for $a = 0.5$, while it increases to about 2.5 for $a = 0.8$.

The relationship between $\alpha_{h,cr}^3$ *and a (fig. 9.4) makes it possible to represent eq. (9.43) graphically with only one parameter: the exponent a.* Such a diagram is shown in fig. 9.5.

A similar diagram can be derived from the Stockmayer–Fixman equation, which reads in reduced form:

$$\frac{[\eta]}{[\eta]_R} = \left(\frac{M}{M_{cr}}\right)^{1/2} + B'\left(\frac{M}{M_{cr}}\right) \tag{9.46}$$

where $B' = BM_{cr}/[\eta]_R$. This equation is represented in fig. 9.6, which shows a certain resemblance to fig. 9.5. As can be seen in fig. 9.7, however, a correlation between a and B' is dependent on the ratio M/M_{cr}.

N.B. Eq. (9.44) in combination with fig. 9.4 offers an interesting possibility to determine M_{cr} of a polymer; the data needed are K and a. For this purpose, eq. (9.44) is rewritten as

$$a \log M_{cr} - \log[\eta]_R = -\log K + \log \alpha_{h,cr}^3 \tag{9.47}$$

If $\log \alpha_{h,cr}^3 - \log K$ is plotted as a function of a, the points may be connected by a straight line, the slope of which corresponds to $\log M_{cr}$. This is shown in fig. 9.8 for polystyrene.

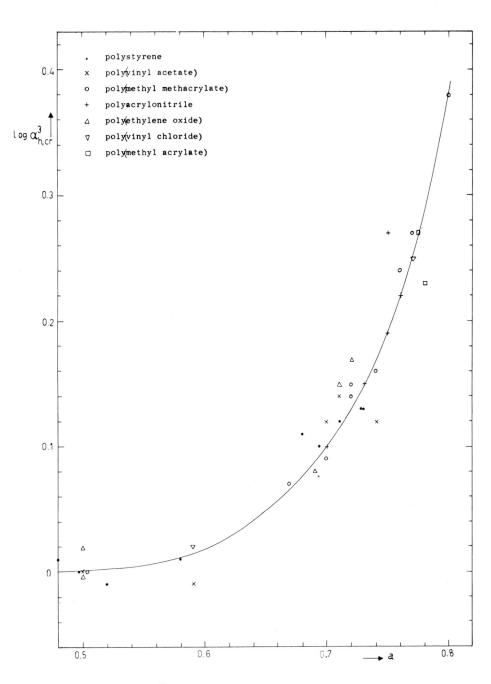

Fig. 9.4. Correlation between $\alpha_{h,cr}^3$ and a.

192

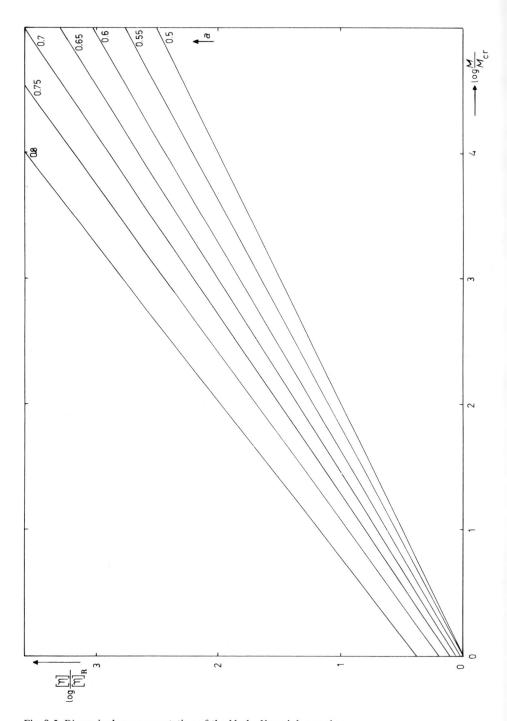

Fig. 9.5. Dimensionless representation of the Mark–Houwink equation.

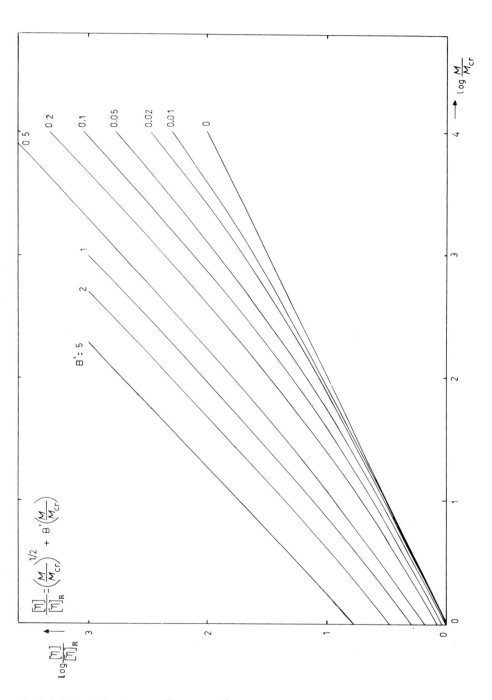

Fig. 9.6. Reduced Stockmayer–Fixman equation.

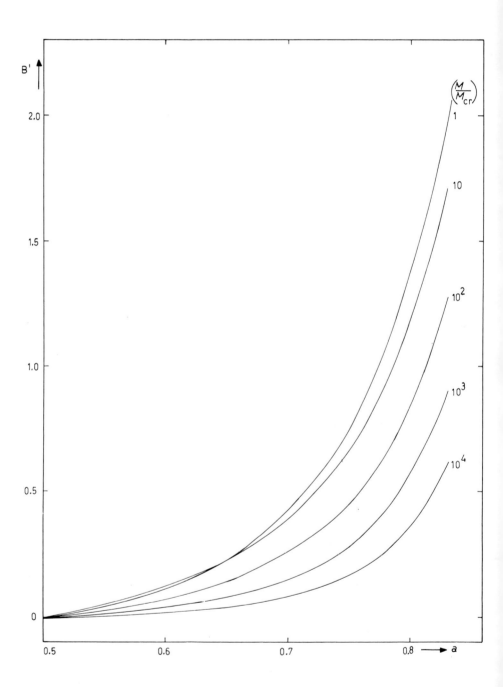

Fig. 9.7. Correlation between a and B'.

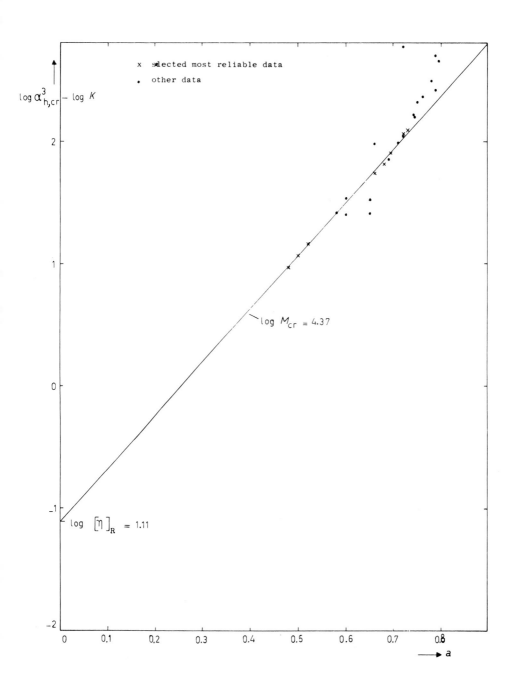

Fig. 9.8. Determination of M_{cr} for polystyrene.

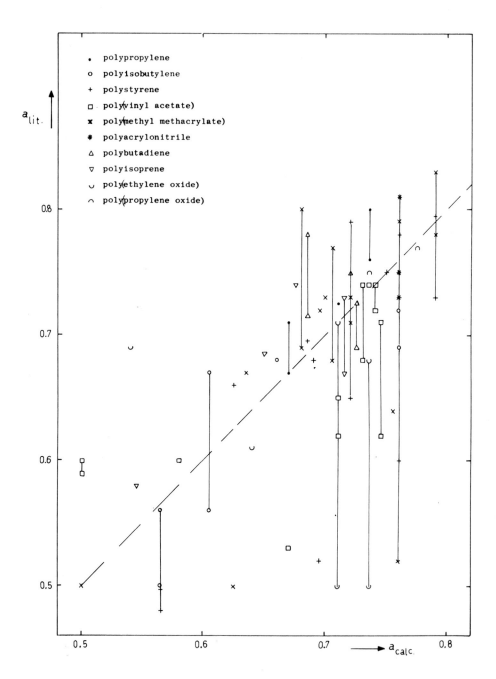

Fig. 9.9. Experimental and calculated values of *a*.

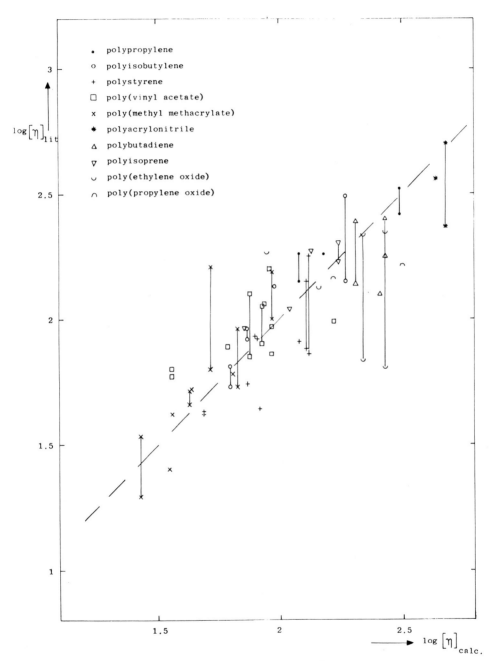

Fig. 9.10. Experimental and calculated values of $[\eta]$ ($M = 2.5 \times 10^5$).

Table 9.4 besides values of a also compares calculated values of the limiting viscosity number at a given molecular weight ($M = 2.5 \times 10^5$) with literature values. In most cases, the correct order of magnitude is predicted.

The comparison between calculated and experimental a-values is shown graphically in fig. 9.9, while the comparison for log $[\eta]$ (at $M = 2.5 \times 10^5$) is given in fig. 9.10.

Example 9.1

Estimate the limiting viscosity number of poly(methyl methacrylate) with a molecular weight $M = 2.5 \times 10^5$ in toluene.

Solution

a. Estimation of a

According to Chapter 7, $\delta_P = (E_{coh}/V)^{1/2}$.

The calculated value of E_{coh} in table 7.3 is $E_{coh} = 31300$ J/mol. With $V = 86.5$ cm^3/mol

$$\delta_P = \left(\frac{31300}{86.5}\right)^{1/2} = 19.05 \text{ J}^{1/2}/\text{cm}^{3/2}$$

In Table VI (Part VII) we find for toluene

$$\delta_S = 18.25 \text{ J}^{1/2}/\text{cm}^{3/2}$$

$\delta_P - \delta_S = 0.80$, so according to eq. (9.37) $a = 0.80 - \dfrac{0.80}{10} = 0.72$.

b. Calculation of M_{cr}

Table 9.2 mentions the following values of the limiting viscosity number function K_i

structural group	K_i
$-CH_2-$	2.35
$\overset{\backslash}{\underset{/}{C}}\overset{/}{\underset{\backslash}{}}$	0
2 $-CH_3$	7.1
$-COO-$	6.4
	15.85

$$K = 15.85 + 4.2 \text{ Z} = 15.85 + 8.4 = 24.25$$

$$K_\Theta = \left(\frac{K}{M}\right)^2 = \left(\frac{24.25}{100.1}\right)^2 = 0.059 \text{ cm}^3 \cdot \text{mol}^{1/2}/\text{g}^{3/2}$$

According to eq. (9.39)

$$M_{cr} = (13/K_\Theta)^2 = 4.9 \times 10^4$$

c. Estimation of $[\eta]$

For this purpose we use figure 9.5.

$$M/M_{cr} = 2.5 \times 10^5/4.9 \times 10^4 = 5.1$$

At this value we find by interpolation between the lines for $a = 0.7$ and $a = 0.75$

$$[\eta]/[\eta]_R = 4.4$$

With $[\eta]_R = 13$, $[\eta] = 57$ cm^3/g.

d. Estimation of K

According to eq. (9.45) we get:

$$\log K = \log K_\Theta - (a - \frac{1}{2}) \log M_{cr} + \log \alpha_{h,cr}^3$$

For $a = 0.72$ we obtain from fig. 9.4:

$$\log \alpha_{h,cr}^3 = 0.13$$

With $K_\Theta = 0.059$ and $M_{cr} = 4.9 \times 10^4$ we get after substitution

$$\log K = -2.13$$

so $K = 0.0074$

With the approximative equation (9.38) we obtain

$$\log K = -2.04$$

so $K = 0.0091$

e. Comparison with literature value

In the "Polymer Handbook" we find two sets of Mark–Houwink parameters for poly(methyl methacrylate) in toluene at $25°C$

1) $[\eta] = 0.0071 \, M^{0.73}$ with $M = 2.5 \times 10^5$, $[\eta] = 61.9 \, cm^3/g$

2) $[\eta] = 0.00812 \, M^{0.71}$ with $M = 2.5 \times 10^5$, $[\eta] = 55.2 \, cm^3/g$

So the agreement between experimental and calculated values for K and $[\eta]$ is very satisfactory.

5. Polymers with special characteristics

Branched polymers

The dilute solution properties of branched polymers differ from those of linear polymers of the same composition. Generally, the Mark–Houwink exponent a is lowered by branching (Zimm and Stockmayer, 1949; Zimm and Kilb, 1959).

For determining the molecular weight of branched polymers gel permeation chromatography can be used. An important quantity in this connection is the hydrodynamic volume of the polymer coil, which is proportional to the product $[\eta]M$. According to Benoit and co-workers (1966) the hydrodynamic volume is the key size parameter in the establishment of a universal calibration curve for gel permeation chromatography columns (see Chapter 2): if $\log (M[\eta])$ is plotted versus the elution volume for a variety of polymers, the data fit a single curve.

For linear and branched molecules having the same hydrodynamic volume or elution volume, it follows that the products of their intrinsic viscosities and molecular weights can be equated:

$$M_1[\eta]_1 = M_b[\eta]_b \qquad \text{(at constant elution volume!)} \qquad (9.48)$$

Eq. (9.48) offers a method to determine the molecular weight of branched polymers via the combination of gel permeation chromatography and viscometry.

The procedure is as follows. If for a certain GPC column the universal calibration curve (for linear polymers) is known, the next step is to determine the elution volume and the intrinsic viscosity of the unknown branched fraction. Then the product $M[\eta]$ corresponding to the mean elution volume of a branched fraction is read from the universal calibration curve; this value divided by the determined intrinsic viscosity gives the molecular weight of the fraction. At the same molecular weight one can also calculate the intrinsic viscosity of the linear polymer by using the Mark–Houwink equation.

Rod-like polymer molecules

The dilute solution properties of polymers discussed so far had to do with randomly coiled macromolecules. In some cases, however, dissolved polymer molecules tend to assume a completely stretched rod-like shape.

This phenomenon can be detected experimentally by a very high value of the Mark–Houwink exponent a, the value of which varies between 0.5 and 0.8 for coiled molecules. Theoretical investigations (Flory, 1953) predict a value $a \approx 1.8$ for rigid stretched molecules. This value is indeed found experimentally in some cases. Another indication of rod-like behaviour of macromolecules is a high ratio of radius of gyration to molecular weight.

Rod-like behaviour has been observed with several types of polymers. It is always an indication of a stiff chain skeleton. Some examples are:

1) polyamides containing a large amount of ring-shaped structural elements. A well-known representative of this group is poly(p-phenylene terephthalamide)

2) some polypeptide helices and other natural polyelectrolytes
3) some synthetic polyelectrolytes with a high degree of ionization in dilute solutions.

Polyelectrolytes

A polyelectrolyte is defined as a polymer in which the monomeric units of its constituent macromolecules possess ionizable groups. In non-aqueous solvents a polyelectrolyte shows the same behaviour as a normal polymer. In aqueous solutions, however, the charged groups of the polyelectrolytes may be surrounded by small, oppositely charged counter-ions. The conformational properties of polyelectrolytes in aqueous solutions are highly dependent on the nature and concentration of the ions present.

These ions may be divided into two groups:

1) Ions from neutralizing substances

In aqueous solutions of poly(acrylic acid), for instance, the carboxyl groups of the polymer can be neutralized by the hydroxide ions of sodium hydroxide. The fraction of the carboxyl groups neutralized is called the degree of ionization α_i. For $\alpha_i = 1$, the polymer is called sodium polyacrylate.

2) Ions from salts

Their concentration is usually expressed in the ionic strength I.

In general, the viscosity η of an aqueous polyelectrolyte solution is a complicated function of

$$
\begin{array}{ll}
c & - \quad \text{polyelectrolyte concentration} \\
\alpha_i & - \quad \text{degree of ionization} \\
I & - \quad \text{ionic strength of salts present} \\
M & - \quad \text{molecular weight}
\end{array}
$$

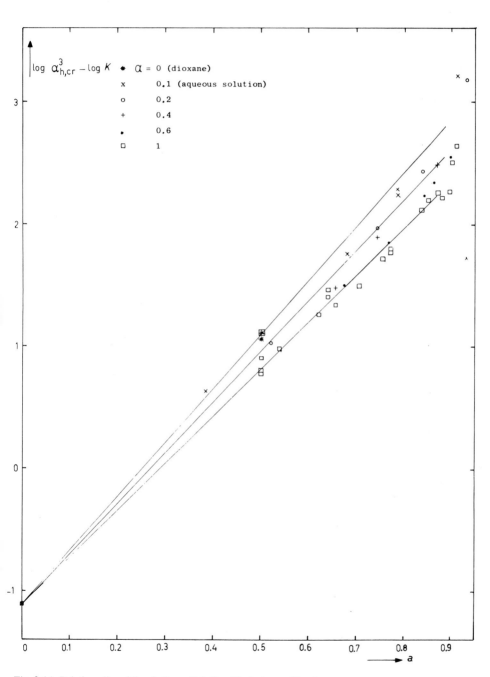

Fig. 9.11. Poly(acrylic acid) solutions. Relationship between K and a.

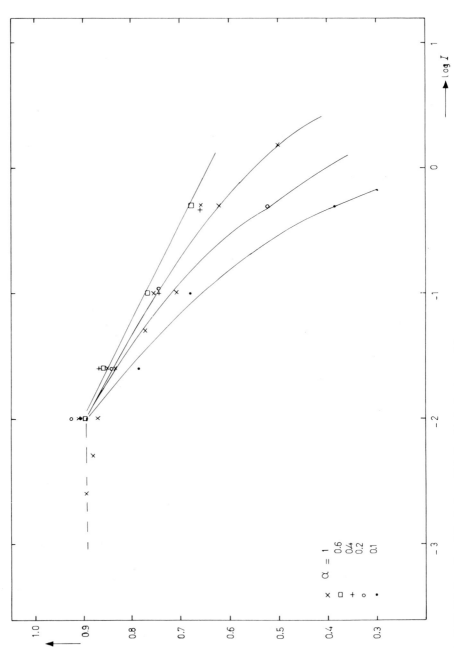

Fig. 9.12. Poly(acrylic acid) solutions. Relationship between a and I.

T – temperature
$\dot{\gamma}$ – rate of shear

In this chapter, we are mainly concerned with the phenomena in very dilute solutions at zero shear rate, as expressed by the limiting viscosity number $[\eta]$, defined in equation (9.14). For several polyelectrolyte solutions, however, it is not even possible to calculate $[\eta]$, as η_{sp}/c does not approach to a constant value for c approaching zero.

In cases where $[\eta]$ can be calculated, the Mark–Houwink equation (9.15) generally holds. The parameters K and a are complicated functions of α_i and I. An extensive literature is devoted to theoretical considerations about this relationship. Some general reviews have been written by Rice et al. (1961), Armstrong and Strauss (1969), Oosawa (1971), but a recent compilation of the relevant literature seems to be lacking.

Here no attempt at a general survey will be made, but only a specific example of polyelectrolyte behaviour will be given, viz. the viscosity data on solutions of poly(acrylic acid). For this polymer, values of a and K can be found in the literature for different values of α_i and I.

In order to establish a relationship between a and K, the method of eq. (9.47) has been applied by plotting $\log \alpha_{h,cr}^3 - \log K$ as a function of a. It appears that the linear relationship of eq. (9.47) holds for constant values of the degree of ionization α_i. The different values of a and K belonging to the same straight line depend on different values of the ionic strength I. This can be seen in fig. 9.11.

There is an interesting analogy with the behaviour of normal polymers:

a. Polyelectrolytes with different degrees of ionization behave as different polymers.

b. At a given value of α_i, aqueous solutions with different ionic strength behave as different solvents.

c. At a low degree of ionization the polyelectrolyte shows the same behaviour in an aqueous solution as in an organic solvent.

Fig. 9.12 shows the influence of the ionic strength I on the Mark–Houwink exponent a. Although there is a large amount of scatter, the data clearly indicate a decrease of a with increasing I. At very low salt concentrations the polyelectrolyte shows a highly expanded state, while at high salt concentrations an unperturbed state is approached. The polymer coil dimensions differ, however, from those of the unperturbed state in organic solvents.

The experimental data on some other polyelectrolytes can be correlated in a similar way, but the relationship between a, K, α_i and I is different for each polymer. At the moment, this behaviour cannot be predicted.

The above discussion dealt exclusively with synthetic polyelectrolytes, which behave in solution more or less as flexible polymers. Another important group, the natural polyelectrolytes, will not be discussed here. They include polynucleic acids, proteins, carbohydrate derivates etc. They generally behave as rigid-chain polymers.

C. INTERRELATIONSHIPS OF "LIMITING" DIFFUSIVE TRANSPORT QUANTITIES

Closely connected with the conformational dimensions of the polymer coil, and therefore with the limiting viscosity number, are some other macroscopic quantities, viz. the limiting sedimentation coefficient and the limiting diffusivity.

Sedimentation

According to Svedberg and Pederson (1940) the sedimentation coefficient is defined as the sedimentation velocity in a unit field of force (e.g. in a centrifuge):

$$s = \frac{dr/dt}{\omega^2 r} \qquad \text{(dimension: second)} \qquad (9.49)$$

where $\dfrac{dr}{dt}$ = instantaneous rate of sedimentation at r

ω = angular velocity.

For a given polymer in a given solvent the sedimentation coefficient is dependent on polymer concentration, molecular weight, temperature and pressure.

Extrapolation of the s-value to zero concentration gives the limiting sedimentation coefficient:

$$s_0 = \lim_{c \to 0} s(c) \qquad (9.50)$$

This limiting sedimentation coefficient is like $[\eta]$ an important polymer property.

The temperature dependence may be approximated by the expression

$$\frac{s(T)}{s(298)} = \frac{\eta_S(298)}{\eta_S(T)} \qquad (9.51)$$

where η_S is the viscosity of the solvent.

In analogy with the Mark–Houwink equation the dependence of the sedimentation coefficient on molecular weight can be expressed as:

$$s_0 = K_s M^c \qquad (9.52)$$

Diffusivity

The diffusivity is defined by Fick's law for unidirectional diffusion

$$D = \frac{\partial c/\partial t}{\partial^2 c/\partial x^2} \qquad \text{(dimension: cm}^2\text{/s)} \qquad (9.53)$$

i.e. the ratio of the rate of change of concentration and the change of the concentration gradient as a function of the distance of transport.

Also the diffusivity is a function of the polymer concentration, the molecular weight, the temperature and – to a lesser extent – the pressure.

Extrapolation of the D-values to zero concentration gives the limiting diffusion coefficient:

$$D_0 = \lim_{c \to 0} D(c) \tag{9.54}$$

The temperature dependence can be described by:

$$\frac{D(T)}{D(298)} = \frac{\eta_S(298)}{\eta_S(T)} \times \frac{T}{298} \tag{9.55}$$

The diffusivity–molecular weight dependence frequently takes the form:

$$D_0 = K_D M^{-d} \tag{9.56}$$

Table 9.5 gives the functional relationships between $[\eta]$, $\langle h^2 \rangle^{1/2}$, s_0 and D_0 and the expressions for the numerical calculation of the exponents b, c and d from a and of the constants K, K_h, K_s and K_D from K_Θ and a.

Example 9.2

Estimate the limiting diffusion coefficient, the limiting sedimentation coefficient and the radius of gyration of poly(methyl methacrylate) ($M = 2.5 \times 10^5$) in toluene.

TABLE 9.5

Interrelationships between transport quantities

Method	Equation $Y = KM^x$	eq.	Relationship between K and x	eq.
Viscometry	$[\eta] = K\bar{M}^a$	(9.15)	approximate: $\log K \approx \log K_\Theta - 3.7(a - \frac{1}{2})$	(9.38)
			accurate: $\log K \approx \log K_\Theta + \log \alpha_{h,cr}^3 - (\log M_{cr})(a - \frac{1}{2})$	(9.45)
Coil statistics	$\langle h^2 \rangle^{1/2} = K_h \bar{M}^b$	(9.10)	$\log K_h = \frac{1}{3} \log(K/\Phi_0) = \frac{1}{3} \log K - 7.8$	(9.57)
Sedimentation	$s_0 = K_s \bar{M}^c$	(9.52)	$\log K_s \approx -14.8 + 5.25(\frac{1}{2} - c)$	(9.58)
Diffusion	$D_0 = K_D \bar{M}^{-d}$	(9.56)	$\log K_D \approx -7.1 + 6.5(d - \frac{1}{2}) - \log \eta_S$ [1]	(9.59)

Relationship between a, b, c and d	eq.
$a = 3b - 1 = 2 - 3c = 3d - 1$	
$b = \frac{1}{3}(a + 1) = 1 - c = d$	(9.60)
$c = \frac{1}{3}(2 - a) = 1 - b = 1 - d$	
$d = \frac{1}{3}(a + 1) = b = 1 - c$	

[1] η_S = viscosity of solvent, expressed in $N \cdot s/m^2$.

Solution

a. Estimation of D_0

According to equation (9.56) and (9.59) (Table 9.5) we have:

$$\log D_0 = \log K_D - d \log \bar{M}$$
$$= -7.1 + 6.5(d - \tfrac{1}{2}) - d \log \bar{M} - \log \eta_S$$

Eq. (9.60) gives the value of d:

$$d = \tfrac{1}{3}(a + 1)$$

In example 1 we have found:

$$a = 0.72, \text{ so } d = \tfrac{1}{3} \times 1.72 = 0.575$$
$$\eta_S = 5.5 \times 10^{-4} \text{ N} \cdot \text{s/m}^2$$

So we get:

$$\log D_0 = -7.1 + 6.5 \times 0.075 - 0.575 \log M - \log \eta_S$$
$$= -6.46$$

so $D_0 = 3.5 \times 10^{-7} \text{ cm}^2/\text{s}$

and $D_0 = 4.4 \times 10^{-4} M^{-0.575} \text{cm}^2/\text{s}$

The literature gives no data, but for PMMA in chloroform it gives:

$$D_0 = 4.5 \times 10^{-4} M^{-0.60} \qquad \text{(Polymer Handbook)}$$

b. Estimation of s_0

Table 9.5 (eqs. (9.52) and (9.58)), gives:

$$\log s_0 = \log K_s + c \log \bar{M}$$
$$= -14.8 + 5.25(\tfrac{1}{2} - c) + c \log \bar{M}$$

since, according to eq. (9.60) $c = 1 - d = \tfrac{1}{3}(2 - a)$, we get with $a = 0.72$ and $d = 0.575$

$$c = 0.425$$

Substitution gives

$$s_0 = 4 \times 10^{-15} M^{0.425} \text{ s}$$

and for $M = 2.5 \times 10^5$

$$s_0 = 7.9 \times 10^{-13} \text{ s}$$

Also in this case the literature does not provide data but for PMMA in ethyl acetate it gives:

$$s_0 = 1.5 \times 10^{-15} M^{0.48} \qquad \text{(Polymer Handbook)}$$

c. Estimation of $\langle h^2 \rangle_0^{1/2}$

With eq. (9.34) we get:

$$\log \frac{\langle h^2 \rangle_0^{1/2}}{\bar{M}^{1/2}} = \tfrac{1}{3}(\log K_\Theta - \log \Phi_0)$$

In example 1 we have found $\log K_\Theta = -1.23$

Since $\log \Phi_0 = 23.4$ we get

$$\log \frac{\langle h^2 \rangle_0^{1/2}}{\bar{M}^{1/2}} = -8.21$$

so $\dfrac{\langle h^2 \rangle_0^{1/2}}{\overline{M}^{1/2}} = 0.62 \times 10^{-8}$ cm $= 0.62 \times 10^{-10}$ m.

The literature (Polymer Handbook) gives $(640 \pm 60) \times 10^{-3}$ Å $= (0.64 \pm 0.06) \times 10^{-10}$ m. So in Θ solution we get

$$\langle h^2 \rangle_0^{1/2} = 0.62 \times 10^{-10} \times (25 \times 10^4)^{1/2}$$
$$\approx 3 \times 10^{-8} \text{ m}$$

d. Estimation of $\langle h^2 \rangle^{1/2}$ and R_G

According to eqs. (9.9) and (9.11) we find

$$\langle h^2 \rangle^{1/2} = R_G \sqrt{6} = \alpha \langle h^2 \rangle_0^{1/2}$$

Since $\alpha^3 = \dfrac{KM^a}{K_\Theta M^{1/2}} = \dfrac{K}{K_\Theta} M^{(a - 1/2)}$

we find $\log \alpha = \frac{1}{3}(\log K - \log K_\Theta + (a - \frac{1}{2})\log M)$

From example 9.1 we get $\log K = -2.13$ and $\log K_\Theta = -1.23$.

So $\log \alpha = 0.097$ and $\alpha \approx 1.25$

and

$\langle h^2 \rangle^{1/2} = 1.25 \times 3 \times 10^{-8} = 3.75 \times 10^{-8}$ m $= 37.5$ nm

$R_G = 1.53 \times 10^{-8}$ m $= 15.3$ nm

This is in fair agreement with eqs. (9.10) and (9.57) from table 9.5 from which we get:

$$\log \langle h^2 \rangle^{1/2} = \log K_h + b \log M$$
$$= \frac{1}{3} \log K - 7.8 + b \log M$$

Since $b = d$, we have $b = 0.575$. Substitution of $\log K$ ($= -2.13$) and $\log M$ ($= 5.4$) gives

$\langle h^2 \rangle^{1/2} = 3.9 \times 10^{-6}$ cm $= 3.9 \times 10^{-8}$ m $= 39$ nm.

BIBLIOGRAPHY, CHAPTER 9

General references

Armstrong, R.W. and Strauss, U.P., "Polyelectrolytes", in "Encyclopedia of Polymer Science and Technology", Interscience, New York, 1969, Vol. 10, p. 781.

Brandrup, J. and Immergut, E.H. (Eds.), "Polymer Handbook", Interscience, New York, 1st ed., 1966; 2nd ed., 1975.

Bueche, F., "Physical Properties of Polymers", Wiley, New York, 1962.

Eirich, F.R., "Rheology", Academic Press, New York, 1956, Vol. I.

Elias, H.G., "Makromoleküle", Hüthig & Wepf, Basel, 1971.

Flory, P.J., "Principles of Polymer Chemistry", Cornell Univ. Press, Ithaca, N.Y., 1953.

Flory, P.J., "Statistical Mechanics of Chain Molecules", Insterscience, New York, 1969.

Morawetz, H., "Macromolecules in Solution", Wiley-Interscience, New York, 1st ed., 1965; 2nd ed., 1975.

Oosawa, F., "Polyelectrolytes", Marcel Dekker, New York, 1971.

Rice, S.A., Nagasawa, M. and Morawetz, H., "Polyelectrolyte Solutions, a Theoretical Introduction", Academic Press, London, 1961.
Tanford, C., "Physical Chemistry of Macromolecules", Wiley, New York, 1961.
Tompa, H., "Polymer Solutions", Academic Press, New York, 1956.
Vollmert, B., "Grundriss der Makromolekularen Chemie", Springer, Berlin, 1962.

Special references

Benoit, H., Grubisic, Z., Rempp, P., Decker, D. and Zilliox, J.G., J. Chim. Phys. 63 (1966) 1507.
Houwink, R., J. prakt. Chem. 157 (1940) 15.
Kratky, O. and Porod, G., Rec. Trav. Chim. 68 (1949) 1106.
Krigbaum, W.R., J. Polymer Sci. 18 (1955) 315.
Kuhn, W., Kolloid-Z. 68 (1934) 2.
Kurata, M. and Stockmayer, W.H., Fortschr. Hochpolymer. Forsch. 3 (1963) 196.
Mark, H., in "Der feste Körper" R. Sänger (Ed.), Hirzel, Leipzig, 1938.
Porod, G., Monatsh. Chem. 80 (1949) 251.
Rouse, P.E., J. Chem. Phys. 21 (1953) 1272.
Rudin, A. and Johnston, H.K., Polymer Letters 9 (1971) 55.
Stockmayer, W.H. and Fixman, M., J. Polymer Sci. C1 (1963) 137.
Svedberg, T. and Pederson, K.O., "The Ultracentrifuge", Clarendon Press, London, 1940.
Van Krevelen, D.W. and Hoftyzer, P.J., J. Appl. Polymer Sci. 10 (1966) 1331; 11 (1967) 1409; 11 (1967) 2189.
Williams, M.C., AIChE J. 21 (1975) 1.
Zimm, B.H., J. Chem. Phys. 24 (1956) 269.
Zimm, B.H. and Kilb, R.W., J. Polymer Sci. 37 (1959) 19.
Zimm, B.H. and Stockmayer, W.H., J. Chem. Phys. 17 (1949) 1301.

PART III

PROPERTIES OF POLYMERS IN FIELDS OF FORCE

CHAPTER 10

OPTICAL PROPERTIES

The index of refraction *and the* specific refractive index increment *(an important quantity in light scattering) can be estimated via additive molar properties.* Light absorption, *on the other hand, does not show additivity, but is a typically constitutive property. Other optical properties, such as* light reflection, *are dependent on both refraction and absorption.*

Introduction

In general the interaction of electromagnetic radiation (light) with matter is controlled by three properties, viz. the *specific conductivity* (σ_{el}), the *electric inductive capacity* [1] (ϵ) and the *magnetic inductive capacity* [2] (μ). These properties are related to the refractive index and the absorption index of the medium.

It is sometimes useful to distinguish between conducting or dissipative ($\sigma_{el} > 0$) media and non-conducting ($\sigma_{el} = 0$) media. For non-conducting media the velocity of an electromagnetic wave is inversely proportional to the product $(\mu\epsilon)^{1/2}$, just as the velocity of a sound wave is inversely proportional to the square root of the compressibility.

All material bodies possess a number of critical frequencies at which radiation is in resonance with some internal vibration of the body. At these critical frequencies such bodies are strong absorbers of radiation, even if they are transparent to radiation on either side of the critical frequency.

Among the optical properties *refraction, absorption, reflection* and *scattering* of light are the most important. While the first three properties are determined by the average optical properties of the medium, scattering is determined by local fluctuations in optical properties within the medium.

Although in principle all media transmit part and reflect part of the incident light, for practical purposes a number of descriptive terms are used to discriminate between quantitatively widely different cases. The *transmittance* of a material, defined as the ratio of the intensity of light passing through to that of light incident on the specimen, is determined by reflection, absorption and scattering. If the second and third effects can be neglected with respect to reflection, the material is called *transparent*. An *opaque* material is one in which practical transmittance is almost zero because of a high scattering power. Materials with negligible absorption but with a transmittance appreciably higher than zero but lower than 90% may be called *translucent*.

---

[1] Usually called *dielectric constant* or *electric permittivity*.
[2] Usually called *magnetic permeability*.

Gloss and *haze* are characteristic terms for polymeric materials. Gloss is the reflectance of a surface responsible for its lustrous appearance, commonly at a maximum near the specular direction, i.e. the direction of mirror reflection. Haze is the percentage of light passing through the specimen but deviating from the direction of incident light by forward scattering.

A. ABSORPTION

A light beam propagating through a medium over a path l suffers a loss of intensity (I) characterized by *Lambert's relationship*

$$I = I_0 \exp\left(-\frac{4\pi n K l}{\lambda}\right).$$
(10.1)[1]

The *absorption index K* is a characteristic function of the wavelength. Most polymers show no specific absorption in the visible region of the spectrum and are therefore colourless in principle.

Infrared absorption

Since all polymers possess specific absorption bands in the infrared part of the spectrum, the infrared spectrum is one of the most valuable tools in the analysis of polymers. The approximate wavelengths of some infrared absorption bands arising from structural group and atomic vibrations found in polymers are shown in fig. 10.1. As some infrared bands are influenced by the conformation of the polymer chain, the IR absorption technique offers a means to determine the crystallinity. Use of polarized IR provides the opportunity to determine the orientation of the amorphous and crystalline parts of a semicrystalline polymer separately.

B. REFRACTION

The index of refraction n is the ratio of the velocity of light in a vacuum to its velocity in the substance considered.

For nonabsorbing media the additive property correlating optical refraction with chemical structure is called *molar refraction*. Several definitions of molar refraction have been proposed in the literature, e.g.:

---

[1] Another formulation of Lambert's relation is in terms of the *mass extinction coefficient* (ϵ_λ), which is defined as

$$\epsilon_\lambda = \frac{1}{\rho l} \ln \frac{I}{I_0}$$
(10.1a)

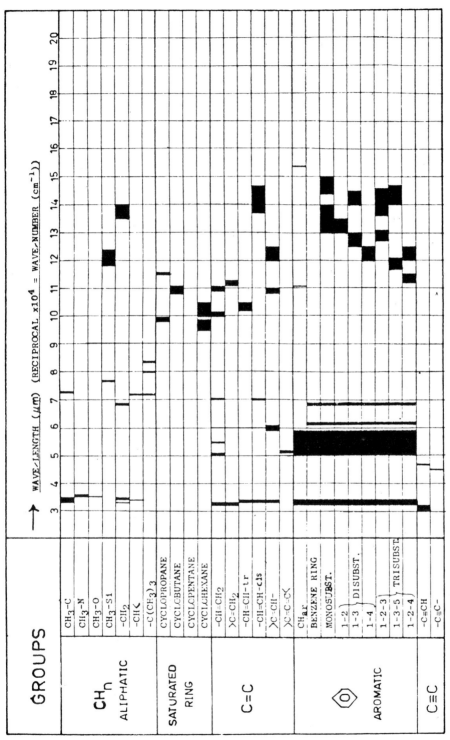

Fig. 10.1.

(Continued on p. 214/215)

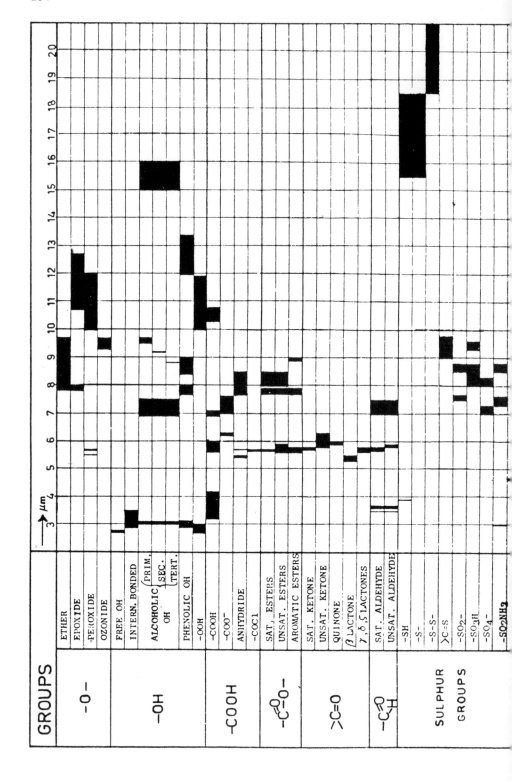

215

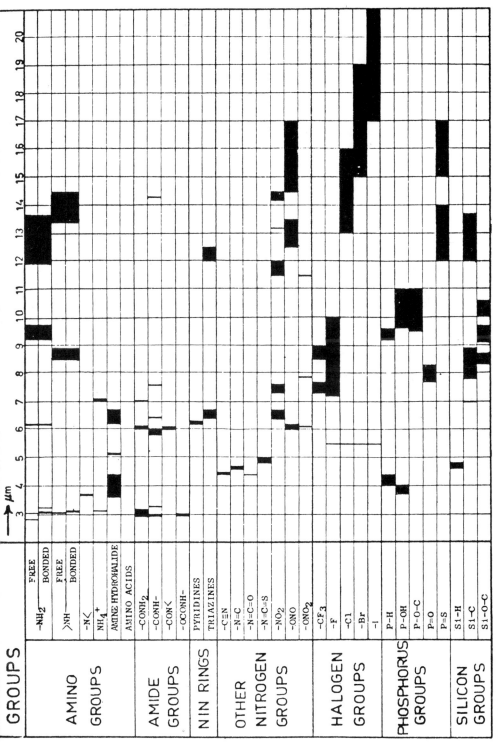

Fig. 10.1. Characteristic absorption bands of structural groups.

a) the molar refraction, according to Lorentz and Lorenz (1880):

$$R_{LL} = \frac{n^2 - 1}{n^2 + 2} \frac{M}{\rho} = \frac{n^2 - 1}{n^2 + 2} V \tag{10.2}$$

b) the molar refraction, according to Gladstone and Dale (1858):

$$R_{GD} = (n - 1)\frac{M}{\rho} = (n - 1)V \tag{10.3}$$

c) the molar refraction, according to Vogel (1948–1954):

$$R_V = nM . \tag{10.4}$$

While b) and c) are purely empirical combinations, a) has its theoretical basis in the electromagnetic wave theory of light. As a standard refractive index usually the index in sodium light (n_D) is used.

Several investigators have calculated the atomic, group or bond contributions to the molecular refraction. Among them are Eisenlohr (1911, 1912), Schoorl (1920), Wibaut et al. (1939), Young and Finn (1940), Vogel (1948) and Huggins (1956).

Goedhart (1969) made an extensive regression analysis based on about a thousand liquid organic compounds containing 43 different functional groups. With his group contributions the quantity $(n - 1)$ can be predicted with a mean standard deviation of about 1%, which means that n itself can be predicted with an average of about 0.4%. Goedhart's values are given in table 10.1.

Because of the relatively strong influence of the benzene ring on other groups, Goedhart made a distinction between groups directly attached to a benzene ring and those separated from the aromatic ring by one or more C atoms. The group contribution of a benzene ring with more substituents is obtained by subtracting an equivalent number of H_{ar} contributions from the contribution of phenyl or phenylene.

A special constitutional increment is the "steric hindrance", which has been introduced to overcome the problem caused by multiple substitution on adjacent C atoms. If, on a chain, groups like CH_3, Cl, or OH are adjacent (on 2 neighbouring C atoms), this steric hindrance increment has to be used.

Table 10.2 shows a comparison between calculated and observed values for a series of solid amorphous polymers. Remarkable is the fact that the very simple formula of Vogel (1948–1954), $R_V = nM$, gives about the same standard deviation as the more complex and theoretically better explicable formulas of Lorentz–Lorenz and Gladstone–Dale.

A polymer always has a higher average refractive index in the crystalline than in the amorphous state. However, since also the density of the crystalline polymer is higher, the molar refraction according to Lorentz–Lorenz and Gladstone–Dale remains practically constant. The molar refraction according to Vogel is not applicable to crystalline polymers, since it does not contain the polymer density.

From the eqs. (10.2) – (10.4) the following expressions for the refractive index can be easily derived:

$$n = \left[\frac{1 + 2\dfrac{R_{LL}}{V}}{1 - \dfrac{R_{LL}}{V}} \right]^{1/2} \quad ; n = 1 + \frac{R_{GD}}{V} ; n = \frac{R_V}{M} . \tag{10.5}$$

TABLE 10.1

Group contributions to the molar refraction (λ = 589 nm)

Groups		R_{LL}	R_{GD}	R_V
$-CH_3$	general	5.644	8.82	17.66
	attached to benzene ring	5.47	8.13	15.4
$-CH_2-$	general	4.649	7.831	20.64
	attached to benzene ring	4.50	7.26	18.7
$\diagdown$CH$-$	general	3.616	6.80	23.49
	attached to benzene ring	3.52	6.34	21.4
$\diagdown$C$\diagup$	general	2.580	5.72	26.37
	attached to benzene ring	2.29	4.96	25.1
(cyclohexyl ring)	cyclohexyl	26.686	44.95	122.66
(phenyl ring)	phenyl	25.51	44.63	123.51
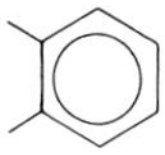 (o-phenylene ring)	o-phenylene	24.72	44.2	129.0
(m-phenylene ring)	m-phenylene	25.00	44.7	128.6
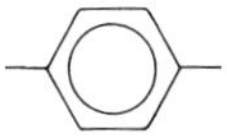 (p-phenylene ring)	p-phenylene	25.03	44.8	128.6
H_{ar}	average value	0.59	0.04	-5.2
$-O-$	methyl ethers	1.587	2.96	23.85
	higher ethers	1.641	2.81	23.18
	attached to benzene ring	1.77	2.84	22.6
	acetals	1.63	2.75	22.99
$-OH$	primary alcohol	2.551	4.13	24.08
	secondary alcohol	2.458	3.95	23.95
	tertiary alcohol	2.453	3.85	24.05
	phenol	2.27	3.53	22.7
$\diagdown$C$=$O	methyl ketone	4.787	8.42	43.01
	higher ketones	4.533	7.91	43.03
	attached to benzene ring	5.09	8.82	41.9
$-\overset{O}{\overset{\|}{C}}-H$	general	5.83	9.63	40.69
$-COOH$	general	7.212	11.99	64.26
$-COO-$	methyl esters	6.237	10.76	65.32
	ethyl esters	6.375	10.94	64.49
	higher esters	6.206	10.47	64.20
	attached to benzene ring	6.71	11.31	64.8
	acetates	6.306	10.87	64.90

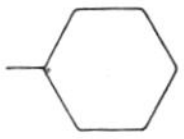

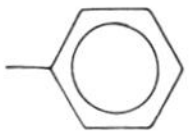

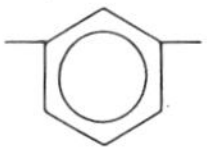

(Continued on p. 218)

TABLE 10.1 (continued)

Groups		R_{LL}	R_{GD}	R_V
−OCOO−	methyl carbonates	7.75	13.39	87.8
	higher carbonates	7.74	13.12	86.8
−NH$_2$	general	4.355	7.25	22.64
	attached to benzene ring	4.89	8.40	23.7
$\diagdown$NH$\diagup$	general	3.585	6.29	24.30
	attached to benzene ring	4.53	8.68	26.9
$\diagdown$N−$\diagup$	general	2.803	5.70	26.66
	attached to benzene ring	4.05	8.67	30.7
−CONH−	general	7.23	15.15	69.75
	attached to benzene ring	8.5	18.1	73
−C≡N		5.528	9.08	36.67
−NO$_2$		6.662	11.01	66.0
−SH	primary	8.845	15.22	50.61
	secondary	8.79	15.14	50.33
	tertiary	9.27	15.66	49.15
−S−	methyl sulphide	7.92	14.30	53.54
	higher sulphides	8.07	14.44	53.33
−SS−		16.17	29.27	107.63
−F	mono	0.898	0.881	22.20
	per	0.898	0.702	20.92
−Cl	primary	6.045	10.07	51.23
	secondary	6.023	9.91	50.31
	tertiary	5.929	9.84	50.75
	attached to benzene ring	5.60	8.82	48.4
−Br	primary	8.897	15.15	118.5
	secondary	8.956	15.26	118.4
	tertiary	9.034	15.29	119.1
−I		13.90	25.0	−
Constitutional increments				
Δ "steric hindrance"	(neighbouring)	−0.118	−0.18	0.41
Δ isopropyl group		0.068	0.05	−0.20
Δ ethylenic bond	general	1.65	1.90	−6.36
(C=C)	cis	1.76	1.94	−5.56
	trans	1.94	2.09	−6.37
Δ ring structure	cyclopentane	−0.18	−1.15	−5.06
	cyclohexane	−0.13	−0.92	−4.44
	tetrahydrofuryl	−0.12	−0.98	−4.36
	furyl	−0.086	−0.78	−4.53
	piperidyl	−0.41	−1.94	−5.63

TABLE 10.2

Observed and calculated values of refractive indices

Polymer	n exper.	n calculated from (10.5)		
		from R_{LL}	from R_{GD}	from R_V
polyethylene	1.49	1.479	1.478	1.469
polystyrene	1.591	1.603	1.600	1.590
poly(methylstyrene)	1.587	1.577	1.585	1.574
poly(isopropylstyrene)	1.554	1.562	1.560	1.555
poly(o-methoxystyrene)	1.593	1.560	1.562	1.575
poly(p-methoxystyrene)	1.597	1.565	1.566	1.572
poly(o-chlorostyrene)	1.610	1.612	1.607	1.583
poly(vinylidene fluoride)	1.42	1.41	1.42	1.43
poly(tetrafluoroethylene)	1.35	1.28	1.28	1.36
poly(vinyl chloride)	1.539	1.544	1.543	1.511
poly(methyl vinyl ether)	1.467	1.450	1.457	1.474
poly(ethyl vinyl ether)	1.454	1.457	1.460	1.465
poly(r-butyl vinyl ether)	1.456	1.463	1.465	1.466
poly(isobutyl vinyl ether)	1.451	1.464	1.466	1.464
poly(n-pentyl vinyl ether)	1.459	1.465	1.467	1.467
poly(hexyl vinyl ether)	1.460	1.466	1.468	1.468
poly(decyl vinyl ether)	1.463	1.469	1.472	1.469
poly(vinyl acetate)	1.467	1.471	1.475	1.472
poly(vinyl benzoate)	1.578	1.583	1.583	1.569
poly(methyl acrylate)	1.479	1.489	1.488	1.477
poly(ethyl acrylate)	1.469	1.487	1.488	1.468
poly(butyl acrylate)	1.466	1.481	1.480	1.466
poly(methyl methacrylate)	1.490	1.484	1.485	1.475
poly(ethyl methacrylate)	1.485	1.488	1.488	1.467
poly(isopropyl methacrylate)	1.552	1.479	1.478	1.464
poly(n-butyl methacrylate)	1.483	1.475	1.475	1.466
poly(tert.-butyl methacrylate)	1.464	1.467	1.472	1.464
poly(isobutyl methacrylate)	1.477	1.480	1.480	1.466
poly(hexyl methacrylate)	1.481	1.476	1.475	1.467
poly(lauryl methacrylate)	1.474	1.476	1.475	1.469
poly(cyclohexyl methacrylate)	1.507	1.515	1.513	1.495
poly(benzyl methacrylate)	1.568	1.563	1.560	1.539
poly(methyl chloroacrylate)	1.517	1.519	1.521	1.500
poly(ethyl chloroacrylate)	1.502	1.516	1.518	1.490
poly(sec.-butyl chloroacrylate)	1.500	1.503	1.502	1.495
poly(cyclohexyl chloroacrylate)	1.532	1.529	1.528	1.508
polyacrylonitrile	1.514	1.528	1.529	1.523
poly(1,3-butadiene)	1.516	1.511	1.513	1.514
polyisoprene	1.520	1.514	1.514	1.504
poly(2-tert.-butyl-1,3-butadiene)	1.506	1.517	1.513	1.489
poly(2-decyl-1,3-butadiene)	1.490	1.487	1.489	1.483
polychloroprene	1.558	1.560	1.560	1.531

(Continued on p. 220)

TABLE 10.2 (continued)

Polymer	n exper.	n calculated from (10.5)		
		from R_{LL}	from R_{GD}	from R_V
poly(methylene oxide)	(1.510)	1.416	1.426	1.453
poly(propylene oxide)	1.457	1.451	1.455	1.463
poly(hexamethylene adipamide)	1.530	1.497	1.521	1.528
poly(ethylene terephthalate)	1.640	1.580	1.581	1.558
poly[1,1-ethane bis(4-phenyl)carbonate]	1.594	1.600	1.602	1.594
poly[2,2-propane bis(4-phenyl)carbonate]	1.585	1.579	1.583	1.590
poly[1,1-butane bis(4-phenyl)carbonate]	1.579	1.585	1.587	1.582
poly[2,2-butane bis(4-phenyl)carbonate]	1.583	1.573	1.577	1.584
poly[1,1-(2-methylpropane)bis(4-phenyl)-carbonate]	1.570	1.580	1.583	1.582
poly[diphenylmethane bis(4-phenyl)carbonate]	1.654	1.637	1.630	1.628
poly[1,1-cyclopentane bis(4-phenyl)carbonate]	1.599	1.589	1.596	1.599
poly[1,1-cyclohexane bis(4-phenyl) carbonate]	1.590	1.583	1.590	1.595

It is clear that the ratios R_{LL}/V, R_{GD}/V and R_V/M are characteristics of the refractive power of the polymer. This is also true of the structural groups. It is obvious that aromatic groups have a high refractive power, while methyl groups and fluorine atoms have a very low refractive power.

Example 10.1

Estimate the refractive index of poly(methyl methacrylate).

Solution

The structure unit is

$$
\left[\begin{array}{c} CH_3 \\ | \\ -CH_2-C- \\ | \\ C=O \\ | \\ OCH_3 \end{array} \right] \quad (M = 100.1)
$$

Using the group contributions of table 10.1 we obtain

$$R_{LL} = 1(-CH_2-) + 2(-CH_3) + 1(-COO-) + 1(\ \overset{|}{\underset{|}{C}}\ ) =$$
$$= 4.649 + 11.288 + 6.237 + 2.580 = 24.754$$

$$V \doteq 86.5 \ cm^3/mol$$

So n_D will be

$$\left(\frac{1 + \dfrac{2 \times 24.754}{86.5}}{1 - \dfrac{24.754}{86.5}} \right)^{1/2} = 1.484$$

which is in fair agreement with the experimental value ($n_D = 1.490$).

Birefringence

If a substance is anisotropic, which means that it has different properties in different directions, it will be doubly refracting or birefringent (when transparent).

Birefringence is evidenced by the ability of a material to rotate the plane of polarized light. It is defined as the difference in refractive indices in the directions parallel and perpendicular to the direction of orientation:

$$\Delta n = n_{/\!/} - n_\perp$$

Orientation in polymers is normally effected by stretching. One therefore observes the phenomenon of birefringence in polymer melts under forced flow (shear stress) or under tension, and in solid polymers after stretch orientation; the oriented polymer is cooled to below its glass transition temperature before the molecules have had a chance to relax to their random coiled configuration.

Birefringence is (as a matter of course) not restricted to visible light.

Some of the infrared absorption bands of oriented polymers show *infrared dichroism*; they absorb different amounts of polarized infrared radiation in different directions (parallel or perpendicular to the direction of orientation). Dyed oriented polymers often show dichroism to visible light due to orientation of the dye molecules (together with the polymer molecules).

For *rubber-elastic materials* (i.e. polymers above their T_g) theory predicts that the retractive stress is directly proportional to the degree of orientation, which in turn is directly proportional to the birefringence. Thus, for uniaxial tension, the birefringence and the retractive stress are related by the simple equation:

$$n_{/\!/} - n_\perp = C\sigma \tag{10.6}$$

C is called the *stress optical coefficient*. The value of C depends on the chemical structure of the polymer and is somewhat temperature-dependent. The theory of rubber elasticity leads to the following expression:

$$C = \frac{2\pi(\alpha_{/\!/} - \alpha_\perp)}{45} \frac{(\bar{n}^2 + 2)^2}{\bar{n}kT} \tag{10.7}$$

where $\alpha_{/\!/} - \alpha_\perp$ is the difference in polarizability of a polymer segment parallel and perpendicular to the direction of the chain. $\bar{n}$ is the average refractive index ($\bar{n}$ equals n of the unoriented polymer). C is normally expressed in 10^{-12} m^2/N which are called brewsters. According to theory, C is independent of the degree of cross-linking. During stress relaxation the birefringence decreases with the stress, so that their ratio remains constant. The same is true during creep.

Rigid amorphous polymers also become birefringent when a stress is applied to them. A much greater stress is required, however, to produce a given value of birefringence in a rigid polymer than in a rubber: the stress optical coefficient is much lower. It usually changes rapidly with temperature in the neighbourhood of the glass–rubber transition. For some polymers it even changes sign at T_g!

Table 10.3 gives C-values for a number of polymers below and above the glass temperature.

TABLE 10.3

Stress-optical coefficients of polymers

Polymer	Temperature (°C)	$C(T < T_g)$ (brewsters)	$C(T > T_g)$ (brewsters)
polyethylene	130/190		1800/2400
polypropylene	210		900
polystyrene	−195	17	
	24	10	
	110/214		4100/5200
poly(α-methylstyrene)	27	2.0	
poly(vinyltoluene)	27	15.5	
poly(p-tert.-butyl styrene)	27	11.0	
poly(p-chlorostyrene)	27	23.7	
poly(2,5-dichlorostyrene)	27	7.2	
poly(vinyl chloride)	180/210		420/530
poly(methyl methacrylate)	18/27	3.8/4.5	
	93		45?
poly(phenyl methacrylate)	27	39.8	
poly(benzyl methacrylate)	27	45	
poly(cyclohexyl methacrylate)	27	5.9	
poly(chloroethyl methacrylate)	27	5.6	
poly(o-nitrophenyl methacrylate)	27	22	
natural rubber	20		1900
gutta-percha	85		3000
poly(dimethyl siloxane)	22/25		135/175
	105/190		190/265

Data from Lamble and Dahmouch (1958), Rudd and Andrews (1958, 1960), Saunders (1956) and Wales (1976).

Crystalline polymers, and especially oriented crystalline polymers (see Chapter 14), show birefringence which is made up of two contributions:
a) *intrinsic birefringence* (contribution of the crystallites themselves)
b) *form birefringence,* resulting from the shape of the crystallites or the presence of voids.
    In crystalline polymers the relations between stress, orientation and birefringence are much more complicated than in amorphous materials.

Polymer solutions show birefringence if orientation is brought about by outside forces; this may occur under the influence of flow (flow birefringence), rotation, electric fields (Kerr effect) or magnetic fields (Cotton–Mouton effect). Janeschitz-Kriegl and Wales (1967) derived dimensionless groups for the correlation of flow birefringence data.

C. LIGHT SCATTERING

Scattering of light is caused by optical inhomogeneities. Molecules act as secondary sources of light, as has been shown by Rayleigh (1871). By integrating the intensity of scattered light per unit volume (i_ϑ) over all angles ϑ, one obtains the turbidity (τ)

$$\tau = \int_0^\pi 2\pi i_\vartheta \sin \vartheta d\vartheta. \tag{10.8}$$

In the absence of absorption, τ is related to the primary intensities of a beam before and after it has passed through a thickness l of the medium, by the equation

$$I = I_0 \exp[-\tau l]. \tag{10.9}$$

In solutions, part of the light scattering arises from fluctuations in refractive index caused by fluctuations in composition. The well-known equation for light scattering from solutions is based on these considerations

$$R_\vartheta = K \frac{RTc}{\left(\dfrac{d\Pi}{dc}\right)} \tag{10.10}$$

where c = polymer concentration

$$R_\vartheta = \frac{r^2 i_\vartheta}{I_0(1 + \cos^2\vartheta)} \quad \text{is called } Rayleigh\text{'}s \ ratio$$

r = distance of scattering molecule

$$K = \frac{2\pi^2}{\lambda_0 N_A} \left[\bar{n} \frac{dn}{dc}\right]^2 \tag{10.11}$$

N_A = Avogadro number
λ_0 = wavelength of the light in vacuo
Π = osmotic pressure
Since

$$\frac{1}{RT}\left(\frac{d\Pi}{dc}\right) = \frac{1}{M} + 2A_2 c$$

(where A_2 is the second virial coefficient), substitution gives

$$\frac{Kc}{R_\vartheta} = \frac{1}{M} + 2A_2 c. \tag{10.12}$$

This equation forms the basis of the determination of polymer molecular weights by light scattering, which is one of the few absolute methods.

The eq. (10.12), however, is correct only for optically isotropic particles, which are small compared to the wavelength. If the particle size exceeds $\lambda/20$ (as in polymer solutions), scattered light waves, coming from different parts of the same particle, will interfere with one another, which will cause a reduction of the intensity of the scattered light to a fraction $P(\vartheta)$ given by

$$P(\vartheta) = 1 - \frac{1}{3} h^2 R_G^2 + \dots \tag{10.13}$$

where R_G is the radius of gyration of the particle (polymer molecule) and $h = 4\pi(\bar{n}/\lambda_0) \sin \vartheta/2$. The formula for the excess light scattered by a polymer solution as compared with pure solvent therefore becomes

$$\frac{Kc}{R_\vartheta} = \frac{1}{\bar{M}_W P(\vartheta)} + 2A_2 c + \ldots \tag{10.14}$$

As $P(\vartheta) \to 1$ for $\vartheta \to 0$, Zimm (1960) suggested a plot of Kc/R_ϑ against $\sin^2 (\vartheta/2) + kc$ (where k is an arbitrary constant of the order of 100). Thus one obtains a grid which allows extrapolation to $c = 0$ and $\vartheta = 0$ (see fig. 10.2). The intercept on the ordinate then gives $1/\bar{M}_W$, and the two slopes provide values to calculate A_2 and R_G^2. By this method polymer molecular weights of the order of $10^4 - 10^7$ can be measured. In order to find the quantity K, the refractive index of the solution $\bar{n}$, and the so-called *specific refractive index increment* (dn/dc), require experimental determination. Because the solutions to be measured are very dilute, the value of $\bar{n}$ may be replaced by n_S, the refractive index of the solvent.

Also for these dilute solutions, the refractive index increment is a constant for a given polymer, solvent and temperature, and is normally measured with an interferometer or with a differential refractometer.

As was shown by Goedhart (1969), it is also possible to calculate (dn/dc) values from group contributions. The best results were obtained with the following simple equation

$$\frac{dn}{dc} = \frac{n_P - n_S}{\rho_P} = \frac{V}{M}\left(\frac{R_V}{M} - n_S\right) \tag{10.15}$$

where the subscripts S and P identify solvent and polymer, respectively. Since n and ρ of polymers can be calculated by means of additive molar quantities, the specific refractive index increment can be calculated, so that measurement of R_ϑ only is sufficient for the determination of $\bar{M}_W$, R_G^2 and A_2.

Table 10.4 shows that experimental and calculated values of (dn/dc) are in fair agreement.

It should be mentioned that light scattering is not restricted to solutions. In fact, the technique can be used to obtain information about the supermolecular structure of solid polymers.

Example 10.2

Estimate the specific refractive index increment (dn/dc) of polystyrene in 1,4-dioxane ($n_D = 1.422$).

Solution

The structural unit of polystyrene is

$$\left[-CH_2-CH- \right] \quad M = 104.1$$

Using the group contributions in tables 4.6 and 10.1 we find

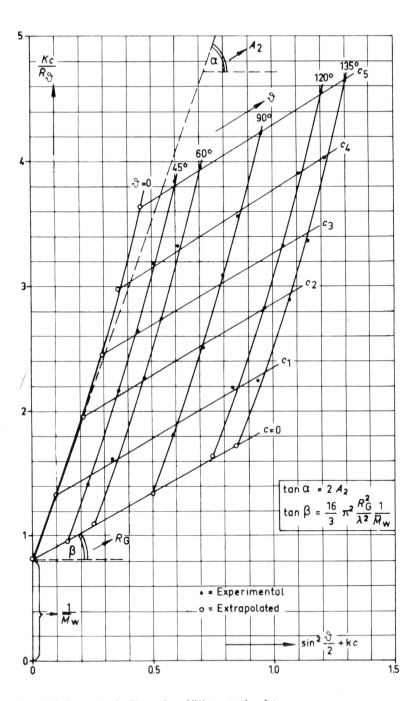

Fig. 10.2. Example of a Zimm plot of light scattering data.

TABLE 10.4

Comparison of calculated and experimental dn/dc values of polymer solutions

Polymer	Solvent	Experimental			Calc. dn/dc with	
		dn/dc	T (°C)	λ (nm)	n_{GD}	n_V
polystyrene	benzene	0.106	25	546	0.093	0.084
	benzene	0.110	25	546	0.093	0.084
	bromobenzene	0.042	25	546	0.038	0.028
	bromonaphthalene	−0.051	25	546	−0.056	−0.025
	carbon tetrachloride	0.146	25	546	0.129	0.120
	chlorobenzene	0.099	−	436	0.071	0.061
	chloroform	0.195	20	436	0.145	0.136
	cyclohexane	0.167	20	546	0.161	0.151
	p-chlorotoluene	0.093	25	436	0.075	0.066
	decalin	0.128	20	546	0.122	0.113
	dichloroethane	0.161	20	546	0.147	0.137
	dioxane	0.168	25	546	0.167	0.158
	tetrahydrofuran	0.189	25	546	0.184	0.175
	toluene	0.104	20	546	0.097	0.088
poly(vinyl chloride)	acetone	0.138	20	546	0.133	0.110
	cyclohexanone	0.078	25	−	0.066	0.043
	dioxane	0.086	−	546	0.087	0.064
	tetrahydrofuran	0.102	−	−	0.100	0.077
poly(vinyl acetate)	acetone	0.095	20	546	0.097	0.094
	acetone	0.104	30	436	0.097	0.094
	acetonitrile	0.104	−	−	0.108	0.105
	benzene	−0.026	25	560	−0.022	−0.025
	chlorobenzene	−0.040	25	560	−0.042	−0.045
	dioxane	0.030	25	560	0.044	0.040
	ethyl formate	0.095	−	−	0.096	0.093
	methanol	0.131	25	546	0.121	0.117
	2-butanone	0.080	25	546	0.079	0.075
	tetrahydrofuran	0.055	25	546	0.060	0.056
	toluene	−0.020	25	560	−0.018	−0.022
poly(methyl methacrylate)	acetonitrile	0.137	25	546	0.120	0.112
	bromobenzene	−0.058	25	546	−0.065	−0.073
	1-bromonaphthalene	−0.147	25	546	−0.151	−0.159
	butyl acetate	0.097	−	546	0.078	0.069
	butyl chloride	0.090	20	546	0.072	0.063
	chlorobenzene	−0.026	25	546	−0.035	−0.043
	isoamyl acetate	0.091	20	546	0.072	0.063
	nitroethane	0.094	25	546	0.082	0.074
	1,1,2-trichloroethane	0.025	−	560	0.012	0.003
	acetone	0.129	25	546	0.109	0.100
	acetone	0.134	25	546	0.109	0.100
	benzene	−0.010	25	546	−0.014	−0.022
	2-butanone	0.109	−	546	0.090	0.081
	2-butanone	0.114	25	546	0.090	0.081
	carbon tetrachloride	0.023	25	546	0.019	0.010

TABLE 10.4 (continued)

Polymer	Solvent	Experimental			Calc. dn/dc with	
		dn/dc	T (°C)	λ (nm)	n_{GD}	n_V
poly(methyl methacrylate)	chloroform	0.055	–	546	0.034	0.025
(continued)	chloroform	0.063	–	546	0.034	0.025
	dioxane	0.071	–	546	0.055	0.046
	ethyl acetate	0.118	–	546	0.098	0.089
	tetrahydrofuran	0.087	–	546	0.070	0.061
poly(propylene oxide)	benzene	−0.045	25	546	−0.046	−0.042
	chlorobenzene	−0.064	25	546	−0.069	−0.065
	hexane	0.078	25	546	0.079	0.083
	2-methylheptane	0.066	35	546	0.061	0.065
	methanol	0.118	25	546	0.123	0.127
poly(hexamethylene adipamide)	m-cresol	−0.016	25	546	−0.017	−0.011
	dichloroacetic acid	0.098	25	546	0.051	0.057
	95% sulphuric acid	0.082	25	546	0.076	0.083

	R_{Vi}	V_i
$1(-CH_2-)$	20.64	15.85
$1(>CH-)$	21.4	9.45

$$1\left(-\bigcirc\right) \quad \frac{123.51}{165.55} \quad \frac{72.7}{98.0}$$

Using eq. (10.15) we get:

$$\frac{dn}{dc} = \frac{V}{M}\left(\frac{R_V}{M} - n_S\right) = \frac{98.0}{104.1}\left(\frac{165.55}{104.1} - 1.422\right) = 0.941(1.590 - 1.422) = 0.158$$

which is in fair agreement with the experimental value of 0.168.

D. REFLECTION

The reflectance of a boundary plane between two non-absorbing media is a function of the refractive indices of the media examined.

If the light strikes the boundary plane perpendicular to this plane, the reflectance r is given by Fresnel's relationship (see Pohl, 1943):

$$r = \frac{(n_2 - n_1)^2}{(n_2 + n_1)^2} \tag{10.16}$$

where n_1 and n_2 denote the refractive indices of the two media.

If the light is absorbed only in the second medium, this relationship changes into Beer's equation (see Pohl, 1943):

$$r = \frac{(n_2 - n_1)^2 + n_2^2 K_2^2}{(n_2 + n_1)^2 + n_2^2 K_2^2} \tag{10.17}$$

where K denotes the absorption index, which is defined by Lambert's relationship for the intensity loss $I_0 - I$ of a light beam propagating over a length of path l

$$I = I_0 \exp\left(-\frac{4\pi n K l}{\lambda_0}\right) \tag{10.18}$$

where λ_0 is the wavelength of the light in vacuo.

At obliquely incident light the reflectance is also dependent on the direction of polarization with respect to the plane of incidence. If the light is polarized parallel to the plane of incidence and the two media do not absorb, Fresnel's relationship applies

$$r = \frac{\tan^2(\vartheta_i - \vartheta_r)}{\tan^2(\vartheta_i + \vartheta_r)} \tag{10.19}$$

where

ϑ_i = angle of incidence
ϑ_r = angle of refraction.

From this formula an important conclusion may be derived, namely that there must exist an angle $\vartheta = \vartheta_B$ at which $\vartheta_i + \vartheta_r = \frac{1}{2}\pi$. Then according to eq. (10.19) $r = 0$, which means that light striking at an angle ϑ_B (polarizing angle or *Brewster angle*) is not reflected. Under these conditions Brewster's relationship holds

$$\tan \vartheta_B = n_2 \tag{10.20}$$

The refractive index of a non-absorbing medium may thus be determined.

With strongly absorbing media (10.19), and hence (10.20), are no longer applicable because the refracted light wave will then be inhomogeneous, which renders the relationship between the reflectance and the angles of incidence and refraction very complicated. Moreover, in the case of strong absorption the indices of refraction and absorption become dependent on the angle of incidence.

BIBLIOGRAPHY, CHAPTER 10

General references
Bellamy, L.J., "Advances in Infrared Group Frequencies", Methuen, London, 1968.
Conley, R.T., "Infrared Spectroscopy", Allyn and Bacon, Boston, 1966.
Dodd, R.E., "Chemical Spectroscopy", Elsevier, Amsterdam, 1962.
Flett, M.St.C., "Characteristic Frequencies of Chemical Groups in the Infrared", Elsevier, Amsterdam, 1963.
Freeman, S.K. (Ed.), "Interpretive Spectroscopy", Reinhold, New York, Chapman, London, 1965.

Hummel, D.O., "Infrared Spectra of Polymers: in the Medium and Long Wavelength Regions", Interscience, New York, 1966. (Polymer Reviews; ed. by Mark, H.F. and Immergut, E.H., Vol. 14).
Oster, G., Chem. Revs. 43 (1948) 319.
Pohl, R.W., "Einführung in die Optik", Berlin, 1943, p. 147.
Stacey, K.A., "Light Scattering in Physical Chemistry", Butterworth, London, 1956.
Stuart, H.A., "Die Physik der Hochpolymeren", Bd.I., Springer, Berlin, 1952.
Szymanski, H.A., "Infrared Band Handbook", Plenum Press, New York, 1964.
Weissberger, A. (Ed.), "Technique of Organic Chemistry", Interscience, New York, 1961.
Wilkes, G.L., J. Macromol. Sci. Rev. Macromol. Chem. 10 (1974) 149.
Zbinden, R., "Infrared Spectroscopy of High Polymers", Academic Press, New York, 1964.

Special references

Debye, P., J. Appl. Phys. 15 (1944) 338; J. Phys. & Coll. Chem. 51 (1947) 18.
Eisenlohr, F., Z. physik. Chem. 75 (1911) 585; 79 (1912) 129.
Gladstone, J.H. and Dale, T.P., Trans. Roy. Soc. (London) A 148 (1858) 887.
Goedhart, D.J., Communication Gel Permeation Chromatography International Seminar, Monaco, Oct. 12–15, 1969.
Heller, W., Phys. Rev. 68 (1945) 5; J. Phys. Chem. 69 (1965) 1123; J. Polymer Sci. A2-4 (1966) 209.
Huggins, M.L., Bull. Chem. Soc. Japan 29 (1956) 336.
Janeschitz-Kriegl, H., Makromol. Chem. 33 (1959) 55; 40 (1960) 140.
Janeschitz-Kriegl, H. and Wales, J.L.S., Nature (1967) 1116.
Lamble, J.H. and Dahmouch, E.S., Brit. J. Appl. Phys. 9 (1958) 388.
Lorentz, H.A., Wied. Ann. Phys. 9 (1880) 641.
Lorenz, L.V., Wied. Ann. Phys. 11 (1880) 70.
Rayleigh, J.W. Strutt, Lord, Phil. Mag. (4) 41 (1871) 107, 224, 447.
Rudd, J.F. and Andrews, R.D., J. Appl. Phys. 29 (1958) 1421 and 31 (1960) 818.
Saunders, D.W., Trans. Faraday Soc. 52 (1956) 1414.
Schoorl, N., "Organische Analyse" I Bd. 14, Centen, Amsterdam, 1920.
Vogel, A., J. Chem. Soc. (1948) 1833.
Vogel, A., Chem. & Ind. (1951) 376; (1952) 514.
Vogel, A., Cresswell, W. and Leicester, I., Chem. & Ind. (1950) 358; (1953) 19.
Vogel, A., Cresswell, W. and Leicester, I., J. Phys. Chem. 58 (1954) 174.
Wales, J.L.S., "The application of flow birefringence to rheological studies of polymer melts", Thesis Delft University of Technology, Delft University Press, 1976.
Wibaut, J.P., Hoog, H., Langendijk, S.L., Overhoff, J. and Smittenberg, J., Rec. Trav. Chim. 58 (1939) 329.
Young, J. and Finn, A., J. Research Natl. Bur. Standards 24 (1940) 759.
Zimm, B.H., "The Normal-Coordinate Method for Polymer Chains in Dilute Solution", Ch. 1 in F.R. Eirich (Ed.), "Rheology", Vol. 3, Academic Press, New York, 1960.

CHAPTER 11

ELECTRICAL PROPERTIES

Two groups of electrical properties of polymers are of interest. The first group of properties is usually assessed from the behaviour of the polymer at low electric field strengths. To this group belong the *dielectric constant*, the *dissipation factor*, the *static electrification*, and the *electrical conductivity*.

The second group consists of properties which are important at very high electric field strengths, such as *electric discharge, dielectric breakdown* and *arc resistance*. They may be regarded as the ultimate electrical properties.

Properties of the first group are directly related to the chemical structure of the polymer; those of the second are greatly complicated by additional influences in the methods of determination.

Only the dielectric constant can be estimated by means of additive quantities.

Introduction

The application of an electric field to a material can produce two effects. It may cause the charges within the material to flow; on removal of the field the flow ceases but does not reverse. In this case the material is called an electric *conductor*.

Alternatively the field may produce finite changes in the relative positions of the electric charges, which change is of the nature of an electric displacement and is completely reversed when the electric field is removed. In this case the material is called a *dielectric*.

The common polymers are all dielectrics.

A. DIELECTRIC POLARIZATION

Dielectric constant (permittivity, electric inductive capacity)

The dielectric constant of insulating materials (ϵ) is the ratio of the capacities of a parallel plate condenser measured with and without the dielectric material placed between the plates. The difference is due to the polarization of the dielectric. It is a dimensionless quantity.

The dielectric constant ϵ of a non-polar insulator may be expressed in terms of the refractive index n by *Maxwell's relationship*:

$$\epsilon = n^2. \tag{11.1}$$

For comparison these two quantities should be measured at the same frequency. However, ϵ is generally measured at relatively low frequencies ($10^2 - 10^6$ cycles per second), whereas n is measured in the range of visible light (5 to 7 times 10^{14} cycles per second, usually at the sodium D line). Simple comparison, however, of ϵ and n_D already gives interesting information. A large disparity of ϵ and n_D^2 may be an indication of semi-conduction; more frequently the disparity is caused by the occurrence of permanent dipoles in the dielectric.

Molar polarization

The molar polarization of a dielectric can be defined as follows:

$$P_{LL} = \frac{\epsilon - 1}{\epsilon + 2} V \quad \text{(compare } R_{LL}) \tag{11.2}$$

or:

$$P_V = \epsilon^{1/2} M \quad \text{(compare } R_V) \tag{11.3}$$

TABLE 11.1

Group contributions to molar dielectric polarization (P) in polymers (cm³/mol)

Group	For $P_{LL} = \dfrac{\epsilon - 1}{\epsilon + 2} V$	For $P_V = \epsilon^{1/2} M$
$-CH_3$	5.64	17.66
$-CH_2-$	4.65	20.64
$\diagdown CH-$	3.62	23.5
$\diagup\diagdown C \diagup\diagdown$	2.58	26.4
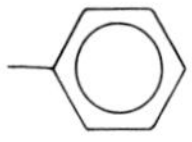 —⬡	25.5	123.5
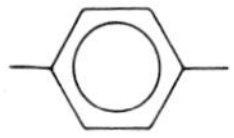 —⬡—	25.0	128.6
$-O-$	5.2	(30)
$\diagdown C{=}O$	(10)	(65)
$-COO-$	15	95
$-CONH-$	30	125
$-O-COO-$	22	125
$-F$	(1.8)	(20)
$-Cl$	(9.5)	(60)
$-C{\equiv}N$	11	(50)
$-CF_2-$	6.25	70
$-CCl_2-$	17.7	145
$-CHCl-$	13.7	90
$-S-$	8	(60)
$-OH$ (alcohol)	(6)	(30)
$-OH$ (phenol)	~20	~100

TABLE 11.2

Dielectrical constants of polymers

Polymer	ϵ exp. [1]	n_D^2	ϵ calc. from (11.2)	ϵ calc. from (11.3)
polyethylene (extrap. to amorphous)	2.3	(2.19)	2.20	2.20
polypropylene (amorph. part)	2.2	(2.19)	2.15	2.15
polystyrene	2.55	2.53	2.55	2.60
poly(o-chlorostyrene)	2.6	2.60	2.82	2.82
poly(tetrafluoroethylene) (am.)	2.1	≈1.85	2.00	1.96
poly(vinyl chloride)	2.8/3.05	2.37	3.05	3.15
poly(vinyl acetate)	3.25	2.15	3.02	3.30
poly(methyl methacrylate)	2.6/3.7	2.22	2.94	3.15
poly(ethyl methacrylate)	2.7/3.4	2.20	2.80	3.00
poly(methyl α-chloroacrylate)	3.4	2.30	3.45	3.32
poly(ethyl α-chloroacrylate)	3.1	2.26	3.20	3.16
polyacrylonitrile	3.1	2.29	3.26	3.15
poly(methylene oxide)	3.1	2.29	2.95	2.85
poly(2,6-dimethylphenylene oxide)	2.6	–	2.65	2.75
Penton® (poly[2,2-bis(chloromethyl)-trimethylene-3-oxide])	3.0	–	2.95	2.80
poly(ethylene terephthalate) (am.)	2.9/3.2	2.70	3.40	3.50
poly(bisphenol carbonate)	2.6/3.0	2.50	3.00	3.05
poly(hexamethylene adipamide)	4.0	2.35	4.14	4.10

[1] Sources of data: Morton and Hearle (1962); Saechtling (1971); Brandrup and Immergut (1975); Hütte (1967).

The group contributions to the molar polarization (for polymers) are given in table 11.1. Application of equations (11.2) and (11.3) permits the calculation of the dielectric constant ϵ if the structural unit is known. Table 11.2 shows the calculated values of ϵ in comparison with the observed values and with n^2. The agreement with the experimental values is satisfactory.

Dipole moment

In the simplest cases, i.e. when the dielectric is a pure compound and the dipole moment (μ) is small ($\mu < 0.6$ debye units), it is possible to use *Debye's equation*:

$$P_{LL} - R_{LL} = \left[\frac{\epsilon - 1}{\epsilon + 2} - \frac{n^2 - 1}{n^2 + 2}\right]\frac{M}{\rho} = \frac{4}{9}\pi N_A \frac{\mu^2}{kT} \approx 20.6\,\mu^2 \quad \text{(at 298 K).} \tag{11.4}$$

The equation shows that if permanent dipoles are present, $\epsilon > n^2$. (Water, for example, possesses the very high dielectric constant of 81, while its value for n^2 is only 1.77.) For all polymers with polar groups $\epsilon > n^2$.

Application of eq. (11.4) to these polymers (as a first orientation) yields values for the mean dipole moment of the structural units varying from 0 debye units for hydrocarbon polymers to about 1

TABLE 11.3

Dipole moments of structural groups in polymers

Group	Effective μ in polymers	μ in low-molecular liquids
$-Cl$	0.45	2.0
$-CCl_2-$	0.40	–
$-CF_2-$	0.25	–
$-C\equiv N$	0.50	3.5
$\overset{\diagdown}{\underset{O}{\diagup}}$	0.45	1.1
$-C\overset{\displaystyle \overset{O}{\parallel}}{\underset{\overset{\diagup}{O}}{\diagdown}}$	0.70	1.7
$-C\overset{\displaystyle \overset{O}{\parallel}}{\underset{\overset{\diagdown}{NH}}{\diagdown}}$	1.00	–

Conversion factor to S.I.: 1 debye unit = 3.34×10^{-30} C · m.

debye unit for polyamides. The measured values are low compared with the dipole moments of the polar groups in liquids.

Table 11.3 gives the effective average dipole moments in polymers in comparison with those measured in liquids.

Example 11.1

Estimate the dielectric constant and the average dipole moment of poly(bisphenol carbonate).

Solution

The structural unit of polycarbonate is

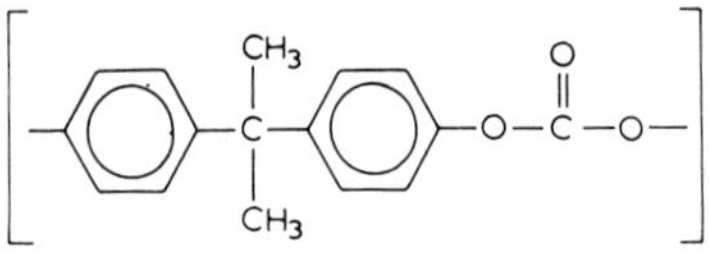

The molar weight is 254 and the molar volume $V(298) = 215$. By means of the group contributions in table 11.1 we get:

Groups	P_{iLL}	P_{iV}
2 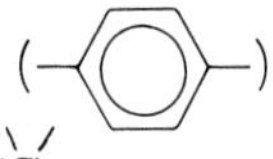 $(-\bigcirc-)$	50.0	257.2
1$(\overset{\diagdown}{\underset{\diagup}{C}})$	2.6	26.4
2$(-CH_3)$	11.3	35.3
1$(-O-COO-)$	22	125
	85.9	443.9

from which we calculate $\epsilon = 3.00$ and $\epsilon = 3.05$ respectively, in good agreement with the experimental value ($\epsilon = 2.6/3.0$).

The average dipole moment is estimated by means of the Lorentz–Lorenz molar refraction (table 10.1)

Groups	R_{iLL}
2 (—⬡—)	50.06
1(C)	2.29
2(—CH$_3$)	11.29
1(—O—COO—)	7.74
	71.38

Substitution in eq. (11.4) gives:

$$20.6\mu^2 = P_{LL} - R_{LL} = 85.9 - 71.4 = 14.5$$

or

$$\mu = \left(\frac{14.5}{20.6}\right)^{1/2} = 0.84$$

Correlation between dielectric constant and solubility parameter

As electrical forces due to polarizability and polar moment determine the cohesive energy, a certain correlation between dielectric constant and solubility parameter may be expected. Darby et al. (1967) suggested such a correlation for organic compounds.

It appeared that a surprisingly simple correlation holds for polymers, viz.:

$$\delta \approx 7.0\epsilon \tag{11.5}$$

Calculated and experimental values of ϵ are compared in table 11.4.

Dielectric loss factor

If the electric field is time-dependent (as in alternating current), the dielectric polarization is time-dependent too. Because of the resistance to motion of the atom groups in the dielectric, there is a delay between changes in the electric field and changes in the polarization. The dielectric behaviour of a polymer in an oscillating electrical field is completely similar to the dynamic-mechanical behaviour under alternating stresses (see Chapter 13). In both cases the delay is expressed as a loss angle δ (see fig. 11.1).

The so-called *loss tangent*, $\tan \delta$, is a very useful dimensionless parameter and is a measure of the ratio of the electric energy lost to energy stored in a periodic field. The product $\epsilon \tan \delta$ is directly proportional to the dielectric loss of energy, e.g. in a high-voltage cable.

As described in Chapter 2E, ϵ may be expressed as a complex quantity:

$$\epsilon^* = \epsilon' - i\epsilon'' \tag{11.6}$$

where ϵ' is the real part (*dielectric constant*) and ϵ'' the imaginary part (*dielectric absorption constant*).

ϵ and $\tan \delta$ are usually measured over a wide frequency range (50 cycles per second to some megacycles per second) (fig. 11.1).

TABLE 11.4

Dielectric constant and solubility parameter

Polymer	δ calc. [1]	ϵ calc.	ϵ exp.
polyethylene	16.0	2.3	2.3
polypropylene	17.0	2.4	2.2
polystyrene	19.1	2.7	2.55
poly(o-chlorostyrene)	18.2 [2]	2.6	2.6
poly(vinyl chloride)	19.7	2.8	2.8/3.05
poly(vinylidene chloride)	20.6	2.9	2.85
poly(tetrafluoroethylene)	11.7	1.7	2.1
poly(chlorotrifluoroethylene)	15.7	2.2	2.3/2.8
poly(vinyl acetate)	19.6	2.8	3.25
poly(methyl methacrylate)	19.0	2.7	2.6/3.7
poly(ethyl methacrylate)	18.6	2.7	2.7/3.4
polyacrylonitrile	25.7	3.7	3.1
poly(methylene oxide)	20.5	2.9	3.1
poly(ethylene terephthalate)	20.5	2.9	2.9/3.2
polycarbonate	20.3 [2]	2.9	2.6/3.0
nylon 6,6	28.0	4.0	4.0

[1] Calculated from the correlation as presented in Chapter 7.
[2] Experimental value.

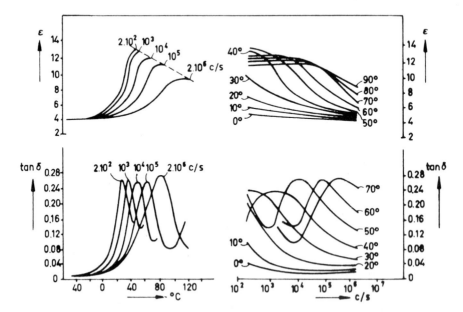

Fig. 11.1. Dispersion curves ϵ and tan δ for poly(vinyl acetate) (after Würstlin, 1951).

Relation between dielectric constant and optical quantities

The complex electric inductive capacity is closely connected with the optical properties, viz. the refractive index (n) and the absorption index (K). The relationships are:

$$\epsilon^* = (n^*)^2 \tag{11.7}$$

$$\epsilon^* = \epsilon' - i\epsilon''; \quad n^* = n(1 - iK) \tag{11.8}$$

$$\epsilon' = n^2(1 - K^2) \tag{11.9}$$

$$\epsilon'' = 2n^2K \tag{11.10}$$

$$\frac{\epsilon''}{\epsilon'} = \tan \delta = \frac{2K}{1 - K^2} \ . \tag{11.11}$$

Relation between dielectric polarizability and dynamic-mechanical properties

Since polarization of a polymer in an electric field occurs by chain-sub-units tending to align their dipolar and highly polarizable bonds with the field direction, some correlation is to be expected between the dynamic-mechanical behaviour (Chapter 13) and the electrical properties in an alternating field.

At one time it was hoped that the more tedious mechanical studies could be entirely replaced by easier electrical measurements. There are indeed close similarities between the general shapes and temperature-dependences of the mechanical and dielectric loss curves, but the quantitative connection between these phenomena is not as simple as was originally believed. Electrical measurements constitute a useful addition to, but not a substitute for, mechanical studies.

Relation between dielectric polarizability and optical dispersion

The main features (simplified) of dielectric polarizability as a function of frequency are shown in fig. 11.2. At low frequencies the total polarization manifests itself completely. However, the orientation of the polar groups is relatively slow and as the frequency increases the orientation lags behind. When the frequency reaches a value of about 10^{12}, the dipoles are unable to follow the oscillations of the field (P_{dip} disappears). Only random orientations are left and these do not contribute to the resultant polarization. Of the total polarization only the atomic (P_{at}) and the electronic polarization (P_{el}) remain.

At a somewhat higher frequency the stretching and bending of the bonds become too sluggish, so that no atomic polarization occurs, either.

The frequency at which this resonance effect occurs (in P_{at}) is of the order of 10^{13}, so dispersion occurs in the infrared region and an infrared absorption band can be observed. Only P_{el} remains above a frequency of 10^{14}.

Finally, at a frequency higher than 10^{15}, which is in the optical range, the distortion of the electronic clouds around the nuclei lags behind, with the consequence that absorption in the optical spectrum occurs.

From fig. 11.2 it can be seen that the polarization (and so the refractive index) increases as it approaches a resonance frequency and temporarily falls to a "too" low value just beyond it. This remarkable and sudden change in behaviour was once considered anomalous and was called anomalous dispersion. The electro-magnetic wave theory showed that the "anomalous" dispersion is just as "normal" dispersion and can be explained as a direct consequence of the equation of motion of nuclei and electrons.

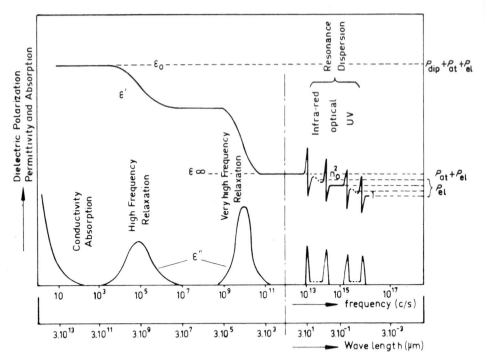

Fig. 11.2. Dispersion curves of the dielectric constant (ϵ') and dielectric absorption (ϵ'') in the regions of electrical, infrared and optical frequencies.

B. STATIC ELECTRIFICATION AND CONDUCTIVITY

Static electrification

When brought into intimate contact with a neutral surface, e.g. by rubbing, polymers become positively or negatively charged on separation. If two polymers are rubbed against each other and separated, one becomes positively charged (i.e. acts as an *electron donor*) whilst the other becomes negative (i.e. acts as an *electron acceptor*). The sequence of polymers according to their charging behaviour is called the *triboelectric series*.

Coehn (1898) derived the general rule that if two substances become charged by mutual contact, the substance with the highest dielectric constant will get the positive charge (i.e. will act as an electron donor). Fig. 11.3 shows that this holds in broad outline: the sequence in the triboelectric series is the same as that of the dielectric constant. Since ϵ for hydrophilic polymers is very moisture-dependent, due to the great influence of the high dielectric constant of water, it is clear that these polymers will be antistatic under humid conditions (wool), but static under very dry conditions. The highest charges observed (500 e.s.u./cm^3) are still caused by the transfer of relatively few charges; one electron for every 10^4 Å^2, which area covers many hundreds of atoms, would be sufficient.

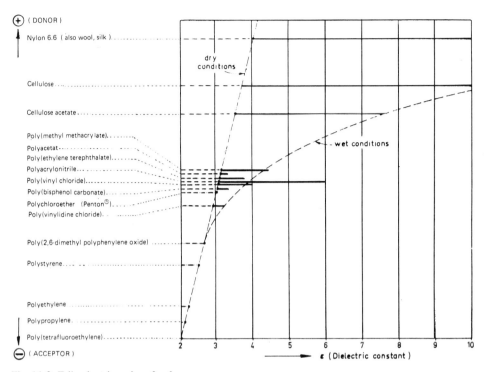

Fig. 11.3. Triboelectric series of polymers.

More important than the electrification itself is the *rate of charge decay*. It was found (Shashoua, 1963) that for a given structural group the fastest charge decay occurs when the group is present as a side chain substituent rather than in the main chain of the polymer. The charge-selective power of a polymer appeared to be related to its ability to bind ions on its surface. This makes it clear how small quantities of impurity can alter the charge-selective power of a given substance (degree of dissociation of ionic impurities).

Conductivity

The *electrical resistance* of most polymers is very high and conductivity probably results from the presence of ionic impurity, whose mobility is limited by the very high viscosity of the medium. The conductivity and also the activation energy of the conduction appear to be practically insensitive to crystallinity. Both surface and volume resistivity are important in the application of polymers as insulating materials.

The conductivity is greatly increased by moisture.

An obvious relationship exists between the volume resistivity of pure (and dry) polymers and the dielectric constant, as is shown in fig. 11.4.

The volume resistivity (in $\Omega \cdot$ cm) can be estimated by means of the expression:

$$\log R = 19 - 2(\epsilon - 2) \quad \text{(at 298 K)} \tag{11.12}$$

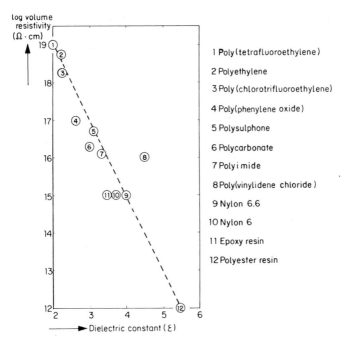

Fig. 11.4. Correlation between electric resistivity and dielectric constant of polymers.

Recently special polymers with semi-conductor properties have been developed. Their electric conductivity depends either on an ionic character (Dolinski and Dean, 1974) or on their backbone structure (systems of conjugated double bonds) (Härtel et al., 1973).

C. ULTIMATE ELECTRICAL PROPERTIES

Dielectric strength

When the voltage applied to an insulator is increased, a point will be reached where physical breakdown of the dielectric causes a catastrophic decrease in resistance. This voltage is called the dielectric strength. Curves of time-to-failure versus voltage can be plotted and usually show two distinct regions of failure. The short-time failure is due to the inability of the conducting electrons to dissipate rapidly enough the energy they receive from the field. The long-time failure is a breakdown mostly due to the so-called corona attack.

The dielectric strength is highly dependent on the form of the material; this effect is sometimes greater than the change in molecular structure.

The average value of the dielectric strength of pure polymers in $kV \cdot cm^{-1}$ is 200. Chlorinated polymers show values up to 500, polymers containing aromatic rings are on the low side (about 160).

There is a great similarity between electrical strength and mechanical strength. This is because electrical breakdown involves physical destruction. Within identical temperature regions both modulus and dielectric strength show a substantial reduction in magnitude.

Arc resistance

When exposed to an electrical discharge, the surface of some polymers may become carbonized and conduct current; the arc resistance, a measure of this behaviour, is an important property in the application as insulating material in engine ignition systems.

The arc resistance has the dimension s; its value varies for different polymers from about 400 (poly(chlorotrifluoroethylene)) to about 50 (poly(vinylidene fluoride)).

No direct correlation with chemical structure can be demonstrated.

BIBLIOGRAPHY, CHAPTER 11

General references

Dielectric polarization

Birks, J.B. and Schulman, J.H. (Eds.), "Progress in Dielectrics", Wiley, New York, 1959.
Böttcher, C.J.F., "Theory of Electric Polarization", Elsevier, Amsterdam, 1st ed. 1952, 2nd ed. 1973.
Brandrup, J. and Immergut, E.H. (Eds.), "Polymer Handbook", Interscience, New York, 1st ed. 1966, 2nd ed. 1975.
Fröhlich, H., "Theory of Dielectrics", Oxford Univ. Press, Oxford, 1949.
Hütte, "Taschenbuch der Werkstoffkunde" ("Stoff-Hütte"), W. Ernst & Sohn, Berlin, 4th ed., 1967.
McCrum, N.G., Read, B.E. and Williams, G., "Anelastic and Dielectric Effects in Polymeric Solids", Wiley, New York, 1967.
Saechtling, H., "Kunststoff Taschenbuch", Carl Hanser, München, 18th ed., 1971.
Würstlin, F. and Thurn, H., "Struktur und Elektrische Eigenschaften", in H.A. Stuart (Ed.), "Die Physik der Hochpolymeren", Vol. IV, Ch. 8, Springer, Berlin, 1956.

Static electrification and conductivity

Gayler, J., Wiggins, R.E. and Arthur, J.B., "Static Electricity; Generation, Measurement and its Effects on Textiles". N. Carolina State University, School of Textiles, Rayleigh, 1965.
Gutman, F. and Lyons, L.E., "Organic Semi Conductors", Wiley, New York, 1967.
Karasz, F.E. (Ed.), "Dielectric Properties of Polymers", Plenum Press, New York, 1972.
Koton, J.E. (Ed.), "Organic Semiconducting Polymers", Marcel Dekker, New York, 1968.
Loeb, L.B., "Static Electrification", Springer, Berlin/New York, 1958.
Morton, W.E. and Hearle, J.W.S., "Physical Properties of Textile Fibres", Chapter 21, The Textile Institute, Butterworths, London, 1962.
Seanor, D.A., Polymer Plast. Techn. Eng. 3 (1974) 69.

Special references

Coehn, A., Ann. Phys. 64 (1898) 217.
Cole, R.H. and Cole, K.S., J. Chem. Phys. 9 (1941) 341.
Darby, J.R., Touchette, N.W. and Sears, K., Polymer Eng. Sci. 7 (1967) 295.
Debye, P., Phys. Z. 13 (1912) 97.
Dolinski, R.J. and Dean, W.R., Polymer News 2, nos 3/4 (1974) 15.

Härtel, M., Kossmehl, G., Manecke, G., Wille, W., Wöhrle, D. and Zerpner, D., Angew. Makromol. Chem. 29/30 (1973) 307.

Mosotti, O.F., a Mem. Matem. e Fisica Moderna 24 (1850) 11.

Müller, F.H. and Schmelzer, Chr., Ergebn. exakt. Naturwiss. 25 (1951) 359.

Schmieder, K. and Wolf, K., Kolloid-Z. 127 (1952) 65.

Shashoua, J. Polymer Sci. A-1, 1 (1963) 169.

Seanor, D.A., Adv. Polymer Sci. 4 (1965) 317.

Würstlin, F., Kolloid-Z. 120 (1951) 102.

CHAPTER 12

MAGNETIC PROPERTIES

The principal magnetic properties of polymers are the *diamagnetic susceptibility* and the *magnetic resonance*. The former is a property of the material as a whole, the latter is connected with special configurations of electrons and nuclei within the material.

Only the diamagnetic susceptibility and the second moment of the nuclear magnetic resonance show additive molar properties.

A. MAGNETIC SUSCEPTIBILITY (MAGNETIC INDUCTIVE CAPACITY)

The magnetic susceptibility χ is defined as the ratio of the intensity of magnetization $\mathcal{I}$ to the magnetic field strength. Matter is diamagnetic, paramagnetic or ferromagnetic. Criteria of this classification are given in the following table:

Class	Susceptibility range in electromagnetic cgs units ($\equiv$cm^3/g)	Dependence on temperature	Dependence on field strength
diamagnetic	$\sim 10^{-6}$	nearly independent	nearly independent
paramagnetic	$10^{-6} - 10^{-3}$	inversely proportional to absolute temperature	nearly independent
ferromagnetic	$10 - 10^5$	highly dependent	dependent, reaches saturation value

Conversion factor: 1 cm^3/g (cgs) = $4\pi \times 10^{-3}$ m^3/kg (SI).

In organic polymers ferromagnetism occurs only when impurities are present. These may completely mask the true susceptibility of the substance to be investigated. In the following we shall only consider substances free from ferromagnetism, since polymers themselves are nonferromagnetic.

Diamagnetism is a universal property of matter. Paramagnetism occurs in only two classes of organic substances: those containing metals of the transition groups of the periodic system, and those containing unpaired electrons in the free radical or the triplet state.

Since

$$\chi_{total} = \chi_{dia} + \chi_{para} \tag{12.1}$$

243

TABLE 12.1

Magnetic susceptibility of the CH_2-group (in 10^{-6} cm^3/mol)

Year	Author	X(CH_2)	Extremes	Error (%)	Type of compounds	Number of compounds
1910	Pascal	11.86	11.5 – 12.5	1.5	11 series liquid and gaseous org. compounds	35
1927	Vaidyanathan	11.2				
1929	Bitter	14.5	13.2 – 16.9	7.3	hydrocarbons (gaseous)	5
1934	Cabrera and Fahlenbrach	11.48	11.08–12.13	2.3	alcohols, esters, acids	6
1934	Bhatnagar et al.	11.36	11.23–11.55	0.9	nitrogenous compounds	20
1935	Gray and Cruikshank	11.86				
1935	Woodbridge	11.67	11.25–12.06	2.1	esters	4
1936	Bhatnagar and Mitra	11.68	10.6 –12.5	2.1	11 different series	82
1937	Farquharson	11.64	11.39–11.86	1.6	acids	5
1943	Angus and Hill	11.68	10.96–11.99	1.4	different homologous series	27
1949	Broersma	11.37			(hydrocarbons, alcohols,	48
1951	Pascal et al.	11.36			esters, acids)	36

the value of χ extrapolated to infinite temperature gives the value of the diamagnetic part of the susceptibility only.

Additivity of the magnetic susceptibility

The diamagnetic properties of homologous series of organic compounds were first investigated by Henricksen (1888), who called attention to the additive character of the magnetic susceptibility per gram molecule.

For a long period, from 1910 to 1952, Pascal worked on the elaboration of a consistent method for calculating the quantity

$$X = M\chi \tag{12.2}$$

He used the formula

$$X = \sum_i X_{Ai} + \sum_i \lambda_i \tag{12.3}$$

where X_A is the so-called atomic susceptibility, while λ_i represents the structure increments (i.e. structural correction factors). Following the work initiated by Pascal, various investigators have screened a large number of homologous series. A survey is given in table 12.1.

Also Dorfman (1964) and Haberditzl (1968) have done important work in this field. They calculated a large number of contributions to the susceptibility per atomic bond, arriving also at a consistent method.

Since this book invariably uses contributions per structural group, Pascal's values (from 1935 and 1952) and those of Dorfman and Haberditzl have been converted into group contributions. They are summarized in table 12.2. The mutual deviations are not large.

Comparison with experimental χ-values of polymers

The number of reliable data on the magnetic susceptibility of polymers is relatively small. Table 12.3 shows that on the whole there is a good agreement with the additively calculated values.

B. MAGNETIC RESONANCE

Magnetic resonance occurs when a material, placed in a steady magnetic field, absorbs energy from an oscillating magnetic field, due to the presence of small magnetic elementary particles in the material. The nature of this absorption always has a resonance character when the steady magnetic field is changed and the frequency of the oscillating field is kept constant. There are two kinds of transition which may be responsible for magnetic resonance:

a. Transitions involving reorientation of the magnetic moment of the electrons in the

TABLE 12.2

Group contributions to molar diamagnetic susceptibility (cgs units) (10^{-6} cm^3/mol)

Group	Pascal (ca. 1935)	Pascal (1952)	Dorfman (1964)	Haberditzl (1968)	Recommended value	
					cgs units	SI units
$-CH_3$	14.04	14.35	14	14.55	14.5	180
$-CH_2-$	11.36	11.36	11.4	11.35	11.35	143
$\diagdown CH-$	8.68	9.4	9.2	8.9	9	110
$\diagup C \diagdown$	6.0	7.4	8	·6.5	7	90
$=CH_2$	8.61	8.65	10.2	9.55	9	110
$=CH-$	5.93	6.65	6.7	6.55	6.6	83
$=C\diagdown$	3.25	4.65	5.5	4.85	4.5	57
$\leftrightarrow CH \leftrightarrow$ ar	9.23	9.1	9.23	9.2	9.2	116
$C-$ ar	5.6	7.1	7.23	6.0	7	90
$C \leftrightarrow$ endo ar	9.7	–	–	9.5	9.5	119
$-C_6H_5$	–	53	–	52	53	670
$-C_6H_4-$	–	51	–	50	50	630
$\equiv CH$	8.30	–	9.1	–	9	110
$\equiv C-$	5.61	–	7.9	–	7	90
$-F$	6.6	6.6	–	6.65	6.6	83
$-Cl$	20	18.5	18	18.5	18.5	230
$-Br$	32	27.8	–	27	27.5	350
$-I$	44	42.2	–	43	43	540
$-CF_3$	–	–	–	25	25	315
$-CH_2Cl$	31.4	–	–	30	30	380
$-CCl_2-$	–	–	43	39	40	500
$-CCl_3$	–	–	60	60	60	750
$-OH$	7.3	7.3	6.7	8.0	7.5	94
$-O-$	4.6	5.3	4.0	5.3	5	60
$-C\diagup^{O}\diagdown_H$	6.45	8.4	8.7	8.35	8.4	106
$\diagdown C=O$	4.3	6.4	7.5	5.5	6.5	82
$-COOH$	15.8	17.15	18.6	20.8	19	240
$-COO-$	13.1	15.15	11.5	14.2	14	180
$-NH_2$	11.2	13.0	10.9	12.5	12	150
$\diagdown NH$	8.5	11.0	8.7	8.4	9	110
$\diagdown N-$	5.5	9.0	6.5	5.5	6	75
N	12.4	–	–	–	12	150
$-C\diagup^{O}-NH_2$	16.8	–	–	18	17	210
$-CONH-$	14.4	–	–	14	14	180

TABLE 12.2 (continued)

Group	Pascal (ca. 1935)	Pascal (1952)	Dorfman (1964)	Haberditzl (1968)	Recommended value	
					cgs units	SI units
$-CON\diagdown^{\diagup}$	11.5	–	–	11	11	140
$-C{\equiv}N$	11	11	12	10	11	140
$-NO_2$	–	–	8.2	–	8	100
$-SH$	17.7	18.9	–	–	18	230
$-S-$	15	16.9	–	–	16	200
$\diagdown_{S=O}^{\diagup}$	–	–	10.4	–	10	130
$\diagdown_{\diagup}Si\diagdown^{\diagup}$	–	–	–	–	11	140

steady magnetic field; this effect is known as electron magnetic resonance or *electron spin resonance* (ESR).

b. Transitions due to reorientation of the magnetic moment of the nuclei in the steady magnetic field; this effect is called *nuclear magnetic resonance* (NMR).

Of all the nuclei the proton is the most widely used in NMR.

Electron resonance occurs at a much higher frequency than nuclear resonance in the same magnetic field, because the magnetic moment of an electron is about 1800 times that of a proton. Electron spin resonance is observed in the microwave region (9–28 GHz), nuclear spin resonance at radio frequencies (10–300 MHz).

In ordinary absorption spectroscopy one observes the interaction between an oscillating electric field and matter, resulting in transition between naturally present energy levels of a system of electrically charged dipoles. So it would be appropriate to call this "electric resonance spectroscopy".

Magnetic resonance spectroscopy deals with the observation of the interaction between an oscillating magnetic field and matter, which results in transition between energy levels of the magnetic dipoles, the degeneracy of which is usually removed by an externally applied steady magnetic field.

The important practical difference between electric and magnetic resonance spectroscopy is that the former technique usually permits observation of transitions in the absence of externally applied fields; in magnetic resonance spectroscopy this is hardly ever possible.

NUCLEAR MAGNETIC RESONANCE (NMR)

The nuclei of some elements possess a net magnetic moment. Quantum-mechanical considerations show that for such a nuclear magnet there are a limited number of stable orientations in an applied magnetic field.

For the hydrogen nucleus, or proton, there are two orientations, which we can think

TABLE 12.3

Comparison of experimental and calculated values of magnetic susceptibilities of polymers (cgs units)

Polymer	Investigator	χ exp. (10^{-6} cm³/g)	X calc. (10^{-6} cm³/mol)	M	χ calc. (10^{-6} cm³/g)
polyethylene	Maklakov (1963); Baltá-Calleja et al. (1965)	0.82	22.7	28.1	0.81
polypropylene	Rákoš et al. (1966)	0.8	34.85	42.1	0.83
polystyrene	Hoarau (1950); Maklakov (1963)	0.705	73.35	104.1	0.705
poly(tetrafluoroethylene)	Wilson (1962)	0.38	40.4	100.2	0.40
poly(methyl methacrylate)	Bedwell (1947)	0.59	61.35	100.1	0.61
poly(2,3-dimethyl-1,3-butadiene)	Hoarau (1950)	0.72	60.7	82.1	0.74
polycyclopentadiene	Hoarau (1950)	0.72	42.6	66.1	0.65
polyoxymethylene	Sauterey (1952)	0.52	16.35	30.0	0.545
poly(ethylene oxide)	Baltá-Calleja et al. (1965)	0.63	27.7	44.1	0.63
poly(2,6-dimethyl-1,4-phenylene oxide)	Baltá-Calleja and Barrales-Rienda (1972)	0.47(?)	80	120.1	0.665
poly(ethylene terephthalate)	Selwood et al. (1950)	0.505	100.7	192.2	0.525
nylon 6,6	Rákoš et al. (1968)	0.76(?)	141.5	226.3	0.63
poly(dimethyl siloxane)	Bondi (1951)	0.62	45	74.1	0.61
poly(methylphenyl siloxane)	Bondi (1951)	0.60	83.5	136.1	0.615

of as parallel and antiparallel to the direction of the applied field. These positions have different energies and, as we have already mentioned, the magnitude of the energy in nuclear transitions is such that it falls into the radio-frequency region of the electromagnetic spectrum. NMR therefore is a branch of radio-frequency spectroscopy and the detection of the resonance signal is possible by means of a television technique. The resonance phenomenon is described by the so-called *Larmor equation*:

$$\nu = KH \tag{12.4}$$

where ν is the resonance frequency, H is the strength of the applied magnetic field and K is a constant which is characteristic of the nuclear species. K itself is defined as:

$$K = \frac{g\beta}{h}$$

where β is the nuclear magneton, h is Planck's constant and g is an experimentally determined constant, the so-called *splitting factor*.

The proton is the most common magnetic species in organic compounds, and proton magnetic resonance (PMR) studies form by far the greater part of NMR work. However, in recent years carbon-13 magnetic resonance (CMR) has become a very powerful tool in the structure elucidation of complex organic compounds. Its potential, especially in the field of macromolecules, may exceed that of proton magnetic resonance. Carbon-13 magnetic resonance deals with the C-13 nuclei which are present in organic compounds in a natural abundance of 1.1%. The most abundant isotope of carbon C-12, has no nuclear spin and is not observable in NMR experiments. Isotope 13, however, has a nuclear spin of $\frac{1}{2}$, just as the proton. Acceptance of C-13 magnetic resonance for the structure analysis of organic compounds has been slow owing to the very weak signals caused by the low natural abundance of C-13 (1.1%). These difficulties have only recently been overcome by the introduction of the pulse-Fourier mode of measurement.

CMR gives information on the carbon skeleton of the molecules, proton magnetic resonance deals with the skin of the molecules, which normally consists of hydrogen atoms.

It is usual to vary ("sweep") the magnetic field at a constant radio frequency or the radio frequency at a constant magnetic field. The most recent and powerful instruments are of the Fourier transform type. At a constant value of the external magnetic field, RF pulses, which contain a wide enough range of frequencies, are given to the sample every few seconds. Between the pulses the magnetic response from the sample is measured. It contains all the information of a complete spectrum. In this way the measuring time is shortened at least 100 times. Fourier transform NMR is very important for carbon-13 NMR where the signals are very weak owing to the low natural abundance of C-13 isotopes. Here computer accumulation of the responses, obtained after each RF pulse, gives spectra of sufficient quality in a relatively short time.

The sensitivity of the NMR measurements is such that even very small changes in the position of the resonance line caused by the environment of the nuclei can be determined with great accuracy. The whole wealth of information on chemical and physical structure that can be obtained by NMR arises from these discrepancies.

The magnetic field experienced by the nuclei is slightly modified by the presence of surrounding electrons (*chemical shift*) and by the presence of interacting neighbouring nuclei (*spin–spin coupling*). In liquids, where the molecules can rotate freely, these factors cause the multisplit structure observed under high resolution (*High-Resolution NMR*).

In solids, where all the nuclei are more or less fixed in position, dipole–dipole interaction causes a broadening of the resonance absorption (*Wide-Line NMR*).

HIGH-RESOLUTION NMR (HR NMR)

The major chemical applications of NMR are derived from three secondary phenomena: *"chemical shift"*, *"spin–spin coupling"* and *"time-dependent effects"*. These can be observed only in samples in gaseous or liquid form or in solution.

Chemical shift

As mentioned before, the chemical shift originates from the different positions of the bonding electrons in the vicinity of protons and C-13 nuclei situated in various chemical environments. The most important differences arise from changes in *electronegativity* of substituents. Other differences, especially in proton magnetic resonance, arise from long-range effects due to movements of electrons in multiple bonds under the influence of the applied magnetic field, setting up magnetic fields of their own. Multiple bonds, for instance, exhibit pronounced magnetic anisotropy; aromatic structures, having delocalized electrons in closed-loop systems, actually show evidence of the presence of "ring currents" under the influence of the magnetic field. The overall effect of the chemical environment can be described in terms of a *screening* or *shielding constant* σ:

$$H_{at\ nucleus} = H_0(1 - \sigma) . \tag{12.5}$$

The magnetic sweep ΔH is only a tiny fraction (10^{-5} for PMR and 10^{-4} for CMR) of the total field strength and therefore the position of the various resonance signals, determined by their chemical shift, cannot be recorded in absolute units. Instead, a reference compound is included in the sample and the chemical shift is defined as:

$$\delta = \frac{H - H_R}{H_R} \times 10^6 \tag{12.6}$$

where H is the magnetic field strength corresponding to the resonance frequency of the nucleus in the compound under investigation, and H_R is the magnetic field strength corresponding to the resonance frequency of the same nucleus in the reference substance.

For proton and C-13 magnetic resonance studies of non-aqueous solutions the most recommended reference compound is tetramethyl silane (($CH_3)_4Si$), which is magnetically and electrically isotropic, chemically reasonably inert, and non-associating with any common compound. When the high-field-absorbing tetramethyl silane is used as a reference, most δ values (defined as in (12.6)) are negative. Fig. 12.1 summarizes the chemical shifts for protons in the principal functional groups. It should be remarked that chemical shifts are, to a certain extent, solvent-dependent. Fig. 12.2 gives the chemical shifts for C-13 in the principal functional groups (see Slothers (1972), Levy and Nelson (1972) and Breitmaier et al. (1971)).

Carbon resonances of organic compounds are found over a range of 600 ppm, compared with 20 ppm for proton nuclei. With modern instrumental methods it is also possible to obtain narrower resonance lines in CMR (by controlled elimination of the spin–spin splitting) than in PMR. These advantages of CMR make this technique superior to PMR,

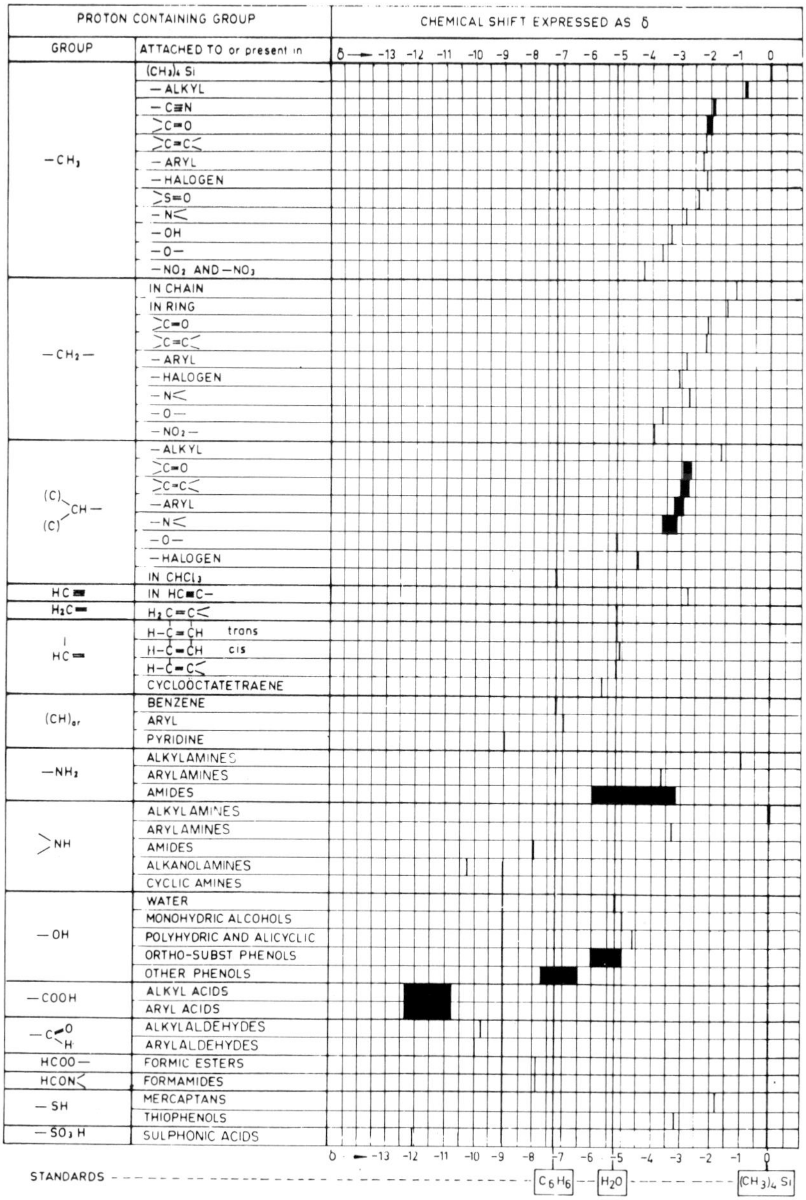

PROTON CONTAINING GROUP		CHEMICAL SHIFT EXPRESSED AS δ
GROUP	ATTACHED TO or present in	δ → -13 -12 -11 -10 -9 -8 -7 -6 -5 -4 -3 -2 -1 0
	(CH₃)₄ Si	
—CH₃	—ALKYL	
	—C≡N	
	⟩C=O	
	⟩C=C⟨	
	—ARYL	
	—HALOGEN	
	⟩S=O	
	—N⟨	
	—OH	
	—O—	
	—NO₂ AND —NO₃	
—CH₂—	IN CHAIN	
	IN RING	
	⟩C=O	
	⟩C=C⟨	
	—ARYL	
	—HALOGEN	
	—N⟨	
	—O—	
	—NO₂—	
(C)⟩CH— (C)	—ALKYL	
	⟩C=O	
	⟩C=C⟨	
	—ARYL	
	—N⟨	
	—O—	
	—HALOGEN	
	IN CHCl₃	
HC≡	IN HC≡C—	
H₂C=	H₂C=C⟨	
HC=	H—C=CH trans	
	H—C=CH cis	
	H—C=C⟨	
	CYCLOOCTATETRAENE	
(CH)ₐᵣ	BENZENE	
	ARYL	
	PYRIDINE	
—NH₂	ALKYLAMINES	
	ARYLAMINES	
	AMIDES	
⟩NH	ALKYLAMINES	
	ARYLAMINES	
	AMIDES	
	ALKANOLAMINES	
	CYCLIC AMINES	
—OH	WATER	
	MONOHYDRIC ALCOHOLS	
	POLYHYDRIC AND ALICYCLIC	
	ORTHO-SUBST PHENOLS	
	OTHER PHENOLS	
—COOH	ALKYL ACIDS	
	ARYL ACIDS	
—C⟨=O,H	ALKYLALDEHYDES	
	ARYLALDEHYDES	
HCOO—	FORMIC ESTERS	
HCON⟨	FORMAMIDES	
—SH	MERCAPTANS	
	THIOPHENOLS	
—SO₃H	SULPHONIC ACIDS	δ → -13 -12 -11 -10 -9 -8 -7 -6 -5 -4 -3 -2 -1 0
STANDARDS		C₆H₆ H₂O (CH₃)₄Si

Fig. 12.1. Proton chemical shifts of principal structural groups.

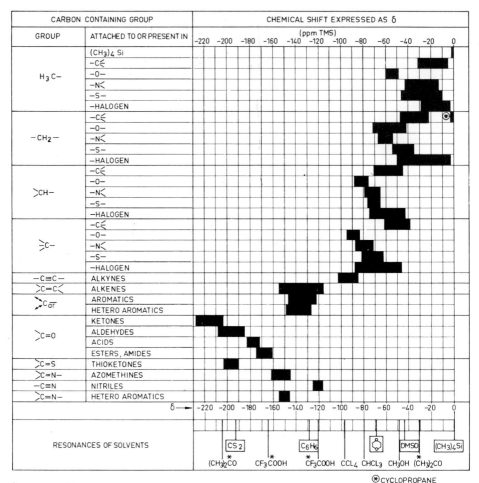

Fig. 12.2. C^{13}-chemical shifts of principal structural groups.

for instance in determining the tacticity of vinyl polymers, the configuration of poly-butadienes, the sequence length of copolymers and the nature and number of side groups in low-density polyethylenes.

Spin–spin coupling

The signals often show a fine structure with a characteristic splitting pattern due to spin–spin interactions with neighbouring nuclei. These interactions occur mostly between nuclei which are one to four bonds away from each other in the molecule. The splitting corresponds to the slightly different energy levels of nuclei whose spins are parallel and anti-parallel to those of their neighbours; in some cases it may lead to a considerable complication of the spectra.

These spin–spin interactions are expressed in coupling constants which can be experimentally determined even in very complex spectra. Coupling constants – e.g. between two protons or a C-13 nucleus and a proton – are molecular parameters, independent of the applied external magnetic field. Expressed in hertz, they can have positive or negative values depending on the numbers of bonds between the two nuclei.

In proton spectra of polymers knowledge of the exact values of the coupling constants and the chemical shifts makes it possible to simulate the experimental spectra by computer calculations. In this way it is possible to interpret quantitatively the complex spectra of many homopolymers and copolymers in terms of configuration (or "tacticity") and monomer sequences (copolymers). The obtained sequence lengths can be directly related to the polymerization mechanism.

As the coupling constants, especially between two protons on adjacent carbon atoms, are very sensitive to rotational changes, one can also derive from them the preferred conformation of the polymer chain (see Diehl et al., 1971).

Time-dependent effects

The NMR signals are sometimes influenced by time-dependent phenomena such as conformational or prototropic changes, which take place at a rate comparable to (or faster than) the inverse of the differences between the frequences of the transitions. This means that kinetic phenomena may be studied by the NMR technique, especially if the temperature of the sample can be adapted.

It is possible to record HR NMR spectra of polymer solutions with the aid of the wide range of solvents available for NMR, sometimes at elevated temperatures. The viscosity of the solution does not always affect the line width. Thus, HR NMR can successfully be applied to elucidate the chemical structure, configuration (tacticity) and conformation of polymers and copolymers.

Since the signal intensity is proportional to the number of absorbing nuclei, HR NMR can also be used as a quantitative tool, e.g. in polymer end group determinations.

The availability of 220–360 MHz proton spectrometers and 25–90 MHz C-13 spectrometers and computers for averaging out noise has greatly enhanced the accuracy of HR NMR polymer analysis.

Reviews of HR NMR polymer analysis have been published by, for instance, Bovey (1969) and Mochel (1972).

WIDE-LINE NMR (WL NMR)

Solids give rise to the "wide-line" spectra, because the local fields arising from nuclear magnetic dipole interactions contribute significantly to the total field experienced by a nucleus in the solid state. A measure of this direct spin–spin interaction is the *spin–spin relaxation time* t_2, which is much shorter in solids than in liquids, and thus gives rise to broader lines (a few gauss). Now the contour of the absorption line provides information as to the relative position of the neighbouring nuclei.

The broadening of the resonance band may be characterized by the line width at half height ($\Delta H_{\frac{1}{2}}$) or by the second moment (S_2) of the curve which is defined as

$$S_2 = \frac{\int\limits_{-\infty}^{+\infty} (H - H_0)^2 f(H) dH}{\int\limits_{-\infty}^{+\infty} f(H) dH} \qquad (12.7)$$

where H_0 is the value of the magnetic field where resonance occurs and $f(H)$ is the shape of the curve if the magnetic field varies and the frequency is kept constant. Correlated with the line width at half height is the above-mentioned spin–spin relaxation time t_2.

$$t_2 \approx \frac{1}{\pi} \times \frac{1}{K\Delta H_{1/2}} \qquad (12.8)$$

In addition to this spin–spin interaction there exists an interaction between the spins and the surroundings, the so-called spin–lattice interaction. The characteristic constant of the order–disorder transition in this case is the *spin–lattice relaxation time* t_1. t_2 is nearly independent of temperature, whereas t_1 is highly temperature-dependent. This provides means of studying the two rate processes separately.

Richards et al. (1955, 1958) measured line widths at low temperatures (90 K) and found that the second moment (S_2) depended very much on the interhydrogen distance. Since the hydrogen atoms in an aromatic ring are more widely spaced than those in aliphatic groups, the variation in the line widths can be associated with variation of the ratio aromatic/aliphatic components. Richards et al. derived additive group contributions to the second moment from the resonance spectra of a number of model substances; they are shown in table 12.4.

The line-width behaviour as a function of temperature may provide useful information on transition temperatures in the solid state.

Since the different types of transitions have different energies of activation, the line width sometimes decreases discontinuously with varying temperature. *At characteristic transition temperatures the spin–lattice relaxation time t_1 reaches a minimum.* Comparative study of this NMR method of measuring transition temperatures with the dynamic-mechanical and dielectric methods is sometimes very valuable to the understanding of structural or conformational effects.

TABLE 12.4

Group contributions to the second moment in NMR (90 K)

Group	Contribution per hydrogen atom to the second moment (gauss)
Aromatic CH	9.7
(Aliphatic CH)	(10)
Aliphatic CH_2	27.5
Aliphatic CH_3	10.0
Peri-CH_3	22.4

The ability of WL NMR to characterize molecular motion in polymers is expected to be greatly enhanced by recent developments (nuclear magnetic relaxation in the rotating frame (McCall et al., 1967)). WL NMR applications to polymers have been reviewed by Slichter (1958, 1970), one of the pioneers in this field.

Another important application of wide-line NMR is the *determination of crystallinity*. Some polymers give spectra which can be graphically separated into a broader and a narrower component. In this way Wilson and Pake (1953) determined the crystallinity of polyethylene and poly(tetrafluoroethylene).

In conclusion, it may be stated that nowadays the nuclear resonance spectrum is a distinct reliable, and extremely useful fingerprint by which any substance containing magnetic nuclei can be identified.

ELECTRON MAGNETIC RESONANCE (ESR)

This type of resonance, often called electron spin resonance, is normally observed in paramagnetic substances and particularly in systems with odd numbers of electrons as for example in organic radicals. The energy of an unpaired electron depends on whether its magnetic moment is oriented parallel or antiparallel to the local magnetic field H.

The energy difference between those two positions is:

$$\Delta E = g\beta_B H \tag{12.9}$$

where g is the spectroscopic splitting factor (whose value is about 2 for organic radicals) and β_B is the Bohr magneton. Thanks to their magnetic dipole moment the unpaired electrons may interact with an electromagnetic field, provided its frequency satisfies the resonance condition

$$\nu = \frac{g\beta_B}{h} H = K'H \tag{12.10}$$

Again, the result of the interaction is net absorption of electromagnetic energy.

It is customary to keep the frequency constant while the field H is varied. Disturbances again cause a band of finite width, characterized by the line width at half height ($\Delta H_{1/2}$). One of the disturbances responsible for a finite line width is the dipole–dipole interaction in the spin system. Characteristic of the order–disorder transition caused by this interaction is the so-called spin–spin relaxation time (t_2), which is correlated with the line width at half height; for a line of Lorentzian shape:

$$t_2 = \frac{h}{\pi g\beta\Delta H_{1/2}} = \frac{1}{\pi}\frac{1}{K'\Delta H_{1/2}} \tag{12.11}$$

In addition to the spin–spin interaction, also in this case there exists interaction between the spins and their surroundings: the so-called spin–lattice interaction. The characteristic constant of the order–disorder transition of this interaction process is the spin–lattice relaxation time (t_1). t_1 is highly dependent on temperature, whereas t_2 is nearly temperature-independent.

In solution, the line width is small enough to observe hyperfine splitting, caused by interaction of the unpaired spin with magnetic nuclei in the radical (e.g. H, F, N).

Thus, electron magnetic resonance is an important tool in the detection and structure analysis of radicals in polymeric systems (during formation, oxidation, irradiation, pyrolysis and mechanical rupture). From these patterns the chemical structure of the radicals may be derived. For the study of short-lived radicals flow systems have been developed. Free radicals in glassy polymers, however, may have an extremely long life.

BIBLIOGRAPHY, CHAPTER 12

General references

Magnetic Susceptibility

Dorfman, J.G., "Diamagnetismus und chemische Bindung", Verlag H. Deutsch, Frankfurt, Zürich, 1964.
Haberditzl, W., "Magnetochemie", Akademie-Verlag, Berlin, 1968.
Selwood, P.W., "Magnetochemistry", Interscience Publishers, New York, 1943.

Nuclear magnetic resonance

Bovey, F.A., "Nuclear Magnetic Resonance Spectroscopy", Academic Press, New York, 1969.
Emsley, J.W., Feeney, J. and Sutcliffe, L.H., "High Resolution Nuclear Magnetic Resonance Spectroscopy", Vol. I and II, Pergamon Press, Oxford, 1965.
Jackman, L.M. and Sternhell, S., "Applications of Nuclear Magnetic Resonance Spectroscopy in Organic Chemistry", 2nd edition, Pergamon Press, Oxford, 1969.
Levy, G.C. and Nelson, G.L., "C-13 Nuclear Magnetic Resonance for Organic Chemists", Wiley Interscience, New York, 1972.
Slothers, J.B., "C-13 NMR Spectroscopy", Academic Press, New York, 1972.

Electron spin resonance

Scheffler, K. and Stegmann, H.B., "Elektronenspinnresonanz", Springer-Verlag, Berlin, 1970.
Wertz, J.E. and Bolton, J.R., "Electron Spin Resonance", McGraw-Hill Co., New York, 1972.

Special references

Magnetic Susceptibility

Angus, W.R. and Hill, W.K., Trans. Faraday Soc. 39 (1943) 185.
Baltá-Calleja, F.J., Hosemann, R. and Wilke, W., Trans. Faraday Soc. 61 (1965) 1912; Kolloid-Z. 206 (1965) 118; Makromol. Chem. 92 (1966) 25.
Baltá-Calleja, F.J., J. Polymer Sci. C 16 (1969) 4311.
Baltá-Calleja, F.J. and Barrales-Rienda, J.M., J. Macromol. Sci., Phys. B 6 (1972) 387.
Bedwell, M.E., J. Chem. Soc. (1947) 1350.
Bhatnagar, S.S., Mitra, N.G. and Das·Tuli, G., Phil. Mag. 18 (1934) 449.

Bhatnagar, S.S. and Mitra, N.G., J. Indian Chem. Soc. 13 (1936) 329.
Bitter, F., Phys. Rev. 33 (1929) 389.
Bondi, A.J., J. Phys. Coll. Chem. 55 (1951) 1355.
Broersma, S., J. Chem. Phys. 17 (1949) 873.
Cabrera, B. and Fahlenbrach, H., Z. Physik 89 (1934) 682.
Cabrera, B. and Colyon, H., Compt. Rend. 213 (1941) 108.
Farquharson, J., Trans. Faraday Soc. 32 (1936) 219; 33 (1937) 824.
Gray, F.W. and Cruikshank, J.H., Trans. Faraday Soc. 31 (1935) 1491.
Hoarau, J., Bull. Soc. Chim. France (1950) 1153.
Maklakov, A.J., Zh. Fiz. Khim. 37 (1963) 2609.
Pascal, P., Ann. Chim. Phys. 16 (1909) 531; 19 (1910) 5; 25 (1912) 289; 28 (1913) 218; Compt. Rend.
    147 (1908) 56, 242, 742; 148 (1909) 413; 150 (1910) 1167; 152 (1911) 862, 1010; 156 (1913)
    323; 158 (1914) 37; 173 (1921) 144; 176 (1923) 1887; 177 (1923) 765; 180 (1925) 1596; Bull. Soc.
    Chim. France 11 (1912) 636; Rev. Gen. Sci. 34 (1923) 388.
Pascal, P., Pacault, A. and Hoarau, J., Compt. Rend. 233 (1951) 1078.
Pascal, P., Gallais, F. and Labarre, J.F., Compt. Rend. 252 (1961) 18, 2644.
Rákoš, M., Šimo, R. and Varga, Z., Czech. J. Phys. B 16 (1966) 112, 167; B 18 (1968) 1456.
Sauterey, R., Ann. Chim. 7 (1952) 5.
Selwood, P.W., Parodi, J.A. and Pace, A., J. Am. Chem. Soc. 72 (1950) 1269.
Vaidyanathan, V.I., Phys. Rev. 30 (1927) 512.
Wilson, C.W., J. Polymer Sci. 61 (1962) 403.
Woodbridge, D.B., Phys. Rev. 48 (1935) 672.

Magnetic resonance

Anet, F.A.L. and Levy, G.C., Science 180 (1973) 141.
Bovey, F.A., "Polymer Conformation and Configuration", Academic Press, New York, 1969.
Breitmaier, E., Jung, G. and Voelter, W., Angew. Chem. 83 (1971) 659.
Diehl, P., Fluck, E. and Kosfeld, R., "NMR Basic Principles and Progress. Vol. 4: Natural and Syn-
    thetic High Polymers", Springer Verlag, Berlin, Heidelberg, New York, 1971.
McCall, D.W. and Falcone, D.R., Trans. Faraday Soc. 66 (1970) 262.
McCall, D.W., Douglass, D.C. and Falcone, D.R., J. Phys. Chem. 71 (1967) 998.
Mochel, V.D., J. Macromol. Sci.-Rev. Macromol. Chem. C 8 (1972) 2, 289.
Richards, R.E. et al.: Newman, P.C., Pratt, L. and Richards, R.E., Nature 175 (1955) 645; Bell, C.L.M.,
    Richards, R.E. and Yorke, R.W., Brennstoff-Chem. 39 (1958) 30.
Slichter, W.P., Fortschr. Hochpolym. Forsch. 1 (1958) 35; J. Chem. Ed. 47 (1970) 193.
Wilson, C.W. and Pake, G.E., J. Polymer Sci. 10 (1953) 503.

CHAPTER 13

MECHANICAL PROPERTIES OF SOLID ISOTROPIC POLYMERS

The only mechanical property which can be calculated from additive
quantities is the *bulk modulus* or its reciprocal, the *compressibility*. Via the
bulk modulus the other elastic quantities can be estimated. They can also
be estimated by means of an empirical relationship between the shear modulus and the characteristic transition temperatures. Also the time- and
temperature-dependence can be estimated if the transition temperatures
are known.

Introduction

The mechanical properties of polymers are of interest in all applications where polymers are used as structural materials. Mechanical behaviour involves the deformation of a
material under the influence of applied forces.

The simplest mechanical properties are those of homogeneous isotropic and purely
elastic materials; their mechanical response can be defined by only two constants. For
anisotropic, oriented-amorphous, crystalline and oriented-crystalline materials more constants are required to describe the mechanical behaviour.

A. ELASTIC QUANTITIES

The most important and most characteristic mechanical properties are called moduli.
A *modulus is the ratio between the applied stress and the corresponding deformation.*
The reciprocals of the moduli are called *compliances.*

The nature of the modulus depends on the nature of the deformation. The three most

TABLE 13.1

Elementary deformations

Elementary mode of deformation	Modulus	Compliance
Isotropic (hydrostatic) compression	Bulk modulus (B)	Bulk compliance or compressibility ($\kappa = 1/B$)
Simple shear	Shear modulus or rigidity (G)	Shear compliance ($J = 1/G$)
Uniaxial extension	Tensile or Young's modulus (E)	Tensile compliance ($D = 1/E$)

259

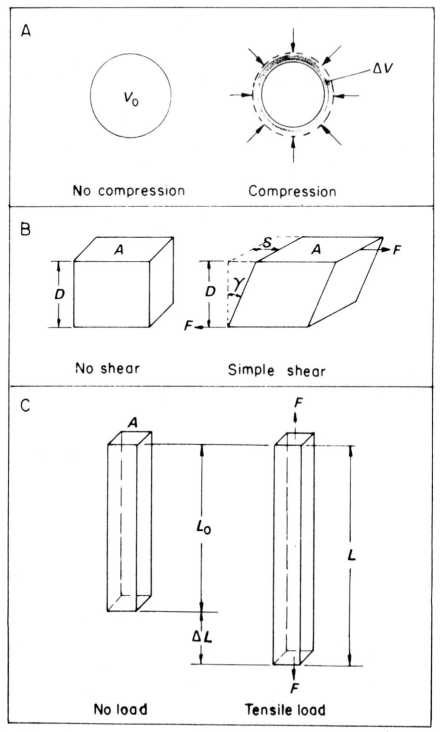

Fig. 13.1. Deformations. A, under hydrostatic pressure; B, under shear; C, under tension.

important elementary modes of deformation and the moduli (and compliances) derived from them are given in fig. 13.1 and table 13.1.

Other very important, but more complicated, deformations are *bending* and *torsion*. From the bending or flexural deformation the tensile modulus can be derived. The torsion is determined by the rigidity.

Definitions

The three elastic moduli mentioned have the dimension force per area (N/m^2). Their precise definition is the following:

1. Bulk modulus (B)

$$B = \frac{\text{Hydrostatic pressure}}{\text{Volume strain}} = \frac{\text{Hydrostatic pressure}}{\text{Volume change per unit volume}} = \frac{p}{\Delta V/V_0} = \frac{pV_0}{\Delta V} \qquad (13.1)$$

2. Shear modulus or rigidity (G)

$$G = \frac{\text{Shear stress}}{\text{Shear strain}} = \frac{\text{Shear force per unit area}}{\text{Shear per unit distance between shearing surfaces}} =$$

$$\frac{F/A}{S/D} = \frac{F/A}{\tan \gamma} = \frac{\tau}{\tan \gamma} \approx \frac{\tau}{\gamma} \qquad (13.2)$$

3. Tensile modulus or Young's modulus (E)

$$E = \frac{\text{Tensile stress}}{\text{Tensile strain}} = \frac{\text{Force per unit cross-sectional area}}{\text{Strain per unit length}} = \frac{F/A}{\ln(L/L_0)} =$$

$$\frac{\sigma}{\epsilon} \approx \frac{F/A}{\Delta L/L_0} \qquad (13.3)$$

The *true stress* is the load divided by the *instantaneous* cross-sectional area of the sample. Engineers often use the nominal stress, which is the load divided by the *initial* (undeformed) cross-sectional area.

Directly measured is the *nominal strain* ϵ_n:

$$\epsilon_n = \frac{L - L_0}{L_0} = \frac{\Delta L}{L_0} \qquad (13.4)$$

The *true strain* is the integral of the nominal strain:

$$\epsilon_{tr} = \int_{L_0}^{L} \frac{dL}{L} = \ln(L/L_0) \qquad (13.5)$$

A fourth important quantity is the *Poisson ratio* (v), which is defined as follows:

$$v = \frac{\text{Change in width per unit width}}{\text{Change in length per unit length}} = \frac{\text{lateral contraction}}{\text{axial strain}} \qquad (13.6)$$

The moduli are interrelated by the following equation:

$$\boxed{E = 2G(1 + v) = 3B(1 - 2v)} \qquad (13.7)$$

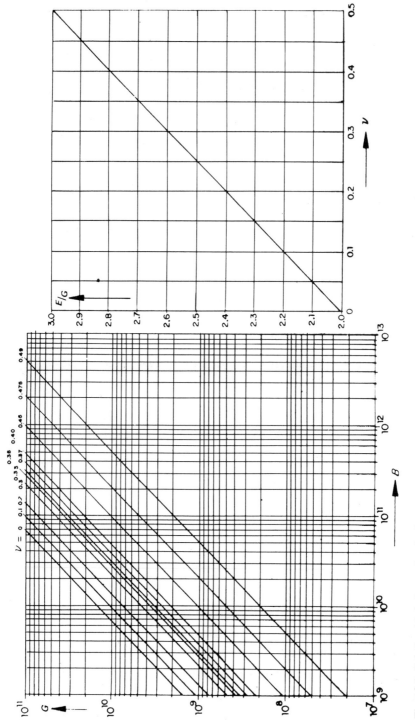

Fig. 13.2. Relationship between the elastic moduli.

Fig. 13.2 shows this equation in graphical form.

Directly connected with the moduli are two special expressions for the rigidity:

$$\text{Flexural rigidity} = \frac{\text{applied force}}{\text{deformation displacement}} \sim Ed^4$$

$$\text{Torsional rigidity} = \frac{\text{applied torque}}{\text{angle of twist}} \sim Gd^4$$

where d is a characteristic dimension of the thickness of the sample.

Numerical values

Table 13.2 gives characteristic values of the moduli and Poisson ratios for different metals, ceramic materials and polymers.

The moduli of polymers cover a wider range than those of other materials (from 10^5 N/m^2 for rubber to 10^{10} N/m^2 for rigid polymers), which is one of the reasons why polymers are so versatile in application. Absolute stiffness and strength of polymers are much lower than those of metals, but on the basis of equal weight polymers compare favourably due to their much lower density. The specific moduli are of the order of one tenth of those of the stronger metals.

For a number of linear polymers, values of E for single crystals have been determined. This has been performed by direct measurements or by calculation from molecular dimensions and force constants for bond stretching and valence angle deformation (Treloar, 1960; Frensdorff, 1964; Sakurada and coworkers, 1962, 1970).

The values of E for polymer crystals are of the order of magnitude of 10^{11} N/m^2, which is much higher that the values mentioned in table 13.2 for commercial polymers.

Relationship between moduli and other physical quantities

The moduli of solid substances are manifestations of intermolecular forces and – as a consequence – are related to other physical quantities.

1. Bulk modulus (B)

The following interrelations are known:

a. with *compressibility* (κ)

The bulk modulus is the reciprocal of the compressibility:

$$B = \frac{1}{\kappa} \tag{13.8}$$

It can therefore be determined by compression experiments.

b. with *sound velocity* (u)

The bulk modulus can also be determined by measuring the velocity of longitudinal elastic waves, i.e. sound.

In a continuous isotropic solid two independent types of elastic waves exist.

In dilatational or compressional waves the solid is subjected to alternate local compressions and ex-

TABLE 13:2

Mechanical properties of various materials

Class of materials	Material	Density ρ (10^3 kg/m³)	Poisson ratio ν	Moduli (10^9 N/m²)			Specific moduli (10^6 N · m/kg)		
				E	G	B	E/ρ	G/ρ	B/ρ
Organic and inorganic liquids	Benzene	0.88	0.5	0	0	1.25	0	0	1.4
	Carbon disulphide	1.26	0.5	0	0	1.5	0	0	1.2
	Water	1.0	0.5	0	0	2.0	0	0	2.0
Polymers	Natural rubber	0.91	(0.49⁵)	10.5×10^{-4}	3.5×10^{-4}	2.0	11.5×10^{-4}	4×10^{-4}	2.2
	Polyethylene (LD)	0.92	0.49	0.2	0.07	3.3	0.22	0.076	3.6
	Nylon	1.14	0.44	1.9	0.7	5.0	1.66	0.61	4.4
	Poly(methyl methacrylate)	1.17	0.40	3.2	1.1	5.1	2.7	0.95	4.4
	Polystyrene	1.05	0.38	3.4	1.2	5.0	3.2	1.14	4.8
	Epoxy resin	1.18	0.4	2.5	0.9	6.4	2.15	0.77	5.5
Metals	Mercury	13.55	0.5	0	0	25	0	0	1.85
	Lead	11.0	0.44	16	6	41	1.45	0.55	3.7
	Gold	19.3	0.42	80	28	165	4.15	1.45	8.5
	Copper	8.9	0.34	110	44	135	12.4	4.95	15.2
	Steel (mild)	7.8	0.28	220	80	160	28	10.2	20.5
	Tungsten	19.3	0.28	390	150	300	20	7.8	15.5
Inorganic solids	Granite	2.7	0.30	30	12	25	11.1	4.45	9.2
	Glass	2.5	0.23	60	25	37	24.0	10.0	14.8
	Vitreous Silica	2.2	0.14	70	30	32	31.8	13.6	14.5
Whiskers	Alumina	3.96	(0)	2000	1000	667	500	250	170
	Carborundum	3.15	(0)	1000	500	333	320	160	106
	Graphite	2.25	(0)	1000	500	333	450	225	150

Conversion factors: 1 kg/m³ = 10^{-3} g/cm³; 1 N/m² = 10 dyn/cm².

pansions. The movements of the individual molecules (atoms) of a solid transmitting a dilatational wave are normal to the advancing wave front and in the direction of propagation of the wave.

The second type of elastic wave is known as a dilatation-free or distortional wave. In a continuous medium transmitting distortional waves the solid is locally subject to shearing forces and the wave consists in the spreading throughout the solid of an oscillating shearing motion. The motion of the individual molecules takes place parallel to the wave front and perpendicular to the direction of propagation of the wave (transverse wave).

In media such as gases or liquids (melts), which have no rigidity, only longitudinal waves can occur. In media which have rigidity but are incompressible only transverse waves can occur.

The relationship between bulk modulus and longitudinal sound velocity for fluids reads as follows:

$$u^2_{long} = \frac{B}{\rho} \tag{13.9}$$

Schuyer (1958, 1959) demonstrated that for *solids* we have the relationship:

$$u^2_{long} = \frac{B}{\rho} \frac{3(1-\nu)}{1+\nu} \tag{13.10}$$

where ν is the Poisson ratio.

c. with *thermodynamic properties*

Grüneisen (1910, 1926) derived a semi-empirical relation between thermal expansion, specific heat and compressibility for *solid crystalline substances*.

$$\frac{\alpha \upsilon}{c_V \kappa} = \text{const} \approx \text{unity} \tag{13.11}$$

d. with *cohesive energy density*

According to Grüneisen (see also Tobolsky, 1960) the following relation applies to simple *molecular crystals*:

$$B \approx 8.04 \frac{E_{subl}}{V} \tag{13.12}$$

where E_{subl} is the lattice energy (sublimation energy) of the molecular crystal.

e. with *surface tension*

McGowan (1967) has demonstrated that *for liquids* the compressibility is closely related to the surface tension:

$$\kappa \gamma^{3/2} = \text{const.} \tag{13.13}$$

2. Shear modulus (G)

The shear modulus determines the *stiffness* (rigidity) of the material and shows the following relations:

a. with *sound velocity*

The shear modulus can be determined by measuring the force necessary for a torsional deformation or by measuring the velocity of propagation of transverse waves.

$$u^2_{dist} = \frac{G}{\rho}. \tag{13.14}$$

b. with *the transition temperatures*

Another way to obtain a fairly good estimation of the rigidity of a polymer at room temperature is the application of an empirical relationship found by Van Krevelen and Hoftyzer (1970)

$$G(298) = G_g(298) + x_c^2[G_c(298) - G_g(298)] \tag{13.15}$$

where x_c is degree of crystallinity, G_c is rigidity of fully crystalline polymer, G_g is rigidity of fully glassy polymer (both isotropic)

$$G_c(298) \approx \frac{T_m - 298}{100} \times 10^9 \text{ N/m}^2 \tag{13.16}$$

$$G_g(298) \approx \frac{3}{1 + \dfrac{600}{T_g}} \times 10^9 \text{ N/m}^2 . \tag{13.17}$$

If $T_g < 298$ K, $G_g(298)$ has to be neglected.

The results of the application of these equations to a number of polymers are given in table 13.3 in comparison with the experimental data. The agreement is very satisfactory.

3. Young's modulus (E)

Young's modulus can be determined by measuring the tension as a function of elonga-

TABLE 13.3

Shear moduli of polymers

State of polymer	Polymer	G exp. (10⁹ N/m²)	G calc. (10⁹ N/m²)
Amorphous	polystyrene	1.1–1.2	1.15
	poly(vinyl chloride)	1.1	1.10
	poly(vinyl acetate)	1.0	1.0
	poly(vinyl carbazole)	1.24	1.33
	poly(methyl methacrylate)	1.0–1.5	1.15
	poly(bisphenol carbonate)	0.8–1.1	1.25
	polyurethane 6,4	0.9	1.0
Semi-crystalline	polyethylene ($x_c \approx 0.8$)	0.1–1.0	0.8
	polypropylene ($x_c \approx 0.5$)	0.7	0.75
	poly(vinyl fluoride) ($x_c \approx 0.25$)	0.1	0.1
	poly(vinylidene chloride) ($x_c \approx 0.75$)	1.2	1.05
	polyoxymethylene ($x_c \approx 1$)	1.2–2.0	1.6
	poly(ethylene oxide) ($x_c \approx 1$)	0.2	0.35
	poly(propylene oxide) ($x_c \approx 0.3$)	0.05	(0.05)
	poly(ethylene terephthalate) ($x_c \approx 0.3$)	~1	1.1
	poly(tetramethylene terephthalate) ($x_c \approx 0.2$)	~1.0	1.0
	nylon 6 ($x_c \approx 0.35$)	~1	1.2

Conversion factor: 1 N/m² = 10 dyn/cm².

tion. It can also be estimated via eq. (13.1) if the Poisson ratio and either B or G are known:

$$E = 3B(1 - 2v) = 2G(1 + v). \tag{13.7}$$

Estimation of the Bulk Modulus by means of additive quantities
The bulk modulus is the only mechanical quantity that can be calculated by means of additive properties. The other moduli, which are technically more interesting and more important, can be calculated from the bulk modulus by means of equation (13.7).

The Rao function or molar sound velocity function
Rama Rao (1940, 1941) demonstrated that for organic liquids the ratio $u^{1/3}/\rho$ is practically independent of temperature and that the combination:

$$U = \frac{M}{\rho} u_{long}^{1/3} \tag{13.18}$$

behaves as an additive molar quantity. The latter is called the *Rao function* or *molar sound velocity function.*
For an isotropic solid the Rao function is different from that of the same substance in the liquid state.
Schuyer (1958, 1959) proved that the generalized expression for the Rao function is:

$$\boxed{U = Vu^{1/3}\left[\frac{1+v}{3(1-v)}\right]^{1/6}} \tag{13.19}$$

For liquids $v = \frac{1}{2}$, so that (13.19) reduces to (13.18).
The group contributions to the Rao function (defined by (13.19)) are given in table 13.4. The numerical values of the Rao function and of its group contributions are expressed in the usual way in $(cm^3/mol) \times (cm/s)^{1/3} = cm^{10/3} \cdot s^{-1/3} \cdot mol^{-1}$.

Rearrangement of (13.19) gives:

$$u_{long} = \left(\frac{U}{V}\right)^3 \left(\frac{3(1-v)}{1+v}\right)^{1/2} \tag{13.20}$$

Schuyer showed that for polyethylenes the Rao function according to (13.19) does not vary with the density, irrespective of whether variations in density are caused by changes in temperature or in structure. Since v is nearly independent of the density, eq. (13.20) predicts that the longitudinal sound velocity will be roughly proportional to the third power of the density of polyethylene. This is confirmed by fig. 13.3.

Combination of (13.10) and (13.20) gives:

$$\frac{B}{\rho} = \left(\frac{U}{V}\right)^6 \tag{13.21}$$

This expression makes it possible to calculate the bulk modulus from the additive quantities U and V.

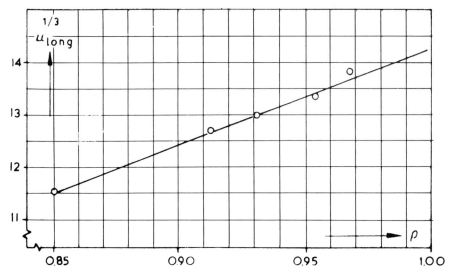

Fig. 13.3. Cubic root of longitudinal sound velocity of polyethylene as a function of density.

Example 13.1
Estimate the bulk modulus of amorphous poly(bisphenol carbonate).

$M = 254$
$V = 212$

Solution
From table 13.4 we obtain as contributions to the Rao function:

	U_i
$2(-C_6H_4-)$	8200
$1(\overset{\backslash/}{\underset{/\backslash}{C}})$	50
$2(-CH_3)$	2800
$1(-O(CO)O-)$	1600
	$\overline{12650 = U}$

So $\dfrac{U}{V} = \dfrac{12650}{212} = 59.7$

and $\left(\dfrac{U}{V}\right)^6 = 4.5 \times 10^{10} = \dfrac{B}{\rho}$

Furthermore $\rho = \dfrac{M}{V} = \dfrac{254}{212} = 1.20$

so that $B = 1.20 \times 4.5 \times 10^{10} = 5.4 \times 10^{10}$ g/cm $\cdot$ s^2 = 5.4×10^9 N/m^2, which is in fair agreement with the experimental value of 5.0×10^9 N/m^2.

TABLE 13.4

Group contributions to the Rao function (in $cm^{10/3}/s^{1/3} \cdot mol$)

(Values for liquids from Sakiadis and Coates, 1955)

Group	U		Group	U	
	in liquids	in solid polymers		in liquids	in solid polymers
$-CH_3$	1360	1400	$-F$		(500)
$-CH_2-$	895	880	$-Cl$	1060	1150
$\diagdown CH-$	460	450	$-Br$	1180	
$\diagdown C \diagdown$	40	50	$-I$	1400	
$=CH_2$	1235		$-O-$	350	400
$=CH-$	745	700	$-OH$	630	600
$=C\diagdown$	255	50			
			$-CO-$	870	900
CH_{ar}	760		$-COO-$	1220	1250
C_{ar}	260		$-OCOO-$	1570	1600
			$-COOH$	1430	
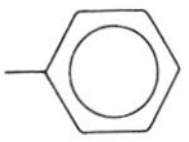 (benzene ring)	4045	4650			
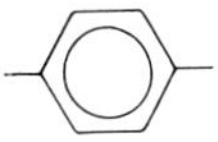 (1,4-disubstituted ring)	3555	4100	$-NH_2$	965	
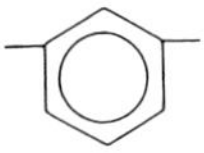 (1,2-disubstituted ring)	3500		$-NH-$	640	
 (1,3-disubstituted ring)	3450		$\diagdown N-$	65	100
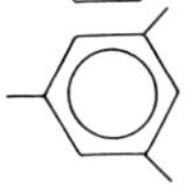 (trisubstituted ring)		3700	$-C \equiv N$	1310	
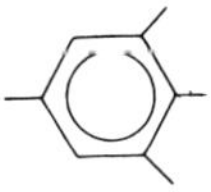 (trisubstituted ring)		3350	$-CONH-$	1365	1700
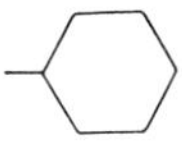 (cyclohexane ring)	4875		$-CONH_2$	1840	
$\equiv CH$	1110		$-S-$	(550)	
$\equiv C-$	620		$-SH$	1050	
			$-SO_2-$		1250

Estimation of the bulk modulus by means of other additive functions

The physical quantities in the dimensionless relations (13.11) and (13.12) may themselves be derived by means of additive groups. This immediately gives us the possibility of estimating the bulk modulus from other additive quantities:

$$\text{from (13.11) } B \approx \frac{c_V}{\alpha v} = \frac{C_V}{E_c} \approx \left(\frac{C_V}{C_p}\right)\left(\frac{C_p}{E}\right) \tag{13.22}$$

$$\text{from (13.12) } B \approx 8.04 \frac{E_{subl}}{V} \approx 8 \frac{E_{coh} + x_c\Delta H_m}{V} \tag{13.23}$$

Results

The results of the three independent methods of calculation of B are given in table 13.5 and compared with experimental values. For the partly crystalline polymers the method of calculation is illustrated in example 13.2.

All methods lead to the right order of magnitude and agree within a factor 2, which is surprisingly good. If no experimental data are available at all, it is best to use the average of the three values obtainable from the additive functions.

Example 13.2

Estimate the bulk modulus of a medium density polyethylene, density 0.95 (degree of crystallinity 70%) by means of the three methods available.

Solution

a. Estimation by means of the Rao function:
   According to eq. (13.21) we have:

$$B/\rho = (U/V)^6$$

For **V** we get:

$$V = M/\rho = 28/0.95 = 29.5 \text{ cm}^3/\text{mol}$$

For **U** we get:

$$U = 2 \times 880 = 1760$$

So

$$(U/V)^6 = \left(\frac{1760}{29.5}\right)^6 = 59.6^6 = 4.5 \times 10^{10} \text{ cm}^2 \cdot \text{s}^{-2}$$

and

$$B = 4.5 \times 10^{10} \times 0.95 = 4.3 \times 10^{10} \text{ g} \cdot \text{cm}^{-1} \cdot \text{s}^{-2} = 4.3 \times 10^9 \text{ N/m}^2$$

b. Estimation by means of the Grüneisen relation:
   According to eq. (13.22) we have:

$$B = \left(\frac{C_V}{C_p}\right)\left(\frac{C_p}{E}\right)$$

For C_p we get:

$$C_p = x_c C_p^s + (1 - x_c)C_p^r = 0.7 \times 51 + 0.3 \times 63 = 54.5 \text{ J/mol} \cdot \text{K}$$

TABLE 13.5

Bulk modulus of some polymers, experimental versus calculated values

Polymers	ρ (g/cm^3)	$B(10^9$ N/m^2)			
		exp. [1]	$(U/V)^6 \times \rho$ eq. (13.21)	C_v/E eq. (13.22)	E_{subl}/V eq. (13.23)
Polyethylene (am) (extrapol.)	0.85	(1.9)	1.95	2.5	2.0
Polyethylene (ld)	0.92	3.4	3.55	3.15	3.0
Polyethylene (md)	0.95	4.5	4.3	4.0	3.7
Polyethylene (hd)	0.97	5.0	5.05	4.35	4.0
Polyethylene (cr) (extrapol.)	1.00	(6.0)	6.3	5.1	4.6
Polypropylene	0.91	3.5	3.85	3.5	3.4
Polybutene-1	0.91	3.8	3.8	3.95	3.4
Polystyrene	1.05	5.0	5.15	4.35	2.7
Poly(vinyl chloride)	1.42	5.5	5.25	5.1	3.2
Poly(vinylidene fluoride)	1.77	5.4	4.2	6.2	2.4
Poly(chlorotrifluoroethylene)	2.15	5.2	4.55	6.6	2.8
Poly(tetrafluoroethylene)	2.35	2.5	3.6	6.6	2.2
Poly(vinyl butyral)	1.11	4.2	3.1	5.2	2.6
Poly(methyl methacrylate)	1.19	5.1	5.25	5.35	2.8
Poly(isobutyl methacrylate)	1.04	2.9	3.2	5.25	2.6
Polyisoprene (natural rubber)	0.91	2.0	1.9	2.4	2.1
Poly(chlorobutadiene)	1.24	2.3	2.3	2.7	2.6
Poly(methylene oxide)	1.43	6.9	7.4	5.8	6.3
Poly(ethylene oxide)	1.21	5.7	6.9	3.4	4.1
Poly(2,6-dimethyl-p-phenyl-ene oxide)	1.07	4.1	4.0	4.35	3.2
Poly(ethylene terephthalate)	1.40	>4	7.4	5.0	4.0
Nylon 6	1.14	5.1	6.05	4.9	7.2
Nylon 66	1.14	8.1	6.05	4.9	7.9
Polyimide	1.44	6.0	6.05	4.15	?
Poly(bisphenol carbonate)	1.20	5.0	5.4	4.6	3.1
Polysulphone	1.24	5.3	6.2	4.2	?
Phenolformaldehyde resin	1.22	7.4	5.4	4.3	−
Epoxy resin	1.18	6.4	6.8	6.2	−

[1] i.a. Warfield and coworkers (1968, 1970, 1972).

and for E:

$$E = x_c E_c + (1 - x_c)E_r = 0.7 \times 92 + 0.3 \times 205 = 126 \times 10^{-10} \text{ m}^3/\text{mol} \cdot \text{K}$$

From fig. 5.4 we read $(C_p/C_v) \approx 1.07$, so that

$$B = \left(\frac{1}{1.07}\right)\left(\frac{54.5}{126}\right) \times 10^{10} = 4.0 \times 10^9 \text{ N/m}^2$$

c. Estimation by means of the Grüneisen–Tobolsky relation:
    From equation (13.23) we get:

$$B = 8.04\left(\frac{E_{subl}}{V}\right)$$

Since $E_{subl} \approx E_{coh} + x_c \Delta H_m$, we first derive E_{coh} and ΔH_m.

From the group contributions mentioned in Chapter 5 for ΔH_m and in Chapter 7 for E_{coh} we derive

E_{coh} = 8380 J/mol and ΔH_m = 7600 J/mol

so

E_{subl} = 8380 + 0.70 × 7600 = 13700 J/mol

and

$$B = 8.04 \left(\frac{E_{subl}}{V} \right) = 8.04 \times \frac{13700}{29.5} \times 10^6 = 3.75 \times 10^9 \text{ N/m}^2$$

The experimental value is 4.5×10^9 N/m^2, in good agreement with the average value of the three estimation methods (= 4.0×10^9 N/m^2).

Poisson ratio (ν)

The Poisson ratio varies from $\frac{1}{2}$ for liquids to low values for purely elastic solids.

Shamov (1966) has pointed out the importance of the time dependence of the Poisson ratio of polymers. Measurements on polymers at very low frequency will yield values near 1/2, whereas data obtained at very high frequencies will yield values asymptotically approaching 1/3. The value of ν is thus a function of the rate of measurement. This fact is illustrated by data of Warfield and Barnet (1972) and Schuyer (1959):

Polyethylene sample $\rho(10^3$ kg/m^3)	Warfield, statically determined	Schuyer's measurements at 2 MHz
0.92	0.49	0.45
0.95	0.45	0.42

The reason of these differences is the viscoelastic nature of polymers (see part C of this chapter).

Fig. 13.4 gives a survey of statically determined ν-values for various materials (data already mentioned in table 13.2). It appears that as a first approximation the following equation can be used for estimating the ν-value:

$$\log (B/\rho) = 8.3 - 4\nu \tag{13.24}$$

Since

$$\frac{B}{\rho} = \left(\frac{U}{V} \right)^6 ,$$

equation (13.24) presents a possibility of estimating the Poisson ratio from the additive properties U and V.

Example 13.3

Estimate the shear modulus and Young's modulus for poly(bisphenol carbonate).

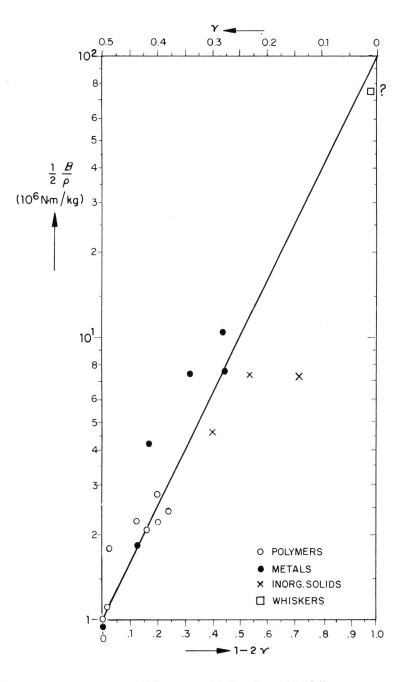

Fig. 13.4. Poisson ratios of different materials (data from table 13.2).

274

Solution

In example 13.1 we found $B = 5.4 \times 10^9$ N/m^2.
Since $\rho = 1200$ kg/m^3, $\frac{1}{2}B/\rho = 2.25 \times 10^6$ N · m/kg.
According to fig. 13.4 the Poisson ratio will be 0.41.
We thus obtain:

$$G = 3/2B \frac{1 - 2\nu}{1 + \nu} = 3/2 \times 5.4 \times 10^9 \times \frac{0.18}{1.41} = 1.03 \times 10^9 \text{ N/m}^2,$$

which is in excellent agreement with the experimental values $(0.8-1.1 \times 10^9$ N/m$^2)$. G may also be estimated by means of eq. (13.17).

Since $T_g = 423$ K we obtain:

$$G_g(298) \approx \frac{3}{1 + \dfrac{600}{423}} \times 10^9 = 1.25 \times 10^9 \text{ N/m}^2$$

Furthermore Young's modulus will be given by (13.7):

$$E = 3B(1 - 2\nu) = 3 \times 5.4 \times 10^9 \times 0.18 = 2.9 \times 10^9 \text{ N/m}^2,$$

in excellent agreement with Warfield's value 2.47×10^9 N/m^2.

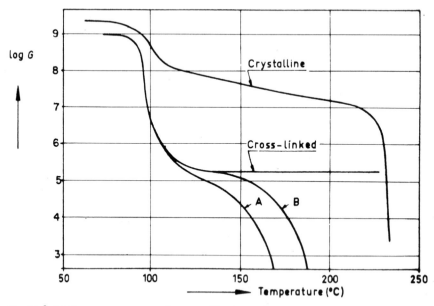

Fig. 13.5. (a) G versus temperature for crystalline isotactic polystyrene, for two linear atactic polystyrene samples A and B (of different molecular weight) and for lightly cross-linked atactic polystyrene (after Tobolsky, 1960).

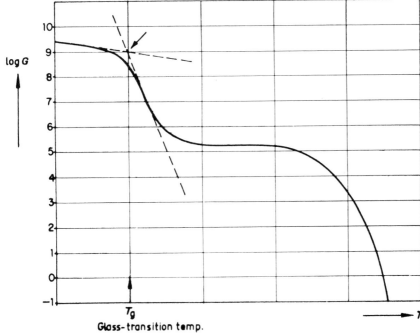

Mechanical Behaviour	Glassy	Leathery	Rubbery-elastic	Rubbery flow	Liquid flow
Molecular Behaviour	Only vibrations of atomic groups	Short-range diffusional motion (chain segments)	Rapid short-range diffusional motions Retarded long-range motions	Slippage of long-range entanglements	Long-range configurational changes (whole molecules)

Fig. 13.5. (b) The regions of viscoelastic behaviour of amorphous polymers.

TEMPERATURE DEPENDENCE OF THE MODULI

If a modulus is plotted as a function of temperature, a very characteristic curve is obtained which is different in shape for the different types of polymer: amorphous (glassy) polymers, semicrystalline polymers and elastomers (cross-linked amorphous polymers).

A typical example is polystyrene. This normally is amorphous (atactic); it can be cross-linked in this state. But it can also be crystalline (isotactic). The curves are shown in fig. 13.5a.

The curve of the shear modulus versus temperature for the amorphous polymer shows five regions of elastic behaviour (fig. 13.5b):

the *glassy* region ($T \leqslant T_g$; $G \approx 10^9$ N/m^2)
the *transition* ("*leathery*") region ($T \approx T_g$; G varies from 10^9 to 10^5 N/m^2)

the *rubbery "plateau"* (G remains fairly constant $\approx 10^{5.3}$ N/m^2)
the region of *rubbery flow* (G varies from $10^{5.3}$ to $10^{3.5}$ N/m^2)
the state of *liquid flow* ($G < 10^3$ N/m^2).

Chain entanglements are the cause of rubber-elastic properties in the liquid. Below the "critical" molecular weight (M_{cr}) there are no indications of a rubbery "plateau". The length of the latter is very much dependent on the length of the molecular chains, i.e. on the molecular weight of the polymer.

As the authors have found, the available data on the moduli of amorphous polymers at the rubbery plateau can be correlated by the following formula:

$$G_r \approx \frac{\rho R T_g}{M_{cr}} \tag{13.25}$$

(describing the "height" of the rubbery plateau), while the "length" of the plateau may be approximated by the equation:

$$\Delta T \approx 10^2 \Delta \log \frac{\overline{M}_n}{M_{cr}} \tag{13.26}$$

or

$$T_B - T_A = 10^2 \log(\overline{M}_B/\overline{M}_A) \tag{13.26a}$$

In these equations ΔT and $T_B - T_A$ express the "shift" of the log G vs. T curve (Fig. 13.5) for the different molecular weights (as indicated). Table 13.6 illustrates the results of eq. (13.25) in comparison with the experimental values.

The rubbery plateau can be "stabilized" by cross-linking, the regions of rubbery flow and liquid flow are completely suppressed if chemical cross-links are introduced to serve as permanent network junctions in place of the temporary chain entanglements. Crystallization is a kind of physical cross-linking with (numerically) many junctions. It is understandable that the amorphous state is more or less "stabilized" by crystallization, so that the transition becomes less pronounced.

We see from fig. 13.5 that at the glass transition temperature the rigidity of the amorphous polymers declines rapidly. In the semi-crystalline polymers there is a decline, too,

TABLE 13.6

Calculated and experimental values of the rubbery shear modulus of some polymers

	M_{cr} $(10^3$ g/mol)	T_g(K)	G_r(calc.) $(10^5$ N/m^2)	G_r(exp.) $(10^5$ N/m^2)
Polypropylene (am)	7	258	2.6	5
Polyisobutylene	16	198	1.0	3
Polystyrene	35	373	1.0	1.3
Poly(vinyl chloride)	6.2	356	6.4	4
Poly(vinyl acetate)	25	301	1.2	1.3

but a certain rigidity is retained up to the melting point. For highly crystalline polymers there is hardly any influence of the glass transition; their rigidity breaks down at the crystalline melting point. In the glassy polymers the rigidity is obviously highly dependent on the glass transition temperature; for the highly crystalline polymers it is mainly the location of the melting point which determines the rigidity. In the semicrystalline polymers both transitions are important.

The empirical expressions (13, 15, 16, 17) of Van Krevelen and Hoftyzer (1970) can be extended to describe the polymer rigidity as a function of temperature.

$$\frac{G_g(T)}{G_g(T_R)} \approx \frac{E_g(T)}{E_g(T_R)} = \frac{T_g/T_R + 2}{T_g/T_R + 2T/T_R} \quad \text{(for } T < T_g) \tag{13.27}$$

$$\frac{G_c(T)}{G_c(T_R)} \approx \frac{E_c(T)}{E_c(T_R)} = \exp\left[-2.65 \frac{T_m/T_R - T_m/T}{T_m/T_R - 1}\right] \quad \text{(for } T > T_R - 100) \tag{13.28}$$

$$G_{sc} = G_g + x_c^2(G_c - G_g) \tag{13.29}$$

where T_R is a reference temperature, e.g. room temperature.

To semicrystalline polymers *with a glass transition temperature well below the reference temperature,* equation (13.28) may directly be applied.

In this special case $\dfrac{G_{sc}(T)}{G_{sc}(T_R)} = \dfrac{G_c(T)}{G_c(T_R)}$

The following form is the easiest for numerical calculations:

$$\log \frac{G(T_R)}{G(T)} \approx \log \frac{E(T_R)}{E(T)} = 1.15 \frac{T_m/T_R - T_m/T}{T_m/T_R - 1} \tag{13.28a}$$

Fig. 13.6 shows how well equation (13.28a) describes the experimental data reported by Ogorkiewicz (1970).

B. RUBBER ELASTICITY

Cross-linked elastomers are a special case. Due to the cross-links this polymer class shows hardly any flow behaviour. The kinetic theory of rubber elasticity leads, for the Young's modulus at low strains, to the following equation:

$$E = 3\frac{RT\rho}{\overline{M}_{crl}} = 3z_{crl}\frac{RT}{V} = 3C_0 \tag{13.30}$$

278

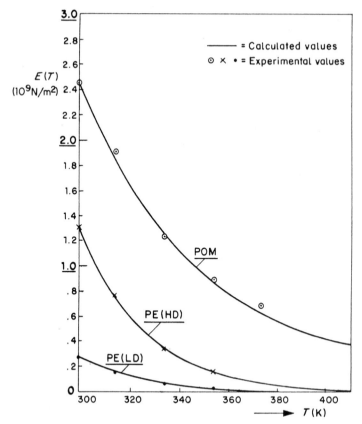

Fig. 13.6. Tensile modulus (10^2s, 0.2% strain).

where

R = gas constant = 8.314 J/mol · K
$\overline{M}_{crl}$ = number average molecular weight of the polymer segments between cross-links
ρ = density
z_{crl} = average number of cross-links per structural unit = $M/\overline{M}_{crl}$
V = molar volume of structural unit
C_0 = $z_{crl}RT/V$

Eq. (13.30) shows that the modulus of a rubber increases with temperature; this is in contrast with the behaviour of polymers that are not cross-linked. The reason of this behaviour is that rubber elasticity is an *entropy elasticity* in contrast with the *energy elasticity* in "normal" solids; the modulus increases with temperature because of the increased thermal or Brownian motion, which causes the stretched molecular segments to tug at their "anchor points" and try to assume a more probable coiled-up shape.

Eq. (13.30) shows that E increases with z_{crl}. Normally z_{crl} is of the order of 10^{-2}, so that $E \approx 10^6$ N/m^2 at 25°C.

The theory of rubber elasticity also leads to the following stress-deformation expression (for unidirectional stretching and compression):

$$\sigma = C_0(\Lambda - \Lambda^{-2}) \tag{13.31}$$

where $\Lambda = L/L_0$ = ratio of stretched length to unstretched length.
    The corresponding expression for simple shear is:

$$\tau = C_0 \tan \gamma \approx C_0(\Lambda - \Lambda^{-1}) \tag{13.32}$$

where γ is the angle through which a vertical edge is tilted.
    The expression (13.31) is valid for small extensions only. The actual behaviour of cross-linked rubbers in unidirectional extension is well described by the empirical *equation of Mooney–Rivlin* (1940, 1948):

$$\sigma = \left(C_1 + \frac{C_2}{\Lambda}\right)(\Lambda - \Lambda^{-2}) \tag{13.33}$$

where C_1 and C_2 are empirical constants.
    In compression and in shear the ideal elastic behaviour is more closely followed.
    Although eq. (13.33) affords a better representation of experimental data than eq. (13.31) it is of little predictive value since the molecular significance of the parameter C_2 remains obscure. The theory of rubber elasticity was extended by Blokland (1968). On the basis of photoelastic, light scattering and electron microscopic studies he found a structure in the networks which can be interpreted as rodlike correlated regions of chain segments or "bundles" (involving about 5% of the chain segments).
    On the basis of this model he derived an equation of the following type:

$$\sigma = C_0(1 - C_3(\Lambda))(\Lambda - \Lambda^{-2}) \tag{13.34}$$

where $C_3(\Lambda)$ is a correction function.
    From this equation the meaning of C_2 in the Mooney–Rivlin equation becomes clearer. Eq. (13.33) may be written as follows:

$$\sigma = \left[(C_1 + C_2) - \left(C_2 - \frac{C_2}{\Lambda}\right)\right](\Lambda - \Lambda^{-2}) . \tag{13.35}$$

or

$$\sigma = (C_1 + C_2)\left[1 - \frac{C_2}{C_1 + C_2}\left(1 - \frac{1}{\Lambda}\right)\right](\Lambda - \Lambda^{-2}) \tag{13.36}$$

    Table 13.7 shows the values of C_1 and C_2 for different families of elastomers.
    It is obvious that if the Mooney–Rivlin equation is written as

$$\sigma = C_0\left[1 - 0.4\left(1 - \frac{1}{\Lambda}\right)\right](\Lambda - \Lambda^{-2}) \tag{13.37}$$

where $C_0 \approx C_1 + C_2$, its form is similar to that of (13.34).
    The value of C_0 ($\approx C_1 + C_2$) is nearly equal to $\frac{1}{3} E_r$, or G_r (the shear modulus of the "rubbery plateau" as calculated according to (13.25)).

TABLE 13.7

Constants of the Mooney–Rivlin equation (numerical values derived from Blokland (1968)). C_1, C_2, expressed in 10^5 N/m^2.

Elastomer	C_1	C_2	$(C_1 + C_2)$	$\dfrac{C_2}{C_1 + C_2}$
Natural rubbers	2.0	1.5	3.5	0.4
	(0.9–3.8)	(0.9–2)		(0.25–0.6)
Butyl rubber	2.6	1.5	4.1	0.4
	(2.1–3.2)	(1.4–1.6)		(0.3–0.5)
Styrene–butadiene rubber	1.8	1.1	2.9	0.4
	(0.8–2.8)	(1.0–1.2)		(0.3–0.5)
Ethene–propene rubber	2.6	2.5	5.1	0.5
	(2.1–3.1)	(2.2–2.9)		(0.43–0.55)
Polyacrylate rubbers	1.2	2.8	3	0.5
	(0.6–1.6)	(0.9–4.8)		(0.3–0.8)
Silicone rubbers	0.75	0.75	1.5	0.4
	(0.3–1.2)	(0.3–1.1)		(0.25–0.5)
Polyurethanes	3	2	5	0.4 ·
	(2.4–3.4)	(1.8–2.2)		(0.38–0.43)

C. VISCOELASTICITY

Sections A and B of this chapter dealt with purely elastic deformations, i.e. deformations in which the strain was assumed to be a time-independent function of the stress. In reality, materials are never purely elastic: under certain circumstances they have non-elastic properties. This is especially true of polymers, which may show non-elastic deformation under circumstances in which metals may be regarded as purely elastic.

It is customary to use the expression viscoelastic deformations for all deformations that are not purely elastic. This means that viscoelasticity deals with a number of quite different phenomena. Literally the term viscoelastic means the combination of viscous and elastic properties. In this sense the non-Newtonian flow of polymer melts (to be discussed in Chapter 15) is a viscoelastic phenomenon. But also stress relaxation of a solid material is called a viscoelastic phenomenon, as the stress—strain relationship in this phenomenon is time-dependent. It is difficult, however, to see stress relaxation as a viscous deformation.

For a better understanding three phenomena may be distinguished, the combination of which is called viscoelasticity. This is elucidated in table 13.8.

This does not mean that these three phenomena can always be easily distinguished. Many practical deformation processes form a complicated combination.

Dynamic-mechanical measurements

Since viscoelastic phenomena always involve the change of properties with time, the

TABLE 13.8

Fundamental viscoelastic phenomena

Phenomenon	Time-dependence of stress–strain relation	Characteristic changing item	Characteristic time
Elastic deformation	Time-independent	Shape	Zero
Viscous deformation	Changes with time	Shape	Short
Relaxation	Changes with time	Structure	Long

measurements of viscoelastic properties of solid polymers may be called dynamic-mechanical.

Many experimental techniques are used to measure dynamic-mechanical properties. Each special technique covers only a small part of the total frequency (or time) range. Therefore a number of different techniques, which supplement one another, are needed. Fig. 13.7 gives a survey of the available methods.

Measurement of the response in deformation of a material to *periodic forces,* for instance during forced vibration, shows that stress and strain are not in phase; the strain lags behind the stress by a phase angle δ, the loss angle.

If the vibration is of a sinusoidal type, one gets:

$$\sigma = \sigma_0 \sin \omega t \qquad \text{(stress)}$$

$$\epsilon = \epsilon_0 \sin(\omega t - \delta) \quad \text{(strain)}$$

(13.38)

Another notation is:

$$\sigma^* = \sigma_0 \exp(i\omega t)$$

$$\epsilon^* = \epsilon_0 \exp\{i(\omega t - \delta)\} .$$

(13.38a)

Then

$$\frac{\sigma^*}{\epsilon^*} = E^* = \frac{\sigma_0}{\epsilon_0} \exp(i\delta) = \frac{\sigma_0}{\epsilon_0}(\cos \delta + i \sin \delta) = \frac{\sigma_0}{\epsilon_0} \cos \delta + i \frac{\sigma_0}{\epsilon_0} \sin \delta$$

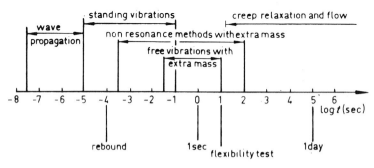

Fig. 13.7. The position of different experimental techniques on logarithmic time scale (Staverman and Schwarzl, 1956).

or

$$\boxed{E^* = E' + iE''} \tag{13.39}$$

where

E^* = the so-called *complex modulus*
E' = $\sigma_0/\epsilon_0 \cos \delta$ is the real part, or *storage modulus*
E'' = $\sigma_0/\epsilon_0 \sin \delta$ is the imaginary part, or *loss modulus*

In the same way also the dynamic shear modulus may be written as a complex modulus. For the complex moduli the basic interrelation formula (13.7) remains valid. The imaginary parts of the complex moduli are damping terms determining the dissipation of energy as heat when the material is deformed; this is why they are called loss moduli. The real parts of the complex moduli are terms determining the amount of recoverable energy stored as elastic energy; hence they are called storage moduli. *The only modulus which is time-independent is the bulk modulus*; hence its advantage as a basis for additivity.

The complex moduli are related to the complex viscosities by the following equations:

$$
\begin{array}{ll}
E'' = \omega\lambda' = 2\pi v_\omega\lambda' & G'' = \omega\eta' = 2\pi v_\omega\eta' \\
E' = \omega\lambda'' = 2\pi v_\omega\lambda'' & G' = \omega\eta'' = 2\pi v_\omega\eta''
\end{array}
\tag{13.40}
$$

where ω is the frequency in radians per second and v_ω the frequence in cycles per second; $\lambda *$ is the so-called complex dynamic *tensile viscosity* and $\eta *$ the complex dynamic *shear viscosity*. Their relation is:

$$\frac{\lambda^*}{\eta^*} = \frac{E^*}{G^*} = 2(1 + \nu). \tag{13.41}$$

For incompressible liquids $\nu = \frac{1}{2}$, so that $\lambda * = 3\eta *$.

The general expressions for the dynamic mechanical parameters are:

$$
\left.
\begin{array}{l}
|E^*| = [(E')^2 + (E'')^2]^{1/2} \\
|G^*| = [(G')^2 + (G'')^2]^{1/2} \\
|J^*| = [(J')^2 + (J'')^2]^{1/2} \quad \text{etc} \\
|\eta^*| = [(\eta')^2 + (\eta'')^2]^{1/2} \quad \text{etc}
\end{array}
\right\}
\tag{13.42}
$$

The loss tangent

The characteristic measure of damping is the ratio of energy dissipated per cycle to the maximum potential energy stored during a cycle; it is called *dissipation factor* or *loss tangent*.

$$\boxed{\frac{E''}{E'} = \tan \delta_E; \frac{G''}{G'} = \frac{J''}{J'} = \frac{\eta'}{\eta''} = \tan \delta_G; \tan \delta_E \approx \tan \delta_G} \tag{13.43}$$

Other related terms are the *logarithmic decrement* (Δ) and the *specific damping capac-*

ity or *internal friction* (ψ). The interrelation is the following:

$$\boxed{\tan \delta \approx \frac{\Delta}{\pi} \approx \frac{\psi}{2\pi}}$$

(13.44)

The heat developed per cycle per unit volume (at deformations with constant amplitude of strain) is

$$Q \approx \pi E'' \epsilon_0^2$$

(13.45)

where ϵ_0 is the maximum amplitude of strain during a cycle.

Resilience

Resilience is a material constant for which different definitions are given in the literature. Most often it is used as an inverse measure of damping. For small damping, different definitions result in:

$$R \approx 1 - 2\Delta \approx 1 - 2\pi \frac{G''}{G'} \approx 1 - 2\pi \tan \delta$$

(13.46)

The resilience of a polymer will be high in temperature regions where no mechanical damping peaks are found. This applies in particular to rubbery networks ($T \gg T_g$), which therefore possess a high resilience.

Dynamic-mechanical data and the structure of polymers

In many investigations dynamic-mechanical properties have been determined not so much to correlate mechanical properties as to study the influence of polymer structure on thermo-mechanical behaviour. For this purpose, complex moduli are determined as a function of temperature at a constant frequency.

In every transition region (see Chapter 2) *there is a certain fall of the moduli accompanied by a definite peak of the loss tangent* (fig. 13.9). These phenomena are called dynamic transitions. The spectrum of these damping peaks is a characteristic fingerprint of a polymer.

Fig. 13.8 shows this for a series of polymers.

Damping peaks between 130 and 170 K are connected with sequences of more than three CH_2 groups in the chain. Also the dispersion region around 200 K is connected with movements (rotations?) of chain segments. The main dispersion region is always related to the conventional glass–rubber transition. (In series of methacrylates it is clear that long side-chains act as plasticizers.) Between glass transition and (pre-)melting there are sometimes transitions in the solid structure which give rise to damping peaks (e.g. poly-(tetrafluoroethylene), polyethylene, poly(methyl methacrylate)).

The temperature at which the damping peak occurs is not the same as that at which the discontinuous change in a thermodynamic quantity is found. The damping peak will always nearly coincide with the point of inflection of the modulus–temperature curve, whereas the conventional transition temperature is at the intersection of the two tangents of the modulus–temperature curve, at least if the frequency is low. For many polymers this difference $T_d - T_{g(dyn)}$ (see fig. 13.9) can be of the order of 25°C.

Very important work on the influence of the chemical structure on the temperature of the damping maximum was done by Heijboer (1956–1965), especially regarding the structure of the ester groups in polymethacrylates.

284

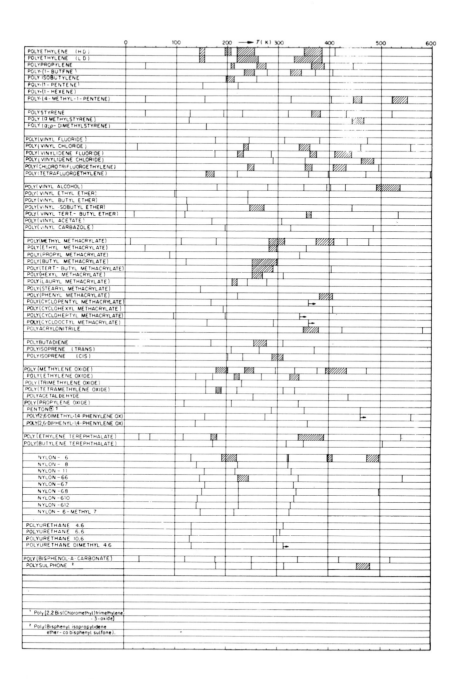

Fig. 13.8. Dynamic transitions of a series of polymers at a frequency of 1 Hz.

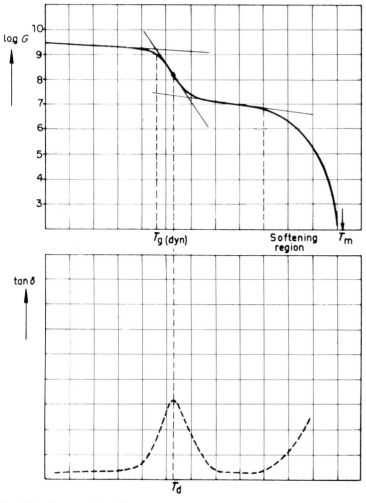

Fig. 13.9. Shear modulus (G) and tan δ as a function of temperature for partly crystalline polymers.

Heijboer (1965) also found an interesting relation between the relative decrease in modulus with temperature and the mean value of the damping (tan δ) between 20 and 60°C; this relationship is reproduced in fig. 13.10 and is valid for hard glassy polymers appreciably below T_g.

STRESS RELAXATION AND CREEP

Stress relaxation and creep are determined by two experimental methods frequently used in the mechanical testing of solid polymers, especially over longer periods.

Stress relaxation

Stress relaxation is the time-dependent change in stress at a constant deformation and

286

temperature. As the shape of the specimen does not change, this is a pure relaxation phenomenon in the sense defined at the beginning of this section. It is common use to call the momentary ratio of tensile stress to strain relaxation modulus (E_{rl}) and to present the results of the experiments in the form of E_{rl} as a function of time. This quantity should be distinguished, however, from the tensile modulus E as determined in elastic deformations.

The stress-relaxation behaviour of polymers is extremely temperature-dependent, especially in the region of the glass temperature.

In the transition region a plot of the logarithm of the tensile relaxation function ($\sigma(t)/\epsilon_0$) against the logarithm of time is nearly a straight line with a negative slope. At both higher and lower temperatures the slope becomes less steep. Fig. 13.11 shows the behaviour of polyisobutylene ($T_g = -76°C$, $T_d = -60°C$).

This behaviour can be approximated by the empirical formula:

$$\frac{\sigma(t)}{\epsilon_0} \equiv E_{rl}(t) = Kt^{-n} \tag{13.47}$$

where K and n are constants.

For amorphous polymers the constant n may vary between 0.5 and 1.0; n, a dimensionless number, is a measure of the relative importance of elastic and viscous contributions to stress relaxation.

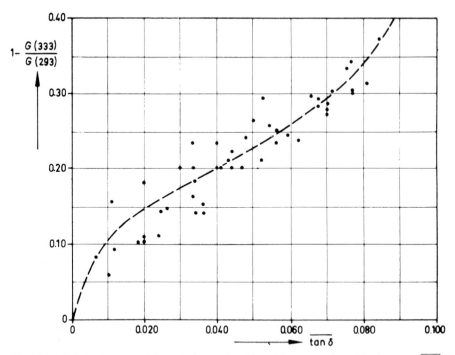

Fig. 13.10. Relative decrease of the modulus as a function of the mean value of the damping ($\overline{\tan \delta}$) between 20°C and 60°C for hard glassy polymers appreciably below T_g. Modulus determined at 1 Hz (after Heijboer, 1965).

n is closely related to tan δ:

$$n\frac{\pi}{2} \approx \tan \delta \ . \tag{13.48}$$

Another approximation of the tensile relaxation function is that of a rheological model, the so-called *Maxwell model*:

$$\frac{o(t)}{\epsilon_0} = E_{rl}(t) = E_0 \exp(-t/\Theta_{rl}) \tag{13.49}$$

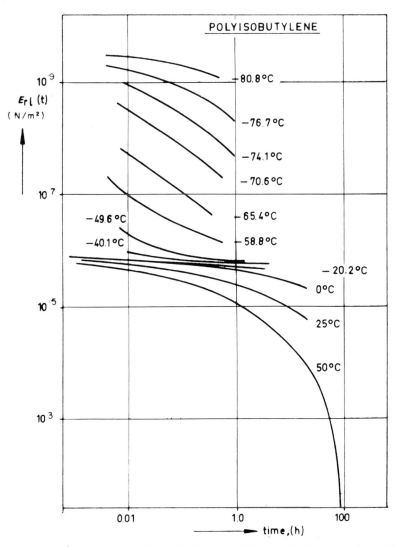

Fig. 13.11. Log E_{rl} (t) vs. log t for unfractionated polyisobutylene between -83 and $25°C$ (after Catsiff and Tobolsky, 1955).

where Θ_{rl} is the *relaxation time,* i.e. the time necessary to reduce σ to a fraction $1/e$ of its original value.

Equation (13.49) is valid only in a rather limited time interval. If the behaviour over a longer time period must be described, a number of equations of this type can be superposed, each with a different relaxation time. Ultimately, a whole *relaxation time spectrum* may be developed.

Creep

Dimensional stability is one of the most important properties of solid materials, but few materials are perfect in this respect.

Creep is the time-dependent relative deformation under a constant force (tension, shear or compression). In contradistinction to stress relaxation, creep is in general a combination of relaxation and viscous deformation phenomena. For small deformations (i.e. under the influence of small forces) relaxation phenomena predominate. It is under these conditions that stress relaxation and creep can be quantitatively correlated.

As the amount of deformation increases, viscous phenomena become increasingly important. At a given moment the specimen may show *yielding,* i.e. rapid viscous deformation.

The results of creep experiments are usually expressed in the quantity creep compliance, the time-dependent quotient of strain/stress.

Creep properties are very much dependent upon temperature. Well below the glass-transition point very little creep will take place, even after long periods of time. As the temperature is raised, the rate of creep increases. In the glass-transition region the creep properties become extremely temperature-dependent. In many polymers the creep rate goes through a maximum near the glass-transition point.

At temperatures well above the glass-transition temperature much greater elongations take place (i.e. the creep compliance is much larger), but the creep rate generally decreases.

A well-known simplified equation for the tensile creep function is *Nutting's empirical formula* (1921):

$$\frac{\epsilon(t)}{\sigma_0} \equiv D_{rt}(t) = K't^n \qquad (13.50)$$

where K' and n are constants.

For n the same reasoning is valid as for the stress relaxation. If $n\pi/2 \ll 1$:

$$n\frac{\pi}{2} \approx \tan\delta . \qquad (13.51)$$

A second approximation of the tensile creep function is derived from a rheological model, the so-called *Voigt model*

$$\frac{\epsilon(t)}{\sigma_0} \equiv D_{rt}(t) = D_0\{1 - \exp(-t/\Theta_{rt})\} \qquad (13.52)$$

where Θ_{rt} is the *retardation time.*

Also in this case, several retardation phenomena with different retardation times may be superposed.

The simple relaxation and retardation phenomena described by eqs. (13.49) and (13.52) show some analogy with a chemical reaction of the first order. The reaction rate constant corresponds with the reciprocal relaxation (or retardation) time. In reality, these phenomena show even more correspondence with a system of simultaneous chemical reactions.

Crystalline polymers may show a complicated behaviour. Their creep properties not only change rapidly with temperature, but at a given temperature crystalline polymers in some cases creep more with time than rigid amorphous or cross-linked polymers. This depends on the degree of crystallinity (which changes with temperature), the relative distance in temperature from the glass-transition, the melting temperature and possible recrystallization phenomena.

THE TIME–TEMPERATURE EQUIVALENCE (SUPERPOSITION) PRINCIPLE (TTEP)

The TTEP for amorphous polymers

Above T_g, the stress relaxation and the creep behaviour of amorphous polymers obey the "time–temperature equivalence (or superposition) principle".

Leaderman (1943) was the first to suggest that in viscoelastic materials time and temperature are equivalent to the extent that data at one temperature can be superimposed upon data taken at a different temperature, merely by shifting curves. Williams et al. (1955), Tobolsky (1960) and Ferry (1970) have worked out this suggestion and demonstrated the validity of the principle; with their procedures it is possible to convert stress-relaxation data at widely different temperatures to a single curve covering many decades of time at some reference temperature.

The principle can be applied as follows: The relaxation modulus:

$$\frac{\sigma}{\varepsilon} = E_{rl}(t)$$

is determined as a function of time (frequency) and temperature.

Fig. 13.11 is chosen as an example showing the curves of polyisobutylene. These curves are first corrected (reduced) for density and temperature. An arbitrary temperature $T_R(K)$ is selected as the reference temperature. The reduced modulus values are calculated by

$$E_{rl}(t)_{red} = \frac{T_R}{T} \cdot \frac{\rho_R}{\rho} E_{rl}(t). \tag{13.53}$$

The correction comes from the kinetic theory of rubber elasticity; it is relatively small and is sometimes neglected. After this reduction the experimental curves are replotted as in fig. 13.12 left. These reduced curves can now be shifted, one at a time, with respect to the reference curve (at $T_R = 25°C$), until portions of the curves superimpose to give a master curve such as shown on the right side of fig. 13.12. The amount each reduced modulus has to be shifted along the logarithmic time axis in making the master curve, the

290

so-called *shift factor,* is a function of temperature (see upper right corner of fig. 13.12).

The generalized formula for the shift factor is, according to *Williams, Landel and Ferry* (1955):

$$\log a_T = \log t/t(T_g) = \frac{-17.44(T - T_g)}{51.6 + (T - T_g)}$$

(13.54)

In this equation T_g is used as the reference temperature.

This WLF equation enables us to calculate the time (frequency) change at constant temperature, which — as far as the dynamic-mechanical behaviour is concerned — is equiva-

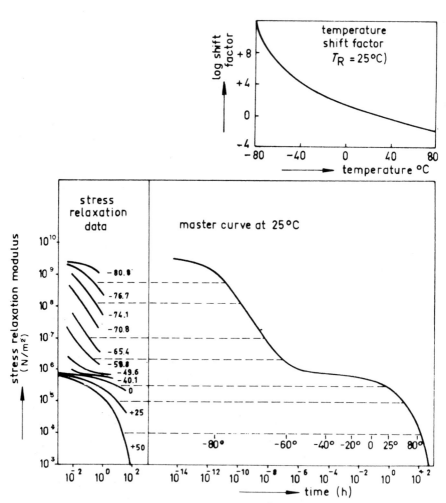

Fig. 13.12. Time—temperature superposition principle illustrated with polyisobutylene data. The reference temperature of the master curve is 25°C. The inset graph gives the amount of curve shifting required at the different temperatures (after Catsiff and Tobolsky, 1955, 1956).

lent to a certain temperature change at constant time (frequency).

Fig. 13.13 gives the graphical representation of the WLF equation (13.54).

For temperatures below T_g, deviations from the WLF equation are to be expected. This has been stated, for instance, by Rusch and Beck (1969).

The shift factor a_T also is the ratio of the relaxation time at temperature T and the relaxation time at T_g, if T_g is chosen as the reference temperature. Since the relaxation time is related to the viscosity η, the following expression can be derived:

$$a_T = \frac{\Theta_{rl}}{\Theta_{rl}(T_g)} = \frac{\eta}{\eta(T_g)} \frac{T_g \rho(T_g)}{T \rho(T)} \approx \frac{\eta}{\eta(T_g)} . \tag{13.55}$$

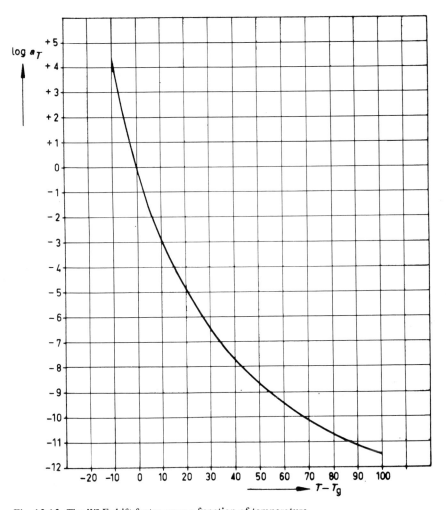

Fig. 13.13. The WLF shift factor a_T as a function of temperature.

The time–temperature equivalence principle can also be applied to the creep behaviour in a similar way. Again, this leads to shift factors which are practically identical with those obtained from stress relaxation.

Example 13.4

The stress relaxation modulus of polyisobutylene at 25°C and a measuring time of 1h is 3 × 10⁵ N/m². Estimate (a) the stress relaxation modulus at a measuring time of 1 h at −80°C, (b) the temperature at which the modulus for a measuring time of 10^{-6} h is the same as that at −80°C for a measuring time of 1 h.

Solution

a. From fig. 13.12 the logarithm of the shift factor at −80° is about 12. The master curve at $t \approx 10^{-12}$ gives a modulus of about 10^9 N/m². The modulus increases by a factor of $10^9/3 \times 10^5 \approx 3000$.

The shift factor at −80°C can also be obtained by applying formula (13.54). For polyisobutylene T_g is 197 K. So

$$\log a(298) = \frac{-17.44 \times 101}{51.6 + 101} = \frac{-1760}{152.6} = -11.5$$

$$\log a(193) = \frac{17.44 \times 4}{51.6 - 4} = \frac{70}{47.6} = 1.5$$

$$\log \frac{a(193)}{a(298)} = 1.5 + 11.5 = 13.0$$

The master curve at $t \approx 10^{-13}$ gives a modulus of about 2×10^9 N/m².

b. The stress relaxation modulus at −80°C and a measuring time of 1 h is 10^9 N/m². We have to calculate the temperature change corresponding to a shift factor of 10^6. We again apply formula (13.54):

$$\log a(193) = 1.5$$

$$\log \frac{a(193)}{a(T)} = 6 = 1.5 + 4.5$$

$$\log a(T) = -4.5 = \frac{-17.44\Delta T}{51.6 + \Delta T}$$

$$-232 - 4.5\Delta T = -17.4\Delta T$$

$$-232 = -12.9\Delta T$$

$$\Delta T = 18$$

or

$$T = T_g + 18 = 197 + 18 = 215 \text{ K} = -58°C$$

The TTEP for (semi)crystalline polymers

For crystalline polymers well below their melting points the WLF equation is not valid. Seitz and Balazs (1968) proved that the interrelation between a_T and T is a simple Arrhenius type of equation

$$\boxed{\log a_T = \log \frac{t}{t_R} = \frac{E_{act}}{2.3R}\left(\frac{1}{T} - \frac{1}{T_R}\right)}$$

(13.56)

In this respect it is interesting that eq. (13.28a) can be written in the following form:

$$\log \frac{E(T)}{E(T_R)} \sim \frac{T_m}{(T_m/T_R) - 1} \left(\frac{1}{T} - \frac{1}{T_R} \right)$$

which means that the activation energy of the creep (and stress relaxation) process is proportional to

$$\frac{T_m}{(T_m/T_R) - 1}.$$

The available data in the literature substantiate this equation as long as $T_g \ll T_R$. Combination of (13.56) with (13.28a) gives:

$$\log \frac{E_R}{E} \approx \log \frac{G_R}{G} \approx A \log \frac{t}{t_R} + B \left(\frac{1}{T_R} - \frac{1}{T} \right) \tag{13.57}$$

where $B \approx T_m(T_m/T_R - 1)$

Some characteristic values for engineering plastics have been derived from the literature data on creep measurements (see, e.g, Ogorkiewicz (1970)) and are given in table 13.9.

The "activation energy" of the shift factor in the formula of Seitz and Balazs (13.56) is:

$$E_{act}/R = 2.3 \, B/A$$

For polyethylene this gives $\frac{E_{act}}{R} \equiv 2.3 \frac{1265}{0.11} = 26{,}500$,

in good agreement with the experimental value obtained by Seitz and Balazs in stress-relaxation measurements, viz. 28,000(E_{act} = 56 kcal).

Significance of the shift factor (a_T)

As we have seen, the shift factor is the *relative* change in time (t/t_R) needed to *simulate* a certain property (which is known at a reference temperature (T_R) and a reference time (t_R)) at a changed temperature.

TABLE 13.9

Values of constants in eq. (13.57)

Polymer	E_R at 298 K; 100s (10^9 N/m²)	A(−)	B(K)	$\dfrac{T_m}{(T_m/T_R) - 1}$
polyethylene HD	1.3	0.11	1265	1170
polypropylene (isot)	1.5	0.08	800	900
polyoxymethylene	2.5	0.06	675	800
nylon 66	2.5	0.1	875	700

The shift factor proves to be the relative *time shortening* to simulate (at the reference temperature) a *low-temperature* property; it is the relative *time lengthening* to simulate (at the reference temperature) a *high-temperature* property.

The time factor is also the relative time *shortening* needed to simulate at a *higher* temperature a property measured at the reference temperature; it is the time *lengthening* to simulate at a *lower* temperature a property measured at the reference temperature.

In order to obtain equal test results, time lengthening at a given reference temperature is *equivalent* to temperature increase at a given reference time. For obtaining the required behaviour of the material, time lengthening can be *compensated* by a temperature decrease and time shortening by a temperature increase. In other words: time (in the form $\log t/t_R$) and temperature (in the form $f(T-T_R)$) are *superposed* in the relationship between property, t and T.

As we have seen, the modulus can be described by a formula of the following form: for amorphous polymers:

$$\log \frac{E_R}{E} = f\left\{\log \frac{t}{t_R} + \frac{17.44(T-T_g)}{51.6+(T-T_g)}\right\} \tag{13.58}$$

for semi-crystalline polymers with $T_R \gg T_g$:

$$\log \frac{E_R}{E} \approx A \log \frac{t}{t_R} + B\left(\frac{1}{T_R} - \frac{1}{T}\right) \tag{13.57}$$

For $E = E_R$, equation (13.58) gives (13.54), the WLF equation, while (13.57) leads to (13.56), the Seitz–Balazs equation.

Example 13.5

The creep modulus of polypropylene at room temperature (298 K) is 1.5×10^9 N/m² (100 s creep modulus). Estimate the creep modulus at 333 K after 10^4 h (= 36×10^7 s).

Solution

Eq. (13.57) is used:

$$\log \frac{E_R}{E} \approx 0.08 \log \frac{3.6 \times 10^7}{10^2} + 800\left(\frac{1}{298} - \frac{1}{333}\right)$$

$$\log \frac{1.5 \times 10^9}{E} \approx 0.08 \times 5.555 + 800(336 - 300)10^{-5}$$

$$\approx 0.445 \qquad + 0.288$$

$$\approx 0.733$$

So $\dfrac{1.5 \times 10^9}{E} \approx 5.4$ or $E(333\ K, 10^4\ h) \approx 0.28 \times 10^9$ N/m²

The experimental value is 0.21×10^9 N/m²

MODELS OF VISCOELASTIC BEHAVIOUR

In order to describe and imitate the viscoelastic behaviour several models have been developed (fig. 13.14).

1. The *ideal elastic element* is represented by a spring which obeys Hooke's law (with a defined modulus of elasticity) (*Hooke element*). The elastic deformation is instantaneous. An ideal rubbery solid exhibits such a simple behaviour.

2. The *ideal viscous element* can be represented by a dashpot filled with a Newtonian fluid, whose deformation is linear with time while the stress is applied, and is completely irrecoverable (*Newton element*). The stress is exactly $90°$ out of phase with the strain.

These two basic elements may be combined in series or parallel, giving:

3. The *Maxwell element* (elastic deformation plus flow), represented by a spring and a dashpot in series. It symbolizes a material which can respond elastically to stress, but can also undergo viscous flow. The two contributions to the strain are additive in this model:

$$\epsilon = \epsilon_e + \epsilon_v \qquad (13.59)$$

The strain will be out of phase with the stress, with a phase angle between $0°$ and $90°$.

4. The *Voigt element* (retarded elastic response), represented by a spring and a dashpot in parallel. The elastic response is not instantaneous but retarded by a viscous resistance. The two contributions to the stress are additive in this model:

$$\sigma = \sigma_e + \sigma_v \qquad (13.60)$$

The basic models contain a modulus E and a viscosity η which are assumed to be time-independent. Many attempts have been made to describe real time-dependent phenomena by combinations of these basic models.

The simplest model that can be used for describing a single creep experiment is Burgers model, consisting of a Maxwell model and a Voigt model in series. More complicated are so-called extended models involving an instantaneous elastic response, viscous flow and a large number of Voigt elements, each with its own modulus and retardation time. Although these models exhibit the chief characteristics of the viscoelastic behaviour of polymers and lead to a spectrum of relaxation and retardation times, they are nevertheless of restricted value: they are valid for very small deformations only. The flow of a polymer is probably not Newtonian and its elastic response not Hookean. The behaviour of real polymers cannot be characterized by discrete relaxation or retardation times, but requires a spectrum of relaxation or retardation times to account for all phases of its behaviour.

In a qualitative way the models are useful.

INTERRELATIONS BETWEEN DIFFERENT VISCOELASTIC FUNCTIONS OF THE SAME MATERIAL

For a given material the viscoelastic properties – the relaxation behaviour for solid materials – can be determined by a number of different techniques. The results obtained by each technique are expressed in the form of a characteristic function. In tensile deformation these functions are:

a. Stress relaxation:
the relaxation modulus as a function of time: $E_{\mathrm{rl}}(t)$

b. Creep:
the retardation compliance as a function of time: $D_{\mathrm{rt}}(t)$

c. Periodic deformation:

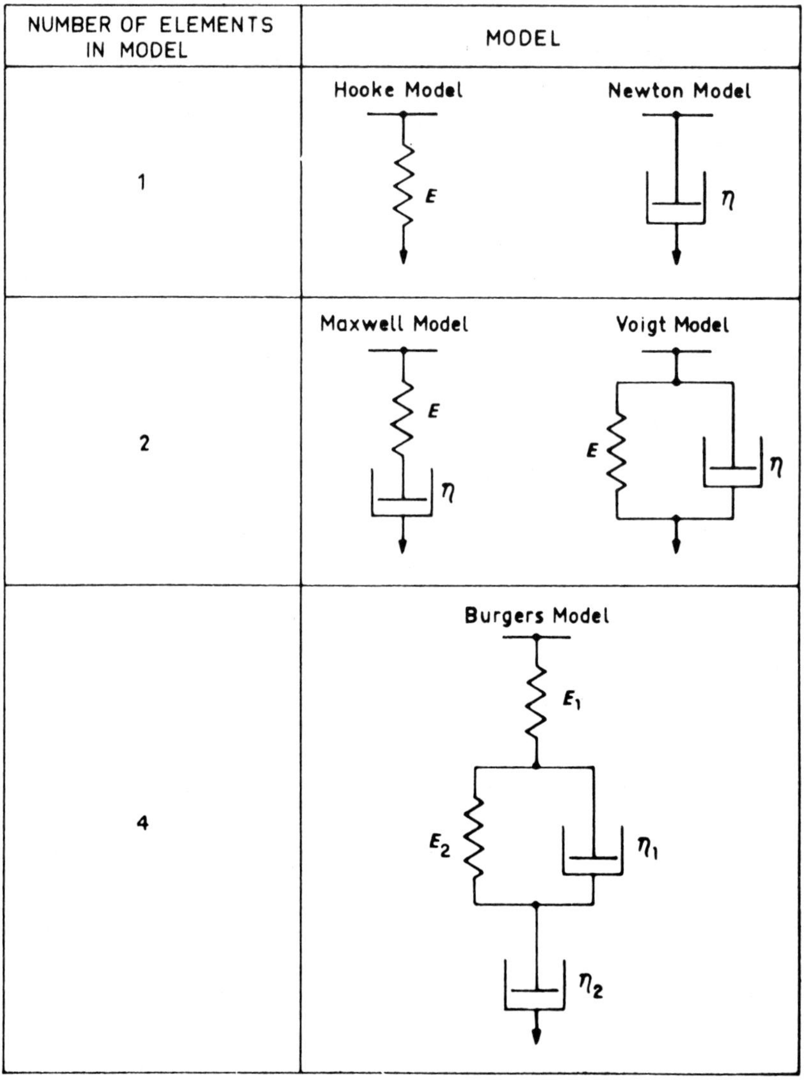
NUMBER OF ELEMENTS IN MODEL
MODEL
1
Hooke Model
E
Newton Model
η
2
Maxwell Model
E
η
Voigt Model
E
η
4
Burgers Model
E1
E2
η1
η2

Fig. 13.14. Models for viscoelastic behaviour.

the components of the dynamic modulus or the dynamic compliance as a function of the frequencies $E'(\omega)$ and $E''(\omega)$ or $D'(\omega)$ and $D''(\omega)$.

It will often be desirable to convert the results of one type of experiment into the characteristic quantities of another type. Unfortunately, there are no rigorous rules for these conversions. The problem may be approached in two ways. In the first place, exact interrelations can be derived from the theory of linear viscoelasticity. This method has two disadvantages.

a. the theory of linear viscoelasticity is applicable to rather small deformations only

b. the exact relations are not very suitable for numerical calculations.

In practice, the exact interrelations will seldom be applicable. This is the reason why a great number of approximate interrelations have been derived by several investigators. For a survey of these relationships the reader is referred to Ferry's monograph (1970).

Schwarzl (1970) studied the errors to be expected in the application of this type of equations, starting from the theory of linear viscoelasticity. His results are given schematically in fig. 13.15. For non-linear viscoelastic behaviour, the exactitude of the approximate formulae cannot be predicted.

As it is impossible to mention all the approximate relationships that have been proposed in the literature, only a few examples will be given.

Stress relaxation from creep

$$E_{rl}(t) = \frac{\sin m\pi}{m\pi D_{rt}(t)} \tag{13.61}$$

in which m = $\dfrac{d \log D_{rt}}{d \log t}$

Stress relaxation from dynamic quantities

$$E_{rl}(0.48t) \approx E'(\omega)| \, t = 1/\omega \tag{13.62}$$

$$E_{rl}(0.48t) \approx E'(\omega) - 0.257 \, E''(0.299\omega)| \, t = 1/\omega \tag{13.63}$$

$$E_{rl}(1.25t) \approx E'(\omega) - 0.5303 \, E''(0.5282\omega)$$

$$-0.021 \, E''(0.085\omega) + 0.042 \, E''(6.37\omega)| \, t = 1/\omega \tag{13.64}$$

Equations (13.62) to (13.64) illustrate how the exactitude of the formula can be increased by the addition of more modulus values at different values of ω. The applicability, however, decreases with an increasing amount of information required.

Dynamic quantities from stress relaxation

$$E'(\omega) \approx E_{rl}(t) + 0.86 \{E_{rl}(t) - E_{rl}(2t)\}| \, t = 1/\omega \tag{13.65}$$

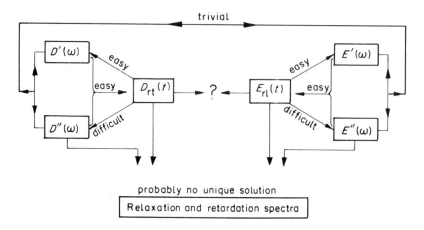

Fig. 13.15. Accuracy of interrelationships between static and dynamic viscoelastic functions.

$$E''(\omega) \approx -0.470\{E_{rl}(2t) - E_{rl}(4t)\} + 1.674\{E_{rl}(t) - E_{rl}(2t)\}$$
$$+ 0.198\{E_{rl}(\tfrac{1}{2}t) - E_{rl}(t)\} + \dots \mid t = 1/\omega \qquad (13.66)$$

D. ULTIMATE MECHANICAL PROPERTIES

Deformation properties

The strength properties of solids are most simply illustrated by the stress—strain diagram, which describes the behaviour of a homogeneous specimen of uniform cross section subjected to uniaxial tension (see fig. 13.16).

Within the linear region the strain is proportional to the stress and the deformation is reversible.

If the material fails and ruptures at a certain tension and a certain small elongation it is called brittle. If permanent or plastic deformation sets in after elastic deformation at some critical stress, the material is called ductile.

During the plastic deformation there is generally an increase in stress with deformation; this is known as *work-hardening*. If at some point the stress is removed, the material recovers along a path nearly parallel to the linear region; the sample then shows a permanent plastic deformation.

There is a basic difference between rupture above the glass transition temperature (where the polymer backbones have an opportunity to change their configurations before the material fails) and well below T_g (where the backbone configurations are essentially immobilized within the period of observation: brittle materials).

Fig. 13.17 shows the stress-strain curves for the different types of polymeric materials.

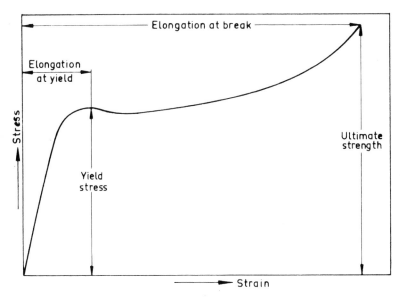

Fig. 13.16. Generalized tensile stress–strain curve for plastics (Winding and Hiatt, 1961).

Ultimate strength of brittle materials

The theoretical value for the brittle strength of a material is of the order of

$$\sigma_{th} \approx \frac{1}{10} E$$

where E is Young's modulus.

The observed brittle strength is generally very variable, but is always 10 to 100 times smaller than the theoretical value. Only some very fine fibres (e.g. silica) have been prepared which have tensile strengths approaching the theoretical value. The source of this "weakness" is the presence of flaws or cracks in the solid, especially at the surface. These cracks act as "stress-multipliers".

If there is a crack in a sample with a length L and a tip radius r, the tensile stress at the tip of the crack is multiplied by a factor of the order $\sqrt{L/r}$. The multiplication factor can easily be of the order of 10–100. But even if the crack-tip tends to zero the material still possesses a certain strength, so that there must be an extra effect to explain the facts.

Griffith (1921) gave the answer to this problem by showing that for a crack to grow, it is not sufficient for the stresses at the crack-tip to exceed the theoretical strength; in addition sufficient elastic energy must be released to provide the extra surface energy that a growing crack demands.

The smallest stress σ_{Gr} capable of producing crack propagation is of the order of

$$\sigma_{Gr} \approx \sigma_{th} \sqrt{\frac{3a}{L}} \tag{13.67}$$

300

where a is the "lattice spacing" in Griffith's model and L is the length of the crack.

Since the surface energy needed must be equal to the work done, we get:

Work done $\sim Ea \sim \gamma$

so that the result after substitution is:

$$\sigma_{Gr} = \sigma_{max} = C\left(\frac{\gamma E}{L}\right)^{1/2} \qquad (13.68)$$

where C is a constant.

Since $\gamma \sim E^{2/3}$, the final result is:

$$\sigma_{max} \sim E^{0.8}$$

Ultimate strength of ductile materials

If a material does not appreciably work-harden after yielding, in tension, its *yield stress* will be very nearly the maximum stress the material can support before it pulls apart, i.e. its ultimate tensile strength.

Description of Polymer	Characteristics of Stress-Strain Curve			
	Modulus	Yield Stress	Ultimate Strength	Elongation at Break
Soft,weak	Low	Low	Low	Moderate
Soft,tough	Low	Low	(Yield Stress)	High
Hard,strong	High	High	High	Moderate
Hard,tough	High	High	High	High
Hard, brittle	High	None	Moderate	Low

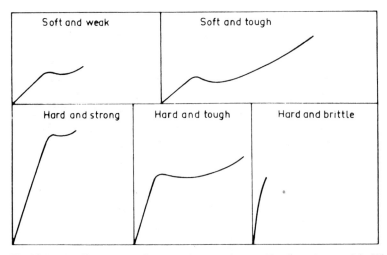

Soft and weak

Soft and tough

Hard and strong

Hard and tough

Hard and brittle

Fig. 13.17. Tensile stress–strain curves for several types of polymeric materials (Winding and Hiatt, 1961).

Tabor (1947) showed that the yield stress of a material is proportional to the indentation hardness (see Chapter 25). Since the latter is a power function of the modulus, the yield stress will be:

$$\sigma_y = \sigma_{max} \sim E^n \tag{13.69}$$

where $n \approx 0.75$.

If a material shows work-hardening, as in many crystalline polymers (due to *orientation* during the plastic deformation), the ultimate strength (if calculated on the basis of original cross section) will of course be higher than the yield stress.

Transition from ductility to brittleness, and vice versa

As we have seen, mobility of the molecules is one of the sources of ductility. However, if the mobility is obstructed by some barrier, an internal crack may form, and initiate crack propagation. In this way a ductile solid may become brittle.

On the other hand a brittle solid may be made ductile by applying hydrostatic pressure. Let us consider a brittle solid which fails at a tensile stress σ. If a hydrostatic pressure p is applied, the tensile stress necessary for failure is $p + \sigma$. Associated with this tensile stress is a shear stress equal to $\frac{1}{2}(p + \sigma)$. If the critical shear stress is less than this, the material will flow in a ductile manner before the tensile stress is large enough to produce brittle failure.

Phenomena like this are well known. At great depths rocks can flow although they are normally very brittle. Even quartz can flow plastically under sufficiently high hydrostatic pressure.

Many polymers which are brittle in tension or bending may readily yield in other types of deformation, and show a high ductility.

In indentation hardness experiments, plastic indentation can often be made in relatively brittle materials; hardness values thus obtained are a measure of the plastic properties of the brittle solid!

Another effect which greatly influences the type of rupture is orientation. If a polymer is heated just above the glass transition temperature, stretched several hundred percent in one direction and cooled to room temperature while under stress, the polymer chains will be trapped in a nonrandom distribution of conformations: more orientation parallel to the stretching direction. The material becomes markedly anisotropic and will be considerably stronger in the direction of orientation (and weaker in the transverse direction). The effect may be dramatic; a glassy polymer which, unoriented, would undergo brittle fracture at $\epsilon_{max} = 0.03$, may, when oriented, exhibit ductile yielding with failure at $\epsilon_{max} = 0.50$. The area under the stress-strain curve, a rough measure of toughness, may be 20 times as large for a properly oriented specimen of the same material (see Chapter 14).

If crystallization and orientation go together, the strength can be further improved. The strongest polymeric materials (synthetic fibres) are oriented crystalline polymers.

Crazing

Crazing is a form of non-catastrophic failure which may occur in glassy polymers, giving rise to irreversible deformation.

Crazes scatter light and are readily visible to the unaided eye as whitened planes *perpendicular* to the direction of stress.

A craze is a narrow zone of highly deformed and voided material (40–60%). The molecular chains in a craze are aligned *parallel* to the direction of stress; they are drawn into a lacework of oriented threads or sheets, separated from each other by a maze of interconnected voids. This leads to visual impairment and enhanced permeability.

Craze formation is now considered to be a mode of plastic deformation peculiar to glassy polymers (or to glassy regions in a polymer) that is competitive with shear ductility.

Thus, when subject to a tensile stress, high-molecular-weight glassy polymers can exhibit three main types of response:
 a. they can extend uniformly
 b. they can extend in a necking mode
 c. they can craze — and finally break (brittle fracture).

It seems reasonable to assume that crazing is a process which can occur quite naturally in any orientation hardening material, which exhibits plastic instability at moderate strains and in which the yield stress is much higher than the stress required for the nucleation of voids (cavitation).

It is interesting to remark that like most mechanical parameters the crazing stress exhibits viscoelastic characteristics, decreasing with increasing temperature and with decreasing strain rate.

Numerical values

Table 13.10 gives the numerical values of the strength properties of a series of polymers.

The data on the tensile strength are graphically reproduced in fig. 13.18, where σ_{max} (i.e. the tensile strength at break of brittle (linear) polymers and the tensile strength at yield of ductile (linear) polymers) is plotted as a function of E, the tensile modulus. As an approximation the following empirical expression may be used (drawn line):

$$\sigma_{max} = 30 \, E^{2/3} \tag{13.70}$$

where σ_{max} and E are expressed in N/m^2.

Table 13.10 permits a comparison of the values of the tensile, flexural and compressive strength. The strength ratios of polymers are compared with those of other materials in table 13.11. Obviously there is a strong influence of the Poisson ratio on the value of the compressive/tensile strength ratio. The following empirical equation provides a good estimate (see fig. 13.19):

$$\log \frac{\sigma_{max}(\text{compressive})}{\sigma_{max}(\text{tensile})} \approx 2.2 - 5\nu \tag{13.71}$$

where ν is the Poisson ratio.

On the other hand, the flexural/tensile strength ratio is nearly constant (average value 1.6) for polymers. (The same is true for the flexural/tensile modulus ratio).

Finally there is a rough relationship between the maximum elongation and the Poisson ratio of polymers.

TABLE 13.10

Ultimate mechanical properties of polymers (unmodified) (moduli in 10^9 N/m^2; strengths in 10^7 N/m^2)

Polymer	Tensile strength at yield	Elongation at yield (%)	Tensile strength at break	Elongation at break (%)	Tensile modulus	Flexural strength	Flexural modulus	Compressive strength	Poisson ratio (stat.)	Polymer ref. No.
Polyethylene (LD)	0.8	20	1.0	800	0.2				0.49	1
Polyethylene (HD)	3.0	9	3.0	600	1	4.5	0.8	2	0.47	2
Polypropylene	3.2	12	3.3	400	1.4	4.9	1.5	4.5	0.43	3
Poly(1-butene)			3.0	350	0.75				0.47	4
Polystyrene			5.0	2.5	3.4	8	3.3	9.5	0.38	5
Poly(vinyl chloride)	4.8	3	5.0	30	2.6	9	3.5	7	0.42	6
Poly(chlorotrifluoroethylene)	3.0	10	3.5	175	1.9	5.5	2	4	0.44	7
Poly(tetrafluoroethylene)	1.3	62.5	2.5	200	0.5		0.35	0.8	0.46	8
Poly(methyl methacrylate)			6.5	10	3.2	11	3	10.5	0.40	9
Poly(methylene oxide)			6.5	40	2.7		2.5	12	0.44	10
Poly(phenylene oxide)			6.5	75	2.3				0.41	11
Poly(phenylene sulphide)			6.5	3	3.4	11				12
Poly(ethylene terephthalate)		6	5.4	275	3.0		2.9		0.43	13
Poly(tetramethylene terephthalate)			5.0		2.5				0.44	14
Nylon 66	5.7	25	8.0	200	2.0		2.3	9	0.46	15
Nylon 6	5.0	30	7.5	300	1.9		2.0	7	0.44	16
Poly(bisphenol carbonate)	6.5	30	6.0	125	2.5	9	2.5	8	0.42	17
Polysulphone			6.5	75	2.5	10			0.42	18
Polyimide			7.5	7	3.0	10			0.42	19
Cellulose acetate	4	6	3	30	2	5	1.25			20
Phenol formaldehyde resin			5.5	1	3.4	9	4	13		21
Uns. polyester resin			6.0	3	5.0	9	5.0	15		22
Epoxy resin			5.5	5	2.4	11	2.5	13		23

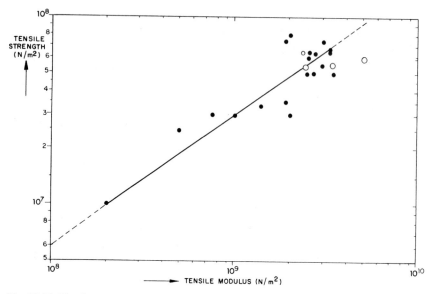

Fig. 13.18. Tensile strength of polymers, correlated with modulus.

This is not unexpected, since the Poisson ratio is a measure of the liquid-like character of a solid. The correlation is illustrated by fig. 13.20.

Rate dependence of ultimate strength

When the rate of elongation is increased, the tensile strength and the modulus also increase; the elongation to break generally decreases (except in rubbers).

Normally an increase of the speed of testing is similar to a decrease of the temperature of testing. To lightly cross-linked rubbers even the time—temperature equivalence principle can be applied.

TABLE 13.11

Strength ratio in different materials

Material	Strength ratio (exp)		Poisson ratio (ν)
	compressive tensile	flexural tensile	
vitreous silica	30	–	0.14
silicate glass	12.5	–	0.225
phenol formaldehyde	2.5	–	0.35
polystyrene	1.9	1.9	0.37
poly(methyl methacrylate)	(1.6)	1.6	0.40
poly(vinyl chloride)	1.4	1.8	0.42
polyethylene (h.d.)	0.67	1.5	0.47

Ultimate stress–strain properties of amorphous elastomers

Lightly cross-linked elastomers follow a simple pattern of ultimate behaviour. Smith (1958) has shown that the ultimate properties of this class of polymers follow a time–temperature equivalence principle just as the viscoelastic response to small non-destructive stresses does.

Curves of stress (divided by absolute temperature) versus the log of time-to-break at various temperatures can be made to coincide by introducing the temperature-dependent shift factor a_T. Application of the same shift factor causes the curves of the elongation

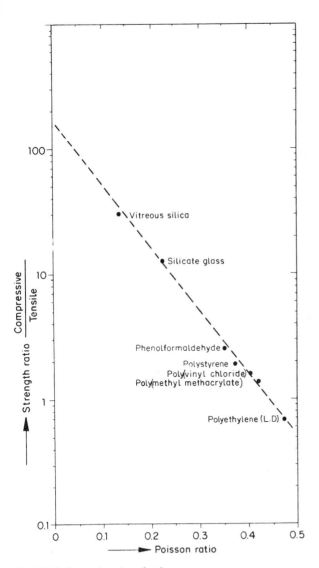

Fig. 13.19. Strength ratios of polymers.

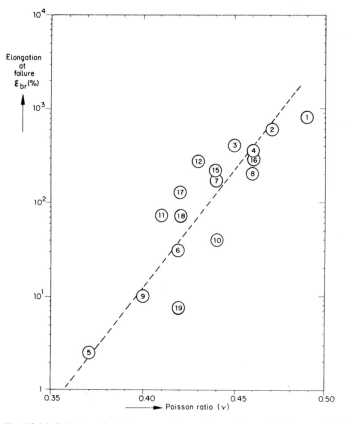

Fig. 13.20. Relationship between maximum elongation and Poisson ratio of polymers (for reference numbers, see table 13.10).

at break ϵ_{br} versus the logarithm of time-to-break at various temperatures to coincide. A direct consequence is that all tensile strengths (divided by absolute temperature), when plotted against elongation at break, fall on a common failure envelope, independent of the temperature of testing.

Fig. 13.21 shows the behaviour of Viton B elastomer.

Crystallization accompanying stretching invalidates the simple time—temperature equivalence principle.

Fig. 13.21c, known as the Smith failure envelope, is of great importance because of its independence of the time scale. Moreover, investigations of Smith, and Landel and Fedors (1963, 1967) proved that the failure envelope is independent of the path, so that the same envelope is generated in stress relaxation, creep, or constant-rate experiments. As such it serves a very useful failure criterion. Landel and Fedors (1967) showed that a further generalization is obtained if the data are reduced to unit cross-link density

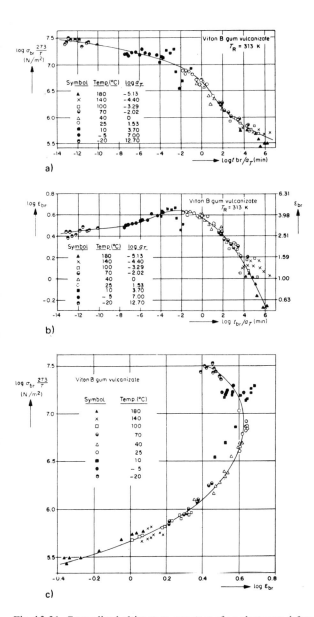

Fig. 13.21. Generalized ultimate parameters of an elastomer (after Smith, 1962, 1964):
(a) Logarithmic plot of stress-at-break ($\sigma_{br}273/T$) versus reduced time-to-break (t_{br}/a_T) for Viton B vulcanizate. Reference temperature for a_T is 313 K (40°C).
(b) Logarithmic plot of ultimate strain (ϵ_{br}) versus reduced time to break (t_{br}/a_T) for Viton B vulcanizate. Reference temperature for a_T is 313 K (40°C).
(c) Failure envelope for Viton B vulcanizate.

(ν_e). The latter is related to the modulus by the formula (13.30)

$$E = 3RT \cdot \nu_e \quad \left(= 3RT \frac{z_{crl}}{V} \right)$$

By plotting

$$\frac{\sigma_{br}}{\nu_e} \cdot \frac{273}{T} \quad \text{vs } \epsilon_{br} = \Lambda_{br} - 1$$

where Λ_{br} is the stretch ratio at break, they obtained a generalized diagram which is somewhat simplified in fig. 13.22. It is valid for polybutadiene, polyisobutylene, silicon and fluorocarbon elastomers and for epoxy resins. At higher temperatures these polymers follow a common response curve, at lower temperatures they diverge due to their different T_g-temperatures, their different chain flexibilities and their different degrees of cross-linking.

For glassy and semicrystalline polymers the number of investigations is very restricted and no generalizations have been found.

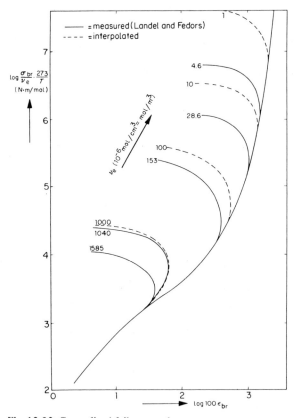

Fig. 13.22. Generalized failure envelope.

Other mechanical properties of polymers

The other mechanical properties of polymers have the typical character of product properties: they are not only dependent on the intrinsic nature of the material but also on the environmental conditions, in other words, they are systemic quantities. They will be treated separately in Chapter 24.

BIBLIOGRAPHY, CHAPTER 13

General references

Alfrey, T., "Mechanical Behaviour of High Polymers", Interscience, New York, 1948.
Andrews, E.H., "Fracture in Polymers", Elsevier, New York, 1968.
Eirich, F.R. (Ed.), "Rheology", Academic Press, New York, 1959, 1960.
Ferry, J.D., "Viscoelastic Properties of Polymers", Wiley, New York, 1970.
Flory, P.J., "Principles of Polymer Chemistry". Cornell University Press, Ithaca, N.Y., 1953.
Gent, A.N., "Rubber Elasticity; a Review", J. Polymer Sci., Polymer Symp. 48 (1974) 1.
Kausch, H.H., Hassel, J.A. and Jaffee, R.J. (Eds.), "Deformation and Fracture of High Polymers", Plenum Press, New York, 1973.
McCrum, N.G., Read, B.E. and Williams, G., "Anelastic and Dielectric Effects in Polymeric Solids", Wiley, New York, 1967.
Nielsen, L.E., "Mechanical Properties of Polymers", Reinhold, New York, 1962.
Ogorkiewicz, R.M. (Ed.), "Thermoplastics, Properties and Design", Wiley-Interscience, London, 1974.
Ogorkiewicz, R.M. (Ed.), "Engineering Properties of Thermoplastics", Wiley-Interscience, London, 1970.
Shen, M. and Croucher, M., "Contribution of Internal Energy to the Elasticity of Rubberlike Materials", J. Macromol. Sci.: Revs. Macromol. Chem. C12 (1975) 287.
Stuart, H.A., "Die Physik der Hochpolymeren", Springer, Berlin, 1956.
Tobolsky, A.V., "Properties and Structure of Polymers", Wiley, New York, 1960.
Treloar, L.R.G., "The Physics of Rubber Elasticity", Clarendon Press, Oxford, 1958.
Winding, C.C. and Hiatt, G.D., "Polymeric Materials", McGraw-Hill, New York, 1961.

Special references

Blokland, R., "Elasticity and Structure of Polyurethane Networks", Thesis, Delft University of Technology, 1968.
Blokland, R. and Prins, W., J. Polymer Sci. (A2) 7 (1969) 1595.
Catsiff, E. and Tobolsky, A.V., J. Colloid Sci. 10 (1955) 375; J. Polymer Sci. 19 (1956) 111.
Fedors, R.F. and Landel, R.F., Trans. Soc. Rheol. 9: 1 (1965) 195.
Frensdorff, H.K., J. Polymer Sci. A2 (1964) 333, 341.
Griffith, A.A., Phil. Trans. Roy. Soc. (London) A221 (1921) 163.
Grüneisen, E., "Handbuch der Physik", Vol. 10, Springer, Berlin, 1926, p. 52.
Heijboer, J., Kolloid-Z. 148 (1956) 36 and 171 (1960) 7; Makromol. Chem. 35A (1960) 86; Proc. Intern. Conf. Physics of Non-crystalline Solids, Delft (1965) p. 231; Brit. Polymer J. 1 (1969) 3; Plastica 10 (1957) 824; 11 (1958) 34; 12 (1959) 110, 598.
Heijboer, J. and Schwarzl, F.R., in "Kunststoffe" (R. Nitsche and K.A. Wolf, Eds.), Springer, Berlin, 1962.
Hertz, H., J. reine angew. Mathem. 92 (1881) 156.
Landel, R.F. and Fedors, R.F., J. Polymer Sci. B1 (1963) 539; Rubber Chem. Technol. 40 (1967) 1049.
Leaderman, H., "Elastic and Creep Properties of Filamentous Materials and other High Polymers", The Textile Foundation, Washington D.C., 1943.
McGowan, J.C., Polymer 8 (1967) 57.

310

Mooney, M., J. Appl. Phys. 11 (1940) 582.

Nutting, P., Proc. Am. Soc. Testing Materials 21 (1921) 1162.

Rao, R., Indian J. Phys. 14 (1940) 109; J. Chem. Phys. 9 (1941) 682.

Rivlin, R.S., Phil. Trans. Roy. Soc. (London) A240 (1948) 459, 491, 509 and A241 (1948) 379.

Rusch, K.C. and Beck, R.H., J. Macromol. Sci. B3 (1969) 365.

Sakiadis, B.C. and Coates, J., A.I.Ch.E.J. 1 (1955) 275.

Sakurada, I., Nakushina, Y. and Ito, T., J. Polymer Sci. 57 (1962) 651.

Sakurada, I. and Keisuke, K., J. Polymer Sci. C 31 (1970) 57.

Schmieder, K. and Wolf, K., Kolloid-Z. 134 (1953) 149.

Schuyer, J., Nature 181 (1958) 1394; J. Polymer Sci. 36 (1959) 475.

Schwarzl, F.R., Kolloid-Z. 165 (1959) 88.

Schwarzl, F.R. and Staverman, A.J., J. Appl. Phys. 23 (1952) 838.

Schwarzl, F.R., Chapter 6 in "Chemie und Technologie der Kunststoffe" (R. Houwink and A.J. Staverman, Eds.), 4th ed., Akademie Verlaggesellschaft, Leipzig, 1963.

Schwarzl, F.R., Pure Appl. Chem. 23 (1970) 219.

Seitz, J.T. and Balazs, C.F., Polymer Eng. Sci. (1968) 151.

Shamov, I., Polymer Mech. (USSR) 1 (1966) 36.

Smith, Th.L., J. Polymer Sci. 32 (1958) 99; A1 (1963) 3597.

Smith, Th.L., J. Appl. Phys. 31 (1960) 1892; 35 (1964) 27.

Smith, Th.L., Rubber Chem. Technol. 35 (1962) 753; 40 (1967) 544.

Smith, Th.L., ASD-TDR 62-572 Report, Wright Patterson Air Force Base, Ohio (1962).

Staverman, A.J. and Schwarzl, F.R., Chapters 1, 2 and 3 in "Die Physik der Hochpolymeren", Vol. 4 (H.A. Stuart, Ed.), Springer, Berlin, 1956.

Tabor, D., Proc. Roy. Soc. (London) 192 (1947) 247.

Treloar, L.R.G., Polymer 1 (1960) 95, 279.

Van Krevelen, D.W. and Hoftyzer, P.J., (1970) unpublished.

Warfield, R.W., Cuevas, J.E. and Barnet, F.R., J. Appl. Polymer Sci. 12 (1968) 1147; Rheologica Acta 8 (1970) 439.

Warfield, R.W. and Barnet, F.R., Angew. Makromol. Chem. 27 (1972) 215; 44 (1975) 181.

Williams, M.L., Landel, R.F. and Ferry, J.D., J. Am. Chem. Soc. 77 (1955) 3701.

CHAPTER 14

PROPERTIES OF ORIENTED POLYMERS

Orientation is extremely important in the use of a polymer as a fibre or film.
The effects of orientation on the physical properties are pronounced.
Some interesting quantitative correlations between the stretch ratio, the degree
of orientation and the mechanical properties have been found, but it is still impossible to derive the basic constants in these correlations from the polymer structure.

Introduction

If an isotropic polymer is subjected to a directed external stress it undergoes a rearrangement called orientation. In amorphous polymers this is simply a rearrangement of
the randomly coiled chain molecules (molecular orientation). In crystalline polymers the
phenomenon is more complex: crystallites may be reoriented or completely rearranged
and *oriented crystallization* may be induced by the stresses applied; the rearrangements
in the crystalline material may be read from the X-ray patterns.

Nearly all polymeric objects have some orientation; during the forming (shaping) of
the specimen the molecules are oriented by viscous flow and part of this orientation is
frozen in as the object cools. But this kind of orientation is negligible compared with the
directed orientation applied in drawing or stretching processes.

Orientation is generally accomplished by deforming a polymer at or above its glass
transition point. Fixation of the orientation takes place if the stretched polymer is cooled
to below its glass transition temperature before the molecules have had a chance to return
to their random orientation. By heating above the T_g the oriented polymer will tend to
retract; in amorphous polymers the retractive force is even a direct measure of the degree
of orientation obtained.

Orientation has a pronounced effect on the physical properties of polymers. Oriented
polymers have properties which vary in different directions, i.e. they are *anisotropic*.
Orientation can convert brittle polymers such as polystyrene and poly(methyl methacrylate) into ductile materials as far as stress is applied in the direction of orientation.

Oriented polymeric materials can be roughly divided into two classes: uniaxially oriented and biaxially oriented materials.

A. DEGREE OF ORIENTATION

Orientation can be measured by a number of methods.

311

1. Birefringence or double refraction

This is often the easiest method (Stein and Tobolsky (1948); De Vries (1953) and Andrews (1954)). The specific birefringence (Δn) of a fibre measured in transverse direction is defined as the difference in refractive index between the two components of a light wave vibrating parallel and perpendicular to the fibre axis ($\Delta n = n_{\parallel} - n_{\perp}$). Birefringence is made up of contributions from the amorphous and crystalline regions.

The increase in birefringence occurring in crystalline polymers by orientation is due to the increase in mean orientation of the polarizable molecular chain segments. In crystalline regions the segments contribute more to the overall birefringence than in less ordered regions. Also the average orientation of the crystalline regions (behaving as structural units) may be notably different from the mean overall orientation.

2. X-ray diffraction (in crystalline polymers)

Unoriented crystalline polymers show X-ray diffraction patterns which resemble powder diagrams of low-molecular crystals, characterized by diffraction rings rather than by spots. As a result of orientation the rings contract into arcs and spots. From the azimuthal distribution of the intensity in the arcs the degree of orientation of the crystalline regions can be calculated (Kratky, 1941).

3. Infrared dichroism

In oriented samples the amount of absorption of polarized infrared radiation may vary greatly when the direction of the plane of polarization is changed. If stretching vibrations of definite structural groups involve changes in dipole moment which are perpendicular to the chain axis, the corresponding absorption bands are strong for polarized radiation vibrating perpendicular to the chain axis (and weak for that vibrating along the axis). Sometimes separate absorptions can be found for crystalline and amorphous regions; in such a case the dichroism of this band gives information about orientation in both regions.

4. Fluorescence polarization (Nishijima et al., 1966; McGraw, 1970)

This recent method not only gives a measure of the orientation in the amorphous regions of the polymer, but also affords more information about the orientation distribution function than other methods.

The quantitative influence of orientation on the different physical properties will be treated later.

B. UNIAXIAL ORIENTATION

Uniaxial orientation is accomplished by stretching a thread, strip or bar in one direction; usually this process is carried out at a temperature just above the glass transition point. The polymer chains tend to line up parallel to the direction of stretching, although in reality only a small fraction of the chain segments becomes perfectly oriented.

Uniaxial orientation is of the utmost importance in the production of man-made fibres. Only by stretching or drawing will the spun filaments become dimensionally stable and lose their tendency to creep – at least at room temperature. The filaments as spun possess a very low orientation, unless spinning is performed at extreme velocities. Normally a separate drawing step is required to produce the orientation necessary for optimum physical properties. In practice a drawing machine consists of two sets of rolls, the second running about four times as fast as the first.

As mentioned already, the effects of orientation on the physical properties are considerable. They result in increased tensile strength and stiffness with increasing orientation. Of course, with increasing orientation the anisotropy of properties increases too. Oriented fibres are strong in the direction of their long axis, but relatively weak perpendicular to it.

If the orientation process in semi-crystalline fibres is carried out well below the melting point (T_m), the thread does not become thinner gradually, but rather suddenly, over a short distance: the neck [1]. The so-called *draw ratio* (Λ) is the ratio of the length of the drawn to that of the undrawn filament; it is about 4 to 5 for many polymers, but may be as high as 10 for linear polyolefins and as low as 2 in the case of regenerated cellulose.

The degree of crystallinity does not change much during drawing if one starts from a specimen with a developed crystallinity (before drawing); if on the other hand, the crystallinity of the undrawn filament is not, or only moderately, developed, crystallinity can be greatly induced by drawing. The so-called "cold drawing" (e.g. nylon 6,6 and 6) is carried out more or less adiabatically. The drawing energy involved is dissipated as heat, which causes a rise of temperature and a reduction of the viscosity. As the polymer thread reaches its yield-stress, it becomes mechanically unstable and a neck is formed.

During the drawing process the crystallites tend to break up into microlamellae and finally into still smaller units, possibly by unfolding or despiralizing of chains. Spherulites present tend to remain intact during the first stages of drawing and often elongate into ellipsoids. Rupture of the filament may occur at spherulite boundaries; therefore it is a disadvantage if the undrawn thread contains spherulites. After a first stage of reversible deformation of spherulites, a second phase may occur in which the spherulites are disrupted and separate helices of chains (in the case of polyamides) become permanently arranged parallel at the fibre axis. At extreme orientations the helices themselves are straightened.

Change of properties by orientation

1. Amorphous polymers

The Young's moduli of uniaxially oriented amorphous polymers are greater in the direction parallel to orientation than in the direction perpendicular to it, but the effect is not great at low degrees of orientation; high orientations are required to give a Young's modulus parallel to orientation which is twice the modulus of an unoriented amorphous polymer.

Much greater are the effects on tensile strength and elongation [2] at break, as well as on impact strength. Fig. 14.1 illustrates this for oriented amorphous polystyrene strips (data from Jackson and Ballman, 1960). Parallel to orientation the tensile strength (σ_{max}) and

---

[1] Also amorphous polymers may show the phenomenon of necking.
[2] Elongation is defined as $(L - L_0)/L_0 = \epsilon_n$ (nominal strain).

314

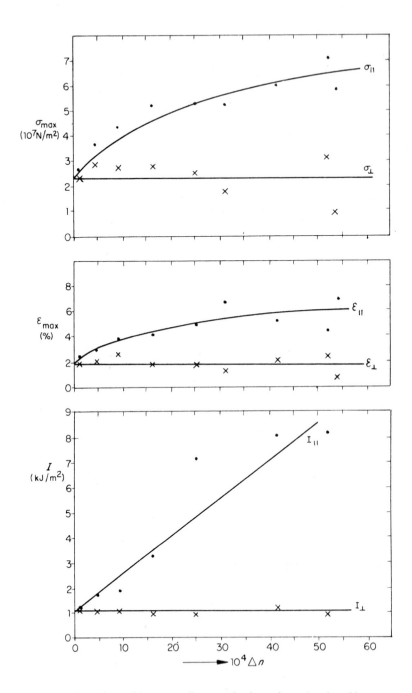

Fig. 14.1. Effect of stretching on tensile strength, elongation at break and impact strength of polystyrene film (after Jackson and Ballman, 1960).

elongation at break (ϵ_{max}) are increased by a factor of 3, while the impact strength (I) can even be increased by a factor of 8!

Also elastomers show great effects of orientation, but here the rubber must be held in stretched condition while the measurements are made. Fig. 14.2 (after Mason, 1961) gives typical results of dynamic-mechanical measurements on natural rubber strips. Rubber beyond about 200% elongation shows induced oriented crystallization, by which the mechanical properties are strongly influenced. The Young's modulus increases rapidly with orientation. Also the loss modulus increases, but less rapidly, so that the damping decreases somewhat.

2. Crystalline polymers

Of the greatest practical importance is the effect of uniaxial orientation on semi-crystalline polymers, since the properties of many man-made fibres depend on it.

The influence of orientation can be studied by investigating a so-called drawing-series, i.e. a series of yarns drawn with different draw ratios. Figs. 14.3a and 14.3b present data of drawing series of nylon 6 and polyester filaments. Additional data (for poly(ethylene terephthalate)) are given in table 14.1 and fig. 14.4 (data from Van der Meer, 1970).

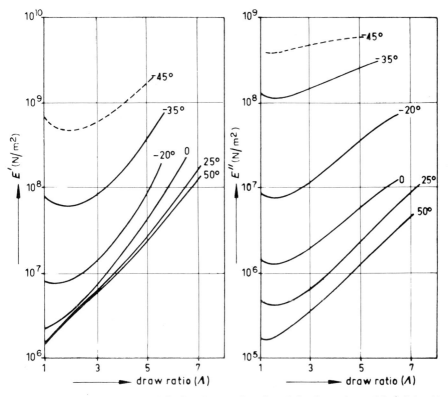

Fig. 14.2. Dynamic Young's moduli of rubber as a function of the elongation at 1 kc/s (after Mason, 1961).

Quantitative relationships
In the following we shall summarize a number of quantitative relationships for some physical quantities after orientation.

1. Density
Density only changes if induced crystallization takes place. In this case the expression (4.3) of Chapter 4 may be applied:

$$\frac{\rho_{sc}}{\rho_a} \approx 1 + 0.13x_c \tag{14.1}$$

2. Thermal expansion
The volume coefficient of expansion of an oriented polymer is the same as that of the isotropic material; for uniaxial orientation the volume coefficient (α) is related to the linear coefficients $\beta_\parallel$ and $\beta_\perp$ in the directions parallel and perpendicular to the chain alignment by the formula:

$$\alpha = 3\beta_{iso} = \beta_\parallel + 2\beta_\perp \tag{14.2}$$

According to measurements of Tjader and Protzman (1956) on stretched poly(methyl methacrylate), $\beta_\perp$ and $\beta_\parallel$ are dependent on the draw ratio:

$$\frac{\beta_\perp}{\beta_\parallel} - 1 \approx \tfrac{1}{3}(\Lambda - 1) \tag{14.3}$$

This gives:

$$\beta_\parallel \approx \frac{\alpha}{3} \frac{1}{1 + \tfrac{2}{9}(\Lambda - 1)} \tag{14.4a}$$

$$\beta_\perp \approx \frac{\alpha}{3} \frac{1 + \tfrac{1}{3}(\Lambda - 1)}{1 + \tfrac{2}{9}(\Lambda - 1)} \tag{14.4b}$$

For oriented crystalline polymers comparable relationships have not yet been published.

3. Thermal conductivity (λ)
Eiermann (1964) found an expression equivalent to (14.2), viz.:

$$\frac{3}{\lambda_{iso}} = \frac{1}{\lambda_\parallel} + \frac{2}{\lambda_\perp} \tag{14.5}$$

Furthermore he demonstrated that for amorphous polymers an interrelation between λ and β exists

$$\frac{\lambda_{iso}}{\lambda_{or}} \approx 0.2 + 0.8 \frac{\beta_{or}}{\beta_{iso}} \tag{14.6}$$

where β_{or} is the linear expansion coefficient of the oriented material; β_{or} may be either $\beta_\parallel$ or $\beta_\perp$.

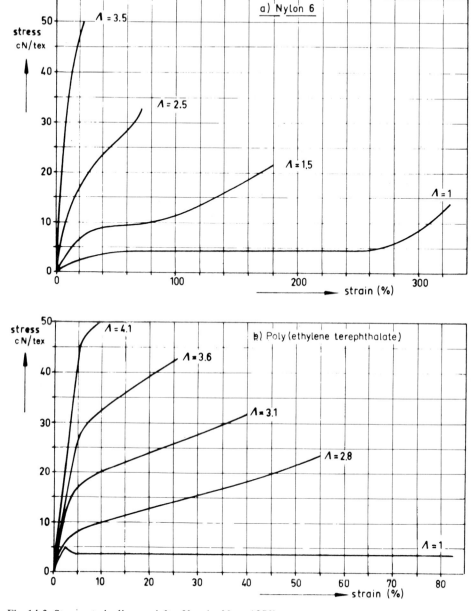

Fig. 14.3. Stress–strain diagram (after Van der Meer, 1970).

Combination of eqs. (14.4) and (14.6) makes it possible to calculate the heat conductivity of oriented amorphous polymers as a function of the draw ratio. A comparable relationship for oriented crystalline polymers is still lacking.

TABLE 14.1

Stretch series of poly(ethylene terephthalate) yarns (data from Van der Meer, 1970)

	Draw ratio (Λ)					
	1	2.77	3.08	3.56	4.09	4.49
density (ρ) (20°C) (g/cm³)	1.3383	1.3694	1.3775	1.3804	1.3813	1.3841
crystallinity (x_c) (%)	3	22	37	40	41	43
birefringence (Δn) (20°C)	0.0068	0.1061	0.1126	0.1288	0.1368	0.1420
tensile strength (σ_{max}) (cN/tex)	11.8	23.5	32.1	43.0	51.6	64.5
elongation at break (%)	(450)	55	39	27	11.5	7.3
Young's modulus (10^9 N/m²)						
E' at 9370 Hz	–	8.3	12.3	17.4	20.2	22.9
E' at 5 Hz	2.6	7.8	11.5	14.9	18.0	19.9
loss factor tan δ	4	0.20	0.165	0.155	0.135	0.12
T_g(dynamic) (°C)	71	72	83	85	90	89
T_d (damping peak) (°C)	84	107	118	124	128	131
ΔT_g (width of tan δ-peak at inflection points)	10	39	43	45	50	55

4. Refractive index (birefringence)

For the refractive index an expression analogous to (14.2) is valid (Hermans and Vermaas, 1946), provided the density remains unchanged

$$3n_{iso} \approx n_{\parallel} + 2n_{\perp} \tag{14.7}$$

As already mentioned, the difference $n_{\parallel} - n_{\perp} = \Delta n$ is called birefringence. Some data on the birefringence of fibres are given in table 14.2.

A general relationship between birefringence and draw ratio (Λ) related to the isotropic state was found by De Vries (1953, 1955, 1959).

$$\frac{d(\Delta n)}{d \ln \Lambda} = m + p\Delta n \tag{14.8}$$

where m and p are constants.

After integration, (14.8) gives for $p \neq 0$:

$$\Delta n = \frac{m}{p}(\Lambda^p - 1) = \frac{m}{p}\left[\left(\frac{d_{iso}}{d}\right)^{2p} - 1\right] \tag{14.9}$$

where d_{iso} and d are the diameters of the thread (yarn) in the isotropic and in the drawn

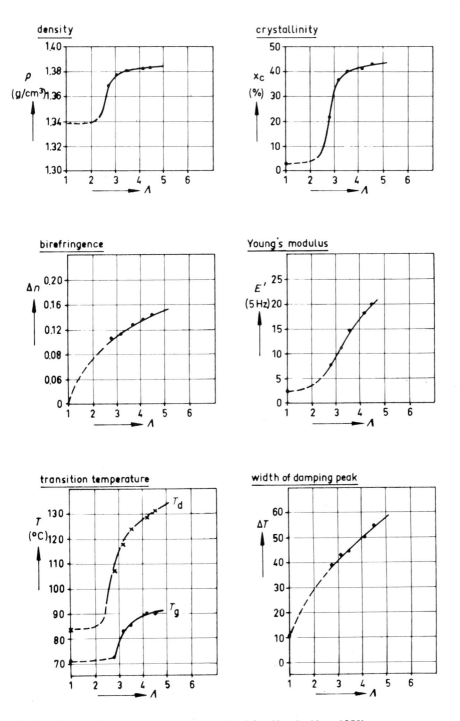

Fig. 14.4. Physical data of polyester drawing series (after Van der Meer, 1970).

TABLE 14.2

Some numerical data on birefringence of fibres (data from Morton and Hearle (1962))

Fibre	$n_\parallel$	$n_\perp$	Δn
poly(ethylene terephthalate)	1.725	1.537	0.188
flax	1.596	1.528	0.068
nylon 6,6	1.582	1.519	0.063
nylon 6	1.580 [1]	1.530 [1]	0.050 [1]
silk	1.591	1.538	0.053
cotton	1.578	1.532	0.046
polyethylene	1.556	1.512	0.044
viscose rayon	1.539	1.519	0.020
wool	1.553	1.542	0.010
cellulose acetate (sec.)	1.539	1.519	0.020
polyacrylonitrile	1.500	1.500	0.000
glass	1.547	1.547	0.000
cellulose triacetate	1.474	1.479	−0.005

[1] Measurements by De Vries (private communication).

state. This expression enables us to estimate the draw ratio of a yarn if Δn is determined and m and p are known.

For a number of polymers De Vries (1959) specified the values of p and m. They are given in table 14.3.

A significant conclusion from these data is that p has a positive value if the polymer chain contains rings, and a negative value if it is a purely aliphatic chain. De Vries gave the following tentative scheme of relations between p-values and chemical structure:

	One repeating chemical unit	Two alternating chemical units
Macromolecules resembling paraffin chains	p = −1/2	p = −1
Chain units incorporating a ring structure	p = +1	p = +1/2

According to (14.8) m represents the initial slope of the Δn versus ln Λ curve.

5. Modulus of elasticity

The modulus of elasticity of an oriented polymer is always higher than that of the un-oriented material. De Vries (1953 and unpublished results) derived a general rule for the sonic modulus of elasticity (E) of semicrystalline polymers after orientation:

$$\ln \Lambda = C_\Lambda \left[\frac{1}{E_{iso}} - \frac{1}{E} \right] \qquad (14.10) [1]$$

[1] Based on this equation an expression for the average orientation in the fibre (f_{or}) may be formulated:

$$f_{or} = \frac{E_{iso}^{-1} - E^{-1}}{E_{iso}^{-1} - E_{max}^{-1}} \approx 1 - \frac{E_{iso}}{E}$$

where E_{max} is the modulus of the (hypothetical) completely oriented material; certainly $E_{max} \gg E_{iso}$.

TABLE 14.3

Values of the constants p and m in eqs. (14.8) and (14.9)

Polymer	Type of deformation	p	m	Source of data
Regenerated cellulose	air-dry extension	1.2	0.024	De Vries (1953)
	spin-stretching	1.0	0.012	Hermans and Vermaas (1946)
Polystyrene	hot drawing	1.0	−0.002	Cleereman et al. (1953)
Poly(ethylene terephthalate)	cold drawing	0.5	0.094	De Vries (1959)
	hot drawing	0.5	0.083	De Vries (1959)
				Kordes et al. (1953)
Nylon 6	cold drawing	−0.5	0.050	De Vries (1959)
Nylon 6,6	cold drawing	−1.0	0.072	De Vries (1959)
Linear polyethylene	hot drawing	−0.5	0.038	De Vries (1953)

where C_Λ is a constant which is typical of the polymer considered. Values of C_Λ for some polymers are given in table 14.4. At high draw ratios eq. (14.10) may show deviations (see fig. 14.5).

TABLE 14.4

Values of C_Λ, E_{iso}, C_ϵ and E_0 for some polymers (data from De Vries (1953, 1955, 1956) and unpublished)

Polymer	Drawing			Elongation		
	C_Λ	E_{iso}	E_{iso}/C_Λ	C_ϵ	E_0[1]	E_0/C_ϵ
regen. cellulose						
(cupramm. process)				9.0	20	2.2
natural silk				8.5	17	2.0
poly(vinyl alcohol)				7.3	34	4.7
regen. cellulose						
(viscose process)	8	5.0	0.63	5.5	10–40	1.8–7.3
keratine (hair)				3.7	6.0	1.6
polyacrylonitrile				3.4	14	4.1
polypropylene (isot.)				3.2	5.5	1.7
poly(tetrafluoroethylene)				3.1	21	6.8
poly(ethylene terephthalate)	4	2.6	0.65	2.3	18.5	8.0
native cellulose (cotton)				2.0 [2]	16	8.0
cellulose acetate				1.8	5	2.8
polyethylene (linear)				1.65	11.7	7.1
poly(vinyl chloride)				1.6	7.0	4.4
nylon 4				1.1	9.4	8.5
nylon 6,6				0.9	7	7.8
nylon 6	2.6	1.45	0.56	0.65	4.5	7.0
nylon 11				0.4	5	12.5

[1] Representative values of fibres.
[2] Measured by Weyland (1961).
C_Λ, C_ϵ, E_{iso} and E_0 expressed in 10^9 N/m². Moduli of elasticity measured at ca 9000 Hz.

322

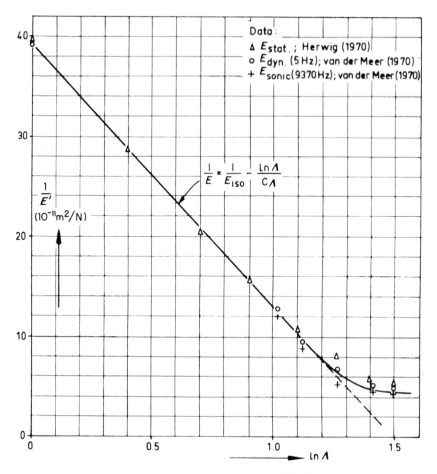

Fig. 14.5. Influence of draw ratio on modulus of elasticity (E'). (Three drawing series of polyester (PETP) yarns.)

De Vries (1953, 1955, 1956) originally found a similar relationship for the elongation (ϵ) of drawn yarns:

$$\ln(1 + \epsilon) = C_\epsilon\left(\frac{1}{E_0} - \frac{1}{E}\right) \tag{14.11}$$

where E_0 is the initial sonic modulus of the drawn yarn.

The constant C_ϵ is of the same order of magnitude as C_Λ but not equal to it.

Since the processes of drawing and elongation are not performed under the same conditions, the difference between C_Λ and C_ϵ is understandable; the ratio C_Λ/C_ϵ may, for instance, be temperature-dependent.

Table 14.4 contains the available C_ϵ values. No correlation between C_ϵ and chemical structure could be detected. The low C_ϵ value for cotton is probably due to the helical structure of the cell walls.

The similarity of eqs. (14.10) and (14.11) can easily be understood, since drawing and elongation are, in principle, very similar; if a yarn with a draw ratio Λ_0 and an initial modulus E_0 (under the same conditions) were subjected to further elongation ϵ, the total resulting draw ratio would be:

$$\Lambda_{tot} = \Lambda_0(1 + \epsilon) . \tag{14.12}$$

Substituting (14.12) in (14.10) leads to an equation of the form of (14.11).

By combining eqs. (14.9) and (14.10) we obtain the following relation between birefringence and modulus

$$\ln\left(1 + \frac{p}{m}\Delta n\right) = pC_\Lambda\left[\frac{1}{E_{iso}} - \frac{1}{E}\right] \tag{14.13}$$

Example 14.1

Estimate the sonic modulus of nylon 6 yarn at a draw ratio of 3.5. For isotropic nylon 6 the sonic modulus is 1.45×10^9 N/m^2.

Solution

According to table 14.4 the C_Λ value of nylon 6 is 2.6×10^9 N/m^2. Applying expression (14.10) we get

$$\frac{1}{E} = \frac{1}{E_{iso}} - \frac{\ln \Lambda}{C_\Lambda} = \left(\frac{1}{1.45} - \frac{2.3 \log 3.5}{2.6}\right)10^{-9} = (0.69 - 0.48)10^{-9} = 0.21 \times 10^{-9}$$

or

$$E = 4.75 \times 10^9 \text{ N/m}^2$$

which is in excellent agreement with the measured value of 4.4×10^9.

Example 14.2

Estimate the birefringence of the same nylon 6 yarn.

Solution

Table 14.3 gives the following values for nylon 6:

$$p = -0.5; \qquad m = 0.05 .$$

Application of expression (14.9) gives:

$$\Delta n = -\frac{0.05}{0.5}(3.5^{-0.5} - 1) = -0.1\left(\frac{1}{1.87} - 1\right) = 0.047$$

The same result is obtained if expression (14.13) is applied:

$$2.3 \log(1 - 10\Delta n) = -0.5 \times 2.6 \times 10^9\left[\frac{1}{1.45} - \frac{1}{4.75}\right]10^{-9}$$

$$\log(1 - 10\Delta n) = -\frac{0.5 \times 2.6}{2.3}(0.69 - 0.21) = -0.27$$

$$1 - 10\Delta n = 0.53$$

$$\Delta n = \frac{0.47}{10} = 0.047 .$$

In contrast to Young's modulus the shear modulus is nearly independent of orientation (the torsional strength, however, decreases!).

6. Mechanical damping

By uniaxial orientation the damping peak of the glass-rubber transition becomes broader and lower; the temperature of the damping maximum is shifted to higher values (see table 14.1: T_g, T_d and ΔT_g). This means that the transition region has broadened in consequence of the molecular order.

From Van der Meer's data one may conclude that for semi-crystalline polymers the following rules are valid (fig. 14.6)

$$\Delta T = a + b\Delta n \tag{14.14}$$

$$T_d - T_g = a' + b'\Delta n \tag{14.15}$$

where ΔT is the width of the damping peak at the inflection points, T_d is the temperature at which the damping has a maximum, a, a', b and b' are constants.

By orientation the total creep and stress relaxation are much reduced, but the rates of creep and stress relaxation are often increased.

7. Generalized stress–strain relationship for polymers

Finally an interesting relation found by Herwig (1970) for a nylon 6 drawing series may be mentioned. Every yarn in such a drawing series, having a certain draw ratio (Λ_0), has its own stress–strain diagram, in which the stress (σ) refers to the cross-section of the yarn and the strain (ϵ) to the initial length of the (drawn) yarn. If, however, the stress is related to the original spinning cross-section and the strain to the original spinning length, it appears that all the stress–strain curves above the yield value merge into one "master curve", as shown in fig. 14.7. This master curve is the stress–strain curve of the undrawn yarn.

For this purpose the "reduced" stress and strain are calculated from the following equations:

$$\sigma_{red} = \sigma_{obs}/\Lambda_0 \tag{14.16}$$

$$1 + \epsilon_{red} = (1 + \epsilon_{obs})\Lambda_0 \tag{14.17}$$

where Λ_0 is the draw ratio at which the yarn has been produced. Comparison of this equation with (14.12) shows that $1 + \epsilon_{red} = \Lambda_{tot}$ as far as the conditions of drawing and elongation are equivalent.

Fig. 14.7 shows that if the stress-strain diagram of the undrawn yarn is determined, the stress–strain diagrams of all the drawn yarns, obtained at definite draw ratios, can be estimated.

The relationships between the stress–strain curves of undrawn and drawn yarn, borne out by the "master curve", again stress the key role of the draw ratio and elongation with respect to the physical properties of yarns, as already shown by the relations to birefringence (14.9) and sonic modulus of elasticity (14.10) and (14.11).

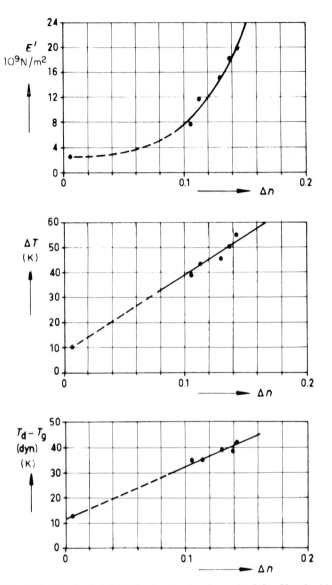

Fig. 14.6. Rheological data of polyester drawing series (after Van der Meer, 1970).

C. BIAXIAL ORIENTATION

Biaxial orientation occurs when a polymer sheet is stretched in two directions at right angles to each other. The polymer chain segments then tend to line up parallel to the plane of the sheet, but in more or less random directions in this plane. In general a biaxial-

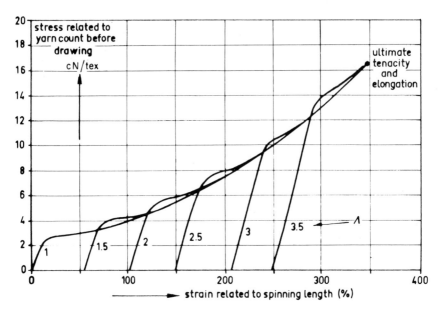

Fig. 14.7. Generalized stress–strain diagram for nylon 6. The tex is a standardized symbol for the linear density of a yarn: 1 tex = 1 gram per 1000 metres. Divided by the density it is proportional to the cross-section of the yarn (after Herwig, 1970).

ly drawn film still possesses a direction of preferred orientation in the plane, although the anisotropy of the film is considerably less than that of uniaxially drawn films.

Biaxial orientation of brittle polymers is used to eliminate the poor strength properties of these uniaxially oriented materials in a direction perpendicular to the axis of orientation. This technique of orientation is very important in the production of crystalline polymer films; in all directions in the plane of the sheet it gives some of the desirable properties shown by uniaxially oriented material in the direction of chain alignment.

Compared with unoriented materials, biaxially oriented sheets and films have higher tensile strengths and higher impact strengths. Typical data collected by Nielsen (1962) are given in table 14.5.

TABLE 14.5

Biaxial orientation of sheets; comparison with unoriented materials

Polymer	Orientation	Tensile strength σ_{max} (10^7 N/m^2)	Elongation to break ϵ_{max} (%)	Impact strength I(kJ/m^2)
Polystyrene	Unoriented	3.5–6	1– 4	1.3–2.6
	Biaxially oriented	5 –8	8–18	>16

The optical properties of biaxially oriented films, especially the biaxial birefringence as influenced by the drawing process, have been investigated by De Vries (1962, 1965).

BIBLIOGRAPHY, CHAPTER 14

General references

Bunn, C.W., "Polymer Texture; Orientation of Molecules and Crystals in Polymer Specimens", Ch. 10 in R. Hill (Ed.), "Fibres from Synthetic Polymers", Elsevier, Amsterdam, 1953.
Hermans, P.H., "Contributions to the Physics of Cellulose Fibres", Elsevier, Amsterdam, 1946.
Morgan, L.B., "The Fibre-Forming Properties of Polymers", in J.C. Robb and F.W. Peaker (Eds.), "Progress in High Polymers", Vol. 1, Academic Press, New York, 1961, pp. 233–277.
Morton, W.E. and Hearle, J.W.S., "Physical Properties of Textile Fibres", The Textile Institute and Butterworths, London, 1962.
Nielsen, L.E., "Mechanical Properties of Polymers", Ch. 10, Reinhold, New York, 1962.
Stein, R.S., "The Optical and Mechanical Properties of High Polymers", in Research Report Nr. 14, High Polymer Series, Chaps. 8 and 9, US Army Quartermaster Res. & Eng. Center, Natick, Mass., 1960.
Stein, R.S. and Onogi, S. (Eds.), US – Japan Seminar in Polymer Physics (J. Polymer Sci., C. 15) Interscience, New York, 1966.

Special references

Andrews, R.D., J. Appl. Phys. 25 (1954) 1223.
Cleereman, K.J., Karam, H.J. and Williams, J.L., Modern Plastics 30 (1953) 119.
De Vries, H., Thesis, Delft (1953); Appl. Sci. Research A3 (1952) 111; Ann. Sci. Text. Belges (1955) nr. 4, 286; Rayon Revue 10 (1956) 53; J. Polymer Sci. 34 (1959) 761; Angew. Chem. 74 (1962) 574; Ned. Tijdschr. Natuurk. 31 (1965) 68.
Eiermann, K., J. Polymer Sci. C 6 (1964) 157.
Hermans, P.H. and Vermaas, D., Trans. Faraday Soc. 42B (1946) 155.
Herwig, H.U., Internal Report Akzo Research & Engineering N.V. (1970).
Jackson, G.B. and Ballman, R.L., Soc. Plastics Eng. J. 16 (1960) 1147.
Kordes, E., Günther, F., Büchs, L. and Göltner, W., Kolloid-Z. 119 (1950) 23.
Kratky, O., Z. physik. Chem. B50 (1941) 255.
McGraw, G.E., J. Polymer Sci. A2, 8 (1970) 1323.
Mason, P., J. Appl. Polymer Sci. 5 (1961) 428.
Nishijima, Y., et al., Rept. Progress Polymer Phys., Japan 9 (1966) 457; J. Polymer Sci. A1, 5 (1967) 1021; J. Polymer Sci. A2, 5 (1967) 23, 37.
Stein, R.S. and Tobolsky, A.V., Textile Research J. 18 (1948) 201, 302.
Tjader, T.C. and Protzman, T.F., J. Polymer Sci. 20 (1956) 591.
Van der Meer, S.J., Thesis, Delft, 1970.
Weyland, H.G., Textile Research J. 31 (1961) 629.

PART IV

TRANSPORT PROPERTIES OF POLYMERS

CHAPTER 15

RHEOLOGICAL PROPERTIES OF POLYMER MELTS

The principal quantities determining the rheological behaviour of polymer melts are the shear and extensional viscosities.

The shear viscosity of polymers depends on the average molecular weight, the molecular weight distribution, the temperature, the shear stress (and shear rate) and the hydrostatic pressure. Semi-empirical relationships for these dependencies permit estimations of shear viscosities of polymer melts under arbitrary experimental conditions.

Much less is known about extensional viscosity. It is obviously dependent on average molecular weight, temperature and rate of extension. But apparently also the tensile strain (degree of extension) is important.

At high shear rates catastrophic deformations are possible which are known as "melt fracture". Empirical expressions for the conditions under which melt fracture occurs are given, but the phenomenon is still not completely understood.

Introduction

The flow behaviour of polymer melts is of great practical importance in polymer manufacturing and polymer processing. Therefore the development of a quantitative description of flow phenomena on the basis of a number of material properties and process parameters is highly desirable.

In the same way as the mechanical behaviour of solid polymers can be described in terms of *moduli* (ratios of stress and deformation), the flow behaviour of polymer melts can be characterized by *viscosities* (ratios of stress and *rate* of deformation).

For common liquids the viscosity is a material constant which is only dependent on temperature and pressure but not on rate of deformation and time. For polymeric liquids the situation is much more complicated: viscosities differ with deformation conditions. Furthermore the flow of polymeric melts is accompanied by elastic effects, due to which part of the energy exerted on the system is stored in the form of recoverable energy [1]. For this reason the viscosities are time and rate dependent: polymer melts are viscoelastic.

---

[1] Some typical viscoelastic phenomena are: a. The *Weissenberg effect.* In a stirred vessel a common liquid shows a vortex with the liquid level at the centre lower than at the wall. In stirring polymer melts the opposite effect is observed. b. The *Barus effect* or *die swell.* If a polymer melt is extruded from a capillary into the air, the jet shows an increase in diameter.

A. MODES OF DEFORMATION AND DEFINITION OF VISCOSITY

Modes of deformation

As in the elasto-mechanical behaviour of solid polymers, so in the flow behaviour of polymer melts the mode of deformation determines the nature of the characteristic property, in this case the viscosity.

There are two prominent elementary modes of deformation, viz. simple shear and simple extension.

1. Simple shear

Under idealized conditions the polymer melt subjected to simple shear is contained between two (infinitely extending) parallel walls, one of which is translated parallel to the other at a constant distance. The result of the shear stress (τ, the force exerted on the moving wall per unit of surface area) is a velocity gradient in the melt in a direction perpendicular to the wall. Under these ideal conditions the velocity profile is linear, so that the gradient ($dv/dx = \dot{\gamma}$, also called rate of shear) is constant. The shear viscosity is obtained as the ratio between shear stress and rate of shear.

Although the geometry of simple shear as defined above is seldom encountered in practice, it may be approximated under real conditions. So the technically important case

1. Poiseuille Flow

2. Couette Flow

3. Parallel Plate Torsion

4. Cone and Plate Torsion

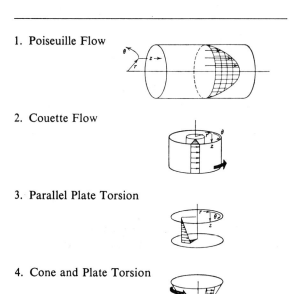

Fig. 15.1. Types of simple shear flow (after Middleman, 1968).

of laminar or Poiseuille flow through cylindrical tubes under ideal conditions is simple shear flow. This and other types of flow geometry are reproduced in fig. 15.1.

2. Simple extension

In this case a cylindrical rod of polymer is subjected to extension in axial direction under the influence of a tensile stress (in the same direction) which is constant over the cross section. The rate of extension is measured and the tensile viscosity is obtained as the ratio between tensile stress and rate of extension.

In practice, simple extension is found in melt spinning of polymeric fibres, although ·the situation is complicated by the non-isothermal character.

Complicated modes of deformation

Several published studies have been devoted to more complicated flow situations, e.g.:

a. *convergent flow,* in which an extensional deformation and a shear deformation are superposed, as encountered in the entry and exit effects of capillary flow.

b. *biaxial shear,* in which shear processes in different directions are superposed, as encountered in the barrel of a screw extruder.

Definitions

The two viscosities mentioned earlier have the dimension: force per area $\times$ time $(N \cdot s/m^2)$. Their precise definitions and those of some connected properties are the following:

1. Shear viscosity (η)

$$\eta = \frac{\text{shear stress}}{\text{shear rate}} = \frac{\text{stress component in the direction of shear deformation}}{\text{velocity gradient perpendicular to the direction of shear deformation}}$$

or

$$\boxed{\eta = \frac{\tau}{\dfrac{dv}{dx}} = \frac{\tau}{\dot{\gamma}}} \qquad (15.1)$$

For ordinary liquids η is a constant; such a behaviour is called *Newtonian.* At very low rates of deformation polymeric melts also show Newtonian behaviour. In this case the shear viscosity will be characterized by the symbol η_0.

As a matter of fact $\eta_0 = \lim_{\dot{\gamma} \to 0} \eta(\dot{\gamma})$ $\qquad (15.2)$

2. Extensional viscosity (λ)

$$\lambda = \frac{\text{tensile stress}}{\text{rate of extension}} = \frac{\text{stress component in the direction of tensile deformation}}{\text{relative increase of length}}$$

or

$$\boxed{\lambda = \frac{\sigma}{\frac{1}{L}\frac{dL}{dt}} = \frac{\sigma}{\dot{\epsilon}}} \tag{15.3}$$

where the extension $\epsilon = \ln (L/L_0)$ $\qquad$ (15.4)

rate of extension $\dot{\epsilon} = \dfrac{d\epsilon}{dt} = \dfrac{1}{L}\dfrac{dL}{dt}$ $\qquad$ (15.5)

Also in this case we have:

$$\lambda_0 = \lim_{\dot{\epsilon}\to 0} \lambda(\dot{\epsilon}) \tag{15.6}$$

Connected with the two viscosities are a number of other quantities which characterize the full shear and extensional behaviour.

3. Other shear properties

For the exact definition of these quantities we use the illustration of the stress components given in fig. 15.2. In this figure the stress components p_{11}, p_{22} and p_{33} are normal stresses, p_{12}, p_{21}, p_{23}, p_{32}, p_{13} and p_{31} are shear stresses. If the shear is in the X_1-direction, we have, in the case of simple shear:

$p_{21} \equiv \tau$ = shear stress
p_{11} = normal stress component in the direction of shear
p_{22} = normal stress component in the direction of the velocity gradient (perpendicular to the direction of shear)
$(p_{33} = 0, p_{31} = 0, p_{32} = 0)$
$p_{11} - p_{22}$ = *normal stress difference*

$$\frac{p_{11} - p_{22}}{p_{21}} \equiv \gamma_e = \textit{elastic shear deformation } [1] \tag{15.7}$$

$$\frac{p_{21}}{\gamma_e} \equiv G = \textit{shear modulus} \tag{15.8}$$

$$\frac{p_{11} - p_{22}}{\dot{\gamma}^2} \equiv \xi = \textit{normal stress coefficient} \tag{15.9}$$

$$\frac{p_{11} - p_{22}}{p_{21}\dot{\gamma}} = \frac{\gamma_e}{\dot{\gamma}} = \Theta = \textit{characteristic shear time} \tag{15.10}$$

NB.: $\boxed{\dfrac{\gamma_e}{\dot{\gamma}} \equiv \Theta = \dfrac{\eta}{G}}$ $\qquad$ (15.11)

For "Newtonian" behaviour G and Θ become material constants, just as η:

$$G_0 = \lim_{\dot{\gamma}\to 0} G(\dot{\gamma}) \tag{15.12}$$

---

[1] According to some theories, this definition should be $\gamma_e = (p_{11} - p_{22})/2p_{21}$.

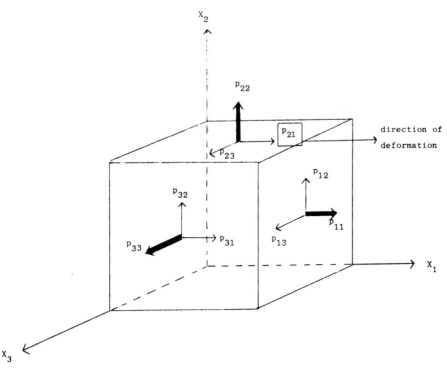

Fig. 15.2. Stress components in simple shear deformation.

$$\Theta_0 = \lim_{\dot{\gamma} \to 0} \Theta(\dot{\gamma}) \tag{15.13}$$

4. Other extensional properties

In the same way some other extensional quantities may be defined:

ϵ_e = elastic part of the tensile strain ($\equiv \ln[1 + (\Delta L)_e/L_0]$)

$$E = \text{tensile modulus} = \frac{\sigma}{\epsilon_e} \tag{15.14}$$

$$\Theta_\epsilon = \frac{\epsilon_e}{\dot{\epsilon}} = \text{characteristic extension time} \tag{15.15}$$

NB.: $\boxed{\dfrac{\epsilon_e}{\dot{\epsilon}} \equiv \Theta_\epsilon = \dfrac{\lambda}{E}}$ $\tag{15.16}$

For "Newtonian" behaviour we get:

$$E_0 = \lim_{\dot{\epsilon} \to 0} E(\dot{\epsilon}) \tag{15.17}$$

$$\Theta_{\epsilon 0} = \lim_{\dot{\epsilon} \to 0} \Theta_\epsilon(\dot{\epsilon}) \tag{15.18}$$

Under Newtonian conditions a simple relationship exists between η_0 and λ_0:

$$\lambda_0 = 3\eta_0 \tag{15.19}$$

According to Cogswell and Lamb (1970) the relationship between E and G for elastic deformations holds, so that

$$E_0 = 3G_0 \tag{15.20}$$

Therefore

$$\Theta_{\epsilon 0} = \Theta_0 \tag{15.21}$$

Experimental determination of viscosity

Since the range of η may extend from 10^{-2} to 10^{11} N $\cdot$ s/m^2, a number of different experimental techniques have been developed to cover this wide range. Some methods are listed in table 15.1.

B. NEWTONIAN SHEAR VISCOSITY OF POLYMER MELTS

This section will be devoted to the Newtonian viscosity η_0, that is to situations where the shear rate is proportional to the shear stress. This is the case *under steady-state conditions at low rates of shear.* Frequently η_0 is not measured directly, but found by extrapolation of viscosity values as a function of shear rate:

$$\eta_0 = \lim_{\dot{\gamma} \to 0} \eta(\dot{\gamma}) \tag{15.2}$$

This may introduce a certain inaccuracy into the values of η_0.

TABLE 15.1

Summary of methods for measuring viscosity

Method	Viscosity range (N $\cdot$ s/m^2)
Capillary pipette	$10^{-3} - 10^2$
Capillary extrusion	$10^{-1} - 10^7$
Parallel plate (plastometer)	$10^3 \ -10^8$
Rotating cylinder (couette)	$10^{-1} - 10^{11}$
Cone and plate viscometer	$10^2 \ -10^{11}$
Tensile creep (very low rates) [1]	$10^5 \ -10^{12}$

The flow geometry of these methods is shown schematically in fig. 15.1.

[1] The calculation of viscosity values from creep data should be performed very cautiously.

Another method to calculate η_0 is from the loss modulus G'' measured in dynamic shear experiments.

$$\eta_0 = \lim_{\omega \to 0} \frac{G''(\omega)}{\omega} \qquad (15.22)$$

ω = angular frequency.

The parameters on which η_0 is dependent for a given polymer are molecular weight, temperature and hydrostatic pressure.

Table 15.2 gives some typical values of η_0 for different polymers.

Effect of molecular weight on η_0

As is to be expected, the viscosity of a polymer melt increases with increasing molecular weight. The difference in behaviour of polymers from low-molecular-weight substances becomes striking, however, for molecular weights higher than a certain critical value, M_{cr}. In this instance

$$\boxed{\log \eta_0 = 3.4 \log \bar{M}_w + A} \qquad (15.23)$$

where A is an empirical constant, dependent on the nature of the polymer and the temperature.

For molecular weights lower than M_{cr}, a number of empirical relationships can be found in the literature, for instance

$$\log \eta_0 = n \log \bar{M}_w + B \qquad (15.24)$$

where $n \approx 1$ and B is a constant, or

$$\log \eta_0 = C_1 (\bar{M}_w)^n + C_2 \qquad (15.25)$$

where $n \approx \frac{1}{2}$ and C_1 and C_2 are constants.

Originally it was supposed that there is a rather sudden transition from eq. (15.23) to eq. (15.24) at $\bar{M}_w = M_{cr}$. Later investigations showed a gradual transition from eq. (15.23) to eq. (15.24). Nevertheless, M_{cr} may still be defined as the molecular weight at which the two extrapolated logarithmic linear relationships intersect.

The very strong influence of molecular weight on the viscosity of polymer melts required some mechanism of molecular interaction for a theoretical interpretation. Bueche (1952) could derive equation (15.23) with certain assumptions on the influence of chain entanglements on polymer flow. Later, numerous other interpretations have been offered which will not be discussed here.

A consequence of these theories is that chain entanglements are not important to flow behaviour if $\bar{M}_w < M_{cr}$. On this ground polymers could be defined as substances composed of molecules, for which $\bar{M}_w > M_{cr}$.

The critical molecular weight M_{cr} may vary from 2000 to 60,000, depending on the structure of the polymer. It was shown by Fox et al. (1956) that the critical value of the number of atoms in the backbone of the polymer chain, Z_{cr}, gives a smaller variation. But the values of Z_{cr} still show great differences.

Fox and Allen (1964) correlated M_{cr} with molecular dimensions, i.e. with the group

$$\frac{R_{Go}}{Mv}$$

where R_{Go} is the unperturbed radius of gyration (see Chapter 9); v is the specific volume.

An even better correlation can be obtained, however, with K_Θ, the coefficient in the equation for the intrinsic viscosity of Θ-solutions (Chapter 9). Approximately

$$\boxed{K_\Theta M_{cr}^{1/2} \approx 0.013} \qquad (m^3/kg) \tag{15.26}$$

In table 15.3 values for M_{cr}, Z_{cr} and the product $K_\Theta M_{cr}^{1/2}$ are listed for a number of polymers.

If the Newtonian viscosity at the critical molecular weight is denoted by η_{cr}, eqs. (15.23) and (15.24) may be rewritten as:

$$\log \eta_0 = \log \eta_{cr} + 3.4 \log (\overline{M}_w/M_{cr}) \text{ if } \overline{M}_w > M_{cr}$$

$$\log \eta_0 = \log \eta_{cr} - \log (M_{cr}/\overline{M}_w) \quad \text{if } \overline{M}_w < M_{cr} \tag{15.27}$$

Effect of temperature on η_0

The effect of temperature on the viscosity of polymer melts is very complicated. Several mathematical formulations of this effect have been presented in the literature, but none has been found to hold for every arbitrary polymer over the whole range of temperatures. This is mainly because for many polymers the temperature range of the viscosity data extends far below the crystalline melting point, often even into the vicinity of the

TABLE 15. 2

Some typical values of η_0

Polymer	T (°C)	$\overline{M}_w$	η_0 (N · s/m²)
polyethylene, high density	190	10^5	2×10^4
polyethylene, low density	170	10^5	3×10^2
polypropylene	220	3×10^5	3×10^3
polyisobutylene	100	10^5	10^4
polystyrene	220	2.5×10^5	5×10^3
poly(vinyl chloride)	190	4×10^4	4×10^4
poly(vinyl acetate)	200	10^5	2×10^2
poly(methyl methacrylate)	200	10^5	5×10^4
polybutadiene	100	2×10^5	4×10^4
polyisoprene	100	2×10^5	10^4
poly(ethylene oxide)	70	3×10^4	3×10^2
poly(ethylene terephthalate)	270	3×10^4	3×10^2
nylon 6	270	3×10^4	10^2
polycarbonate	300	3×10^4	10^3
poly(dimethyl siloxane)	120	4×10^5	2×10^3

Conversion factor: 1 N · s/m² = 10 poise.

TABLE 15.3

Critical molecular weight for a number of polymers

Polymer	M_{cr} (g/mol) (lit.)	Z_{cr}	K_Θ ($cm^3 \cdot mol^{1/2}$/ $g^{3/2}$)	$K_\Theta M_{cr}^{1/2}$ (cm^3/g)
Polyethylene	3500	250	0.219	13
Polypropylene	7000	330	0.135	11
Polyisobutylene	16000	570	0.102	13
Polystyrene	35000	670	0.084	16
Poly(α-methylstyrene)	40000	680	0.076	15
Poly(vinyl chloride)	6200	200	0.149	12
Poly(vinyl alcohol)	7500	340	0.205	18
Poly(vinyl acetate)	25000	580	0.081	13
Poly(methyl acrylate)	24000	560	0.065	10
Poly(methyl methacrylate)	30000	600	0.059	10
Poly(butyl methacrylate)	60000	840	0.049	12
Poly(hexyl methacrylate)	61000	720	0.044	11
Poly(octyl methacrylate)	110000	1100	0.042	14
Polyacrylonitrile	1300	50	0.258	9
Polybutadiene	6000	440	0.166	13
Polyisoprene	10000	590	0.129	13
Poly(ethylene oxide)	3400	230	0.156	9
Poly(propylene oxide)	5800	300	0.116	9
Poly(tetramethylene adipate)	6000	360	0.190	15
Poly(decamethylene succinate)	4000	250	0.196	12
Poly(decamethylene adipate)	4500	285	0.198	13
Poly(decamethylene sebacate)	4000	260	0.202	13
Poly(ethylene terephthalate)	6000	310	0.178	14
Poly(ϵ-caprolactam)	5000	310	0.226	16
Polycarbonate	3000	140	0.214	12
Poly(dimethyl siloxane)	30000	810	0.077	13

glass transition temperature. Obviously, the flow behaviour of a polymer changes essentially over such a temperature range. For temperatures far enough above the melting point of a given polymer, the temperature dependence of viscosity follows a simple exponential relationship

$$\eta = B \exp(E_\eta/RT) \tag{15.28}$$

where E_η is an activation energy for viscous flow and B is a constant.

This expression was first formulated by Andrade (1930). Eyring (1941) interpreted this equation with the aid of his hole-theory of liquids. According to this theory a liquid contains unoccupied sites or holes, which move at random throughout the liquid as they are filled and created anew by molecules jumping from one site to another. Each jump is made by overcoming an energy barrier of height E_η. This energy of activation is (for low-molecular liquids) related to the heat of vaporization of the liquid, since the removal of a molecule from the environment of its neighbours forms part of both processes.

In polymers, however, E_η levels off at a value independent of molecular weight. This means that in long chains the unit of flow is considerably smaller than the complete molecule. It seems that viscous flow in polymers takes place by successive jumps of segments until the whole chain has shifted.

As was stated by Magill and Greet (1969), eq. (15.28) does not hold in the vicinity of the melting point, even for liquids of low molecular weight. So it is quite obvious that eq. (15.28) cannot be used for polymers in the temperature range between T_m and T_g. Sometimes values of E_η for this situation are mentioned in the literature, but these relate to formal application of eq. (15.28) over a small temperature range. Such values of E_η increase with decreasing temperature.

The decrease of E_η with increasing T may be explained by the extra free volume created by thermal expansion. This was suggested by Batchinski in 1913 already. Several attempts have been made to formulate a joint temperature function for polymer melts and rubbery amorphous polymers on this basis. Doolittle (1951) formulated the equation:

$$\eta = A \exp(B/\phi_f) \text{ or } \ln \eta = \ln A + \frac{B}{\phi_f} \tag{15.29}$$

where A and B are constants and ϕ_f is the free volume fraction.

If it is assumed that ϕ_f increases linearly with temperature, e.g. $\phi_f = \phi_g + a(T - T_g)$, substitution into eq. (15.29) gives

$$\ln \frac{\eta(T)}{\eta(T_g)} = -\frac{B}{\phi_g} \left(\frac{T - T_g}{\phi_g/a + T - T_g} \right) \tag{15.30}$$

This equation was proposed by Williams, Landel and Ferry (1955). In its generalized form the equation reads:

$$\log \eta(T) = \log \eta(T_S) - \frac{C_1(T - T_S)}{C_2 + (T - T_S)} \tag{15.31}$$

where T_S is a standard temperature. If T_g is chosen as standard temperature, the values of

TABLE 15.4

T_g and T_S values for different polymers

Polymer	T_S	T_g	$T_S - T_g$
poly(hexene-1)	268	223	45
polyisobutylene	243	197	46
polystyrene	413	373	40
poly(vinyl chloride)	395	358	37
poly(vinyl acetate)	350	305	45
poly(methyl acrylate)	324	282	42
poly(methyl methacrylate)	433	387	46
poly(cis-isoprene)	249	206	43
polyurethane	283	238	45
	Average		43

C_1 and C_2 are 17.44 and 51.6, respectively. If the standard temperatures are arbitrarily selected in order to obtain the best universal function (see table 15.4 for these T_S-values of different polymers), the values of the constants C_1 and C_2 are 8.86 and 101.6, respectively. The difference $T_S - T_g$ is about 43°C for a wide range of polymers. As we have seen, the WLF equation also plays an important role in the time-temperature superposition principle in viscoelastic processes (see Chapter 13).

Eq. (15.31) gives a fair description of the effect of temperature on viscosity for a number of polymers. For some other polymers, however, considerable deviations are found. According to eq. (15.31), $\eta(T)/\eta(T_g)$ should be a universal function of $(T - T_g)$, which is not confirmed by experimental data.

Another attempt to derive an equation for the whole temperature range based on a free-volume theory was made by Litt (1973). His equation reads:

$$\log \frac{\eta(T)}{\eta(T_R)} = \left(\frac{T_R}{T}\right)^{3/2} \frac{\exp(T_R/T)}{1 + (T_R/T)} \tag{15.32}$$

in which T_R is a reference temperature. Litt found T_R to be proportional to T_g for a number of polymers ($T_R \approx 2.8\ T_g$).

Eq. (15.32) would imply that $\eta(T)/\eta(T_g)$ is a universal function of T_g/T. But this relationship is not confirmed, either, by experimental data.

Finally a quite empirical equation, proposed by Fox and Loshaek (1955), should be mentioned:

$$\log \eta = A + \frac{B}{T^{(1+a)}} \tag{15.33}$$

where A, B, and a are constants (usually $a \approx 1$).

A similar formula was proposed by Cornelissen and Waterman (1955) for several oils, bituminous products, silicones and glasses.

A new viscosity–temperature relationship [1]

As no completely satisfactory equation is available for the effect of temperature on η_0, a correlation of the available experimental data will be given here in graphical form. Such a correlation should satisfy eq. (15.28) for high temperatures and should correspond to some WLF-type relationship in the neighbourhood of T_g. This can be realized by plotting T_g/T along the horizontal axis.

By plotting $\log \eta$ against T_g/T, the same temperature effect is found for all polymers if $T \leqslant 1.2\ T_g$ (in the region where also the WLF correlation approximately holds). So a generalized $\eta - T$ correlation may be obtained by plotting

$$\frac{\eta_0(T)}{\eta_0(1.2\ T_g)} \left(= \frac{\eta_{cr}(T)}{\eta_{cr}(1.2\ T_g)}\right)$$

as a function of T_g/T. This is shown in fig. 15.3 in which the available experimental data on zero-shear viscosities of polymer melts are plotted. It can be seen that for T_g/T values exceeding $1/1.2$ ($= 0.83$) all points indeed lie on a single curve. For higher temperatures,

---

[1] The viscosity–temperature relationship presented in the 1st edition was dependent on the system of units used. Here an improved relationship is given.

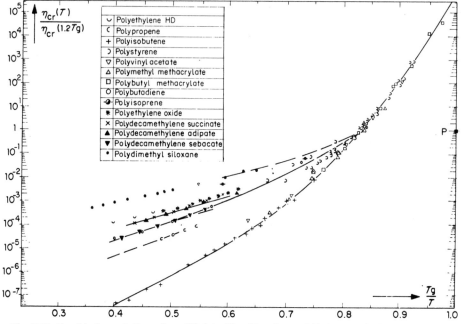

Fig. 15.3. Graphical correlation of η_{cr} (T) data (Van Krevelen and Hoftyzer, 1976).

however, the curves for different polymers follow completely different paths. For high values of T, i.e. low values of T_g/T, the curves asymptotically approach to straight lines.

It is remarkable that all these lines, when extrapolated, pass through one point, indicated by P in fig. 15.3. The coordinates of this point are

$$\log\ [\eta_{cr}(T)/\eta_{cr}(1.2\ T_g)] = 0$$

$$T_g/T = 1$$

The general formula of these asymptotes is:

$$\log \frac{\eta_0(T)}{\eta_0(1.2\ T_g)} = \log \frac{\eta_{cr}(T)}{\eta_{cr}(1.2\ T_g)} = A\left(\frac{T_g}{T} - 1\right) \qquad (15.34)$$

Comparison with eq. (15.28) shows that

$$E_\eta(\infty) = 2.3\ ART_g \quad \text{or} \quad A = \frac{1}{2.3}\frac{E_\eta(\infty)}{RT_g} \qquad (15.35)$$

So with the aid of fig. 15.3 log η_{cr} at a given temperature can be estimated if E_η and log η_{cr} (1.2 T_g) are known. Table 15.5 gives a survey of the available data. It should be borne in mind that there are rather large differences between the values of E_η and log η_{cr} (1.2 T_g) obtained from the data of different investigators. The data mentioned in table 15.5 are mean values.

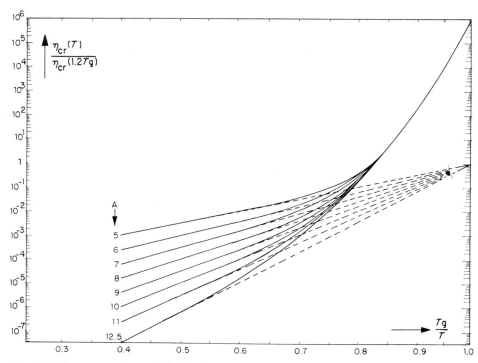

Fig. 15.4. Master curves for η_{cr} (T) (Van Krevelen and Hoftyzer, 1976).

For practical use, a number of master curves for η_{cr} $(T)/\eta_{cr}$ $(1.2\ T_g)$ against T_g/T have been drawn in fig. 15.4, for different values of A, in correspondence with fig. 15.3.

It would, of course, be very desirable to have a method for using the curves of fig. 15.4 with polymers for which E_η and η_{cr} $(1.2\ T_g)$ are not yet known. This means that these quantities have to be predicted from the structure of the polymer, a task which is facilitated by the existence of a correlation between E_η and η_{cr} $(1.2\ T_g)$ [1]. In order to demonstrate this, equation (15.28) may be rewritten as

$$\log \eta_{cr}(T) = \log \eta_{cr}(\infty) + \frac{E_\eta(\infty)}{2.3\ RT} \tag{15.36}$$

where $\eta_{cr}(\infty)$ is a formally defined viscosity at $T = \infty$.

Combination with eq. (15.34) gives

$$\log \eta_{cr}(\infty) = \log \eta_{cr}(1.2\ T_g) - A \tag{15.37}$$

In fig. 15.5 $\log \eta_{cr}(\infty)$ is plotted against E_η. The data approximately satisfy the simple equation

$$\log \eta_{cr}(\infty) = -1.4 - 8.5 \times 10^{-5}\ E_\eta(\infty) \qquad (E_\eta(\infty) \text{ in J/mol}) \tag{15.38}$$

Combination of (15.37), (15.38) and (15.35) gives:

$$\log \eta_{cr}(1.2\ T_g) = -1.4 - 8.5 \times 10^{-5} E_\eta(\infty) + 0.052\ \frac{E_\eta(\infty)}{T_g}$$

[1] Such a correlation is often found in related activated mass transfer processes (diffusion, chemosorption, etc.).

or

$$\log \eta_{cr}(1.2\,T_g) = E_\eta(\infty)\left(\frac{0.052 - 8.5 \times 10^{-5}\,T_g}{T_g}\right) - 1.4 \qquad (15.39)$$

As can be seen from table 15.5, there exists a general correlation between E_η and polymer structure. A low value of E_η, 25 kJ/mol, is found for an unbranched polymethylene chain. About the same value is found for linear polymers, containing methylene groups and oxygen or double bonds. For linear polymers, containing other groups, E_η increases with increasing bulkiness of these groups.

Higher values of E_η are found for polymers containing side chains, and E_η increases with increasing length of the side chain.

The activation energy of poly(dimethyl siloxane) is evidently much lower than the value to be expected for the corresponding carbon-containing polymer.

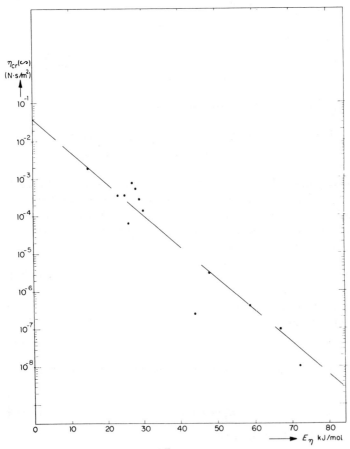

Fig. 15.5. η_{cr} (∞) as a function of E_η.

TABLE 15.5

Parameters of the $\eta_{cr}(T)$ correlation

	A (−)	$E_\eta(\infty)$ (kJ/mol)	Log $\eta_{cr}(1.2T_g)$ (N·s/m²)	T_g (K)	$E_\eta(\infty)$ (calc.) (kJ/mol)
Polyethylene	8.5	25	5.05	195	27
Polypropylene	9.0	44	2.4	253	43
Polyisobutylene	12.5	48	7.8	198	48
Polystyrene	8.2	59	1.8	373	58
Poly(vinyl chloride)	≈12.5	≈85	≈6	354	85
Poly(vinyl acetate)	11.5	67	4.45	301	63
Poly(methyl methacrylate)	9.0	65	3.1	378	64
Poly(butyl methacrylate)	12.5	72	4.5	300	75
Polybutadiene (cis)	8.0	26	3.8	171	26
Polyisoprene	5.5	23	2.05	220	26
Poly(ethylene oxide)	6.7	27	2.6	206	27
Poly(decamethylene succinate)	7.0	28	3.75	210	30
Poly(decamethylene adipate)	7.0	29	3.45	217	29
Poly(decamethylene sebacate)	7.8	30	3.95	197	29
Poly(ethylene terephthalate)	≈7	≈45	≈2	343	47
Nylon 6	≈6	≈36	≈1	323	36
Polycarbonate	≈11	≈85	≈2	414	85
Poly(dimethyl siloxane)	5.2	15	2.5	150	15

Conversion factors: 1 kJ/mol = 240 cal/mol; 1 N·s/m² = 10 poise.

It was found (Van Krevelen and Hoftyzer, 1976) that the function

$$H_\eta = ME_\eta^{1/3}(\infty) \qquad \text{(dimension: g · J}^{1/3} \cdot \text{mol}^{-4/3})$$

has additive properties. Table 15.6 gives the group contributions to this function, and the last column of table 15.5 gives the $E_\eta(\infty)$ values as calculated by means of these increments. The correlation is very satisfactory. The function H_η will be called *molar viscosity—temperature function.*

Table 15.6 enables the prediction of E_η for other polymers. Unaccuracies in the prediction of E_η are reduced by the compensative character of eq. (15.39).

Example 15.1

Estimate the Newtonian viscosity of poly(ethylene terephthalate) with a molecular weight $\bar{M}_w = 4.7 \times 10^4$ at a temperature of 280°C.

Solution

1. According to table 15.6 the H_η-function of PETP is calculated as follows

$-C_6H_4-$	3200
2 $-COO-$	2900
2 $-CH_2-$	840
H_η	6940

TABLE 15.6

Group contributions to the molar viscosity–temperature function $(g \cdot J^{1/3} \cdot mol^{-4/3})$

Group	$H_{\eta i}$	Group	$H_{\eta i}$
Bivalent		Monovalent	
$-CH_2-$	420	$-CH_3$	810
$-CH(CH_3)-$	1060	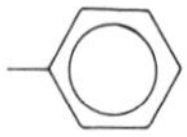	3350
$-C(CH_3)_2-$	1620		
$-CH(C_6H_5)-$	3600		
$-CHCl-$	2330	$-Cl$	2080
		Trivalent	
$-O-$	480		
$-COO-$	1450	$\diagdown CH-$	250
$-OCOO-$	3150	$=CH-$	380
$-CONH-$	1650		
		Tetravalent	
	3200	$\diagdown C \diagup$	0
$-Si(CH_3)_2-$	1350	$\diagdown C=$	0
		$\diagdown Si \diagup$	-270
		Extra effect of side chain, per $-CH_2-$ or other bivalent group	250

Since M = 192 we find

$$E_\eta(\infty) = \left(\frac{H_\eta}{M}\right)^3 = \left(\frac{6940}{192}\right)^3 = 47 \times 10^3 \text{ J/mol.}$$

2. Substitution in eq. (15.39) gives:

$$\log \eta_{cr}(1.2 \, T_g) = 47 \times 10^3 \left[\frac{0.052 - 8.5 \times 10^{-5} \times 343}{343}\right] - 1.4 = 1.7$$

3. According to eq. (15.35) we get:

$$A = \frac{1}{2.3} \frac{47 \times 10^3}{8.3 \times 343} = 7.2$$

4. In fig. 15.4, the curve for A = 7.2 runs close to that for A = 7. At $T_g/T = 343/553 = 0.62$, interpolation gives

$$\log \frac{\eta_{cr}(T)}{\eta_{cr}(1.2 \, T_g)} = -2.7$$

So $\log \eta_{cr}(553) = 1.7 - 2.7 = -1.0$.

5. The critical molar weight M_{cr} of PETP is 6×10^3. So

$$\log \overline{M}_w/M_{cr} = \log(4.7 \times 10^4/6 \times 10^3) = 0.89.$$

According to eq. (15.27)

$$\log \eta_0(553) = \log \eta_{cr}(553) + 3.4 \log \frac{4.7 \times 10^4}{6 \times 10^3}$$

$$= -1.0 + 3.4 \times 0.89 = 2.0 \ (N \cdot s/m^2).$$

This is in fair agreement with the experimental value as determined by Gregory (1972), viz. $\log \eta_0(553) = 2.54 \ (N \cdot s/m^2)$.

Effect of hydrostatic pressure on viscosity

Just as for liquids of low molecular weight, the viscosity of polymers increases with the hydrostatic pressure. The *pressure coefficient of viscosity*, $\mathcal{X}$ is defined as

$$\mathcal{X} = \frac{1}{\eta}\left(\frac{\partial \eta}{\partial p}\right) \qquad (15.40)$$

Experimental data of $\mathcal{X}$ for polymers are scarce; the available data are mentioned in table 15.7. In principle, for a prediction of $\mathcal{X}$, the following equation which can be derived from thermodynamics might be used

$$\frac{\mathcal{X}}{\mathcal{A}} \approx -\frac{\kappa}{\alpha} \qquad (15.41)$$

where

$$\mathcal{A} = \textit{temperature dependence of viscosity} = \frac{1}{\eta}\left(\frac{\partial \eta}{\partial T}\right)$$

κ = compressibility

α = thermal expansion coefficient.

However, as a rule the thermodynamic data for the calculation of the quotient κ/α are not readily available. In this case the mean value of the $\mathcal{X}/\mathcal{A}$ ratio of table 15.7 can be used:

TABLE 15.7

The pressure coefficient of viscosity

Polymer	T (°C)	$\mathcal{X}$ $(10^{-8}$ m²/N)	$\mathcal{A}$ (K^{-1})	$-\dfrac{\mathcal{X}}{\mathcal{A}}$ $(10^{-7}$ m² $\cdot$ K/N)	References
Polyethylene	190	1.4	−0.028	5.0	Westover (1961)
Polyethylene LD	210	1.43	−0.027	5.3	Cogswell and McGowan (1972)
Polyethylene HD	170	0.68	−0.025	2.7	Cogswell and McGowan (1972)
Polypropylene	210	1.50	−0.028	5.4	Cogswell and McGowan (1972)
Polystyrene	165	4.3	−0.078	5.5	Hellwege et al. (1967)
Polystyrene	190	3.5	−0.103	3.4	Cogswell and McGowan (1972)
Poly(methyl methacrylate)	235	2.14	−0.057	3.8	Cogswell and McGowan (1972)
Polycarbonate	270	2.35	−0.058	4.1	Cogswell and McGowan (1972)
Poly(dimethyl siloxane)	40	0.73	−0.018	4.0	Holzmüller and Dinter (1960)

348

$$\frac{\mathcal{K}}{\mathcal{A}} \approx 4 \times 10^{-7} \text{ m}^2 \cdot \text{K} \cdot \text{N}^{-1} \tag{15.41a}$$

So

$$\frac{\partial \ln \eta}{\partial p} \approx -4 \times 10^{-7} \frac{\partial \ln \eta}{\partial T}$$

or

$$\frac{\Delta \ln \eta}{\Delta p(\text{bar})} \approx -4 \times 10^{-2} \frac{\Delta \ln \eta}{\Delta T}$$

This means that a pressure increase of 1000 bar has about the same effect as a temperature decrease of 40°C.

C. NON-NEWTONIAN SHEAR VISCOSITY OF POLYMER MELTS

Viscosity as a function of shear rate

The most obvious viscoelastic phenomenon in polymer melts is the decrease of viscosity with increasing shear rate. This decrease may amount to several decades. At the same time, elastic behaviour may be observed.

A number of empirical equations have been proposed to describe the influence of shear rate on viscosity. The most popular equation represents the so-called power law formulated by Ostwald (1925) and De Waele (1923):

$$\tau = K\dot{\gamma}^n \text{ or } \eta = K\dot{\gamma}^{(n-1)} \tag{15.42}$$

Table 15.8 gives values of the exponent n for some typical polymers. Other empirical equations have been used by Ferry (1942):

$$\dot{\gamma} = \frac{\tau}{\eta_0}\left(1 + \frac{\tau}{G_i}\right) \text{ or } \eta = \frac{\eta_0}{1 + \tau/G_i} \tag{15.43}$$

and by Spencer and Dillon (1949):

$$\dot{\gamma} = \frac{\tau}{\eta_0} \exp(\tau/b) \text{ or } \eta = \eta_0 \exp(-\tau/b) \tag{15.44}$$

In these equations, η_0 is the viscosity at zero rate of shear and K, n, G_i and b are constants.

These empirical equations have a limited applicability, and the constants involved have different values for different polymer samples.

In this chapter a general empirical correlation of rheological properties of polymer melts will be given. The form of this correlation is based on theoretical interpretations of the decrease of viscosity with increasing rate of shear. The pioneer in this field has been Bueche (1962), who based his derivations on a simplified model of polymer structure. A more intricate theory, which is often cited, is that of Graessley (1967). For details of these models the reader is referred to the literature.

TABLE 15.8

Values of power-law index, n, for six materials

Shear rate	Poly(methyl methacrylate)	Acetal copolymer	Nylon 6,6	Propylene–ethylene copolymer	Low-density polyethylene	Unplasticized PVC
(s^{-1})	$230°C$	$200°C$	$285°C$	$230°C$	$170°C$	$150°C$
10^{-1}	–	–	–	0.93	0.7	–
1	1.00	1.00	–	0.66	0.44	–
10	0.82	1.00	0.96	0.46	0.32	0.62
10^2	0.46	0.80	0.91	0.34	0.26	0.55
10^3	0.22	0.42	0.71	0.19	–	0.47
10^4	0.18	0.18	0.40	0.15	–	–
10^5	–	–	0.28	–	–	–

After P.C. Powell (1974).

One important aspect of polymer structure should be mentioned here, however, viz. the very important role of very long polymer molecules in the viscoelastic behaviour. As a consequence, the viscoelastic phenomena are strongly dependent on the molecular weight distribution.

Rheological quantities and their interrelations

The viscoelastic quantities η, γ_e, G, ξ and Θ were defined at the beginning of this section. The following interrelations exist between these rheological quantities:

$$\eta = G\Theta = \frac{\xi}{\Theta} = (\xi G)^{1/2}$$

$$G = \frac{\eta}{\Theta} = \frac{\eta^2}{\xi} = \frac{\xi}{\Theta^2}$$

$$\xi = \eta\Theta = G\Theta^2 = \frac{\eta^2}{G}$$

$$\Theta = \frac{\eta}{G} = \frac{\xi}{\eta} = \left(\frac{\xi}{G}\right)^{1/2}$$

$$\gamma_e = \dot{\gamma}\Theta$$

(15.45)

Experimental methods

Of the quantities mentioned in equations (15.45) at least two should be measured as a function of the rate of shear $\dot{\gamma}$ for a description of viscoelastic shear flow. One of these quantities is always the shear stress τ, from which the viscosity η can be calculated.

A number of experimental techniques have been developed for measuring characteristic elastic shear quantities. These methods always involve the determination of either the elastic part of the shear deformation γ_e or the normal stress difference $p_{11} - p_{22}$, both of which can be measured directly or calculated from other quantities. Table 15.9 gives a survey of these methods.

TABLE 15.9

Methods for the determination of elastic shear quantities

Method	Quantity measured directly	Quantity determined	Investigators
Cone-and-plate rheometer recovery	γ_e	γ_e	Cogswell and Lamb (1970) Mills (1969) Vinogradov et al. (1970)
Weissenberg cone-and-plate rheogoniometer	$p_{11} - p_{22}$	$p_{11} - p_{22}$	King (1966) Mills (1969)
Die-swell measurements	$\dfrac{\text{diameter extrudate}}{\text{diameter capillary}}$	γ_e	Cogswell and Lamb (1970)
		$p_{11} - p_{22}$	Metzner et al. (1961, 1969) Vinogradov and Prozorovskaya (1964)
Shear measurements in series of capillaries with varying L/D ratio	End correction	γ_e	Thomas and Hagan (1969)

All these experimental techniques are rather intricate, so that the calculated visco-elastic quantities may show a considerable scatter.

The above-mentioned methods deal with steady-state conditions. Measurements under transient conditions show a dependence of viscosity on time. Meissner (1971) and Vinogradov et al. (1969) describe investigations in which the course of the shear stress was measured at the start of a shear experiment before a steady state had developed.

The results of dynamic shear measurements may also be used for calculating the viscosity if the elastic component G' and the loss component G'' of the complex shear modulus G^* are given as a function of the angular frequency ω. Cox and Merz (1958) found empirically that the steady-state shear viscosity at a given shear rate is practically equal to the absolute value of the complex viscosity $|\eta^*|$ at a frequency numerically equal to this shear rate:

$$\eta(\dot{\gamma}) \approx |\eta^*|(\omega) \tag{15.46}$$

in which

$$|\eta^*| = \frac{|G^*|}{\omega} = \frac{\sqrt{(G')^2 + (G'')^2}}{\omega} \tag{15.47}$$

This rule was afterwards confirmed by many investigators.

Up to now, however, no method has been published for the exact calculation of other viscoelastic quantities from the results of dynamic measurements. An approximate method has been proposed by Adamse et al. (1968). These investigators assumed that

$$p_{11} - p_{22} \approx 2\,G' \tag{15.48}$$

Another method to calculate viscoelastic quantities uses measurements of flow birefringence (see Chapter 10). In these measurements two quantities are determined as functions of the shear rate $\dot{\gamma}$:

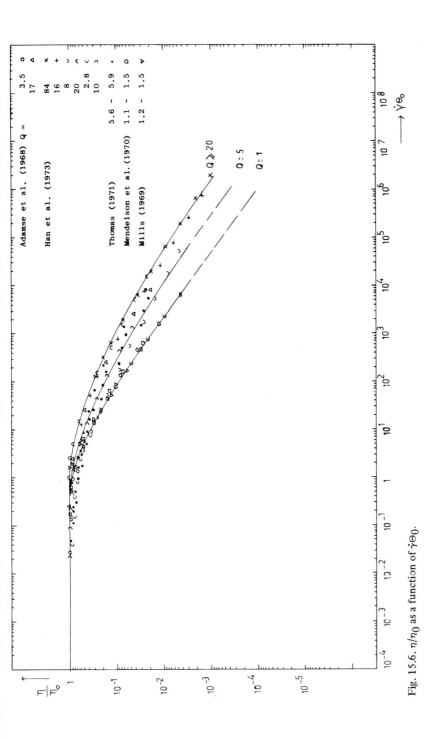

Fig. 15.6. η/η_0 as a function of $\dot{\gamma}\Theta_0$.

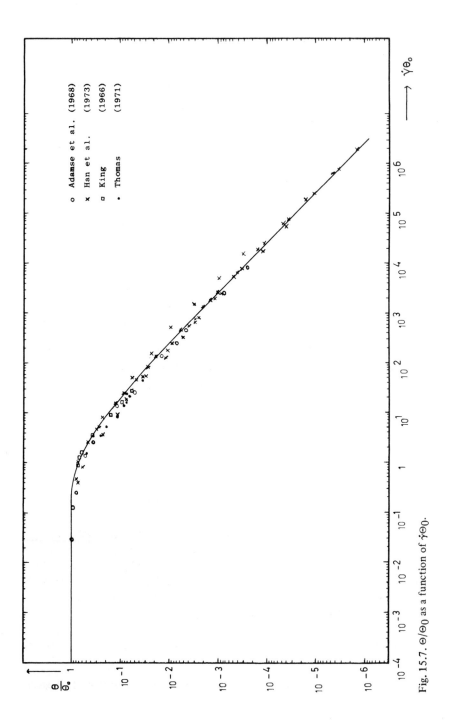

o Adamse et al. (1968)
x Han et al. (1973)
□ King (1966)
• Thomas (1971)

Fig. 15.7. Θ/Θ_0 as a function of $\dot\gamma\Theta_0$.

the birefringence Δn and the extinction angle χ. The following relationships exist with the stress tensor components:

$$2\,p_{21} = C\,\Delta n\,\sin 2\chi \tag{15.49}$$

$$p_{11} - p_{22} = C\,\Delta n\,\cos 2\chi \tag{15.50}$$

where C is the so-called stress-optical coefficient, the value of which depends on the nature of the polymer.

Even if the value of C is not known beforehand, the normal stress component can be estimated by using the quotient of equations (15.49) and (15.50):

$$p_{11} - p_{22} = 2\,p_{21}\,\cot\chi \tag{15.51}$$

The (approximate) validity of equation (15.51) has been confirmed by experiments of Adamse et al. (1968).

Correlation of non-Newtonian shear data

It proved possible to correlate all the available data on viscoelastic shear quantities. The basis for this correlation has been laid by Bueche (1962) and by Vinogradov and Malkin (1964).

In order to elucidate the correlation method it may be recalled that the viscosity η approaches asymptotically to the constant value η_0 with decreasing shear rate $\dot{\gamma}$. Similarly, the characteristic time Θ approaches a constant value Θ_0, and the shear modulus G has a limiting value G_0 at low shear rates.

Bueche already proposed that the relationship between η and $\dot{\gamma}$ be expressed in a dimensionless form by plotting η/η_0 as a function of $\dot{\gamma}\Theta_0$. According to Vinogradov, also the ratio Θ/Θ_0 is a function of $\dot{\gamma}\Theta_0$ [1]. Consequently, the ratio G/G_0 and the elastic deformation γ_e should also be functions of $\dot{\gamma}\Theta_0$, as

$$(G/G_0) = (\eta/\eta_0)/(\Theta/\Theta_0)$$

and

$$\gamma_e = (\dot{\gamma}\Theta_0)(\Theta/\Theta_0)$$

The product $\dot{\gamma}\Theta_0$ is sometimes called the Weissenberg number, N_{Wg}.

The relationship between η/η_0 and $\dot{\gamma}\Theta_0$ appears to be dependent on the molecular weight distribution. As a first approximation this influence may be taken into account by using the distribution factor $Q = \bar{M}_w/\bar{M}_n$ as a parameter. The available experimental data do not show an influence of the molecular weight distribution on the relationship between Θ/Θ_0 and $\dot{\gamma}\Theta_0$. As a consequence, the factor Q should also be used as a parameter in correlating the data on G/G_0 as a function of $\dot{\gamma}\Theta_0$.

Figs. 15.6 to 15.9 show the correlation between η/η_0, Θ/Θ_0, G/G_0, γ_e and $\dot{\gamma}\Theta_0$, with Q as a parameter. For low shear rates ($\log \dot{\gamma}\Theta_0 < -0.5$)

---

[1] Vinogradov originally correlated with the product $\dot{\gamma}\eta_0$ instead of $\dot{\gamma}\Theta_0$.

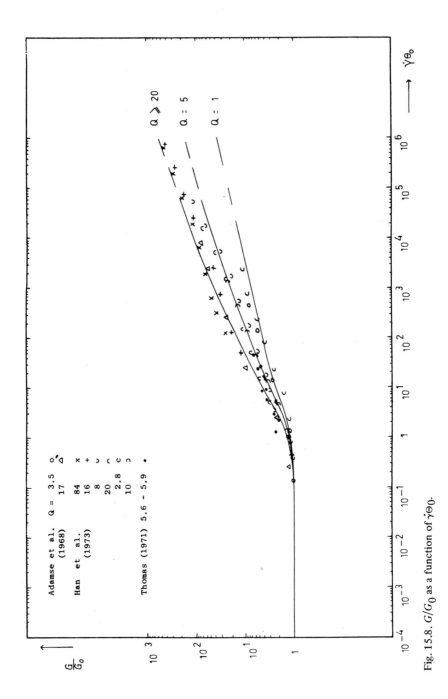

Fig. 15.8. G/G_0 as a function of $\dot{\gamma}\Theta_0$.

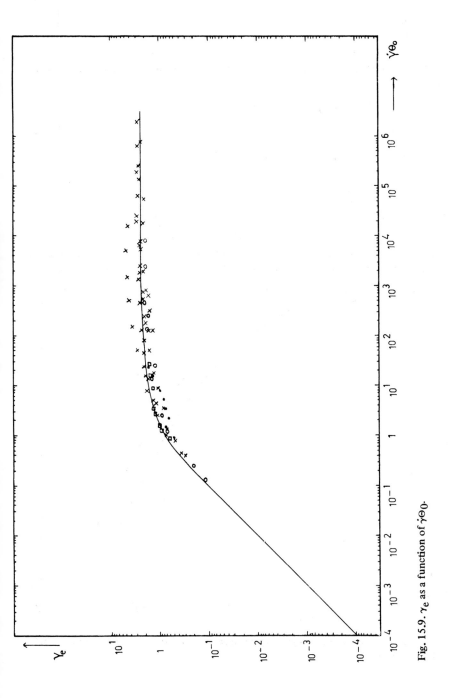

Fig. 15.9. γ_e as a function of $\dot\gamma\Theta_0$.

$$\eta/\eta_0 = 1$$

$$\Theta/\Theta_0 = 1$$

$$G/G_0 = 1$$

$$\gamma_e = \dot{\gamma}\Theta_0 = \dot{\gamma}\frac{\eta_0}{G_0}$$

(15.52)

For high shear rates ($\log \dot{\gamma}\Theta_0 > 3$), the curves can be described by the following linear relationships:

$$\log (\eta/\eta_0) = 0.5 - 0.75 \log (\dot{\gamma}\Theta_0) \qquad \text{(for } Q = 1)$$

$$\log (\Theta/\Theta_0) = 0.4 - \log (\dot{\gamma}\Theta_0)$$

$$\log (G/G_0) = 0.1 + 0.25 \log (\dot{\gamma}\Theta_0) \qquad \text{(for } Q = 1)$$

$$\log \gamma_e = 0.4$$

(15.53)

The correlations given hold for steady-state shearing conditions. Some literature data are also available about the transient state at the start of a shearing experiment at constant shear rate $\dot{\gamma}$, for instance for the experiments of Meissner (1972) with low-density polyethylene.

During the transient period the viscosity increases with time. For a correlation of the viscoelastic quantities two dimensionless groups are needed: $\dot{\gamma}\Theta_0$ and Θ_0/t. These correlations will not be discussed

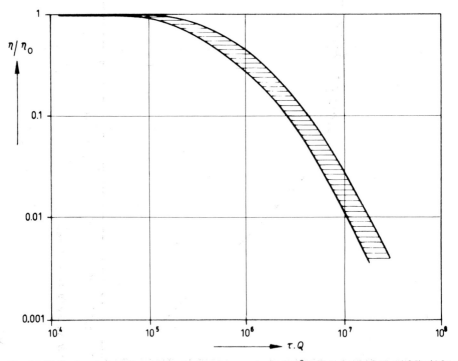

Fig. 15.10. Reduced viscosity of 33 polypropylene grades at 210°C (Q between 3.5 and 25). (After Van der Vegt, 1964.)

here.

Also for the correlation of dynamic viscoelastic shear quantities two dimensionless groups are needed: $\Theta_0\omega$ and $\Theta_0\omega\gamma_0$, as was shown by Vinogradov et al. (1970, 1971). γ_0 is the amplitude of the imposed dynamic shear. These correlations will not be discussed, either.

Prediction of viscosity as a function of shear rate

For many technical calculations a method for the prediction of polymer melt viscosity as a function of shear rate would be very valuable. A basis for this prediction forms fig. 15.6, where η/η_0 has been plotted against $\dot{\gamma}\Theta_0$, with Q as a parameter. Obviously, η_0 and Θ_0 should be known if η is to be calculated as a function of $\dot{\gamma}$.

A method for the prediction of η_0 as a function of molecular weight and temperature has been given earlier in this chapter. There remains the prediction of the characteristic time constant Θ_0.

Calculations with molecular structure models, as performed by Bueche and others, predict that for monodisperse polymers

$$G_0 = \frac{\pi^2}{6} \frac{\rho RT}{M} \tag{15.54}$$

so that

$$\Theta_0 = \frac{\eta_0}{G_0} = \frac{6}{\pi^2} \frac{\eta_0 M}{\rho RT} \tag{15.55}$$

The available data on (nearly) monodisperse polymers seem to confirm these rules.

For polydisperse polymers, however, the situation is more complicated. For a number of polydisperse polymer samples, experimental values of Θ_0 can be found in the literature. These values of Θ_0 are always larger than those calculated with eq. (15.55), using M_w for the molecular weight.

An empirical method to cope with the effect of molecular weight distribution was proposed by Van der Vegt (1964). He determined viscosities of several grades of polypropylenes with different $\bar{M}_w$ and MWD as a function of the shear stress τ. A plot of η/η_0 versus the product $\tau \times Q$ proved to give practically coinciding curves. This generalized curve has been reproduced in fig. 15.10.

The results of Van der Vegt suggest that for polydisperse polymer melts Θ_0 can be predicted by

$$\Theta_0 \approx \frac{6}{\pi^2} \frac{\eta_0 \bar{M}_w}{\rho RT} Q \tag{15.56}$$

so that again η can be calculated with the aid of fig. 15.6.

A more direct prediction method uses a formal time constant Θ_M

$$\Theta_M = \frac{6}{\pi^2} \frac{\eta_0 \bar{M}_w}{\rho RT} \tag{15.57}$$

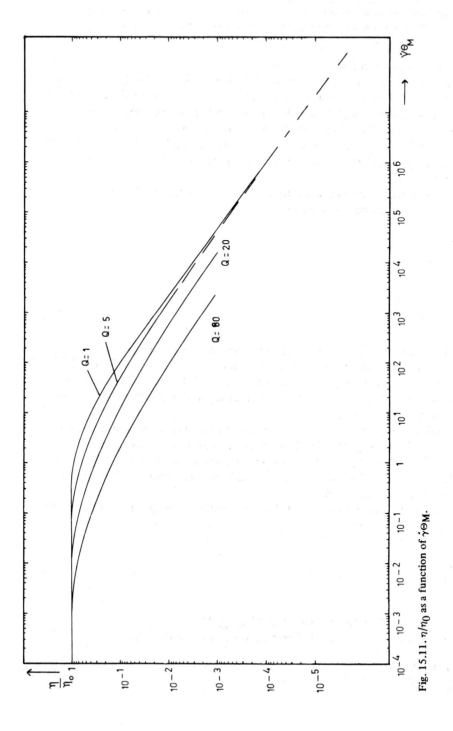

Fig. 15.11. η/η_0 as a function of $\dot{\gamma}\Theta_M$.

Experimental values of η/η_0 are plotted against the product $\dot{\gamma}\Theta_M$, with Q as a parameter. A graph of this type is shown in fig. 15.11. This correlation, however, should be considered as a first approximation only. Some literature values show considerable deviations. This will at least partly be caused by large inaccuracies in the values of $\bar{M}_w$.

It is interesting to note that an analogous result is obtained with a theoretical derivation of η as a function of $\dot{\gamma}$ by Graessley (1967, 1970). This calculation can be used with an arbitrary molecular weight distribution. Calculations carried out with Graessley's formulae by Cote and Shida (1973) showed that the parameter $Q = \bar{M}_w/\bar{M}_n$ was insufficient for a complete description of the effect of molecular weight distribution.

A disadvantage of Graessley's method is that it involves rather complicated calculations, for which computer programs have been developed. A more serious drawback, however, is that the calculations are based on an unspecified time constant. According to experiments of Saeda (1973) this time constant does not correspond with Θ_0 or Θ_M. This makes the method less suited for prediction purposes.

Example 15.2

Estimate the decrease in the viscosity of a poly(ethylene terephthalate) melt at a shear rate of 5000 s^{-1}. $\bar{M}_w = 3.72 \times 10^4$; $Q = 3.5$; $T = 553$ K; $\eta_0 = 156$ N $\cdot$ s/m^2.

Solution

According to eq. (15.57):

$$\Theta_M = \frac{6}{\pi^2} \frac{\eta_0 \bar{M}_w}{\rho R T} = \frac{6}{\pi^2} \frac{156 \times 3.72 \times 10^4}{1160 \times 8310 \times 553} = 6.6 \times 10^{-4}$$

$\dot{\gamma}\Theta_M = 5000 \times 6.6 \times 10^{-4} = 3.3$

In fig. 15.11 we read at $\dot{\gamma}\Theta_M = 3.3$ and $Q = 3.5$: $\eta/\eta_0 \approx 0.50$. So the estimate is $\eta \approx 80$ N $\cdot$ s/m^2 under the conditions given. The experimental value mentioned by Gregory (1972) is $\eta = 81.5$ N $\cdot$ s/m^2.

Second Newtonian flow region

Up to now, two regions of shear flow have been discussed: Newtonian flow at low shear rates and non-Newtonian flow at high shear rates. In the first region the viscosity is independent of the shear rate, while in the second region the viscosity decreases with increasing shear rate.

Under special experimental conditions a third region may be found at still higher shear rates. In this region, the viscosity becomes again independent of the shear rate. Therefore this region is called second Newtonian flow region.

Data on the existence of this region for polymer melts and on the role of molecular weight have been discussed by Porter et al. (1968).

In practice, the second Newtonian flow region will not often be encountered, as under normal conditions melt fracture will occur in the second flow region already.

D. EXTENSIONAL VISCOSITY OF POLYMER MELTS

Experimental techniques

Measurement of rheological quantities on the tensile deformation of polymer melts is extremely difficult and requires the development of special techniques. In fact, adequate experimental techniques have been applied in rather recent investigations only, so that the older literature can be left out of consideration.

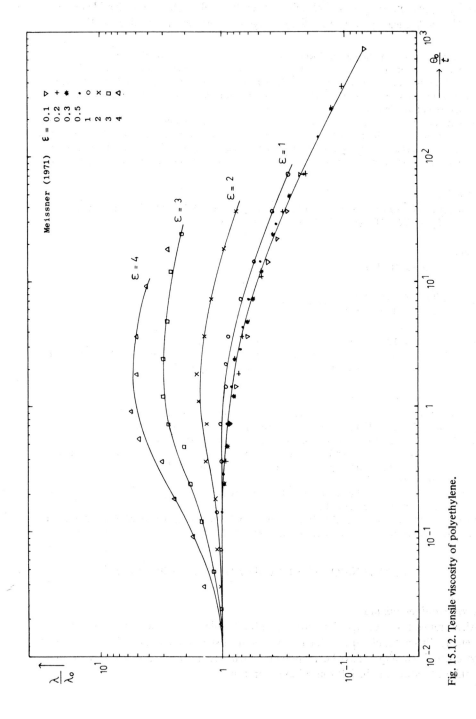

Fig. 15.12. Tensile viscosity of polyethylene.

The usual shear measurements on polymer melts are performed as steady-state experiments in which a stationary state of shear deformation is maintained. A steady-state experiment on tensile deformation, however, means an imitation of a melt spinning process. This type of experiment has several disadvantages:

(1) the deformation conditions (rate of deformation, tensile stress, temperature) vary from point to point;

(2) the local deformation conditions cannot easily be determined;

(3) die-swell occurs in the first stages of deformation.

In a number of publications in this field an incorrect interpretation of the experimental results may have been presented.

Therefore in a number of investigations on tensile deformation non-steady-state techniques have been used. In these experiments, a cylindrical beam of the material is gradually extended from its original length L_0 at $t = 0$ to a length L at time t. From the definition of the rate of deformation $\dot{\epsilon}$, a constant value of $\dot{\epsilon}$ cannot be obtained by moving one end of the beam at a constant linear velocity. A constant rate of deformation could be realized by special experimental devices.

In these experiments, the tensile force is measured as a function of time, so that at a constant rate of deformation $\dot{\epsilon}$ it is possible to calculate the true tensile stress and the extensional viscosity $\lambda = \sigma/\dot{\epsilon}$ at an arbitrary time t. The elastic properties of the deformation can be determined by measuring the elastic strain ϵ_e.

Correlation of extensional viscosity data

For correlating extensional viscosity data it is obvious to attempt the same method as was used for non-steady state shear viscosity. Thus the ratio λ/λ_0 is presumed to be determined by two dimensionless groups: $\dot{\epsilon}\Theta_0$ and Θ_0/t. As $\dot{\epsilon}$ is constant, the ratio of these groups is equal to the tensile deformation ϵ. So λ/λ_0 will likewise be a function of Θ_0/t and ϵ.

By way of example, the experimental results of Meissner (1971) on low-density polyethylene have been represented in fig. 15.12, by plotting λ/λ_0 against Θ_0/t with ϵ as a parameter. For low values of ϵ, all points lie in a single curve, which shows some correspondence to the curves of fig. 15.6 for η/η_0 against $\dot{\gamma}\Theta_0$. If $\epsilon > 1$, however, the extensional viscosity increases considerably with increasing extension.

This effect may be responsible for the popular belief that the extensional viscosity of polymer melts increases with increasing rate of deformation. Obviously this statement is too simplistic, as one more parameter is needed to describe the relationship between extensional viscosity and rate of deformation. The situation is even more complicated! Although extensional viscosity data on other polymers are scarce, it is certain that the correlation of fig. 15.12 has no universal validity, but depends on the nature of the polymer. So at the moment it is not possible to predict the extensional viscosity behaviour of an arbitrary polymer.

The available data on continuous tensile deformation indicate that in this situation the same conclusions hold as given above for non-steady state deformation:

1. The ratio λ/λ_0 is not a simple function of the group $\dot{\epsilon}\Theta_0$, but requires an additional parameter (e.g. ϵ) for correlation.

2. This correlation is dependent on the nature of the polymer.

The available data on continuous tensile deformation are insufficient to justify a presentation at this place.

The elastic properties of tensile deformation may, in principle, be correlated by plotting Θ/Θ_0, E/E_0 or ϵ_e against $\dot{\epsilon}/\Theta_0$ or Θ_0/t. The same types of correlation are found as for shear viscosity, but also in this case the data are too scarce to provide general relationships.

362

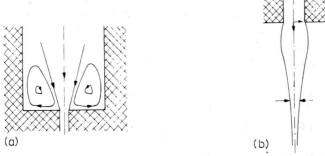

Fig. 15.13. (a) Efflux of an elastic fluid into a narrow tube from a large reservoir. (b) Die swell at efflux of an elastic fluid from a capillary.

E. ELASTIC EFFECTS IN POLYMER MELTS

Converging flow phenomena

Converging flow occurs in a wedge or tapering tube (restrained converging flow) and in the drawing of a molten filament (unrestrained converging flow). Polymer melts often behave very differently from Newtonian fluids under these circumstances.

The most extreme case of converging flow arises when a melt is forced from a large reservoir into a narrow tube. Fig. 15.13a gives a diagrammatic indication for a highly elastic

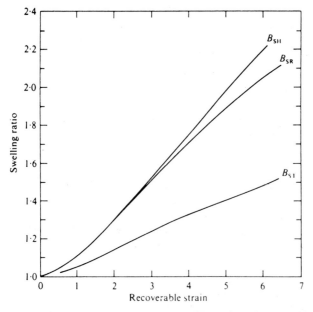

Fig. 15.14. The relationship between swelling ratio and recoverable shear strain for long capillary and slot dies (after Powell, 1974).

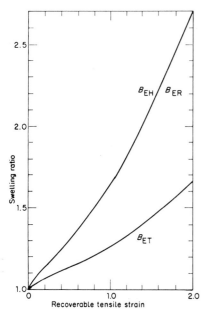

Fig. 15.15. The relationship between swelling ratio and recoverable tensile strain for short capillary and slot dies (after Powell, 1974).

fluid. Tordella (1957) and Clegg (1958) have already observed the large ring vortex as shown with many polymer melts. The phenomenon is a direct consequence of a high extensional (Trouton) viscosity linked with a relatively low shear viscosity; the material flowing into the tube is restricted to a narrow-angle cone and the large recirculating vortex occupies a "dead" volume around it.

In general, when a thermoplastic melt flowing in a channel encounters an abrupt decrease in channel diameter, the material conforms to a natural angle of convergence for streamline flow. Cogswell (1972) derived the following expressions:

for coni-cylindrical flow: $\tan \alpha = \left(\dfrac{2\eta}{\lambda}\right)^{1/2}$

for wedge-flow: $\tan \beta = \dfrac{3}{2}\left(\dfrac{\eta}{\lambda}\right)^{1/2}$

where α and β are in both cases the half angle of natural convergence.

In appendix II of this chapter the most important rheological equations for converging flow are summarized.

Die swell

Most polymer melts, when extruded, expand in diameter once they emerge into an essentially unrestrained environment. Especially in short dies (in the extreme case in dies of "zero length") the tensile component of flow induced by convergence of the flow cannot relax before reaching the die exit. In long capillaries die swell occurs as a consequence of the recoverable shear strain corresponding to the shear stress at the wall at the die exit (fig. 15.13b).

Fig. 15.14 shows the relationships between swelling ratio and recoverable strain as derived by Cogswell (1970) for long capillaries and slot dies. B_{SR} represents the swelling ratio in capillaries, B_{SH} and B_{ST} that in slot dies in the thickness direction and in the transverse direction respectively.

Fig. 15.15 shows the analogous relationships for very short (zero length) dies. B_{ER} is the swelling ratio in radial direction in a very short circular die, whereas B_{EH} and B_{ET} give the corresponding relationships for slot dies in the thickness and transverse directions.

In appendix II the expressions for the swelling ratio in different cases of convergent flow are given.

Unstable flow

Newtonian shear flow of polymer melts is a stable process. This means that small disturbances in the flow conditions, caused by external effects, are readily suppressed. As the rate of shear increases, however, the elastic response of the melt becomes more pronounced relative to the viscous response. In other words, components of the stress tensor in directions different from the direction of the shear stress become more important. As a result, small disturbances are not so readily compensated and may even be magnified.

In extrusion, for instance, high shear rates may result in rough surfaces of the extrudate, poor surface gloss and poor transparency. The ultimate disastrous effect of melt flow instability is melt fracture.

There is an extensive literature on attempts to give quantitative criteria for the onset of melt fracture. The simplest criterion has been proposed by Benbow and Lamb (1963), viz. that melt fracture occurs if the shear stress exceeds 1.25×10^5 N/m^2.

Bartos (1964) suggested a critical value of viscosity reduction

$$\frac{\eta_{MF}}{\eta_0} = 0.025 \tag{15.58}$$

Barnett (1967) defined a "melt fracture number"

$$N_{MF} = \frac{\eta_0 \dot{\gamma}}{Q} \tag{15.59}$$

where $Q = \bar{M}_w/\bar{M}_n$. Melt fracture is observed if $N_{MF} > 10^6$ N/m^2 (η_0 is expressed in N·s/m^2 and $\dot{\gamma}$ in s^{-1}).

It is doubtful, however, if melt fracture can be predicted from shear rate criteria alone, without taking the geometry of the apparatus into account. Especially the form of the channel at the entrance of the die is very important. In using extrusion dies with a conical entrance, flow instabilities are suppressed by decreasing the cone angle. This effect has been found experimentally by Tordella (1956), Clegg (1958) and Ferrari (1964).

From these results Everage and Ballman (1974) concluded that melt fracture originates at a point where fluid elements are subjected primarily to extensional deformation. They could correlate the results of Ferrari with a critical extension rate of about 1000 s^{-1}.

Some important rheological equations

Class of flow	Pressure drop		Die entry	Swell ratio
	Shear	Extensional		
(1) Constant section die				
Circular: long	$2L\tau/R$	0	$\dfrac{4\sqrt{2}}{3(n+1)}\dot{\gamma}(\eta\lambda)^{1/2}$	$B_{SR} = \left[\dfrac{2}{3}\gamma_R\left(\left(1+\dfrac{1}{\gamma_R^2}\right)^{3/2} - \dfrac{1}{\gamma_R^3}\right)\right]^{1/2}$
Circular: zero length	0	0	$\dfrac{4\sqrt{2}}{3(n+1)}\dot{\gamma}(\eta\lambda)^{1/2}$	$B_{ER} = (\exp.\ \epsilon_R)^{1/2}$
Slot: long	$2L\tau/H$	0	$\dfrac{4}{3(n+1)}\dot{\gamma}(\eta\lambda)^{1/2}$	$\begin{cases} B_{ST} = \left\{\dfrac{1}{2}\left[(1+\gamma_R^2)^{1/2} + \dfrac{1}{\gamma_R}\ln\{\gamma_R + (1+\gamma_R^2)^{1/2}\}\right]\right\}^{1/3} \\ B_{SH} = B_{ST}^2 \end{cases}$
Slot: zero length	0	0	$\dfrac{4}{3(n+1)}\dot{\gamma}(\eta\lambda)^{1/2}$	$\begin{cases} B_{ET} = (\exp.\ \epsilon_R)^{1/4} \\ B_{EH} = B_{ET}^2 \end{cases}$
(2) Tapered section die				
Coni-cylindrical	$\left[\dfrac{2\tau}{3n\cdot\tan\theta}\left[1 - \left(\dfrac{R_1}{R_0}\right)^{3n}\right]\right.$	$\dfrac{1}{3}\lambda\dot{\gamma}\tan\theta\left[1 - \dfrac{R_1^3}{R_0^3}\right]$ $\left(\hat{\dot{\epsilon}} = \dfrac{1}{2}\left(\dfrac{3n+1}{n+1}\right)\dot{\gamma}\tan\theta\right)$	$\dfrac{4\sqrt{2}}{3(n+1)}\dot{\gamma}_0(\eta\lambda)^{1/2}$ $(\hat{\sigma} = \dfrac{3}{8}(3n+1)P_0)$	$\begin{cases} B_{SR} = \left[\dfrac{2}{3}\gamma_R\left(\left(1+\dfrac{1}{\gamma_R^2}\right)^{3/2} - \dfrac{1}{\gamma_R^3}\right)\right]^{1/2} \\ B_{ER} = (\exp.\ \epsilon_R)^{1/2} \end{cases}$
Wedge	$\dfrac{\tau}{2n\cdot\tan\theta}\left[1 - \left(\dfrac{H_1}{H_0}\right)^{2n}\right]$	$\dfrac{1}{2}\sigma_{av}\left[1 - \dfrac{H_1^2}{H_0^2}\right]$ $(\hat{\dot{\epsilon}} = \dfrac{1}{3}\dot{\gamma}\tan\theta)$	$\dfrac{4}{3(n+1)}\dot{\gamma}(\eta\lambda)^{1/2}$	$B_{ET} = (\exp.\ \epsilon_R)^{1/4}$ $B_{EH} = B_{ET}^2$

(Continued on p. 366)

TABLE 15.10 (continued)

Class of flow	Pressure drop		Swell ratio	
	Shear	Extensional	Die entry	

(3) Spreading disc flow

(Circular disc, centre gate)

Class of flow	Shear	Extensional	Die entry	Swell ratio
Isothermal	$\dfrac{2CQ^nR^{1-n}}{(1-n)x^{1+2n}}$	$\dfrac{\lambda Q}{4\pi xR^2}$		
Non-isothermal	$\dfrac{2CQ^nR^{1-n}}{(1-n)(xZ)^{1+2n}}$	$\dfrac{\lambda Q}{4\pi xR^2 Z}$		

Data from Powell (1974); Cogswell (1970); Cogswell and McGowan (1972); Barrie (1970).

B_{SR} – swelling ratio in radial direction; B_{ST} – swelling ratio in transverse direction; B_{SH} – swelling ratio in thickness direction; B_{ER} – tensile swelling ratio in radial direction for $L \to 0$; B_{ET} – tensile swelling ratio in transverse direction for $L \to 0$; B_{EH} – tensile swelling ratio in thickness direction for $L \to 0$; C – power law constant; H – die gap; H_0 – entry die gap; H_1 – exit die gap; L – length of section; n – power law exponent; P_0 – entry pressure; Q – volume flow rate; R – radius; R_0 – entry radius; R_1 – exit radius; W – width of wedge; x – separation of plates; Z – effective thickness correction factor; $\dot{\gamma}$ – shear rate $= 4Q/\pi R^3$ or $3Q/2WH^2$; γ_R – recoverable shear strain $= \tau/G$; ϵ – tensile strain; ϵ_R – recoverable tensile strain $= \sigma/E$; $\dot{\epsilon}$ – tensile strain rate; η – shear viscosity; θ – half angle of taper; λ – extensional viscosity; σ – tensile stress; τ – shear stress $= C(4Q/\pi R^3)^n$.

APPENDIX I

Flow of polymer melts through narrow tubes and capillaries
For the flow of a Newtonian fluid through a capillary the Hagen–Poiseuille law is:

$$\Phi = \frac{\pi r^4}{8\eta} \frac{dp}{dL} \tag{15.60}$$

where Φ is the volume flow rate, r the capillary radius and dp/dL the pressure gradient. The shear stress at the wall and the shear rate of a Newtonian fluid will be:

$$\tau_N = \frac{r}{2} \frac{dp}{dL} \quad \text{and} \quad \dot{\gamma}_N = \frac{4\Phi}{\pi r^3} . \tag{15.61}$$

If the melt is non-Newtonian, corrections have to be made. The first correction is for entrance and end effects and was suggested by Bagley (1957). Due to the end effects one has to use an effective flow length L_{eff}:

$$\tau = \frac{r}{2} \frac{\Delta p}{L_{\text{eff}}} = \frac{\Delta p}{2\left(\frac{L}{r} + e\right)} \tag{15.62}$$

e being a correction factor which can be determined by plotting (at constant $\dot{\gamma}$) Δp versus L/r. The second correction is for the non-Newtonian character as such. It is the so-called correction of Rabinowitsch (1929)

$$\dot{\gamma} = \frac{4\Phi}{\pi r^3} \frac{3n+1}{4n} \tag{15.63}$$

where

$$n = \lim_{L/r \to \infty} \frac{d \ln\left(\frac{r}{2} \frac{dp}{dL}\right)}{d \ln\left(\frac{4\Phi}{\pi r^3}\right)}$$

(n is the Ostwald–de Waele constant). n may be determined by plotting $\ln\left(\frac{1}{2} r \, dp/dL\right)$ versus $\ln\left(4\Phi/\pi r^3\right)$ for different L/r ratios and extrapolating to $L/r = \infty$.
The real viscosity is then obtained as $\eta = \tau/\dot{\gamma}$.

APPENDIX II

Analysis of flow in processing operations
In the processing equipment of thermoplastics many kinds of complicated flow configurations exist. The flow in a tapered die, for example, produces three components of

deformation: that due to flow from the reservoir into the die; that due to telescopic shear within the die; that to extensional flow within the die. These may be assumed to be separable and the separately calculated pressure drops may be added to give the total pressure drop. But in addition, each deformation mechanism contributes to post extrusion swelling. The components due to simple shear and extension at the die exit determine the swell ratio.

Table 15.10 gives a survey of the more important rheological equations. Figs. 15.14 and 15.15 show the relationship between swelling ratio and recoverable strain.

BIBLIOGRAPHY, CHAPTER 15

General references

Bueche, F., "Physical Properties of Polymers", Interscience, New York, 1962.
Eirich, F.R. (Ed.), "Rheology", Academic Press, New York, 1956.
Ferry, J.D., "Viscoelastic Properties of Polymers", Wiley, New York, 1961; 2nd ed., 1970.
Glasstone, S., Laidler, K.J. and Eyring, H., "The Theory of Rate Processes", McGraw-Hill, New York, 1941.
McKelvey, J.M., "Polymer Processing", Wiley, New York, 1962.
Mason, P. and Wookey, N. (Eds.), "The Rheology of Elastomers", Pergamon Press, New York, 1958; 2nd ed., 1964.
Middleman, S., "The Flow of High Polymers", Interscience, New York, 1968.
Reiner, M., "Deformation and Flow", Lewis, London, 1948.

Special references

Adamse, J.W.C., Janeschitz-Kriegl, H., Den Otter, J.L. and Wales, J.L.S., J. Polymer Sci. A2-6 (1968) 871.
Andrade, E.N. da Costa, Nature 125 (1930) 309, 582.
Bagley, E.B., J. Appl. Phys. 28 (1957) 624; Trans. Soc. Rheol. 5 (1961) 355.
Barnett, S.M., Polymer Eng. Sci. 7 (1967) 168.
Barrie, I.T., Plastics and Polymers 38 (1970) 47.
Bartos, O., J. Appl. Phys. 35 (1964) 2767.
Batchinski, A.J., Z. physik. Chem. 84 (1913) 643.
Benbow, J.J. and Lamb, P., SPE Trans. 3 (1963) 1.
Bueche, F., J. Chem. Phys. 20 (1952) 1959; 22 (1954) 603; 25 (1956) 599.
Bueche, F., (1962): see General references.
Clegg, P.L., in "Rheology of Elastomers" (1958): see General references; Brit. Plastics 39 (1966) 96.
Cogswell, F.N., Plastics and Polymers 38 (1970) 391.
Cogswell, F.N., Polymer Eng. Sci. 12 (1972) 64.
Cogswell, F.N. and Lamb, P., Plastics & Polymers 38 (1970) 331.
Cogswell, F.N. and McGowan, J.C., Brit. Polymer J. 4 (1972) 183.
Cogswell, F.N., Webb, P.C., Weeks, J.C., Maskell, S.G. and Rice, P.D.R., Plastics & Polymers 39 (1971) 340.
Cornelissen, J. and Waterman, H.I., Chem. Eng. Sci. 4 (1955) 238.
Cote, J.A. and Shida, M., J. Appl. Polymer Sci. 17 (1973) 1639.
Cox, W.P. and Merz, E.H., J. Polymer Sci. 28 (1958) 619.
De Waele, A., J. Oil Col. Chem. Assoc. 4 (1923) 33.
Doolittle, A.K., J. Appl. Phys. 22 (1951) 1031, 1471; 23 (1952) 236.
Everage, A.E. and Ballman, R.L., J. Appl. Polymer Sci. 18 (1974) 933.
Eyring, H., (1941): see General references Glasstone et al.

'Ferrari, A.G., Wire and Wire Products 39 (1964) 1036.

Ferry, J.D., J. Am. Chem. Soc. 64 (1942) 1330.

Fox, T.G. and Allen, V.R., J. Chem. Phys. 41 (1964) 344.

Fox, T.G., Gratch, S. and Loshaek, S., in "Rheology" (F.R. Eirich, Ed.), Academic Press, New York, Vol. 1, 1956, p. 431.

Fox, T.G. and Loshaek, S., J. Polymer Sci. 15 (1955) 371.

Graessley, W.W., J. Chem. Phys. 47 (1967) 1942.

Graessley, W.W. and Segal, L., A.I.Ch.E. J. 16 (1970) 261.

Gregory, D.R., J. Appl. Polymer Sci. 16 (1972) 1479, 1489.

Han, C.D., Kim, K.U., Siskovic, N. and Huang, C.R., J. Appl. Polymer Sci. 17 (1973) 95.

Hellwege, K.H., Knappe, W., Paul, P. and Semjonow, V., Rheol. Acta 6 (1967) 165.

Holzmüller, W. and Dinter, R., Exp. techn. Physik 8 (1960) 118.

King, R.G., Rheol. Acta 5 (1966) 35.

Litt, M., Polymer Preprints 14 (1973) 109.

Magill, J.H. and Greet, R.J., Ind. Eng. Chem. Fundamentals 8 (1969) 701.

Meissner, J., Kunststoffe 61 (1971) 576, 688.

Meissner, J., Trans. Soc. Rheol. 16 (1972) 405.

Mendelson, R.A., Bowles, W.A. and Finger, F.L., J. Polymer Sci. A2-8 (1970) 127.

Metzner, A.B., Houghton, W.T., Sailor, R.A. and White, J.L., Trans. Soc. Rheol. 5 (1961) 133.

Metzner, A.B., Uebler, E.A. and Chan Man Fong, C.F., A.I.Ch.E.J. 15 (1969) 750.

Mills, N.J., Europ. Polymer J. 5 (1969) 675.

Ostwald, Wo., Kolloid-Z. 36 (1925) 99.

Porter, R.S., Mac Knight, W.J. and Johnson, J.F., Rubber Chem. Techn. 41 (1968) 1.

Powell, P.C., "Processing methods and properties of thermoplastic melts", Ch. 11 in "Thermoplastics" (R.M. Ogorkiewicz, Ed.), Wiley, London, 1974.

Rabinowitsch, B., Z. physik. Chem. A145 (1929) 1.

Saeda, S., J. Polymer Sci. (Phys.) 11 (1973) 1465.

Spencer, R.S. and Dillon, R.E., J. Colloid Sci. 4 (1949) 241.

Thomas, D.P., Polymer Eng. Sci. 11 (1971) 305.

Thomas, D.P. and Hagan, R.S., Polymer Eng. Sci. 9 (1969) 164.

Tordella, J.P., J. Appl. Phys. 27 (1956) 454; Trans. Soc. Rheol. 1 (1957) 203; Rheol. Acta 2/3 (1961) 216.

Van der Vegt, A.K., Trans. Plastics Inst. 32 (1964) 165.

Van Krevelen, D.W. and Hoftyzer, P.J. Angew. Makromol. Chem. 52 (1976) 101.

Vinogradov, G.V., Pure Appl. Chem. 26 (1971) 423.

Vinogradov, G.V. and Malkin, A.Ya., J. Polymer Sci. A2 (1964) 2357.

Vinogradov, G.V., Malkin, A.Ya. and Kulichikhin, V.G., J. Polymer Sci. A2-8 (1970) 333.

Vinogradov, G.V., Malkin, A.Ya., Yanovsky, Yu.G., Dzyura, E.A., Schumsky, V.F. and Kulichikhin, V.G., Rheol. Acta 8 (1969) 490.

Vinogradov, G.V. and Prozorovskaya, N.V., Rheol. Acta 3 (1964) 156.

Vinogradov, G.V., Radushkevich, B.V. and Fikhman, V.D., J. Polymer Sci. A2-8 (1970) 1.

Vinogradov, G.V., Yanovsky, Yu. and Isayev, A.I., J. Polymer Sci. A2-8 (1970) 1239.

Westover, R.F., S.P.E. Trans. 1 (1961) 14.

Williams, M.L., Landel, R.F. and Ferry, J.D., J. Am. Chem. Soc. 77 (1955) 3701.

CHAPTER 16

RHEOLOGICAL PROPERTIES OF POLYMER SOLUTIONS

The viscosity of a polymer solution increases with the polymer concentration. A discontinuity exists at the so-called critical concentration (which decreases with increasing molecular weight), separating "dilute" from "concentrated" solutions.

The viscosity of dilute polymer solutions can be estimated with fair accuracy.

For concentrated polymer solutions the viscosity is proportional to the 3.4th power of the molecular weight and about the 5th power of the concentration. The effects of temperature and concentration are closely interrelated. A method is given for predicting the viscosity of concentrated polymer solutions.

Introduction

The viscosity of polymer solutions is a subject of considerable practical interest. It is important in several stages of the manufacturing and processing of polymers, e.g. in the spinning of fibres and the casting of films from solutions, and especially in the paints and coatings industry.

Despite the large amount of literature on this subject, the viscosity of polymer solutions is less completely understood than that of polymer melts. This is because two more parameters are involved: the nature and the concentration of the solvent.

Theoretical investigations of the properties of polymer solutions may use two different starting points:

a. the very dilute solution (the nearly pure solvent)

b. the pure solute (polymer melt).

These two approaches can be clearly distinguished in the literature on the viscosity of polymer solutions. It is remarkable that both approaches use quite different methods. Only a few authors have tried to establish a relationship between the two fields of investigation.

In conformity with the literature, dilute polymer solutions and concentrated polymer solutions will be discussed separately in this chapter.

It is difficult to give an exact definition of the terms "dilute" and "concentrated". Usually there is a gradual transition from the behaviour of dilute to that of concentrated solutions, and the concentration range of this transition depends on a number of parameters. As a rule of thumb, however, a polymer solution may be called concentrated if the solute concentration exceeds 5 per cent by weight.

A. DILUTE POLYMER SOLUTIONS

In Chapter 9 the following definition of the limiting viscosity number was given

$$[\eta] = \lim_{c \to 0} \frac{\eta_{sp}}{c} \tag{16.1}$$

where $\eta_{sp} = \dfrac{\eta - \eta_S}{\eta_S}$

$\quad \eta \quad$ = viscosity of the solution
$\quad \eta_S \;$ = viscosity of the solvent
$\quad c \quad$ = solute concentration

Equation (16.1) implies that the relationship between η_{sp} and c can be approximated by a linear proportionality as c approaches zero. At finite concentrations, however, the relationship between η_{sp} and c is certainly not linear. Therefore some extrapolation method is required to calculate $[\eta]$ from viscosity measurements at a number of concentrations.

The most popular extrapolation method was introduced by Huggins (1942):

$$\eta_{sp} = [\eta]c + k_H[\eta]^2 c^2 \tag{16.2}$$

where k_H is called the Huggins constant.

Another well-known extrapolation formula was proposed by Kraemer (1938):

$$\ln\left(\frac{\eta}{\eta_S}\right) = [\eta]c - k_K[\eta]^2 c^2 \tag{16.3}$$

where k_K is the so-called Kraemer constant.

In fact, several authors used both extrapolation methods for the calculation of $[\eta]$. In several cases this led to identical values of $[\eta]$. Moreover, it was found that

$$k_H + k_K \approx 0.5 \tag{16.4}$$

which was to be expected theoretically.

Equations (16.2) and (16.3) are truncated versions of the complete virial equation

$$\frac{\eta_{sp}}{c} = [\eta]\{1 + k_1[\eta]c + k_2[\eta]^2 c^2 + k_3[\eta]^3 c^3 + ...\} \tag{16.5}$$

where $k_1 \equiv k_H$.

Rudin et al. (1973) used a computer program for the correlation of eq. (16.5) with experimental data. They compared correlations with one, two and three terms of eq. (16.5) and found that a two-term equation provided very accurate values of $[\eta]$. With a one-term equation (i.e. the Huggins equation) slightly different values of $[\eta]$ were found, but for most purposes the accuracy of these $[\eta]$ values was sufficient.

The coefficients of eq. (16.5), however, proved to be very sensitive to the number of terms applied. Especially the coefficient k_1 ($\equiv k_H$) showed a large amount of scatter if it was calculated with the one-term equation (16.2). The scatter of k_1 was considerably reduced with the two-term or three-term equation.

This conclusion is confirmed by the large amount of scatter found in the literature values of k_H. These data generally cannot be correlated with other system parameters.

There seems to exist a correlation between k_H and the exponent a of the Mark–Houwink equation in the same polymer–solvent system, but owing to large variations in both k_H and a values, such a correlation cannot be determined exactly. As a general rule, for ordinary polymer solutions, showing values of $a \approx 0.7$, the Huggins constant is about $k_H \approx 0.4$. For Θ-solutions, $0.5 < k_H < 0.64$, according to Sakai (1970). On the other hand, under conditions where the exponent a approaches the value 1.0, as in solutions of nylon 6,6 in formic acid, $k_H \approx 0.1$.

Very approximately, the relationship between k_H and a could therefore be described as:

$$k_H \approx 1.1 - a . \tag{16.6}$$

Table 16.1 shows values of k_H and a for some polymer–solvent systems.

Equation (16.2) can be used for predicting the viscosity of a dilute polymer solution if the Huggins constant k_H is known. But literature values of k_H or values predicted with eq. (16.6) are rather inaccurate. So they do not permit a good prediction of η.

Application of eq. (16.5) would provide a prediction of the viscosity with a greater accuracy if the coefficients k_1, k_2, etc. were available. Lack of these data prohibits the application of this equation.

TABLE 16.1

Huggins constants and a-values of polymer–solvent systems

Polymer	Solvent	k_H	a	$k_H + a$
Poly(methyl methacrylate)	toluene	0.43	0.73	1.16
	chloroform	0.32	0.82	1.14
	benzene	0.35	0.76	1.11
	acetone	0.48	0.70	1.18
	butanone	0.40	0.72	1.12
Poly(vinyl acetate)	acetone	0.37	0.70	1.07
	chlorobenzene	0.41	0.56	0.97
	chloroform	0.34	0.74	1.08
	dioxane	0.34	0.74	1.08
	methanol	0.47	0.59	1.06
	toluene	0.50	0.53	1.03
	benzene	0.37	0.65	1.02
Polystyrene	toluene	0.37	0.72	1.09
	cyclohexane	0.55	0.50	1.05
	benzene	0.36	0.73	1.09
	chloroform	0.33	0.76	1.09
	butanone	0.38	0.60	0.98
	ethylbenzene	0.23	0.68	0.91
	decalin	0.60	0.56	1.16
Polybutadiene	benzene	0.49	0.76	1.25
	isobutyl acetate	0.64	0.50	1.14
	cyclohexane	0.33	0.75	1.08
	toluene	0.33	0.70	1.03
(average)		—	—	1.08

In order to overcome this difficulty, Rudin and Strathdee (1974) developed a semi-empirical method for predicting the viscosity of dilute polymer solutions. The method is based on an empirical equation proposed by Ford (1960) for the viscosity of a suspension of solid spheres:

$$\frac{\eta_S}{\eta} = 1 - 2.5\,\phi + 11\,\phi^5 - 11.5\,\phi^7 \qquad (16.7)$$

where ϕ is the volume fraction of the suspended spheres.

Rudin and Strathdee assume that eq. (16.7) may be used for dilute polymer solutions if ϕ is replaced by ϕ_{solv}, the volume fraction of the solvated polymer. They calculate ϕ_{solv} by

$$\phi_{solv} = \frac{N_A c V_{solv}\epsilon}{M} \approx \frac{c\epsilon}{\rho} \qquad (16.8)$$

where N_A = Avogadro number
$\quad\quad c$ = polymer concentration
$\quad\quad V_{solv}$ = volume of a solvated polymer molecule
$\quad\quad \epsilon$ = swelling factor
$\quad\quad M$ = molecular weight of polymer
$\quad\quad \rho$ = bulk polymer density.

They further assume that ϵ is a linear function of ϕ_{solv} between two limits:
a) $\phi_{solv} = 0$, i.e. at infinite dilution. Here the swelling has its maximum value: $\epsilon = \epsilon_0$
b) $\phi_{solv} = 0.524$, i.e. the occupied volume in cubical packing of uniform spheres. It is assumed that there is no swelling in this situation: $\epsilon = 1$.

This function is:

$$\frac{1}{\epsilon} = \frac{1}{\epsilon_0} + \frac{c}{0.524\rho}\,\frac{\epsilon_0 - 1}{\epsilon_0} \qquad (16.9)$$

Substituting (16.9) into (16.8) gives:

$$\phi_{solv} = \frac{0.524 c\epsilon_0}{0.524\rho + c(\epsilon_0 - 1)} \qquad (16.10)$$

Finally ϵ_0 is calculated by combining eq. (16.8) with the Einstein equation

$$\frac{\eta}{\eta_S} = 1 + 2.5\phi \qquad (16.11)$$

or

$$[\eta] = \lim_{c \to 0} \frac{\eta - \eta_S}{c\eta_S} = 2.5\,\frac{\phi_{solv}}{c} = 2.5\,\frac{\epsilon_0}{\rho} \qquad (16.11a)$$

resulting in

$$\epsilon_0 = \frac{[\eta]\rho}{2.5} = \frac{KM^a\rho}{2.5} \qquad (16.12)$$

where K and a are the Mark–Houwink constants. Combination of (16.10) and (16.12) gives:

$$\boxed{\phi_{solv} = \frac{1}{2.5} \frac{[\eta]c}{1 + 0.765[\eta]c - 1.91c/\rho}} \qquad (16.13)$$

So η can be calculated as a function of c by means of eqs. (16.7), (16.10) and (16.12) if the following parameters are known:

the Mark–Houwink constants K and a
the bulk polymer density ρ
the solvent viscosity η_S.

Rudin and Strathdee tested their method against available literature data with remarkably good results, at least for concentrations not exceeding 1% by weight.

For dilute polymer solutions, the effect of temperature on the viscosity can be described with Andrade's equation:

$$\eta = B \exp(E_\eta/RT) \qquad (16.14)$$

where B = constant
$\quad E_\eta$ = energy of activation of viscous flow
$\quad R$ = gas constant
$\quad T$ = temperature.
As a first approximation

$$E_\eta(\text{solution}) = E_\eta(\text{solvent}) + \phi_P \{E_\eta(\infty)(\text{polymer}) - E_\eta(\text{solvent})\} \qquad (16.15)$$

where ϕ_P = volume fraction of polymer
$\quad E_\eta(\infty)$ = the value of E_η of the polymer for $T \gg T_g$.
This quantity has been described in Chapter 15.

Example 16.1
Estimate the viscosity of a solution of polystyrene in toluene at 20°C, if $c = 0.02$ g/cm^3 and $[\eta] = 124$ cm^3/g
a. with Huggins' equation
b. with the method of Rudin and Strathdee.

Solution
a. Literature values of k_H for polystyrene in toluene range from 0.31 to 0.39. The lower value gives in eq. (16.2)

$$\eta_{sp} = [\eta]c + k_H[\eta]^2c^2 = 124 \times 0.02 + 0.31 \times 124^2 \times 0.02^2 = 4.39$$

$$\eta_S = 5.56 \times 10^{-4}\ \text{N} \cdot \text{s/m}^2$$

$$\eta = \eta_S(\eta_{sp} + 1) = 5.56 \times 10^{-4} \times 5.39 = 3.00 \times 10^{-3}\ \text{N} \cdot \text{s/m}^2.$$

The higher value of k_H gives $\eta = 3.27 \times 10^{-3}$ N · s/m^2. With the Mark–Houwink exponent $a = 0.72$, eq. (16.6) predicts $k_H = 1.1 - 0.72 = 0.38$. This corresponds with $\eta = 3.23 \times 10^{-3}$ N · s/m^2.
b. With eq. (16.13) and $\rho = 1.05$

$$\phi_{solv} = \frac{1}{2.5} \frac{[\eta]c}{1 + 0.765[\eta]c - 1.91\,c/\rho} = \frac{1}{2.5} \frac{124 \times 0.02}{1 + 0.765 \times 124 \times 0.02 - 1.91 \times 0.02/1.05} = 0.347$$

Eq. (16.7) gives

$$\frac{\eta_S}{\eta} = 1 - 2.5\,\phi_{\text{solv}} + 11\,\phi_{\text{solv}}^5 - 11.5\,\phi_{\text{solv}}^7 = 1 - 0.868 + 0.055 - 0.007 = 0.180.$$

$$\eta = \frac{\eta_S}{0.180} = \frac{5.56 \times 10^{-4}}{0.180} = 3.09 \times 10^{-3}\ \text{N} \cdot \text{s/m}^2$$

The experimental value mentioned by Streeter and Boyer (1951) is $\eta = 3.16 \times 10^{-3}\ \text{N} \cdot \text{s/m}^2$. From their experimental results these authors calculated $k_H = 0.345$. With this value, the calculated viscosity is $\eta = 3.11 \times 10^{-3}\ \text{N} \cdot \text{s/m}^2$.

B. CONCENTRATED POLYMER SOLUTIONS

The rheology of concentrated polymer solutions shows a striking correspondence with that of polymer melts, which has been discussed in Chapter 15. The influences of the parameters molecular weight, temperature and shear rate on the viscosity are largely analogous, but the situation is made more complicated by the appearance of a new parameter: the concentration of the polymer.

Like polymer melts, concentrated polymer solutions show the phenomenon of a critical molecular weight. This means that in a plot of $\log \eta$ against $\log M$ the slope of the curve changes drastically if M exceeds a critical value M_{cr}. For polymer solutions, M_{cr} increases with decreasing polymer concentration. A similar phenomenon is observed if $\log \eta$ is plotted against $\log c$ for a constant value of M: the slope of the curve changes at $c = c_{cr}$.

These critical phenomena will now be described before the influence of the parameters mentioned is discussed.

Critical values of molecular weight and concentration

As was mentioned in Chapter 15, the strong effect of M on η if $M > M_{cr}$ is attributed to entanglements between coiled polymer molecules. Obviously, the conditions become less favourable for entanglements as the polymer concentration decreases. So M_{cr} increases with decreasing concentration, and vice versa.

Onogi et al. (1966) investigated the mutual influence of c and M on η for a number of polymer–solvent systems. They found that the critical conditions obeyed the general formula

$$c_{cr}^p \cdot M_{cr} = \text{constant} \tag{16.16}$$

where $p \approx 1.5$.

It is difficult, however, to derive accurate values of c_{cr} and M_{cr} from experimental data, because the change of slope in a $\log \eta - \log M$ curve or a $\log \eta - \log c$ curve is very gradual. An additional difficulty is that the concentration is expressed in different units in different articles. Moreover, the values mentioned for the polymer molecular weight are not completely comparable.

With these restrictions as to accuracy, a number of literature data on $c_{cr} - M_{cr}$ combinations will now be correlated. For this purpose the concentrations will be expressed in

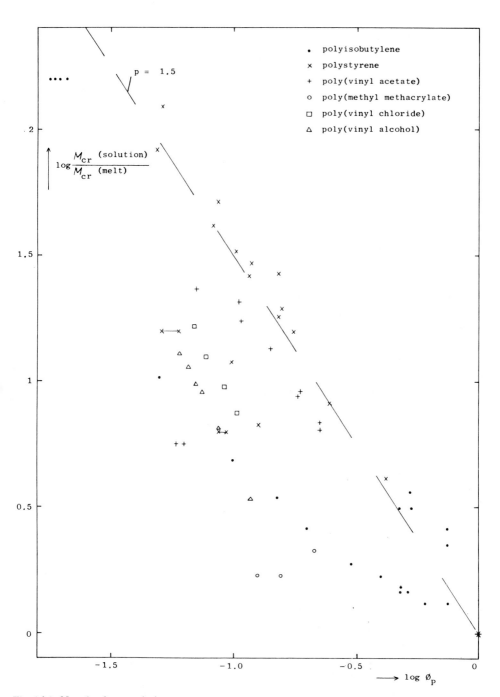

Fig. 16.1. M_{cr} of polymer solutions.

ϕ_p, the volume fraction of (unsolvated) polymer. This makes it possible to compare values of M_cr for polymer solutions with those for polymer melts ($\phi_\mathrm{p} = 1$). In fig. 16.1 log $[M_\mathrm{cr}(\mathrm{solution})/M_\mathrm{cr}(\mathrm{melt})]$ is plotted against log ϕ_p for a number of polymer–solvent systems.

In agreement with the rules mentioned by Onogi et al., the majority of the data on polystyrene and poly(vinyl acetate) fall on a straight line, with a slope of -1.5. This corresponds with p = 1.5 in eq. (16.16). For a number of other polymers, however, lower values of p are found. The available literature data do not permit more definite conclusions about the relationship between M_cr and c_cr.

Rudin and Strathdee (1974) remarked that the equations presented for the viscosity of dilute polymer solutions were valid approximately up to the critical concentration. This leads to a more general definition of a concentrated polymer solution, viz. a solution for which $c > c_\mathrm{cr}$.

Effect of molecular weight and concentration on the viscosity of concentrated polymer solutions

In accordance with the foregoing remarks, the influences of molecular weight and concentration should be discussed simultaneously. This principle is actually applied in the literature, but in two different ways.

The first method uses the power-law equation:

$$\eta = Kc^\alpha M^\beta \qquad (16.17)$$

where K = constant, dependent on the nature of the system.

This equation was applied by Onogi et al. (1966), but had already been proposed in principle by Johnson et al. (1952). The exponent of the molecular weight, β, is always quite close to the value of 3.4 found for polymer melts. The value α, however, may vary from 4.0 to 5.6. The mean value is about $\alpha \approx 5.1$, corresponding with $\alpha/\beta = p = 1.5$.

By way of illustration this method of correlation is applied to the experimental data of Pezzin and Gligo (1966) on poly(vinyl chloride) in cyclohexanone. In fig. 16.2 log η is plotted against log $c + 0.63$ log M, and indeed all the data points fall approximately on one curve. This curve approaches asymptotically to a straight line with a slope of 5.4 for the higher concentrations. So for concentrated solutions eq. (16.17) is valid:

$$\eta = Kc^{5.4} M^{3.4}$$

The other method has been described by Simha and Utracki in several articles (1963–1973). The method is called a corresponding states principle. A reduced viscosity $\tilde{\eta}$ is plotted against a reduced concentration $\tilde{c}$, where

$$\tilde{\eta} = \frac{\eta_\mathrm{sp}}{c[\eta]} \qquad (16.18)$$

and

$$\tilde{c} = c/\gamma$$

γ is a shift factor, depending on molecular weight and temperature.

Simha and Utracki show that indeed all the experimental data for a given polymer–

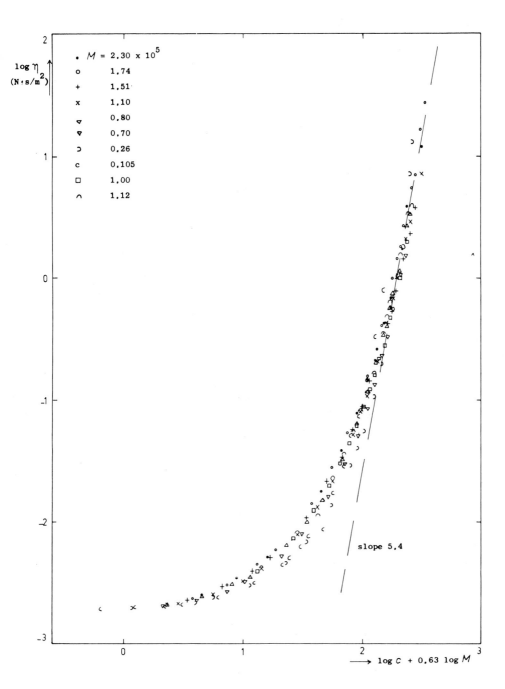

Fig. 16.2. Viscosity of solutions of PVC in cyclohexanone (power-law method).

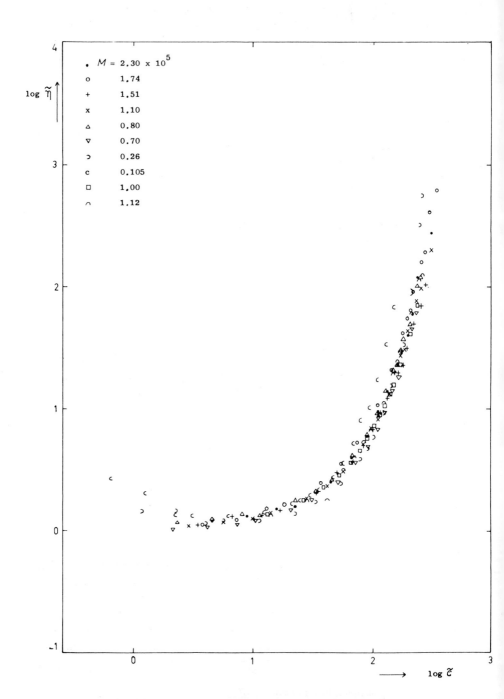

Fig. 16.3. Viscosity of solutions of PVC in cyclohexanone (method of reduced parameters)

solvent system fall on the same master curve. The master curve is different, however, for each different polymer–solvent system, while the shift factors γ differ also. Therefore this method is less suited for predicting the viscosity of a new polymer–solvent system.

To illustrate the application of this method the same data of fig. 16.2 are plotted in fig. 16.3 as log $\tilde{\eta}$ against log $\tilde{c}$, where log $\tilde{c} = \log c + 0.63 \log M$.

A peculiar effect of concentration and molecular weight on viscosity show solutions of rod-like macromolecules. These phenomena have originally been described by Flory (1956) and Hermans (1962) for polypeptides, but they were also observed by Papkov et al. (1974) with polyparabenzamide and by Sokolova et al. (1973) with poly(paraphenylene terephthalamide).

Solutions of these substances at first show the normal increase of viscosity with concentration. Above a certain critical concentration, however, the viscosity decreases rapidly. This phenomenon is explained by orientation of the rod-like macromolecules in the flow direction. An analogous behaviour is observed, if the viscosity is plotted as a function of molecular weight at constant concentration.

Flory (1956) proposed the following equation for the critical concentration, at which transition from an isotropic to an anisotropic state takes place

$$\phi^* = \frac{8}{r}\left(1 - \frac{2}{r}\right) \tag{16.19}$$

where ϕ^* = critical concentration (expressed in volume fraction)
$\quad$ r = length-to-diameter ratio of the rod-like particles.

The effect of temperature on the viscosity of concentrated polymer solutions

It is to be expected that the influence of temperature on the viscosity of a polymer solution lies somewhere between that of the pure solvent and that of a polymer melt.

The temperature effect on the viscosity of solvents can be described by Andrade's equation

$$\eta_S = B \exp(E_\eta/RT) \tag{16.14}$$

where B = a constant
$\quad R$ = gas constant
$\quad E_\eta$ = energy of activation.

For most solvents E_η varies between 7 and 14 kJ/mol.

As was discussed in Chapter 15, a plot of log η against $1/T$ for polymer melts shows a curved line with increasing slope. This slope approaches very high values as T approaches T_g. For low values of $1/T$, that is for temperatures far above T_g, eq. (16.14) holds, but even in this region the energy of activation of polymer melts is much higher than that of solvents. Values of $E_\eta(\infty)$ for most polymers range from 25 to 85 kJ/mol.

For a number of polymer solutions experimental data on the effect of temperature on viscosity are available. By way of example, fig. 16.4 shows log η against $1/T$ for polystyrene in xylene, together with the curve for the melt and the straight line for the pure solvent.

For concentrated polymer solutions the relationship between log η and $1/T$ often is a curved line, its slope (so the activation energy) varying with the polymer concentration.

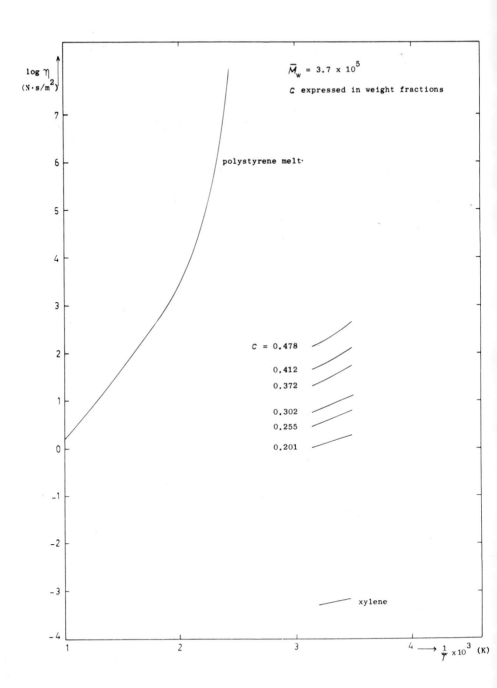

Fig. 16.4. Viscosity of solutions of polystyrene in xylene.

Summarizing we may state:

for solvents $\qquad E_\eta = f(T)$
for polymer melts $\qquad E_\eta = f(T, T_g)$
for polymer solutions $\quad E_\eta = f(T, T_g, c)$.

Furthermore we know (a) that in concentrated solutions $\eta \sim c^\alpha$ (with $\alpha \approx 5$) and (b) that T_g is a function of the solvent concentration (the well-known plasticizer effect). An important conclusion can be drawn: the effects of concentration and temperature on the viscosity of polymer solutions show complicated interactions, so that they should not be treated separately. Especially at high polymer concentrations part of the effect of concentration on viscosity is caused by the variation of T_g and only part of the effect is a proper dilution effect.

The glass transition temperature of polymer solutions

It is a well-known fact that the glass transition temperature of a polymer is lowered if a liquid of low molecular weight is dissolved into the polymer. In fact some commercial polymers, e.g. several brands of poly(vinyl chloride), contain considerable amounts of plasticizers.

Unfortunately, there are only a few literature data on this subject. One of the most extensive investigations, that of Jenckel and Heusch, dates back to 1953. Moreover, published T_g values of polymer solutions are rather inaccurate and generally cover a limited concentration range.

A theoretical treatment of the plasticizer effect has been developed by Bueche (1962), who gave the following equation for the glass transition temperature of a plasticized polymer:

$$T_g = \frac{T_{gP} + (KT_{gS} - T_{gP})\phi_S}{1 + (K - 1)\phi_S} \qquad (16.20)$$

where T_{gP} = glass transition temperature of polymer
$\qquad T_{gS}$ = glass transition temperature of plasticizer (solvent)
$\qquad \phi_S$ = volume fraction of plasticizer (solvent)

$\qquad K \quad$ = constant $\approx \dfrac{\alpha_{1S} - \alpha_{gS}}{\alpha_{1P} - \alpha_{gP}}$

$\qquad \alpha_1$ = volume coefficient of expansion above T_g
$\qquad \alpha_g$ = volume coefficient of expansion below T_g.

The constant K normally has values between 1 and 3.

From eq. (16.20) one can easily derive

$$\frac{T_{gP} - T_g}{T_{gP} - T_{gS}} = \frac{1 - \phi_P}{1 - \phi_P\left(1 - \dfrac{1}{K}\right)} \qquad (16.21)$$

where ϕ_P = volume fraction of polymer.

In order to check this expression, the T_g values of solvents should be known. Actually this is the case for a few solvents only. Table 16.2 gives a survey. It is striking that also for these small molecules the relationship found for polymers:

$$T_g/T_m \approx 2/3 \qquad\qquad (16.22)$$

appears to be valid. So if T_g s is unknown, $2/3\ T_m$ s may be used as a good approximation.

Fig. 16.5 gives a graphical representation of eq. (16.21) for different values of K in comparison with the available T_g data of polymer—solvent systems in the literature. If no K value for the system is known, one should take as an average K = 2.5.

TABLE 16.2

Experimental values of T_g for a number of compounds of low molecular weight

Compound	T_g (K)	T_m (K)	T_g/T_m
pentane	64	142	0.45
hexane	70	179	0.39
heptane	84	182	0.46
octane	85	216	0.39
2,3-dimethylpentane	83	~149	~0.56
3-methylhexane	~85	154	~0.55
cyclohexane	80	280	0.29
methylcyclohexane	85	147	0.58
toluene	106	178	0.60
ethylbenzene	111	180	0.62
n-propylbenzene	122	171	0.71
isopropylbenzene (cumene)	123	176	0.70
n-butylbenzene	124	192	0.65
sec.-butylbenzene	127	190	0.67
tert.-butylbenzene	142	215	0.66
n-pentylbenzene	128	195	0.66
methanol	110	175	0.63
ethanol	100	157	0.64
n-propanol	109	146	0.75
n-butanol	118	183	0.64
tert.-butanol	180	299	0.60
n-pentanol	124	194	0.64
isopropanol	121	184	0.66
glycerol	187	293	0.64
butanone	97	187	0.52
isobutyl chloride	88	142	0.62
dimethyl sulphoxide	153	291	0.53
abietic acid	320	446	0.72
glucose	298	418	0.71
sulphur	243	353	0.69
selenium	303	488	0.63
boron trioxide	513	723	0.71
silicon dioxide	1410	1975	0.72

Example 16.2

Estimate the glass transition temperature for a solution of polystyrene in benzyl alcohol with $\phi_P = 0.85$.

Solution

According to fig. 16.5 at $\phi_P = 0.85$ and $K = 2.5$

$$\frac{T_{gP} - T_g}{T_{gP} - T_{gS}} = 0.29.$$

For polystyrene $T_{gP} = 373$ K. The value of T_{gS} for benzyl alcohol cannot be found in the literature. So the estimated value is derived from $T_{mS} = 258$ K:

$$T_{gS} = \frac{2}{3} T_{mS} = 172 \text{ K}.$$

With these data, the estimated value is $T_g = 315$ K. The experimental value of Kambour et al. (1973) is $T_g = 324$ K.

A new method for estimating the viscosity of concentrated polymer solutions

In the preceding sections it was shown that there can be two causes for the decrease in viscosity upon addition of a solvent to a polymer:

a) a decrease of the viscosity of the pure polymer as a result of a decrease of the glass transition temperature

b) a real dilution effect, which causes the viscosity of the solution to fall between that of the pure polymer (as mentioned under a) and that of the pure solvent.

For this reason the effects of concentration and temperature on the viscosity of polymer solutions cannot be separated.

In reality the interactions between polymer and solvent molecules, which determine the solution viscosity, are very complicated and dependent on a great number of parameters. The literature mentions the solubility parameters of polymer and solvent, polymer chain stiffness, free volume of the solution, etc. In principle, all these factors should be taken into account in predicting the viscosity of a polymer solution. However, the available experimental data are insufficient for this purpose.

Instead, a simple prediction method has been developed, which provides approximate values of the viscosity for a number of polymer–solvent systems. This method is based on the following three assumptions:

1) The glass transition temperature of the solution can be calculated with the method described in the preceding section (eqs. 16.21 and 16.22)

2) The viscosity of the undiluted polymer (η_P^*) at the new T_g (glass transition temperature of the solution) can be calculated from the normal log η vs. T_g/T relationship given in Chapter 15. The glass transition temperature of the solution has to be used in the T_g/T ratio in fig. 15.4.

3) For a description of the dilution effect, a modified form of eq. (16.17) can be applied: it is assumed that η is proportional to the 5th power of ϕ_P, the volume fraction of the polymer. As $\eta = \eta_P^*$ at $\phi_P = 1$,

$$\log \eta = \log \eta_P^* + 5 \log \phi_P \tag{16.23}$$

The applicability of this method will be demonstrated in the following example.

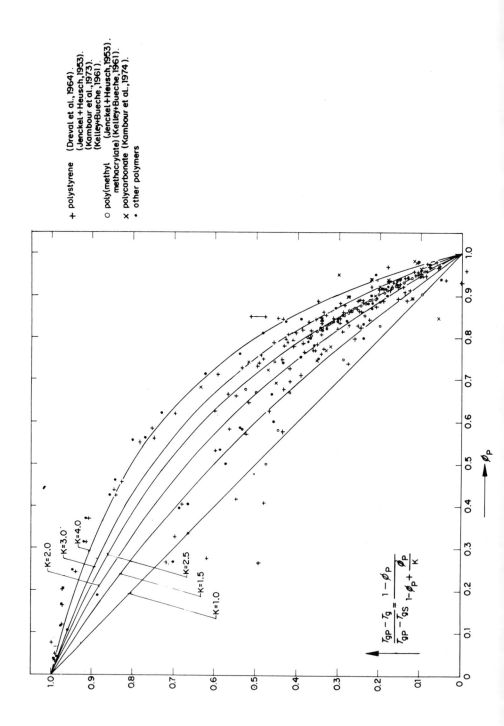

+ polystyrene (Dreval et al.,1964).
(Jenckel+Heusch,1953).
(Kambour et al.,1973).
(Kelley+Bueche,1961).

○ poly(methyl (Jenckel+Heusch,1953).
methacrylate) (Kelley+Bueche,1961).

× polycarbonate (Kambour et al.,1974).

• other polymers

$$\frac{T_{gP} - T_g}{T_{gP} - T_{gS}} = \frac{1 - \phi_P}{1 - \phi_P + \dfrac{\phi_P}{K}}$$

K=2.0

K=3.0

K=4.0

K=2.5

K=1.5

K=1.0

ϕ_P

Example 16.3

For concentrated solutions of polyisobutylene in decalin ($\phi_P > 0.1$), estimate the viscosity as a function of the volume fraction of polymer at a temperature of 20°C. The viscosity of the bulk polymer at this temperature is $\eta_P = 6.5 \times 10^9$ N · s/m². (Experimental data of Tager et al., 1963.)

Solution

1. The glass transition temperatures. For the polymer, the literature value is $T_{gP} = 198$ K. A glass transition temperature of decalin has not yet been published. Therefore T_{gS} is estimated by

$T_{gS} = 2/3 T_{mS} = 2/3 \times 230 = 150$ K.

Now for the solutions T_g can be calculated with the aid of fig. 16.5, using K = 2.5. These values are mentioned in table 16.3.
2. For the calculation of η^* use can be made of fig. 15.4, where $\eta_P(T)/\eta_P(1.2T_g)$ is plotted against the ratio T_g/T. This graph shows a number of curves for different values of a parameter A. As has been mentioned in Chapter 15, for polyisobutylene A = 12.5. $\eta(1.2T_g)$ can be calculated from the viscosity of the bulk polymer. With $T_{gP} = 198$ K and $T = 293$ K, $T_g/T = 0.676$. According to fig. 15.4 this corresponds to $\log\{\eta_P(T)/\eta_P(1.2T_{gP})\} = -3.5$. So $\log \eta_P(1.2T_{gP}) = 9.8 + 3.5 = 13.3$. For each value of T_g in table 16.3, $\eta_P(T)/\eta_P(1.2T_{gP}) \equiv \eta_P^*/\eta_P(1.2T_{gP})$ can be read in fig. 15.4 and η_P^* can be calculated.
3. Application of eq. (16.23) gives the estimated values of $\log \eta$. These are compared in table 16.3 with the experimental values of Tager et al.

TABLE 16.3

Solutions of polyisobutylene in decalin (η in N · s/m²)

ϕ_P	T_g (K)	T_g/T	$\log \dfrac{\eta_P^*}{\eta_P(1.2 T_{gP})}$	$\log \eta_P^*$	$5 \log \phi_P$	$\log \eta$ calc.	$\log \eta$ exp.
1.00	198	0.676	−3.5	9.8	0	9.8	9.81
0.77	178	0.608	−4.7	8.6	−0.58	8.0	8.30
0.70	174	0.594	−4.9	8.4	−0.77	7.65	7.83
0.61	170	0.580	−5.1	8.2	−1.08	7.1	7.24
0.51	165	0.563	−5.3	8.0	−1.48	6.5	6.51
0.42	162	0.553	−5.4	7.9	−1.89	6.0	5.94
0.31	159	0.543	−5.65	7.65	−2.54	5.1	5.04
0.21	156	0.532	−5.8	7.5	−3.41	4.1	3.87
0.10	151	0.515	−6.0	7.3	−4.94	2.35	2.23

While in this example the agreement between calculated and experimental viscosity values is excellent, it should be mentioned that for several series of experimental data it is less.

An equation for the viscosity of polymer solutions over the whole concentration range

In this chapter, different methods for predicting the viscosity are described that are valid for dilute or concentrated polymer solutions. The same distinction is made in most of the literature. This has a natural justification, because a discontinuity in behaviour can be observed near the critical concentration.

Nevertheless, Lyons and Tobolsky (1970) proposed an equation for the concentration-dependence of the viscosity of polymer solutions which is claimed to be valid for the whole concentration range from very dilute solutions to pure polymer. The equation reads:

$$\frac{\eta_{sp}}{c[\eta]} = \exp \frac{k_H [\eta] c}{1 - bc} \tag{16.24}$$

where

η_{sp} = specific viscosity
$[\eta]$ = intrinsic viscosity
c = concentration
k_H = Huggins constant
b = constant.

For a given polymer–solvent system, k_H and $[\eta]$ can be determined in the usual manner. The only remaining constant, b, can be calculated from the bulk viscosity of the polymer, where $c = \rho$ (polymer density).

Lyons and Tobolsky successfully applied eq. (16.24) to the systems poly(propylene oxide)–benzene and poly(propylene oxide)–methylcyclohexane. The application was restricted, however, to a polymer of molecular weight 2000, that is below the critical molecular weight M_{cr}.

The applicability of eq. (16.24) will be limited by the fact that the bulk viscosity of the polymer is often extremely high and unknown at the temperature at which the solution viscosities are determined. On the basis of theoretical considerations, Rodriguez (1972) concludes that the applicability of eq. (16.24) is limited to systems for which $M < M_{cr}$.

A certain generalization is permitted with respect to the relationship between the effects of concentration and molecular weight on the viscosity of polymer solutions. It is restricted to solutions of polymers with $M > M_{cr}$ in good solvents.

At high concentrations eq. (16.17) holds, according to which η is proportional to c^α and M^β, and $\alpha/\beta \approx 1.5$. At very low concentrations η_{sp} is proportional to the first power of c and, according to the Mark–Houwink equation, to a power of M of about 0.7. This gives the same power ratio of about 1.5. This ratio seems to hold over the whole concentration range.

As the intrinsic viscosity $[\eta]$ is proportional to $M^\alpha \approx M^{\beta/\alpha}$, the product $c[\eta]$ is proportional to c and M in the correct power ratio. Therefore η_{sp} will be a unique function of the product $c[\eta]$. This was discussed by Vinogradov et al. (1973).

Viscoelastic properties of polymer solutions in simple shear flow

Viscoelastic properties of polymer solutions may be of practical importance, e.g. in the flow of these solutions through technical equipment.

For concentrated polymer solutions the viscoelastic properties show great analogy with those of polymer melts. For dilute solutions ($c < c_{cr}$) the analogy decreases with decreasing concentration. The following discussion will be limited to concentrated solutions.

The viscoelastic quantities involved have been defined in Chapter 15.

At low rates of shear (i.e. for $\dot{\gamma}\Theta_0 < 1$) polymer solutions, as polymer melts, show Newtonian behaviour. This is determined by the Newtonian viscosity η_0 and the Newtonian shear modulus G_0. The ratio η_0/G_0 equals Θ_0, the Newtonian time constant. In fact, the foregoing part of this chapter was devoted to the estimation of η_0.

Prediction of G_0 is possible for solutions of monodisperse polymers with the equation

$$G_0 \approx \frac{\pi^2}{6}\frac{cRT}{M} \tag{16.25}$$

where c = polymer concentration
       R = gas constant
       T = temperature
       M = molecular weight

Eq. (16.25) is the equivalent of eq. (15.54), in which the polymer density ρ has been replaced by c. As η_0 is proportional to approximately the 5th power of c and G_0 is proportional to the 1st power, the ratio $\Theta_0 = \eta_0/G_0$ is proportional to about the 4th power of c.

Eq. (16.25) does not apply, however, to polydisperse polymers. This leads to the same difficulties as discussed in Chapter 15 for polymer melts.

For $\dot{\gamma}\Theta_0 > 1$, the viscosity η and the time constant Θ decrease with increasing shear rate, while the shear modulus G increases. The value of η can be estimated as a function of $\dot{\gamma}$ with the aid of fig. 15.6, which was derived for polymer melts.

The corresponding graphs of G and Θ for polymer melts cannot be used, however, for the estimation of these quantities for polymer solutions. Apparently, the shear modulus of polymer solutions shows only a very slight increase with increasing shear rate. This means that also the influence of the shear rate on the time constant is smaller for polymer solutions than for polymer melts. But the available data show a large amount of scatter, so that more definite statements cannot be made at the moment.

Finally a phenomenon should be mentioned which polymer solutions show more often than polymer melts: viz. *a second Newtonian region.* This means that with increasing shear rate the viscosity at first decreases, but finally approaches to another constant value. As the first Newtonian viscosity is denoted by η_0, the symbol η_∞ is generally used for the second Newtonian viscosity.

The ratio η_0/η_∞ increases with the molecular weight of the polymer and with the concentration. Experimental data are scarce and show a large amount of scatter, but the order of magnitude of η_0/η_∞ can be estimated in the following way

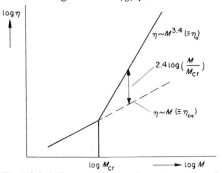

Fig. 16.6. Influence of entanglements on viscosity.

If it is assumed that the influence of entanglements on viscosity starts at $M = M_{cr}$, while

$\eta \sim M$ for unentangled molecules

$\eta \sim M^{3.4}$ for entangled molecules

and η_∞ represents unentangled conditions, the distance between the two lines in fig. 16.6 corresponds with $\log(\eta_0/\eta_\infty)$ for polymer melts and

$$\log(\eta_0/\eta_\infty) = 2.4 \log(M/M_{cr}) .$$

For polymer solutions, the difference between η_0 and η_∞ decreases with decreasing concentration. A number of literature data could approximately be correlated with the following empirical equation

$$\log(\eta_0/\eta_\infty) = 2.4 \log(\overline{M}_w/M_{cr}) + 2 \log \phi_p \tag{16.26}$$

Example 16.4
Estimate the viscosity of a solution of polystyrene in diethyl phthalate under the following conditions:
temperature $20°C$
polymer concentration: $c = 0.44$ g/cm^3
$\overline{M}_w = 3.5 \times 10^5$ $Q = \overline{M}_w/\overline{M}_n = 2$
$\eta_0 = 4 \times 10^3$ N $\cdot$ s/m^2
shear rates 0.1, 10 and 10^3 s^{-1}.
(Experimental data of Ito and Shishido, 1975).

Solution
The time constant Θ_0 may be estimated with eq. (15.56).

$$\Theta_0 \approx \frac{6}{\pi^2} \frac{\eta_0 \overline{M}_w Q}{cRT} = \frac{6 \times 4 \times 10^3 \times 3.5 \times 10^5 \times 2}{\pi^2 \times 0.44 \times 10^3 \times 8.31 \times 10^3 \times 293} = 1.6 \text{ s.}$$

The values of η/η_0 can be read in fig. 15.6

$\dot{\gamma}(\text{s}^{-1})$	$\dot{\gamma}\Theta_0$	η/η_0	$\eta(\text{N} \cdot \text{s/m}^2)$	η exp.$(\text{N} \cdot \text{s/m}^2)$
0.1	0.16	1.00	4.0×10^3	4.0×10^3
10	16	0.30	1.2×10^3	1.0×10^3
10^3	1.6×10^3	0.016	64	≈ 150

There is a reasonable correspondence between the experimental and calculated viscosity values at a shear rate of 10 s^{-1}. The calculated η value at $\dot{\gamma} = 10^3$ s^{-1} is too low, however, because at this shear rate the second Newtonian region is approached. To estimate η_∞, eq. (16.26) can be applied with

$M_{cr} = 3.5 \times 10^4$

$\phi_p \approx c/\rho(\text{polymer}) = 0.44/1.05 = 0.42$

$\log(\eta_0/\eta_\infty) = 2.4 \log(\overline{M}_w/M_{cr}) + 2 \log \phi_p = 2.4 \log 10 - 2 \times 0.38 = 2.4 - 0.76 = 1.64$

$\eta_0/\eta_\infty = 44$

$\eta_\infty = 4000/44 = 91$ N $\cdot$ s/m^2 .

An alternative method for the estimation of η/η_0 is the use of fig. 15.11. In this case Θ_M must be calculated with eq. (15.57); for the example $\Theta_M = 0.8$ s and at $\dot{\gamma} = 10$ s^{-1} the product $\dot{\gamma}\Theta_M = 8$. According to fig. 15.11 $\eta/\eta_0 = 0.35$ at $Q = 2$.

C. EXTENSIONAL DEFORMATION OF POLYMER SOLUTIONS

Extensional deformation of polymer solutions is applied technically in the so-called dry spinning of polymer fibres.

The literature data in this field are scarce, so that only a qualitative picture can be given here.

For concentrated polymer solutions, the behaviour in extensional deformation shows a great correspondence to that of polymer melts. At low rates of deformation the extensional viscosity has the theoretical value of three times the shear viscosity. At higher rates of deformation, the experimental results show different types of behaviour. In some cases, the extensional viscosity decreases with increasing rate of extension in the same way as the shear viscosity decreases with increasing shear rate. In other cases, however, a slight increase of the extensional viscosity with increasing rate of extension was observed. But all the experimental data on concentrated polymer solutions show extensional viscosities of the same order of magnitude as the shear viscosities.

By contrast, quite different results have been obtained with dilute polymer solutions. Here the extensional viscosity may be as much as thousand times the shear viscosity.

An explanation of this phenomenon has been presented by Acierno et al. (1974). They assume that in the extensional flow field there occur uncoiling and alignment of the macromolecules. This does not occur in a shear field because of the rotational nature of such a motion. Under extreme conditions the macromolecules may behave as uncoiled, rigid molecules in extensional flow.

The order of magnitude can be estimated by

$$\left(\frac{\lambda}{\eta_0}\right)_{max} \approx 3N \qquad (16.27)$$

where N = number of statistical segments in the coiled molecule.

In the extensional flow of concentrated polymer solutions, however, the dominating phenomenon is the decrease of effective entanglements with increasing rate of deformation, which causes a decrease of the viscosity.

D. OTHER TRANSPORT PROPERTIES IN POLYMER SOLUTIONS

In Chapter 9 the limiting sedimentation coefficient s_0 and the limiting diffusion coefficient D_0 have been discussed. These are the values of the sedimentation coefficient s and the diffusion coefficient D, extrapolated to zero concentration c.

The dependence of s_0 and D_0 on polymer molecular weight and temperature is also mentioned in Chapter 9.

For dilute polymer solutions, the effect of concentration on s and D may be described by equations which show great analogy with eq. (16.2) as far as the effect of concentration on viscosity is concerned. These equations are

$$\frac{\eta_{sp}}{[\eta]c} = 1 + k_H [\eta] c \tag{16.28}$$

$$\frac{s_0}{s} = 1 + k_s [\eta] c \tag{16.29}$$

$$\frac{D}{D_0} = 1 + k_D [\eta] c \tag{16.30}$$

where

k_H = Huggins' constant
k_s = concentration coefficient of sedimentation (dimensionless)
k_D = concentration coefficient of diffusion (dimensionless)

The literature (see Brandrup and Immergut, 1975) contains a number of data of k_s for several polymer–solvent systems. It is found that k_s, *as defined in eq. (16.29)*, is independent of the molecular weight of the polymer. The order of magnitude is $k_s \approx 1$.

Since only few experimental data on k_D are available, no general conclusions can be drawn.

BIBLIOGRAPHY, CHAPTER 16

General references

Brandrup, J. and Immergut, E.H. (Eds.), "Polymer Handbook", Interscience, New York, 2nd ed., 1975.
Bueche, F., "Physical Properties of Polymers", Wiley, New York, 1962.
Eirich, F.R., "Rheology", Vol. I, Academic Press, New York, 1956.
Flory, P.J., "Principles of Polymer Chemistry", Cornell Univ. Press, Ithaca, N.Y., 1953.
Tanford, C., "Physical Chemistry of Macromolecules", Wiley, New York, 1961.
Tompa, H., "Polymer Solutions", Academic Press, New York, 1956.
Vollmert, B., "Grundriss der Makromolekularen Chemie", Springer, Berlin, 1962.

Special references

Acierno, D., Titomanlio, G. and Greco, R., Chem. Eng. Sci. 29 (1974) 1739.
Bondi, A., "Physical Properties of Molecular Crystals, Liquids and Glasses", Wiley, New York, 1968.
Dreval, V.Ye., Tager, A.A. and Fomina, A.S., Polymer Sci. U.S.S.R. 5 (1964) 495.
Fitzgerald, E.R. and Miller, R.F., J. Coll. Sci. 8 (1953) 148.
Flory, P.J., Proc. Royal Soc. A234 (1956) 73.
Ford, T.F., J. Phys. Chem. 64 (1960) 1168.
Hermans, J., J. Colloid Sci. 17 (1962) 638.
Hoftyzer, P.J. and Van Krevelen, D.W., Angew. Makromol. Chem. 54 (1976) in press.
Huggins, M.L., J. Am. Chem. Soc. 64 (1942) 2716.
Ito, Y. and Shishido, S., J. Polymer Sci., Polymer Phys. 13 (1975) 35.
Jenckel, E. and Heusch, R., Kolloid-Z. 130 (1953) 89.

Johnson, M.F., Evans, W.W. and Jordan, T., J. Coll. Sci. 7 (1952) 498.
Kambour, R.P., Gruner, C.L. and Romagosa, E.E., J. Polymer Sci., Polymer Phys. 11 (1973) 879; Macromol. 7 (1974) 248.
Kambour, R.P., Romagosa, E.E. and Gruner, C.L., Macromol. 5 (1972) 335.
Kelley, F.N. and Bueche, F., J. Polymer Sci. 50 (1961) 549.
Kraemer, E.O., Ind. Eng. Chem. 30 (1938) 1200.
Lyons, P.F. and Tobolsky, A.V., Polymer Eng. Sci. 10 (1970) 1.
Onogi, S., Kimura, S., Kato, T., Masuda, T. and Miyanaga, N., J. Polymer Sci. C15 (1966) 381.
Papkov, S.P., Kulichikhin, V.G., Kalmykova, V.D. and Malkin, A. Ya., J. Polymer Sci.: Polymer Phys. 12 (1974) 1753.
Pezzin, G. and Gligo, N., J. Appl. Polymer Sci. 10 (1966) 1.
Rodriguez, F., Polymer Letters 10 (1972) 455.
Rudin, A. and Strathdee, G.B., J. Paint Techn. 46 (1974) 33.
Rudin, A., Strathdee, G.B. and Brain Edey, W., J. Appl. Polymer Sci. 17 (1973) 3085.
Sakai, T., Macromol. 3 (1970) 96.
Simha, R. and Chan, F.S., J. Phys. Chem. 75 (1971) 256.
Simha, R. and Utracki, L., J. Polymer Sci. A2-5 (1967) 853.
Simha, R. and Utracki, L., Rheol. Acta 12 (1973) 455.
Sokolova, T.S., Yefimova, S.G., Volokhina, A.V., Kudryavtsev, G.I. and Papkov, S.P., Polymer Sci. U.S.S.R. 15 (1973) 2832.
Streeter, D.J. and Boyer, R.F., Ind. Eng. Chem. 43 (1951) 1790.
Tager, A.A., Dreval, V.Ye. and Khasina, F.A., Polymer Sci. U.S.S.R. 4 (1963) 1097.
Utracki, L. and Simha, R., J. Polymer Sci. A1 (1963) 1089.
Vinogradov, G.V., Malkin, A.Ya., Blinova, N.K., Sergeyenkov, S.I., Zabugina, M.P., Titkova, L.V., Yanovsky, Yu.G. and Shalganova, V.G., Europ. Polymer J. 7 (1973) 1231.

CHAPTER 17

TRANSPORT OF THERMAL ENERGY

In this chapter it is demonstrated that the *heat conductivity* of amorphous
polymers (and polymer melts) can be calculated by means of additive quantities
(Rao function, molar heat capacity and molar volume). Empirical rules then also
permit the calculation of the heat conductivity of crystalline and semi-crystalline
polymers.

The rate of heat transport in and through polymers is of great importance. For good
thermal insulation the thermal conductivity has to be low. On the other hand, polymer
processing requires that the polymer can be heated to the processing temperature and
cooled to ambient temperature in a reasonable time.

THERMAL CONDUCTIVITY

No adequate theory exists which may be used to predict accurately the thermal conductivity of polymeric melts or solids. Most of the theoretical or semi-theoretical expressions proposed are based on Debye's treatment of heat conductivity (1914), which leads
to the equation:

$$\lambda = \Lambda c_v \rho u L \tag{17.1}$$

where c_v is specific heat capacity, ρ is density, u is velocity of elastic waves (sound velocity), L is average free path length and Λ is a constant in the order of magnitude of unity.
Kardos (1934) and, later, Sakiadis and Coates (1955, 1956) proposed an analogous
equation:

$$\lambda \approx c_p \rho u L \tag{17.2}$$

in which L represents the distance between the molecules in "adjacent isothermal layers".
Most theories have the common feature that they explain the phenomenon of heat conductivity (in
melts and amorphous solids) on the basis of the so-called "phonon" model. The process is supposed
to occur in such a way that energy is passed quantumwise from layer to layer with sonic velocity and
the amount of energy transferred is assumed to be proportional to density and heat capacity. No large-
scale transfer of molecules takes place.
In crystalline solids, and therefore also in highly crystalline solid polymers, the thermal conductivity
is enlarged by a concerted action of the molecules.

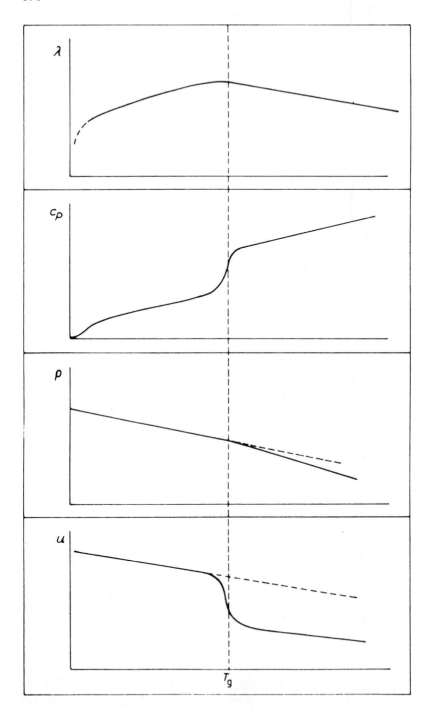

Fig. 17.1. Thermal conductivity λ and its components for amorphous polymers.

Amorphous polymers and polymer melts

The general shape of the $\lambda - T$ curve of amorphous polymers and of polymer melts is given in fig. 17.1. The curve passes through a rather flat maximum at T_g and shows a gradual but slow decline in the liquid state. In the same figure also the slopes of the $c_p - T$, $\rho - T$ and $u - T$ curves are shown, being the components of the $\lambda - T$ curve according to eqs. (17.1) and (17.2). Indeed, multiplication of c_p, ρ and u gives the expected behaviour of λ. Assuming that ΛL in (17.1) or L in (17.2) are nearly constant and independent of temperature, it may be expected that a direct proportionality exists between the thermal diffusivity $\lambda/c_p\rho$ and the sound velocity u. Using the method of calculation of u, explained in Chapter 13, i.e. putting

$$u_{long} = \left(\frac{U}{V}\right)^3 \left[\frac{3(1-\nu)}{1+\nu}\right]^{1/2} \tag{17.3}$$

one may expect

$$\boxed{\frac{\lambda}{c_p\rho} = L\left(\frac{U}{V}\right)^3 \left[\frac{3(1-\nu)}{1+\nu}\right]^{1/2}} \tag{17.4}$$

The factor $(3\frac{1-\nu}{1+\nu})^{1/2}$ is nearly constant for solid polymers (≈ 1.05). Table 17.1 gives the adequate data at room temperature as published by Hellwege, Eiermann and Knappe (see references) and by Hands et al. (1973). The value of L is of the expected order of magnitude with an average of $L \approx 5 \times 10^{-11}$ m.

Since $c_p\rho = \frac{C_p}{V}$, the approximate value of λ can be estimated by means of the expression:

$$\lambda(298) = L\left(\frac{C_p}{V}\right)\left(\frac{U}{V}\right)^3 \qquad (J/s \cdot m \cdot K) \tag{17.4a}$$

where $L \approx 5 \times 10^{-11}$ m.

The thermal conductivity of polymers is temperature-dependent. Fig. 17.2 shows a generalized curve as a function of T/T_g, based on the available experimental data.

Highly crystalline polymers

Crystalline polymers show a much higher thermal conductivity. As an example fig. 17.3 gives the measured values of polyethylenes as a function of the degree of crystallinity.

Using an extrapolation method, Eiermann (1962–1965) found the following relationship for polymers such as polyethylene and polyoxymethylene of "100% crystallinity".

$$\lambda \approx \frac{C}{T} \; J/K \cdot m \cdot s \tag{17.5}$$

where C is a constant with a value of about 210.

Therefore the thermal conductivity at room temperature of these highly regular polymers is found to be approximately 0.71 $J/K \cdot m \cdot s$ as compared with about 0.17 $J/K \cdot m \cdot s$ for the same polymers in the amorphous state.

398

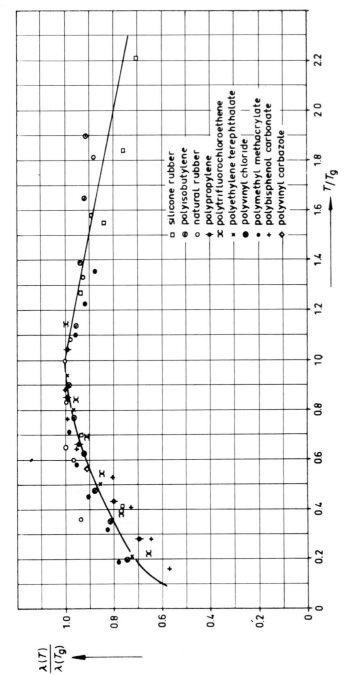

Fig. 17.2. Generalized curve for the thermal conductivity of amorphous polymers.

□ silicone rubber
⊖ polyisobutylene
○ natural rubber
◆ polypropylene
✕ polytrifluorochloroethene
✕ polyethylene terephthalate
● polyvinyl chloride
● polymethyl methacrylate
✚ polybisphenol carbonate
◇ polyvinyl carbazole

$\dfrac{\lambda(T)}{\lambda(T_g)}$

T/T_g

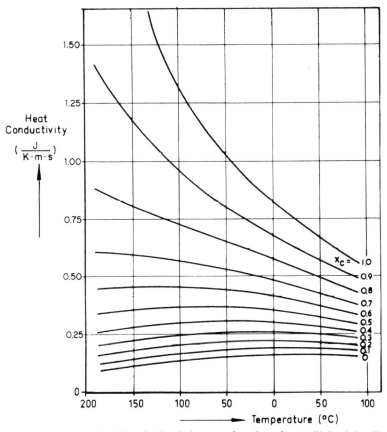

Fig. 17.3. Heat conductivity of polyethylene as a function of crystallinity (after Eiermann, 1965).

For the highly regular polymers one may, as a rule of thumb, use the equation:

$$\frac{\lambda_c}{\lambda_a} \approx \left(\frac{\rho_c}{\rho_a}\right)^6 \tag{17.6}$$

by which the heat conductivity at room temperature of fully crystallized polymers can be calculated if the ratio ρ_c/ρ_a is known.

For the "normal" crystalline polymers Eiermann (1965) found the following relationship:

$$\frac{\lambda_c}{\lambda_a} - 1 = 5.8\left(\frac{\rho_c}{\rho_a} - 1\right). \tag{17.7}$$

Partly crystalline polymers

Eiermann also derived equations for partly crystalline polymers of which the degree of crystallinity x_c and the ratio λ_c/λ_a are known. These equations are graphically reproduced in fig. 17.4.

TABLE 17.1

Heat conductivities of amorphous polymers

Polymer	λ (J/s·m·K)	c_p (10^3 J/kg·K)	ρ (10^3 kg/m³)	$\dfrac{\lambda}{c_p\rho}$ (10^{-8} m²/s)	u_{long} (calc) (m/s)	L (10^{-}
Polypropylene (at.)	0.172	2.14	0.85	9.5	1715	5.5
Polyisobutylene	0.130	1.97	0.86	7.7	1770	4.3
Polystyrene	0.142	1.21	1.05	11.1	2600	4.3
Poly(vinyl chloride)	0.168	0.96	1.39	12.5	2000	6.3
Poly(vinyl acetate)	0.159	1.47	1.19	9.1	1610	5.7
Poly(vinyl carbazole)	0.155	1.26	1.19	10.4	2460	4.4
Poly(methyl methacrylate)	0.193	1.38	1.17	11.8	2370	5.0
Polyisoprene	0.134	1.89	0.91	7.8	1470	5.3
Polychloroprene	0.193	1.59	1.24	9.8	1360	7.2
Poly(ethylene oxide)	0.205	2.01	1.13	9.0	2120	4.1
Poly(ethylene terephthalate)	0.218	1.13	1.34	14.3	2140	6.7
Polyurethane	0.147	1.7	1.05	8.3	1710	4.8
Poly(bisphenol carbonate)	0.193	1.20	1.20	13.5	2350	5.8
Poly(dimethyl siloxane)	0.163	1.59	0.98	10.4	1700	6.1
Phenolic resin	0.176	1.05	1.22	13.7	2320	5.9
Epoxide resin	0.180	1.25	1.19	12.0	2680	4.5
Polyester resin	0.176	1.25	1.23	11.3	2430	4.6

Conversion factor: $1 \text{ J/s·m·K} = 2.4 \times 10^{-3} \text{ cal/s·cm·°C}$.

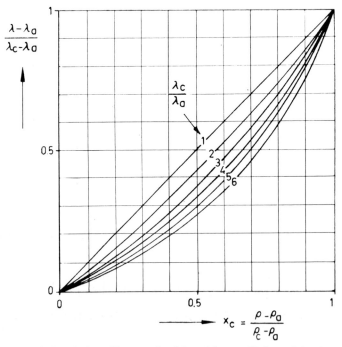

Fig. 17.4. Correlation of heat conductivity with crystallinity and density.

Example 17.1

Estimate the heat conductivity of amorphous poly(methyl methacrylate), a. at room temperature, b. at 200°C.

Solution

a. We use formula (17.4) with $c_p = 1380$ J/kg · K (Chapter 5), $\rho = 1.17$ g/cm³ = 1170 kg/m³ (Chapter 4), $\nu = 0.40$ (Chapter 13) and M = 100.1. We first calculate the Rao function (Chapter 13)

	U_i
1($-CH_2-$)	880
1(C)	50
2($-CH_3$)	2800
1($-COO-$)	1250
	————
	4980

So $U/V = \frac{4980}{100.1/1.17} = 58.2$ (cm$^{1/3}$/s$^{1/3}$) and $(U/V)^3 = 1.97 \times 10^5$ cm/s = 1.97×10^3 m/s. According to eq. (17.4)

$$\lambda = c_p \rho L (U/V)^3 \left[\frac{3(1-\nu)}{1+\nu} \right]^{1/2} = 1380 \times 1170 \times 5 \times 10^{-11} \times 1.97 \times 10^3 \times 1.13 = 0.180 \text{ J/s} \cdot \text{m} \cdot \text{K}.$$

This is in fair agreement with Eiermann's data (0.193).

b. We first calculate by means of fig. 17.2, λ at T_g. Since $T_g = 387$ K we find at room temperature

$$T/T_g = \frac{298}{387} = 0.77; \qquad \lambda(T)/\lambda(T_g) = 0.96,$$

so that

$$\lambda(T_g) = (0.180/0.96) = 0.188.$$

This being known we find at $T = 200°C = 473$ K:

$$T/T_g = \frac{473}{387} = 1.22$$

and from fig. 17.2

$$\frac{\lambda(473)}{\lambda(T_g)} = 0.95.$$

So λ at 200°C will be 0.178.

Example 17.2

The heat conductivity of amorphous poly(ethylene terephthalate) at room temperature is 0.218 J/s · m · K. Calculate the heat conductivity of semi-crystalline PETP at a degree of crystallinity of 0.40.

Solution

Since $\rho_c = 1.465$ and $\rho_a = 1.335$, we can calculate λ_c by means of eq. (17.7)

$$\lambda_c = \lambda_a \left(1 + 5.8 \left(\frac{\rho_c}{\rho_a} - 1 \right) \right) = 0.218 \left(1 + 5.8 \left(\frac{1.465}{1.335} - 1 \right) \right) = 0.218 \times 1.56 = 0.340.$$

By means of fig. 17.4 we may find $\lambda(x_c = 0.4)$. At $\lambda_c/\lambda_a = 1.58$ and $x_c = 0.4$ we read from the graph:

$$\frac{\lambda - \lambda_a}{\lambda_c - \lambda_a} \approx 0.36 \qquad \text{or} \qquad \frac{\lambda - 0.218}{0.340 - 0.218} = 0.36.$$

$\lambda = 0.044 + 0.218 = 0.262$ J/s $\cdot$ m $\cdot$ K, in good agreement with the experimental value (0.272).

BIBLIOGRAPHY, CHAPTER 17

General references

Bridgman, P.W., Proc. Am. Acad. Arts and Sci. 59 (1923) 154.
Carslaw, H.S. and Jaeger, J.C., "Conduction of Heat in Solids", Clarendon Press, Oxford, 2nd ed., 1959.
Debye, P., Math. Vorlesungen Univ. Göttingen 6 (1914) 19.
Stuart, H.A., "Die Physik der Hochpolymeren", Vol. I, Springer, Berlin, 1952.

Special references

Eiermann, K. Kolloid-Z. 180 (1962) 163; 198 (1964) 5, 96; 199 (1964) 63, 125; 201 (1965) 3.
Eiermann, K., Kunststoffe 51 (1961) 512; 55 (1965) 335.
Eiermann, K. and Hellwege, K.H., J. Polymer Sci. 57 (1962) 99.
Eiermann, K., Hellwege, K.H. and Knappe, W., Kolloid-Z. 171 (1961) 134.
Hands, D., Lane, K. and Sheldon, R.P., J. Polymer Sci., Symp. No. 42 (1973) 717.
Hellwege, K.H., Henning, J. and Knappe, W., Kolloid-Z. 186 (1962) 29; 188 (1963) 121.
Kardos, A., Forsch. Geb. Ingenieurw. 5B (1934) 14.
Knappe, W., Z. angew. Physik 12 (1960) 508; Kunststoffe 51 (1961) 707; 55 (1965) 776.
Sakiadis, B.C. and Coates, J., A. I. Ch. E. J. 1 (1955) 275; 2 (1956) 88.

CHAPTER 18

PERMEATION OF POLYMERS

THE DIFFUSIVE TRANSPORT OF GASES, VAPOURS AND LIQUIDS IN POLYMERS

Permeation of polymers by small molecules depends on their solubility and diffusivity. For both quantities reasonable estimations are possible if some basic data of the permeating molecules (critical temperature, diameter) and of the polymer (structure, glass transition temperature, crystallinity) are known.

Introduction

Diffusion and permeation of gases and vapours are of great practical importance in the manufacture and processing of polymers and especially in their subsequent use as protective coatings and films.

Definitions

The following notations and definitions can be formulated:

1. Diffusivity or coefficient of diffusion: D

D is the amount of matter (m) passing per second through a unit area, under the influence of a unit gradient of concentration (the "driving force"), as expressed in the equation:

$$\frac{dm}{dt} = DA \left(\frac{dc}{dx} \right) \tag{18.1}$$

The dimension of D is m^2/s or, more usual in the literature: cm^2/s.

2. Permeability or permeation coefficient: P

P is the amount of substance passing through a polymer film of unit thickness, per second, per unit area, and at a unit pressure difference. It is normally expressed in the following dimensions:

$$cm^3(STP)/cm \cdot s \cdot bar = 10^{-9} \, m^3(STP)/m \cdot s \cdot Pa$$

where $cm^3(STP)$ is the amount of gas in cm^3 at standard temperature and pressure (273 K, 1 bar) [1].

---

[1] 1 bar = $10^5 \, N/m^2 = 10^5$ Pa (pascal).

3. Solubility or solubility coefficient: S

S is the amount of substance (gas) per unit volume of solvent (polymer) in equilibrium with a unit partial pressure (1 bar), as expressed in the equation:

$$c = Sp \text{ (Henry's law)} \tag{18.2}$$

For simple gases S is usually given in $cm^3(STP)$ per cm^3 polymer per bar, its dimension therefore being:

$$cm^3(STP)/cm^3 \cdot bar = 10^{-5} \, m^3(STP)/m^3 \cdot Pa$$

N.B. For organic vapours the solubility is normally expressed in weight per weight of polymer at equilibrium vapour pressure. In order to convert this into $cm^3(STP)/cm^3 \cdot$ bar one has to multiply by the factor:

$$\frac{22{,}400 \times \rho(\text{polymer})}{M(\text{vapour}) \times p(\text{vapour})}$$

where 22,400 is the STP molar volume of vapour (in cm^3/mol) (M expressed in g/mol).

The three quantities mentioned are interrelated by the equation:

$$\boxed{P = D \cdot S} \tag{18.3}$$

Experimental determination

The *permeability* of a gas can be directly measured by determining the rate of mass transfer through a polymer film, expressed per unit area, per unit thickness, and per unit pressure difference across the film.

The *solubility* of gases in polymers is not so easy to determine, since the solubilities of simple gases in polymers are low. The most accurate procedure is to establish sorption equilibrium between polymer and gas at known pressure and temperature, followed by desorption and measurement of the quantity of gas desorbed.

For fairly soluble organic vapours the determination of S is easier; a sample of polymer of known weight is kept at a fixed temperature and pressure in contact with the vapour and the weight increase is measured, usually by means of a quartz spiral.

The *diffusivity* can be determined directly either from sorption or from permeation experiments.

In the first case the reduced sorption $(c(t)/(c_\infty - c_0))$ is plotted versus the square root of the sorption time and D is calculated from the equation:

$$D = \frac{\pi}{16}\delta^2 K^2 \tag{18.4}$$

where δ = film thickness and K is the slope of the reduced sorption curve.

In the second case D can be calculated from the *permeation time lag* by means of the equation:

$$D = \frac{1}{6}\frac{\delta^2}{\Theta} \tag{18.5}$$

where Θ is the time lag in seconds obtained by extrapolating the linear part of the pressure-versus-time graph to zero pressure.

Indirectly D can be determined by measuring the permeability and solubility, and applying eq. (18.3).

A. SOLUBILITY OF GASES AND VAPOURS IN POLYMERS

A survey of the numerical data of the solubilities of the most important simple gases in polymers at room temperature is given in table 18.1.

It is evident that for a given gas the solubilities in the different polymers do not show large variations. The nature of the gas, however, is important. Taking the solubility of nitrogen as 1, that of oxygen is *roughly* 2, that of carbon dioxide 25 and that of hydrogen 0.75 (see later).

A simple linear relationship has been found by Van Amerongen (1950, 1964) between the solubility of various gases in rubber and their boiling points or their critical tempera-

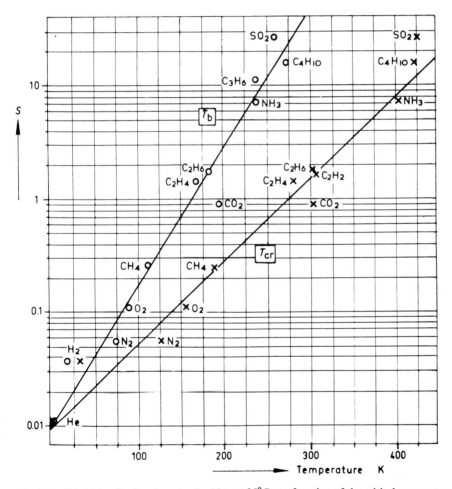

Fig. 18.1. Solubility, S, of gas in natural rubber at 25°C as a function of the critical temperature and the boiling point of the gas: S in cm^3 (NTP) per cm^3 rubber at 1 bar (Van Amerongen).

tures. The solubility of these simple gases in natural rubber is shown in fig. 18.1.

The drawn lines can be described by the following expressions (S in $cm^3/cm^3 \cdot bar$):

$$\log S(298) = -2.1 + 0.0074 T_{cr} \qquad (18.6a)$$

$$\log S(298) = -2.1 + 0.0123 T_b \qquad (18.6b)$$

The nature of the polymer affects the solubility and is probably related to the solubility parameter of the polymer. For amorphous elastomers without strong polar groups (and even for amorphous polymers in general!) the expression (18.6) may be used as a first approximation.

Van Amerongen found a pronounced selective effect of the polarity of the polymer on gas solubility in butadiene-acrylonitrile copolymers. As the acrylonitrile content of the copolymer increases, the solubility of carbon dioxide increases, whereas that of hydrogen, nitrogen and oxygen decreases.

TABLE 18.1

Solubility of simple gases in polymers ($S(298)$ in cm^3 (STP)/$cm^3 \cdot bar$)

	N_2	O_2	CO_2	H_2
Elastomers				
polybutadiene	0.045	0.097	1.00	0.033
cis-1,4-polyisoprene (natural rubber)	0.055	0.112	0.90	0.037
polychloroprene	0.036	0.075	0.83	0.026
styrene–butadiene rubber	0.048	0.094	0.92	0.031
butadiene–acrylonitrile rubber 80/20	0.038	0.078	1.13	0.030
butadiene–acrylonitrile rubber 73/27	0.032	0.068	1.24	0.027
butadiene–acrylonitrile rubber 68/32	0.031	0.065	1.30	0.023
butadiene–acrylonitrile rubber 61/39	0.028	0.054	1.49	0.022
poly(dimethyl butadiene)	0.046	0.114	0.91	0.033
polyisobutylene (butyl rubber)	0.055	0.122	0.68	0.036
polyurethane rubber	0.025	0.048	(1.50)	0.018
silicone rubber	0.081	0.126	0.43	0.047
Semicrystalline polymers				
polyethylene H.D.	0.025	0.047	0.35	–
polyethylene L.D.	0.025	0.065	0.46	–
trans-1,4-polyisoprene (Gutta-percha)	0.056	0.102	0.97	0.038
poly(tetrafluoroethylene)	–	–	0.19	–
polyoxymethylene	0.025	0.054	0.42	–
poly(2,6-diphenyl-1,4-phenylene oxide)	0.043	0.1	1.34	–
poly(ethylene terephthalate)	0.039	0.069	1.3	–
Glassy polymers				
polystyrene	–	0.055	0.65	–
poly(vinyl chloride)	0.024	0.029	0.48	0.026
poly(vinyl acetate)	0.02	0.04	–	0.023
poly(bisphenol A-carbonate)	0.028	0.095	1.78	0.022

The temperature dependence of the solubility obeys the *Clausius–Clapeyron equation*:

$$\frac{\Delta H_s}{R} = -\frac{\text{d} \ln S}{\text{d}\left(\frac{1}{T}\right)} \tag{18.7}$$

where ΔH_s = heat of solution, expressed in J/mol.

For the smallest gas molecules dissolving in elastomers ΔH_s is positive (endothermic effect); for the larger gas molecules the reverse is true (exothermic effect). The process is exothermic if the sorption energy evolved exceeds the energy needed to make a hole of molecular size in the polymer.

Van Amerongen measured the heat effects of various gases in several elastomers; his data are plotted in fig. 18.2 and can be described by the following expression:

$$-\frac{\Delta H_{sr}}{R} \times 10^{-3} = 1.1 + \log S(298) \tag{18.8}$$

where the subscript r refers to the rubbery state.

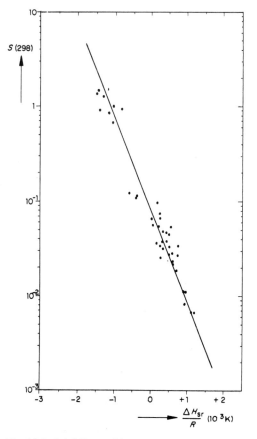

Fig. 18.2. Solubility and heat of solution of gases in elastomers.

So, if the critical temperature or the boiling point of a gas or vapour is known, not only $S(298)$ but also ΔH_s may be calculated in the case of elastomers $(T > T_g)$. The full relationship for the solubility of gases in elastomers (above T_g) therefore becomes:

$$S(T) = S_0 \exp\left(-\frac{\Delta H_{sr}}{RT}\right) = S(298) \exp\left[\frac{\Delta H_{sr}}{R}\left(\frac{1}{298} - \frac{1}{T}\right)\right]. \tag{18.9}$$

Meares (1954, 1957) found that at T_g there is a change in the heat effect of solution. For poly(vinyl acetate) (fig. 18.3) this change may be described by the following equation:

$$\frac{\Delta H_{sg}}{R} \approx 1.67\frac{\Delta H_{sr}}{R} - 2500 \tag{18.10}$$

where subscripts g and r refer to the glassy and rubbery state.

With some reserve the formula may be applied to other polymers also, to calculate heat effects in the glassy state, which are generally more exothermic than in the rubbery state. By means of figs. 18.1 to 18.3 it is possible to estimate the solubility of gases in amorphous polymers in general, if one assumes that at the glass transition point the solubilities in the glassy and rubbery states are equal.

The solubility of gases in (semi-)crystalline polymers depends on the degree of crystal-

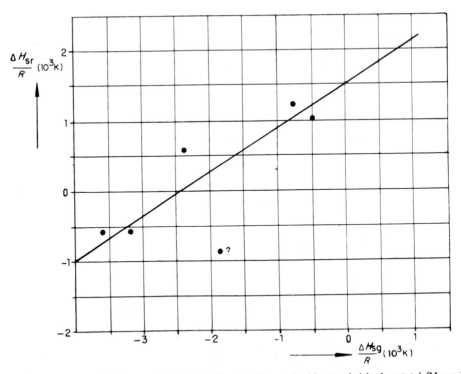

Fig. 18.3. Relationship between heats of solution in glassy and rubbery poly(vinyl acetate) (Meares) for a number of simple gases.

linity. Michaels and Bixler (1961) demonstrated that the following simple rule is valid for a considerable number of gases:

$$S(298) = S_a(298)(1 - x_c) \tag{18.11}$$

where x_c is the degree of crystallinity and S_a the solubility in the amorphous state.

Formulae (18.6) to (18.11) permit the estimation of solubilities of gases and vapours in polymers in different states.

We may conclude that solubilities of simple gases in polymers can be estimated if the boiling point (or the critical temperature) of the gas, the glass transition temperature of the polymer and the degree of crystallinity of the polymer are known.

Example 18.1

Estimate the solubility of oxygen (T_b = 90 K, T_{cr} = 155 K) in poly(vinyl acetate) (T_g = 303 K), a) at 316 K (i.e. above the glass transition temperature) and b) at 280 K (i.e. below the glass transition temperature).

Solution:

a) Slightly above T_g, poly(vinyl acetate) is a rubber. Applying eq. (18.6) (a and b) we obtain for $S(298)$ (in the assumed rubbery state):

(18.6a) $\log S(298) = -2.1 + 0.0074 \times 155 = -2.1 + 1.145 = 0.045 - 1$

(18.6b) $\log S(298) = -2.1 + 0.0123 \times 90 = -2.1 + 1.105 = 0.005 - 1.$

The two values for $S(298)$ are 0.11 and 0.10 respectively or $S(298)$ = 0.105 as an average. With (18.8) we obtain:

$$(\Delta H_s/R) \times 10^{-3} = -1.1 - \log S(298) = -1.1 + 0.98 = -0.12$$

so that

$$S(316) = 0.105 \exp\left[-120\left(\frac{1}{298} - \frac{1}{316}\right)\right] = 0.105 \times 0.98 = 0.10 (cm^3(STP)/cm^3 \cdot bar).$$

The experimental value (Van Amerongen, 1946) is 0.06.

b) We first calculate the solubility at T_g (= 303 K)

$$S(303) = 0.105 \exp\left[-120\left(\frac{1}{298} - \frac{1}{303}\right)\right] \approx 0.105.$$

Applying eq. (18.10) we find for glassy poly(vinyl acetate):

$$\Delta H_{sg}/R = 1.67 \Delta H_{sr}/R - 2500 = -200 - 2500 = -2700$$

The experimental value (Meares, 1954) is −3125.

We now calculate the value of S_0 for the glassy state.

$$S(T_g) = 0.105 = S_0 \exp\left(-\frac{\Delta H_{sg}}{RT_g}\right) = S_0 \exp(9.0)$$

or

$$S_0 = \frac{0.105}{\exp(9.0)} = \frac{0.105}{8 \times 10^3} = 1.3 \times 10^{-5}$$

With this S_0-value we calculate:

$$S(280) = S_0 \exp\left(-\frac{\Delta H_{sg}}{R \cdot 280}\right) = 1.3 \times 10^{-5} \exp(9.7) = 0.21$$

B. DIFFUSIVITY

1. Diffusion of simple gases

For simple gases the interactions with polymers are weak, with the result that the diffusion coefficient is independent of the concentration of the penetrant. In this case the penetrant molecules act effectively as "probes of variable size" which can be used to investigate the polymer structure.

In general, diffusion of gases may be regarded as a thermally activated process, expressed by an equation of the Arrhenius type:

$$D = D_0 \exp(-E_D/RT) \tag{18.12}$$

where D_0 and E_D are constants for the particular gas and polymer.

All the known data on the diffusivity of gases in various polymers were collected by Stannett (1968).

Table 18.2 gives a survey of the data of the most important simple gases. It is evident that the diffusivities – in contradistinction to the solubilities – of a given gas in different polymers show large variations; also the nature of the gas plays an important part.

If the values of $\log D_0$ are plotted versus E_D, a remarkably simple relationship is observed, as is shown in fig. 18.4 for all the known elastomers. For the amorphous glassy polymers the correlation is less accurate but shows a similar tendency, as is clear from fig. 18.5.

So if for a certain gas–polymer combination the activation energy, E_D, is known, the diffusivity can be calculated. Formulae to be used are:

for elastomers:

$$\log D_0 = \frac{E_D \times 10^{-3}}{R} - 4.0 \tag{18.13}$$

for glassy polymers:

$$\log D_0 \approx \frac{E_D \times 10^{-3}}{R} - 5.0 . \tag{18.14}$$

Expressions (18.13) and (18.14) are interesting examples of the so-called *compensation effect* (partial offset of the effect of higher E_D by higher D_0).

Combination of (18.12) with (18.13) or (18.14) gives:

for rubbery polymers:

$$\log D = \log D_0 - \frac{E_D}{2.3RT} = \frac{-E_D}{2.3R}\left(\frac{1}{T} - \frac{1}{T_R}\right) - 4.0 \tag{18.15}$$

for glassy polymers:

$$\log D \approx \log D_0 - \frac{E_D}{2.3RT} = \frac{-E_D}{2.3R}\left(\frac{1}{T} - \frac{1}{T_R}\right) - 5.0 \tag{18.16}$$

where

$$T_R = 435 \text{ K}$$

The remaining problem was to find a relationship between E_D and the intrinsic properties of the gas and the polymer.

The activation energy E_D is needed to enable the dissolved molecule to jump into an-

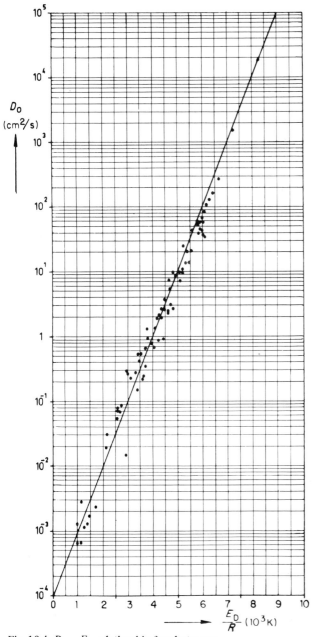

Fig. 18.4. $D_0 - E_D$ relationship for elastomers.

TABLE 18.2

Diffusivity of simple gases in polymers

Values of $D(298)$ in 10^{-6} cm^2/s; D_0 in cm^2/s; E_D/R in 10^3 K.

Polymers	Diffusing gas			
	N$_2$			O$_2$
	$D(298)$	D_0	E_D/R	$D(298)$
Elastomers				
polybutadiene	1.1	0.22	3.6	1.5
cis-1,4-polyisoprene (natural rubber)	1.1	2.6	4.35	1.6
polychloroprene (Neoprene)	0.29	9.3	5.15	0.43
styrene–butadiene rubber	1.1	0.55	3.9	1.4
butadiene–acrylonitrile rubber 80/20	0.50	0.88	4.25	0.79
butadiene–acrylonitrile rubber 73/27	0.25	10.7	5.2	0.43
butadiene–acrylonitrile rubber 68/32	0.15	56	5.85	0.28
butadiene–acrylonitrile rubber 61/39	0.07	131	6.35	0.14
poly(dimethyl butadiene)	0.08	105	6.2	0.14
polyisobutylene (butyl rubber)	0.05	34	6.05	0.08
polyurethane rubber	0.14	55	5.35	0.24
silicone rubber	15	0.0012	1.35	25
Semicrystalline polymers				
polyethylene H.D.	0.10	0.33	4.5	0.17
polyethylene L.D.	0.35	5.15	4.95	0.46
trans-1,4-polyisoprene (Gutta-percha)	0.50	8	4.9	0.70
poly(tetrafluoroethylene)	0.10	0.015	3.55	0.15
polyoxymethylene	0.021	1.34	5.35	0.037
poly(2,6-diphenyl-1,4-phenylene oxide)	0.43	11.2×10^{-5}	1.0	0.72
poly(ethylene terephthalate)	0.0014	0.058	5.25	0.0036
Glassy polymers				
polystyrene	0.06	0.125	4.25	0.11
poly(vinyl chloride)	0.004	295	7.45	0.012
poly(vinyl acetate)	0.03	30	6.15	0.05
poly(ethyl methacrylate)	0.025	0.68	5.1	0.11
poly(bisphenol-A-carbonate)	0.015	0.0335	4.35	0.021

other "hole". It is clear that larger holes need to be formed in the polymer for the diffusion of larger molecules; hence the activation energy will be larger for the diffusion of bigger molecules and the diffusivity will be smaller. This is indeed found to be true in all cases.

The available data show a somewhat scattered correlation between the energy of activation and the diameter of the gas molecule, varying between the first and the second power of the molecular diameter of the penetrant molecule. In our experience the best correlation is obtained if E_D is assumed to be proportional to d^2. The molecular diameters of the gases are shown in table 18.3 (d expressed in Å units). If $(d_{N_2}/d_X)^2 \times E_D/R$ is plotted as a function of T_g of the polymer considered, one obtains the curves given in fig. 18.6 (Van Krevelen, 1970). This figure clearly shows that the activation energy of

| Diffusing gas | | | | | | | |
O₂		CO₂			H₂		
D_0	E_D/R	$D(298)$	D_0	E_D/R	$D(298)$	D_0	E_D/R
0.15	3.4	1.05	0.24	3.65	9.6	0.053	2.55
1.94	4.15	1.1	3.7	4.45	10.2	0.26	3.0
3.1	4.7	0.27	20	5.4	4.3	0.28	3.3
0.23	3.55	1.0	0.90	4.05	9.9	0.056	2.55
0.69	4.05	0.43	2.4	4.6	6.4	0.23	3.1
2.4	4.6	0.19	13.5	5.35	4.5	0.52	3.45
9.9	5.15	0.11	67	6.0	3.85	0.52	3.5
13.6	5.45	0.038	260	6.7	2.45	0.92	3.8
20	5.55	0.063	160	6.4	3.9	1.3	3.75
43	5.95	0.06	36	6.0	1.5	1.36	4.05
7	5.1	0.09	42	5.9	2.6	0.98	3.8
0.0007	1.1	15	0.0012	1.35	75	0.0028	1.1
0.43	4.4	0.12	0.19	4.25	–	–	–
4.48	4.8	0.37	1.85	4.6	–	–	–
4.0	4.6	0.47	7.8	4.9	5.0	1.9	3.8
0.0017	3.15	0.10	0.00093	3.4	–	–	–
0.22	4.65	0.024	0.20	4.75	–	–	–
6.75×10^{-5}	1.15	0.39	9×10^{-6}	0.9	–	–	–
0.38	5.5	0.0015	0.75	5.95	–	–	–
0.125	4.15	0.06	0.128	4.35	4.4	0.0036	2.0
42.5	6.55	0.0025	500	7.75	0.50	5.9	4.15
6.31	5.55	–	–	–	2.1	0.013	2.6
0.039	3.8	0.030	0.021	3.95	–	–	–
0.0087	3.85	0.005	0.018	4.5	0.64	0.0028	2.5

diffusion in the glassy state is lower than that in the rubbery state ($E_{Dg} \approx 0.8\, E_{Dr}$).

By means of fig. 18.6 it is possible to estimate E_D if the diameter of the gas and the glass transition temperature of the polymer are known. E_D being known, D can be estimated by means of the equations (18.15) and (18.16).

Crystallization of polymers tends to decrease the volume of amorphous material available for the diffusion; crystalline regions obstruct the movement of the molecules and increase the average length of the paths they have to travel.

As a first approximation the following equation for (semi-)crystalline polymers

$$D = D_a(1 - x_c) \tag{18.17}$$

may be used, where x_c = degree of crystallinity.

414

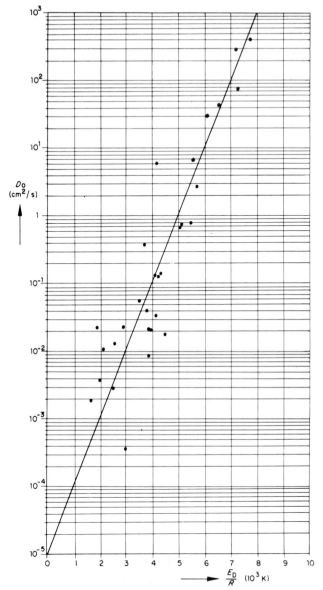

Fig. 18.5. $D_0 - E_D$ relationship for glassy polymers.

This equation has been experimentally verified by Michaels et al. (1963) for the diffusion of several gases in poly(ethylene terephthalate).

The value of D_a in (18.17) follows from fig. 18.6 and eqs. (18.13) − (18.16); it depends on the absolute value of T_g whether in fig. 18.6 the curve of elastomers or that of glassy polymers has to be used for the calculation of D_a.

TABLE 18.3

Diameters of simple molecules

Molecules (Gas)	d (Å)	V_{cr} (cm^3)	T_b (K)	T_{cr} (K)
He	2.55	58	4.3	5.3
H_2O	eff. 3.7	56	373	647
H_2	2.82	65	20	33
Ne	2.82	(42)	27	44.5
NH_3	2.90	72.5	240	406
O_2	3.47	74	90	155
A	3.54	75	87.5	151
CH_3OH	3.63	118	338	513
Kr	3.66	92	121	209
CO	3.69	93	82	133
CH_4	3.76	99.5	112	191
N_2	3.80	90	77	126
CO_2	(3.8)	94	195	304
Xe	4.05	119	164	290
SO_2	4.11	122	263	431
C_2H_4	4.16	124	175	283
CH_3Cl	4.18	143	249	416
C_2H_6	4.44	148	185	305
CH_2Cl_2	4.90	193	313	510
C_3H_8	5.12	200	231	370
C_6H_6	5.35	260	353	562

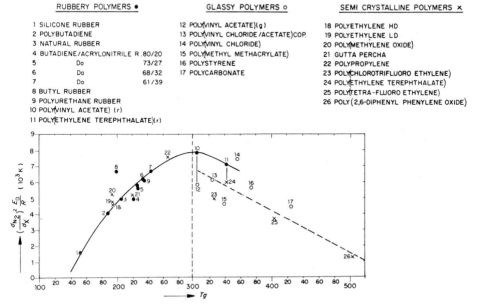

RUBBERY POLYMERS ●

1 SILICONE RUBBER
2 POLYBUTADIENE
3 NATURAL RUBBER
4 BUTADIENE/ACRYLONITRILE R.80/20
5   Do   73/27
6   Do   68/32
7   Do   61/39
8 BUTYL RUBBER
9 POLYURETHANE RUBBER
10 POLY(VINYL ACETATE) (r)
11 POLY(ETHYLENE TEREPHTHALATE)(r)

GLASSY POLYMERS o

12 POLY(VINYL ACETATE)(g)
13 POLY(VINYL CHLORIDE /ACETATE)COP.
14 POLY(VINYL CHLORIDE)
15 POLY(METHYL METHACRYLATE)
16 POLYSTYRENE
17 POLYCARBONATE

SEMI CRYSTALLINE POLYMERS ×

18 POLYETHYLENE HD
19 POLYETHYLENE LD
20 POLY(METHYLENE OXIDE)
21 GUTTA PERCHA
22 POLYPROPYLENE
23 POLY(CHLOROTRIFLUORO ETHYLENE)
24 POLY(ETHYLENE TEREPHTHALATE)
25 POLY(TETRA-FLUORO ETHYLENE)
26 POLY(2,6-DIPHENYL PHENYLENE OXIDE)

Fig. 18.6. Relationship between activation energy of diffusion, size of diffusing molecules and glass transition temperature of polymer.

We may conclude that the diffusivity of simple gases in polymers can be estimated at any temperature if the molecular diameter of the gas, the glass transition temperature and the degree of crystallinity of the polymer are known.

Example 18.2

Estimate the diffusion coefficient of oxygen ($d = 3.47$ Å) in rubbery and glassy poly(vinyl acetate) ($T_g = 303$) at room temperature.

Solution

a. The rubbery state. Using fig. 18.6 we obtain at $T_g \doteq 303$ K:

$$\left(\frac{d_{N_2}}{d_{O_2}}\right)^2 \frac{E_D}{R} \approx 7.8 \times 10^3 \text{K} \qquad \text{or} \qquad \frac{E_D}{R} = \left(\frac{3.47}{3.80}\right)^2 \times 7.8 \times 10^3 = 6500.$$

This gives a value of E_D of 54.0 kJ/mol or 13 kcal/mol.
(The experimental value (Meares, 1954) is 14.5 kcal/mol.) Substituting this value in (18.15) gives:

$$\log D(298) = - \frac{E_D}{2.3R}\left(\frac{1}{298} - \frac{1}{435}\right) - 4.0 = -2800(0.00335 - 0.0023) - 4.0 = -2.95 - 4.0 = 0.05 - 7$$

or

$$D(298) \approx 1.1 \times 10^{-7}$$

b. The glassy state. Using fig. 18.6 again we obtain at $T_g = 303$ K for the glassy state

$$\left(\frac{d_{N_2}}{d_{O_2}}\right)^2 \frac{E_D}{R} \approx 6.5 \times 10^3 \text{K} \qquad \text{or} \qquad \frac{E_D}{R} = \left(\frac{3.47}{3.80}\right)^2 \times 6.5 \times 10^3 = 5400$$

so that

$$\log D(298) = - \frac{E_D}{2.3R}\left(\frac{1}{298} - \frac{1}{435}\right) - 5.0 = -2350(0.00335 - 0.0023) - 5.0 = -2.46 - 5.0 = 0.54 - 8$$

or

$$D(298) = 0.35 \times 10^{-7}$$

The experimental value (Meares, 1954) is 0.51×10^{-7}, which is in fair agreement with our calculation.

2. Diffusion of organic vapours

The diffusion behaviour of organic vapours is much more complicated than that of simple gases. Normally the interaction is much stronger, so that the diffusion coefficient becomes dependent on the concentration of the penetrant:

$$D = D_{c=0} f(c) \tag{18.18}$$

Empirical equations for $f(c)$ are:

$$
\left.
\begin{array}{ll}
f(c) = \exp(\alpha c) & c = \text{concentration} \\
f(c) = \exp(\beta\phi) & \phi = \text{volume fraction} \\
f(c) = \exp(\gamma a) & a = \text{activity}
\end{array}
\right\} \text{ of penetrant} \tag{18.19}
$$

α, β and γ are temperature-dependent constants.

Usually the concentration dependence of D is reduced as the temperature is raised. The general equation for D then becomes:

$$D = D_0 \exp(-E_{D,0}/RT)f(c) \tag{18.20}$$

If for a small temperature range a mean activation energy E_D is defined by

$$D = D_0 \exp(E_D/RT)$$

we get from the last two equations:

$$E_D = E_{D,0} - \left[R\frac{\partial \ln f(c)}{\partial(1/T)}\right] \tag{18.21}$$

So the apparent activation energy is also concentration-dependent! If $f(c)$ is a monotonically increasing function, E_D will decrease continuously with increasing c. If $f(c)$ is a monotonically decreasing function, E_D increases continuously with c.

For the diffusion of benzene in natural rubber the apparent activation energy decreases from 48 kJ/mol at $c = 0$ to 35 kJ/mol at a volume fraction of 0.08. $E_{D,0}$ shows a discontinuity at transition temperatures.

For organic vapours the correlation $E_D \sim d^2$ which was found for simple gases cannot be used any longer. Zhurkov and Ryskin (1954) and Duda and Vrentas (1968) correlated the energy of activation E_D with the molar volume of the diffusing molecules (V_D). Their results are reproduced in fig. 18.7 and show that there is a linear correlation between E_D and V_D at very low concentrations of the diffusate (where the polymer does not show any swelling).

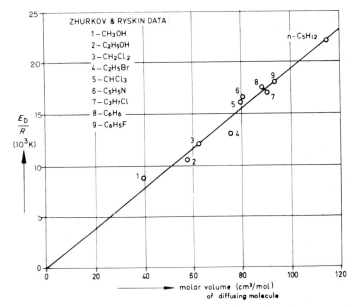

Fig. 18.7. Correlation of activation energy for diffusion in polystyrene with molar volume for temperature range $T_g < T$.

418

The general isokinetic relationship (18.13) and (18.14) is also valid in this case, so that if E_D is known from the $E_D - V_D$ expression, D_0 and D can be calculated.

3. Diffusion of liquids

Diffusion coefficients of organic liquids in rubber have been determined by Southern and Thomas (1967), who followed the kinetics of mass uptake of a rubber sheet immersed in the liquid. Anomalies in the mass uptake–time relation were found and are due to stresses set up in the sheet during swelling and to their variation as swelling proceeds. These anomalies could be eliminated by the use of specimens constrained laterally by bonding to metal plates, which maintains boundary conditions constant during swelling. At liquid concentrations used (up to volume fractions of 0.8 for the best swelling agents!) the diffusion coefficient was shown to depend on the liquid viscosity rather than on the compatibility of rubber and liquid. Fig. 18.8 shows the relationship found, which might have a more general significance.

4. General description of polymer–penetrant system

Hopfenberg and Frisch (1969) succeeded in describing all observed behavioural features for a given polymer–penetrant system in a diagram of temperature versus penetrant activity, which seems to be of general significance for amorphous polymers. It is reproduced in fig. 18.9.

Concentration-independent diffusion only occurs at low temperatures and/or low penetrant "activities". At high penetrant activities over a range of temperatures well below T_g the transport of penetrant into the polymer is accompanied by solvent crazing or cracking: the osmotic stresses produced by the penetrant are sufficiently large to cause local fracture of the material.

Between these two extremes there are a series of transitions. The so-called "Case II" transport (Alfrey et al., 1966) or "partial penetrant stress controlled transport" is characterized by an activation energy which increases with the penetrant activity. It is a highly

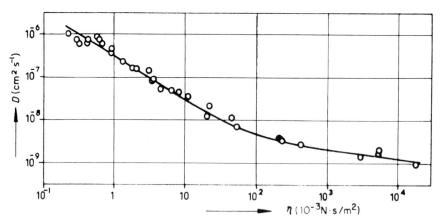

Fig. 18.8. Relation between diffusion coefficient D and liquid viscosity η for various liquids in natural rubber at 25°C (after Southern and Thomas, 1967).

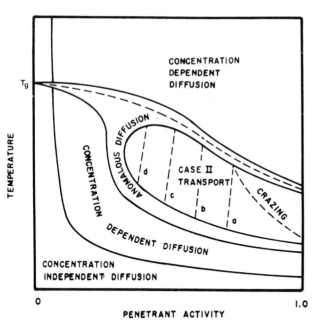

Fig. 18.9. Transport features in the various regions of the temperature–penetrant activity plane. Lines a, b, c, d are lines of constant activation energy. $E_{act_a} > E_{act_b} > E_{act_c} > E_{act_d}$ (after Hopfenberg and Frisch, 1969)

activated process (80–200 kJ/mol) and is confined to temperatures in the vicinity of and below the effective T_g of the system (dashed line in the figure).

The region of "Case II" sorption (relaxation-controlled transport) is separated from the Fickian diffusion region by a region where both relaxation and diffusion mechanisms are operative, giving rise to diffusional anomalies: time-dependent or anomalous diffusion.

Next to it is the concentration-dependent Fickian diffusion zone which is characteristic of many small organic molecules of moderate to high activity at temperatures above or sufficiently below the effective T_g of the system.

5. Self-diffusion

Self-diffusion is the exchange of molecules in a homogeneous material by a kind of internal flow. It has a direct bearing on *tackiness*, which depends on interpenetration by diffusion of polymer molecules at the interface; this effect is well known in elastomers.

Bueche et al. (1952) derived that the coefficient for self-diffusion of poly(n-butyl acrylate) is inversely proportional to the bulk viscosity of this polymer [1]. Also in the

---

[1] The following expression may be used as a good approximation:

$$D\eta \approx CkT \qquad (18.22)$$

where k is the Boltzmann constant (1.38×10^{-23} J · K^{-1}) and C $\approx 10^9$ m^{-1}.

natural rubber–polyisoprene diffusion system a clear connection appears to exist between diffusion coefficient and bulk viscosity.

The energy of activation for self-diffusion of polymers is almost exactly equal to that of viscous flow, as was demonstrated by Bueche et al. Van Amerongen (1964) suggested that the activation energy for self-diffusion of low-molecular-weight material increases with molecular weight, levelling off above a molecular weight corresponding to that of a polymer chain section capable of making independent diffusion jumps. The limiting value would be the same as that of the activation energy for viscous flow.

C. PERMEABILITY OF GASES

For practical purposes the permeability is the most important of the permeation properties. Since methods of estimation of solubility and diffusivity are available, estimation of permeability is possible by means of equation (18.3).

As an illustration, fig. 18.10 shows the permeability of nitrogen (at room temperature) for a great variety of polymers (elastomers, semicrystalline polymers and glassy polymers). It can be seen that the values of P vary by a factor of nearly a million if silicone rubber on the one hand is compared with poly(vinylidene chloride) on the other!

Stannett and Szwarc (1955), Rogers et al. (1956) and Frisch (1963) have shown that simple relationships exist between the ratios of the permeability constants for either a series of gases through two polymers or the ratio between two gases through a series of polymers. If we take nitrogen as the standard gas, the permeabilities of the other gases can be calculated by a simple factor which is given in table 18.4.

A similar relationship as for the permeabilities is valid for the diffusivities and for the solubilities, although here the range in actual values is less impressive than with the permeability constants. These ratios are also given in table 18.4.

Finally, even the activation energies of diffusion and permeation can be estimated in this way, as was already quantitatively described by the relationship $E_D \sim d^2$. We may conclude that if two of the three quantities D, S and P are known (or can be estimated) for nitrogen in a given polymer, those for the other gases can be estimated very quickly and rather accurately.

D. MOISTURE ABSORPTION AND TRANSPORT

The behaviour of water in polymers presents a special case, due to the nature of the water molecule. This molecule is relatively small and has a strong tendency towards hydrogen bond formation in its own liquid and solid state as well as with other polar groups. In polar polymers both equilibrium sorption and diffusivity are strongly influenced by these interactions, but also in less polar polymers anomalies, e.g. association of sorbed water molecules may occur ("clustering").

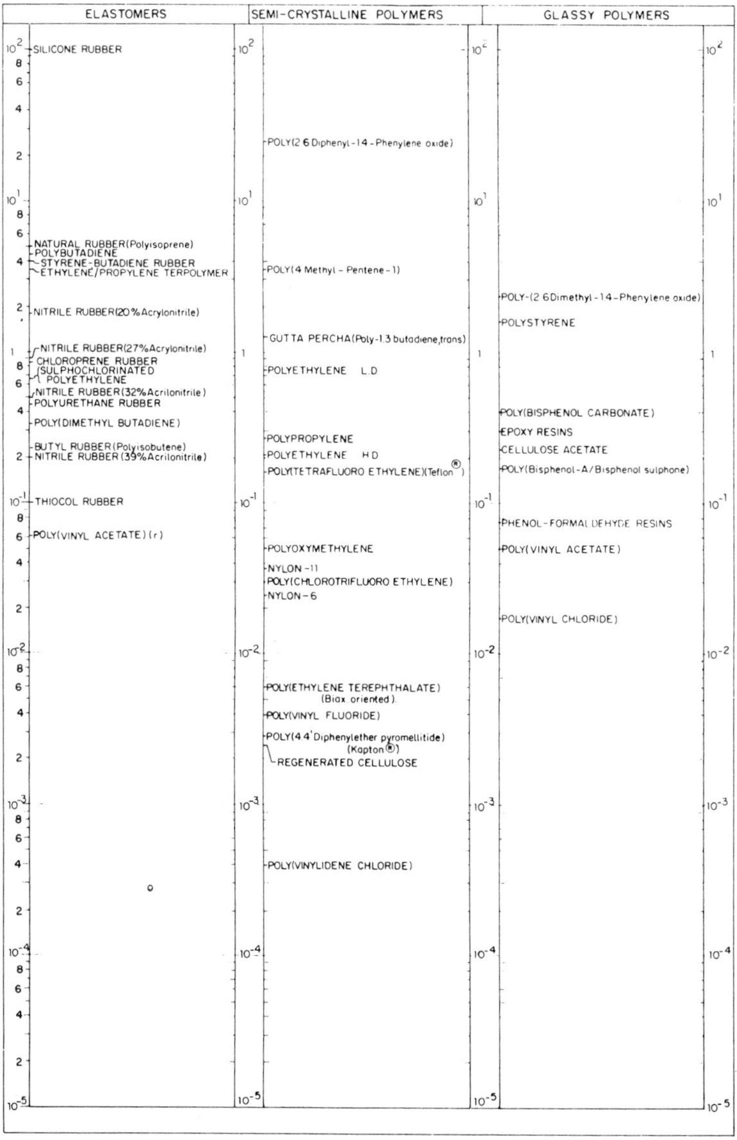

ELASTOMERS		SEMI-CRYSTALLINE POLYMERS		GLASSY POLYMERS	
10^2 −SILICONE RUBBER	10^2		10^2		10^2
8					
6					
4					
		−POLY(2 6 Diphenyl-14-Phenylene oxide)			
2					
10^1	10^1		10^1		10^1
8					
6					
−NATURAL RUBBER(Polyisoprene)					
−POLYBUTADIENE					
4 −STYRENE-BUTADIENE RUBBER		−POLY(4 Methyl-Pentene-1)			
−ETHYLENE/PROPYLENE TERPOLYMER					
				−POLY-(2 6Dimethyl-14-Phenylene oxide)	
2 −NITRILE RUBBER(20%Acrylonitrile)				−POLYSTYRENE	
−NITRILE RUBBER(27%Acrylonitrile)		−GUTTA PERCHA(Poly-1.3 butadiene,trans)			
1	1		1		1
8 −CHLOROPRENE RUBBER		−POLYETHYLENE L.D			
6 −(SULPHOCHLORINATED					
−POLYETHYLENE					
−NITRILE RUBBER(32%Acrilonitrile)				−POLY(BISPHENOL CARBONATE)	
4 −POLYURETHANE RUBBER				−EPOXY RESINS	
−POLY(DIMETHYL BUTADIENE)		−POLYPROPYLENE		−CELLULOSE ACETATE	
−BUTYL RUBBER (Polyisobutene)		−POLYETHYLENE H.D		−POLY(Bisphenol-A/Bisphenol sulphone)	
2 −NITRILE RUBBER (39%Acrilonitrile)		−POLYTETRAFLUORO ETHYLENE)(Teflon®)			
10^{-1} −THIOCOL RUBBER	10^{-1}		10^{-1}		10^{-1}
8				−PHENOL-FORMALDEHYDE RESINS	
6 −POLY(VINYL ACETATE)(r)		−POLYOXYMETHYLENE		−POLY(VINYL ACETATE)	
4		−NYLON-11			
−POLY(CHLOROTRIFLUORO ETHYLENE)					
−NYLON-6					
2				−POLY(VINYL CHLORIDE)	
10^{-2}	10^{-2}		10^{-2}		10^{-2}
8					
6		−POLY(ETHYLENE TEREPHTHALATE)			
		(Biax oriented)			
4		−POLY(VINYL FLUORIDE)			
		−POLY(4 4'Diphenylether pyromellitide)			
2		(Kapton®)			
		−REGENERATED CELLULOSE			
10^{-3}	10^{-3}		10^{-3}		10^{-3}
8					
6					
4		−POLY(VINYLIDENE CHLORIDE)			
2					
10^{-4}	10^{-4}		10^{-4}		10^{-4}
8					
6					
4					
2					
10^{-5}	10^{-5}		10^{-5}		10^{-5}

Fig. 18.10. Permeability of polymers (10^{-8} cm^2/s · bar).

Equilibrium sorption of water (solubility) is described by the different isotherms of the Brunauer–Emmett–Teller classification.

In most hydrophilic polymers, such as cellulose and proteins, each polar group interacts strongly with only one water molecule. In hydrophobic polymers such as polyolefins, on the other hand, Henry's law is obeyed over the complete range of relative pressures and only minute quantities of water are sorbed.

TABLE 18.4

Relative values of permeability parameters

Gas	P	D	S	E_P	E_D	d^2
N_2 (= 1)	1	1	1	1	1	1
CO	1.2	1.1	1.1	1	1	0.95
CH_4	3.4	0.7	4.9	(1)	(1)	0.98
O_2	3.8	1.7	2.2	0.86	0.90	0.83
He	15	60	0.25	0.62	0.45	0.45
H_2	225	30	0.75	0.70	0.65	0.55
CO_2	24	1	24	0.75	1.03	1.0
H_2O	(550)	5	–	0.75	0.75	0.94

TABLE 18.5

Molar water content of polymers per structural group at different relative humidities at 25°C

Group	Relative humidity				
	0.3	0.5	0.7	0.9	1.0
$-CH_3$ $-CH_2-$ $-CH\backslash$	(1.5×10^{-5})	(2.5×10^{-5})	(3.3×10^{-5})	(4.5×10^{-5})	(5×10^{-5})
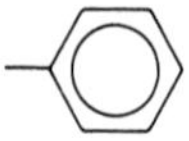 ⬡	0.001	0.002	0.003	0.004	0.005
$C=O$	0.025	0.055	(0.11)	(0.20)	(0.3)
$-C\overset{O}{\underset{O-}{}}$	0.025	0.05	0.075	0.14	0.2
$\backslash O /$	0.006	0.01	0.02	0.06	0.1
$-OH$	0.35	0.5	0.75	1.5	2
$-NH_2$	0.35	0.5	0.75	(1.5)	(2)
$-NH_3^{\oplus}$			2.8	5.3	
$-COOH$	0.2	0.3	0.6	1.0	1.3
$-COO^-$	1.1	2.1	4.2		
$-C\overset{O}{\underset{NH-}{}}$	0.35	0.5	0.75	1.5	2
$-Cl$	0.003	0.006	0.015	0.06	(0.1)
$-CN$	0.015	0.02	0.065	0.22	(0.3)

The more polar groups are present in the polymer matrix, the higher its sorptive affinity for water will be. However, the accessibility of the polar groups, the relative strength of the water–water versus the water–polymer bonds and the degree of crystallinity of the polymer matrix are very important factors, which explain the fact that no simple correlation between number of polar groups and solubility exists. For instance, well-defined crystallites are inaccessible to water, but on the surfaces of the crystallites the polar groups will "react with water".

Barrie (1968) collected all the known data on water sorption. From these data it is possible to estimate the effect of the different structural groups on water sorption at different degrees of humidity. Table 18.5 presents the best possible approach to the sorptive capacity of polymers versus water, namely the amount of water per structural group at equilibrium expressed as molar ratio. From these data the solubility (cm^3 water vapour (STP) per cm^3 of polymer) can be easily calculated. (The multiplication factor is $22.4 \times 10^3/V$, where V is the molar volume per structural polymer unit.)

The heat of sorption is of the order of 25 kJ/mol for non-polar polymers and 40 kJ/mol for polar polymers.

Example 18.3

Estimate the moisture content of nylon 6,6 at 25°C and a relative humidity of 0.7. The crystallinity is 70%.

Solution

The structural unit is

$[-NH(CO)-(CH_2)_4-(CO)NH-(CH_2)_6-]$

From table 18.5 it is evident that the sorptive capacity of the CH_2 groups may be neglected. So we have two CONH groups per structural unit with a molar water content (at a relative humidity of 0.7) of

$2 \times 0.75 = 1.5$ mole/structural unit.

The molar weight of the structural unit is 226.3, so that 1.5×18 g water is absorbed on 226.3 g of polymer or 12 grams per 100 g. Taking the crystallinity into account and using formula (18.11) we get for the solubility of the (semi-)crystalline polymer:

$0.3 \times 12 = 3.6$ grams per 100 g polymer.

This is in good agreement with the experimental value (4 g/100 g).

Also the diffusivity of water in polymers is highly dependent on the polymer–water interaction.

When a polymer contains many hydrogen-bonding groups (cellulose, poly(vinyl alcohol), proteins, etc., and to a lesser extent synthetic polyamides) the diffusivity increases with the water content. This is explained by the strong localization of the initially sorbed water over a limited number of sites, whereas at higher water contents the polymer matrix will swell and the sorbed water will be more and more mobile. As a good approximation the following expression can be used:

$$\log D = \log D_{w=0} + 0.08w \tag{18.23}$$

where w = water content in weight per cent.

Compared with the nonhydrophilic polymers the diffusivity as such is greatly retarded by the strong interaction forces: instead of (18.13) and (18.14) one now finds the relationship:

for water in hydrophilic polymers

$$\log D_0 = \frac{E_D \times 10^{-3}}{R} - 7 \tag{18.24}$$

with E_D expressed in J/mol.

The other extreme is formed by the less hydrophilic polymers such as polyethers and polymethacrylates. Here the diffusivity markedly decreases with increasing water content. This is explained by the increasing "clustering" of water in the polymer (at polar "centres" or in microcavities) so as to render part of the water comparatively immobile. In this case the influence of water can be approximated by the expression:

$$\log D = \log D_{w=0} - 0.08w \tag{18.25}$$

where w = water content in weight per cent.

Furthermore the relationship between D_0 and E_D is the same as for other simple gases.

The third case is that of really hydrophobic polymers, such as polyolefins and certain polyesters. Here the solubility is very low (thermodynamically "ideal" behaviour) and the diffusivity is independent of the water content. Water vapour then diffuses in exactly the same way as the other simple gases.

It will be clear that the diffusive transport (permeability) of water in and through polymers is of extreme importance, since all our clothes are made of polymeric materials and water vapour transport is one of the principal factors of physiological comfort.

BIBLIOGRAPHY, CHAPTER 18

General references

Barrer, R.M., "Diffusion in and through Solids", Cambridge University Press, London, 1941; 2nd ed., 1951.
Crank, J., "The Mathematics of Diffusion", Oxford University Press, London, 1956.
Crank, J. and Park, G.S. (Eds.), "Diffusion in Polymers", Academic Press, London, New York, 1968.
Glasstone, S., Laidler, K.J. and Eyring, H., "The Theory of Rate Processes", McGraw-Hill, New York, 1941.
Hopfenberg, H.B. (Ed.), "Permeability of Plastic Films and Coatings to Gases, Vapours and Liquids", Plenum Press, New York, 1974.

Special references

Alfrey, T., Gurnee, E.F. and Lloyd, W.G., J. Polymer Sci. C12 (1966) 249.
Barrie, J.A., Chapter 8 in "Diffusion in Polymers" (1968) (see General references).
Bueche, F., Cashin, W.M. and Debye, P., J. Chem. Phys. 20 (1952) 1956.
Duda, J.L. and Vrentas, J.S., J. Polymer Sci. A2, 6 (1968) 675.
Frisch, H.L., Polymer Letters 1 (1963) 581.

Fujita, H. Kishimoto, A. and Matsumoto, K., Trans. Faraday Soc. 54 (1958) 40; 56 (1960) 424.

Hopfenberg, H.B. and Frisch, H.L., Polymer Letters 7 (1969) 405.

Meares, P., J. Am. Chem. Soc. 76 (1954) 3415; Trans. Faraday Soc. 53 (1957) 101; 54 (1958) 40.

Michaels, A.S. and Bixler, H.J., J. Polymer Sci. 50 (1961) 393 and 50 (1961) 413.

Michaels, A.S., Vieth, W.R. and Barrie, J.A., J. Appl. Phys. 34 (1963) 1 and 13.

Rogers, C., Meyer, J.A., Stannett, V. and Szwarc, M., Tappi 39 (1956) 741.

Southern, E. and Thomas, A.G., Trans. Faraday Soc. 63 (1967) 1913.

Stannett, V., Chapter 2 in "Diffusion in Polymers" (1968) (see General references).

Stannett, V. and Szwarc, M., J. Polymer Sci. 16 (1955) 89.

Van Amerongen, G.J., J. Appl. Phys. 17 (1946) 972; J. Polymer Sci. 2 (1947) 381; 5 (1950) 307; Rubber Chem. Technol. 37 (1964) 1065.

Van Krevelen, D.W., (1970) unpublished work.

Zhurkov, S.N. and Ryskin, G.Y., J. Techn. Phys. (USSR) 24 (1954) 797.

CHAPTER 19

PROPERTIES OF PHASE CHANGE

CRYSTALLIZATION AND DISSOLUTION

Crystallization of polymers depends on the possibilities of nucleation and growth. The structural regularity of the polymer has a profound influence on both. Interesting correlations were found for estimating the rate of crystallization.

Dissolution of polymers is controlled by processes of diffusion and mass transfer. The rate of dissolution may be estimated from the intrinsic properties of the polymer and the Reynolds number of the dissolving agent.

Introduction

Most pure substances have a definite melting temperature below which the change from a random liquid structure to a well ordered, periodic crystalline structure can occur; this transformation is called *crystallization*; the reverse process is called *melting*.

Crystallization is also possible from solutions; the reverse process is called *dissolving*.

Melts of high-molecular substances have a high viscosity, which increases rapidly on cooling. Only polymers with rather regular molecular chains are able to crystallize fast enough from a melt, notwithstanding the high viscosity. Many polymers solidify into glassy solids.

Crystallization from a solution largely depends on the rate of cooling and on the rate of change in solubility connected with it. Again, the polymers with a regular molecular chain without side groups crystallize fast.

Solidification and melting of polymers are mainly matters of heat transfer. The basic concepts of heat transfer have been discussed in Chapter 17.

Generally, the melting of polymers is more complicated than the solidification.

Melting of polymers usually occurs in a plasticating apparatus, e.g., an extruder. Two different mechanisms can then be distinguished: the first is heat transfer from a heated surface (barrel of the extruder) to the polymer particles; the second is a dissipation of mechanical energy into heat through the deformation of the solid plastic. The first mechanism is controlled by heat conductivity and is governed roughly by the hot surface area. The second mechanism is limited by the amount of mechanical power that can be transmitted.

An investigation by Maddock (1959) revealed details of the melting process. The process starts when the polymer particles in contact with the hot barrel surface partially melt and smear a film of molten polymer over the surface (surface melting). In this phase heat transfer at contact points is the limiting factor. As soon as sufficient molten material is formed, the solid particles are suspended in the melt; because of the motion of the melt

427

heat transfer between barrel and fluid is good. Once this "slush" stage is reached, melting occurs quite rapidly.

In the case of "soft" plastics, such as semicrystalline polyethylene, it is possible (by means of a suitable screw construction) to supply nearly all the melting energy in the form of mechanical energy; the extrusion then is almost completely independent of external heating.

A. CRYSTALLIZATION

The concept "crystallinity"

Since polymers cannot be completely crystalline (i.e. cannot have a perfectly regular crystal lattice) the concept "crystallinity" has been introduced. The meaning of this concept is still disputed (see Chapter 2). According to the original micellar theory of polymer crystallization the polymeric material consists of numerous small crystallites (ordered regions) randomly distributed and linked by intervening amorphous areas. The polymeric molecules are part of several crystallites and of amorphous regions.

In recent years it has been shown that many polymeric solids consist largely of folded chain lamellae and that the breadth of X-ray diffraction lines must be interpreted as a result of either a mosaic structure or as a disorder within the lamellae. However, not all the evidence is in accord with such an extreme viewpoint.

TABLE 19.1

Definitions of crystallinity (x_c) (after Kavesh and Schultz, 1969)

Based on	Definition
specific volume (v)	$x_c = \dfrac{v_a - v}{v_a - v_c}$
specific heat (c_p)	$x_c = \dfrac{c_p^a - c_p}{c_p^a - c_p^c}$
specific enthalpy (h)	$x_c = \dfrac{h_a - h}{h_a - h_c}$
specific enthalpy of fusion (Δh_m)	$x_c = \dfrac{\Delta h_m}{\Delta h_m^c}$
infrared mass extinction coefficient (ϵ) of characteristic vibrational mode	$x_c = \dfrac{\epsilon_\lambda}{\epsilon_\lambda^{(c)}} = 1 - \dfrac{\epsilon_\lambda}{\epsilon_\lambda^{(a)}}$
X-ray scattering intensity (I = area under selected peak)	$x_c = \dfrac{I_c}{I_c + I_a} \approx 1 - \dfrac{I_a}{(I_a)_{melt}}$
nuclear magnetic resonance	$\dfrac{x_c}{1 - x_c} = \dfrac{\text{area of broad component}}{\text{area of narrow component}}$

The several definitions of the weight fraction crystallinity (x_c) are presented in table 19.1. A critical discussion of meaning and measurement of crystallinity in polymers was given by Kavesh and Schultz (1969).

It is understandable that the various methods of determination of crystallinity may lead to somewhat different figures for the same polymer.

Table 19.2 gives the highest degrees of crystallinity measured for a number of polymers. It is obvious that polymers with a high degree of molecular order along the chain and a great simplicity of unit structure possess the highest crystallinity.

Nucleation and growth

The general theory of crystallization was developed by Gibbs, and lateron extended by Becker and Döring (1935), and by Turnbull and Fisher (1949). The derivation is based on the assumption that in supercooled melts there occur fluctuations leading to the formation of a new phase. The phase transformation begins with the appearance of a number of very small particles of the new phase.

For very small particles the decrease in free energy due to phase transition is exceeded by the increase in interfacial free energy. So the possible growth of new particles depends on the ratio of surface area to volume. There is a critical size separating those particles whose free energy of formation increases during growth from those whose energy decreases. So the small particles will tend to redissolve and the larger ones will tend to grow. A particle which has just the critical size acts as a nucleus for growth.

LINEAR GROWTH RATE (v)

The linear growth rate (of spherulites) of several polymers has been investigated. A more or less generalized diagram is reproduced in fig. 19.1 (a). Empirically this figure may be characterized by the following data:

a. The maximum rate of growth v_{max} (at temperature T_k).

TABLE 19.2

Crystallinities of some polymers

Polymer	x_c (max)
polyethylene (HD)	0.80
polypropylene (isot.)	0.63
poly(1-butene)(isot.)	0.50
polyisoprene (cis)	0.45
polystyrene (isot.)	0.32
nylon 6	0.35
nylon 66	0.70
poly(ethylene terephthalate)	0.5
polycarbonate	0.25
poly(chlorotrifluoroethylene)	0.70

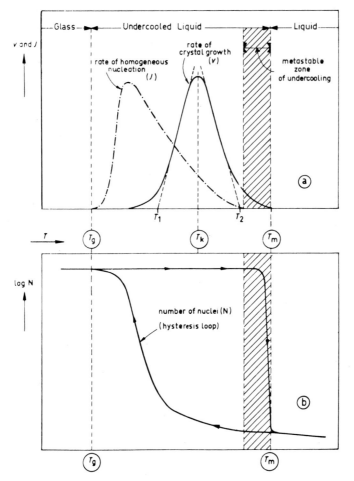

Fig. 19.1. (a) Crystal growth and nucleation as functions of degree of undercooling in viscous liquid. (b) Influence of the thermal history on the number of nuclei.

b. The temperatures T_1 and T_2 obtained as intersections of the T-axis by the tangents of the growth curve.

The basic equation describing the growth rate of polymer crystals reads as follows:

$$v = v_0 \exp\left(-\frac{E_{act}}{RT}\right) \exp\left(-\frac{\Delta W^*}{kT}\right) \tag{19.1}$$

Here E_{act} is the activation energy for the transport process at the interface, ΔW^* is the work required to form a crystal nucleus of critical size and k is the Boltzmann constant.

Hoffman (1958, 1966) proposed the following particular relations for the growth rate (see also Suzuki and Kovacs, 1970):

$$\frac{E_{act}}{RT} = \frac{C_1'}{C_2 + (T - T_g)} \qquad \text{(WLF formulation)} \tag{19.2}$$

$$\frac{\Delta W^*}{kT} = \frac{4b_0 \gamma_\| \gamma_\perp T_m}{k\Delta h_m T\Delta T} = \frac{C_3 T_m}{T(T_m - T)} \tag{19.3}$$

where b_0 = thickness of the chain molecules
$\gamma_\|$ = interfacial free energy (per unit area) parallel to the chain
$\gamma_\perp$ = interfacial free energy (per unit area) perpendicular to the chain
Δh_m = heat of melting per unit volume
T_m = equilibrium melting point
C_1', C_2 and C_3 are "constants" with the following values
C_1' = 2060 K [1]
$C_2 \approx 51.6$ K
$C_3 \approx 265$ K
so that the final expression for the growth rate becomes:

$$\frac{v}{v_0} = \exp\left[-\frac{C_1'}{C_2 + (T - T_g)}\right]\exp\left[-\frac{C_3 T_m}{T(T_m - T)}\right] \tag{19.4}$$

where $v_0 \approx 10^4$ μm/s

This equation has been widely used although the validity of applying the WLF equation to spherulitic growth rate is merely a repetitive assertion (Hoffman et al., 1959; Hoffman and Weeks, 1962), not involving any direct proof of substantiation, as Mandelkern has stated.

Mandelkern et al. (1968) have proved that the WLF formulation, which has had an outstanding success in explaining the segmental mobility and flow properties of completely amorphous polymers, is *not applicable* to the transport process involved in the growth of spherulites in melts of semicrystalline polymers. Rather, a temperature-independent energy of activation, specific to a given polymer and dependent on its glass temperature, suffices to explain the experimental data now available. Mandelkern's equation reads:

$$\frac{v}{v_0} = \exp\left[-\frac{E_D}{RT}\right]\exp\left[-\frac{C_3 T_m^0}{T(T_m^0 - T)}\right] \tag{19.5}$$

where v_0 is a universal constant for semicrystalline polymers: $v_0 \approx 7.5 \times 10^8$ μm/s
E_D is an activation energy for transport
T_m^0 is an "effective" melting point.

Table 19.3 gives a survey of the data.
T_m^0 generally is in the neighbourhood of the crystalline melting temperature as given in the literature, although it may show deviations of more than 10°C. Mandelkern stated

---

[1] $C_1' = 2.3\, C_1 C_2$, where C_1 and C_2 are the WLF constants as defined in eq. (15.31).

TABLE 19.3

Survey of Mandelkern's data on crystallization

Polymer	T_m^0 (K)	T_m (K)	E_D (10^3 J/mol)	T_g (K)
polyethylene	419	414	29.3	195
polypropylene	438	456	50.2	264
polybutene (isot.)	407	415	44.4	249
polystyrene (isot.)	527	513	84.6	373
poly(chlorotrifluoroethylene)	499	491	59.4	325
polyoxymethylene	456	456	41.0	191
poly(ethylene oxide)	347	339	23.0	206
poly(tetramethylene oxide)	462	453	56.1	193
poly(propylene oxide)	354	348	40.6	201
poly(decamethylene sebacate)	356	358	12.6	–
poly(decamethylene terephthalate)	418	411	46.5	268
nylon 6	505	502	56.5	330
nylon 5,6	541	531	61.1	318
nylon 6,6	553	540	64.5	330
nylon 9,6	529	515	56.9	–
nylon 6,10	516	499	53.6	323

Conversion factor: 1 J/mol = 0.24 cal/mol.

that E_D increases monotonically with T_g. After thorough analysis the author of this book found that the following expression is a good approximation of Mandelkern's data:

$$\frac{E_D}{R} \approx 5.3 \times \frac{T_m^2}{T_m - T_g} \tag{19.6}$$

Fig. 19.2 shows this function, together with the experimental data.

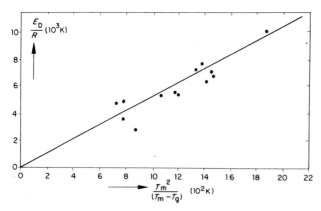

Fig. 19.2. Correlation for the activation energy for transport.

So the final result for the linear growth rate as derived from Mandelkern's work is obtained by substitution of (19.6) into (19.5):

$$\log \frac{v}{v_0} \approx -\frac{1}{2.3} \frac{T_m}{T} \left(\frac{5.3\, T_m}{T_m - T_g} + \frac{265}{T_m - T} \right)$$

or

$$\log \frac{v}{v_0} \approx -2.3 \frac{T_m}{T} \left(\frac{T_m}{T_m - T_g} + \frac{50}{T_m - T} \right) \tag{19.7}$$

where $v_0 = 7.5 \times 10^8\ \mu m/s$.

Steiner et al. (1966), Magill (1967) and Van Antwerpen and Van Krevelen (1972) found that at low to moderate molecular weights the value of v_0 is dependent on the molecular weight; its value increases with decreasing molecular weight, due to increased molecular mobility.

The maximum linear growth rate

It is possible to derive mathematically from eq. (19.7) the conditions at which the growth rate reaches its maximum. This proves to be the case at a temperature T_k related to T_g and T_m by the following equations:

$$T_k/T_m \approx 0.825; \quad T_k/T_g \approx 1.25$$

$$\frac{T_k}{T_g + T_m} \approx 0.5 \tag{19.8}$$

These correlations are in full agreement with the experimental data (see table 19.4).

Substituting these results into equation (19.7) gives a useful relationship for the estimation of the maximum growth rate:

$$\log \frac{v_{max}}{v_0} \approx -\left(2.8 \frac{T_m}{T_m - T_g} + \frac{800}{T_m} \right) \tag{19.9}$$

$(v_0 \approx 7.5 \times 10^8\ \mu m/s)$

Another, purely empirical, expression for v_{max} was found by Van Krevelen and Hoftyzer (1970); it is based on the observation that the growth rate is high if the regularity of the molecular structure is great (high symmetry):

$$v_{max} \approx 83 \left(\frac{n_{CH_2}}{Z} \times \frac{1}{1 + \beta} \right)^4\ \mu m/s \tag{19.10}$$

where

Z = number of backbone chain atoms in structural unit
n_{CH_2} = number of CH_2 groups or equivalent groups in structural unit (backbone)
β = degree of bulkiness of a side group, expressed as the number of carbon atoms or equivalent atoms in.the side group.

As CH_2-equivalent groups are considered $-CF_2-$ and, moreover, $-CX_2-$ and $-S-$ when these are bridges between aromatic rings in the chain.

As CH_3-equivalent side group is considered the Cl atom.

Table 19.4 shows the calculated values of v_{max} according to (19.9) and (19.10) in comparison with the measured values. The agreement is fair. Both expressions (19.9) and (19.10) lead to the right sequence and the right order of magnitude for the growth rate. The Hoffman formulae (19.1–3) do not lead to satisfactory results, as Mandelkern has already stated.

On the basis of the maximum linear growth rate, Gandica and Magill (1972) derived a universal dimensionless relationship for the crystallization kinetics of polymeric materials:

$$\log \frac{v}{v_{max}} = f\left(\frac{T - T_\infty}{T_m - T_\infty}\right) = f(T_{rel}) \tag{19.11}$$

where T_∞ is a characteristic temperature at which polymer chain segmental transport tends to zero; it is generally about 50 K below the glass temperature T_g. Their master curve, which is shown in fig. 19.3, peaks at about $T_{rel} = 0.63 \pm 0.01$ and tends to zero at T_∞ and T_m, respectively.

Taking $\dfrac{T_k - (T_g - 50)}{T_m - (T_g - 50)} \approx 0.63$

one can easily derive: $\dfrac{T_k}{T_m} \approx 0.63 + 0.37 \times \dfrac{T_g}{T_m} - \dfrac{18.5}{T_m}$

TABLE 19.4

Characteristic parameters of polymer crystallization

Polymer	T_k	T_m	T_k/T_m	v_{max} (μm/s)		
				calculated from		exp.
				eq. (19.9)	eq. (19.10)	
polyethylene	–	414	–	45	83	33
polypropylene (isot.)	–	456	–	30 $\times 10^{-1}$	3.3 $\times 10^{-1}$	3.3 $\times 10^{-1}$
poly(1-butene) (isot.)	–	415	–	8 $\times 10^{-1}$	0.7 $\times 10^{-1}$	1.5 $\times 10^{-1}$
polystyrene (isot.)	449	513	0.87	1.2 $\times 10^{-3}$	2.2 $\times 10^{-3}$	4.2 $\times 10^{-3}$
poly(chlorotrifluoroethylene)	–	491	–	2.7 $\times 10^{-1}$	3.3 $\times 10^{-1}$	4.5 $\times 10^{-1}$
polyisoprene (cis)	248	313	0.79	0.14 $\times 10^{-1}$	3.3 $\times 10^{-1}$	–
polyoxymethylene	–	455	–	2 $\times 10^2$	5	7
poly(ethylene oxide)	–	339	–	3 $\times 10^{-1}$	17	–
poly(propylene oxide)	290	348	0.83	9.8 $\times 10^{-1}$	0.7 $\times 10^{-1}$	8.3 $\times 10^{-1}$
poly(ethylene terephthalate)	459	543	0.825	6.5 $\times 10^{-1}$	1.4 $\times 10^{-1}$	1.2 $\times 10^{-1}$
polycarbonate	–	540	–	3 $\times 10^{-5}$	4 $\times 10^{-3}$	1.7 $\times 10^{-4}$
nylon 6	413	502	0.825	1.4 $\times 10^{-1}$	22	3.3
nylon 66	420	540	0.78	1.6	22	20

Since $T_g/T_m \approx 0.65$ and T_m normally varies between 350 and 550 K, we get as an average $(T_m \approx 450)$:

$$\frac{T_k}{T_m} \approx 0.63 + 0.24 - 0.04 \approx 0.83$$

which is in very good agreement with (19.8).

Another interesting (empirical) correlation is that between the crystallinity $x_{c\,max}$ and v_{max} (see tables 19.2 and 19.4). As fig. 19.4 shows, the correlation is obvious. It is not unexpected either, since very simple and regular unit structures will result in high crystallinities as well as high growth rates.

Example 19.1

Estimate for isotactic polystyrene:
a. the temperature of maximum crystallization velocity

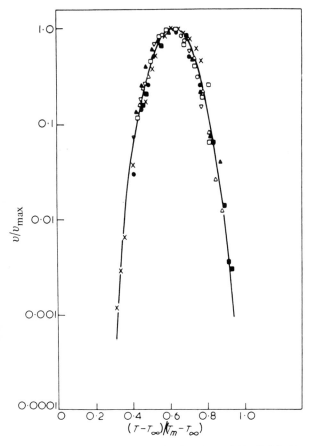

Fig. 19.3. Master curve suggested by Gandica and Magill (1972).

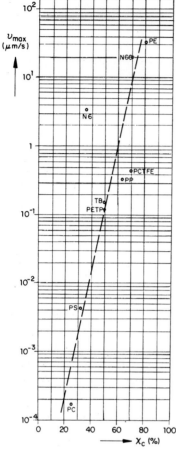

Fig. 19.4. Maximum rate of growth versus maximum degree of crystallinity.

    b. the linear growth rate at this temperature
    c. the probable degree of crystallinity

Solution
a. Using equation (19.8) and putting $T_m \approx 513$, we get

$$T_k \approx 0.825 \times 513 \approx 425 \text{ K}$$

which is in fair agreement with the experimental value of 449 K

b. Applying eq. (19.9) and putting $T_m = 513$ and $T_g = 373$, we get

$$\log v_{max} \approx 8.875 - \left(2.8 \times \frac{513}{513 - 373} + \frac{800}{513} \right) = 0.07 - 3$$

or $v_{max} = 1.2 \times 10^{-3} \ \mu\text{m/s}$

    Using eq. (19.10) we find:

$$v_{max} \approx 83 \left(\frac{1}{2} \times \frac{1}{1+6} \right)^4 = 2.2 \times 10^{-3} \ \mu\text{m/s}$$

The experimental value (Boon, 1966) is $4.2 \times 10^{-3} \ \mu\text{m/s}$; both results are of the right order of magnitude.
c. Using fig. 19.4, we may expect for values of v_{max} between 1.2 and $2.2 \times 10^{-3} \ \mu\text{m/s}$ a probable maximum degree of crystallinity of about 30%, in fair agreement with the experimental value of 32%

NUCLEATION

The rate of homogeneous nucleation (J) should be very similar to the linear growth rate, since both processes are nucleation processes. The former takes place through three-dimensional, the latter through two-dimensional nuclei (or crystallite surfaces). The temperature-dependence of J is given by the equation (Turnbull and Fisher, 1949):

$$J = J_0 \exp\left(\frac{-E_{act}}{RT}\right) \exp\left[-\frac{32\gamma_\parallel^2 \gamma_\perp T_m^2}{k(\Delta H_m)^2 T(T_m - T)^2}\right] \tag{19.12}$$

where J_0 is a constant proportional to the number of effective molecule segments per unit volume.

Fig. 19.1 graphically represents the rates of both homogeneous nucleation and crystal growth as a function of temperature.

For polymeric molecules the temperature interval just below the equilibrium melting temperature is a metastable zone in which nuclei do not form at a detectable rate, but in which crystals, once nucleated, can grow. Below this metastable temperature zone nuclei may form spontaneously, either homogeneously or heterogeneously, but as the substance cools further, a high-viscosity zone is reached where again the formation of nuclei is inhibited and growth does not take place at a detectable rate. Both nucleation and growth show maxima in their rates, because at higher temperatures the driving force (supersaturation) decreases and at lower temperatures the rate of mass transfer is strongly decreased by the high viscosity. Homogeneous nucleation followed by growth of crystallites can only occur in the temperature range where the two curves overlap. The metastable zone of undercooling (supersaturation) is supposed to be due to the greater solubility of microscopic embryonic crystallites as compared with macroscopic crystals and, hence, to the fact that nucleation requires a higher activation energy than growth.

It is very difficult to investigate the homogeneous nucleation, because heterogeneities, which are inevitably present in polymeric melts, greatly promote the (heterogeneous) nucleation.

The nucleation of many polymers is found to be highly dependent on its thermal history. It is affected by the conditions of any previous crystallization as well as by the melting temperature and the time spent in the molten state. Tiny regions of a high degree of order, often stabilized by heterogeneities, may persist in a melt for a long time (resistant nuclei) and will act as predetermined nuclei for recrystallization on cooling. The number and size of the nuclei which remain in the melt depend upon three factors: a. temperature of any previous crystallization; b. temperature of the melt; c. melting time.

In the special case of a very slowly crystallizing polymer interesting effects have been observed (Boon, 1966; Boon et al., 1968). On severe supercooling, "induced" nuclei are created which may grow into effective nuclei at higher temperatures. The crystallization of a severely supercooled polymer is completely governed by these induced nuclei, because they outnumber the resistant nuclei by some orders of magnitude. The number of these induced nuclei can be decreased by purifying the polymer. When cooled polymers are heated to temperatures just above the melting point, the induced nuclei are destroyed and only the resistant nuclei, which are few in number, remain (fig. 19.1, b).

OVERALL RATE OF CRYSTALLIZATION

The overall rate of crystallization of a supercooled liquid is determined by the two factors mentioned: the rate of formation of nuclei (above the critical size) and the rate of growth of such nuclei to the final crystalline aggregates.

The usual procedure in studying the rate of crystallization is to cool the polymer sample quickly from the molten state to the temperature of measurement and then measure the development of crystallinity at constant temperature (isothermal crystallization).

When the crystallization gives rise to well-defined spherulites visible under a microscope it is sometimes possible to follow simultaneously the rate of formation of the nuclei and their rate of growth into spherulites (in μm per min). Since growing spherulites soon interfere with one another's development, measurements are confined to early stages in the crystallization.

If nucleation and growth cannot be studied independently, the overall conversion of amorphous into crystalline polymer may be followed with the aid of any technique giving a measure of the degree of crystallinity. For instance, the specific volume may be followed by enclosing the crystallizing sample in a dilatometer. It is costumary to define the rate of crystallization at a given temperature as the inverse of the time needed to attain one-half of the final crystallinity $(t_{\frac{1}{2}}^{-1})$.

According to Avrami (1939–1941) the progress of the isothermal crystallization can be expressed by the equation:

$$x(t) = 1 - \exp(-Kt^n) \tag{19.13}$$

where $x(t)$ is the fraction of material transformed (into the spherulitic state) at time t. K and n are constants.

The constant K contains nucleation and growth parameters, n is an integer whose value depends on the mechanism of nucleation and on the form of crystal growth. The numerical value of K is directly connected with the overall rate of crystallization $t_{\frac{1}{2}}^{-1}$ by means

TABLE 19.5

Constants n and K of Avrami equation

Form of growth	Type of nucleation			
	Predetermined (constant number of nuclei per cm³)		Spontaneous (sporadic) (constant nucleation rate)	
	n	K	n	K
Spherulitic (spheres)	3	$\frac{4}{3}\pi v^3 N \rho^*$	4	$\frac{\pi}{3} v^3 J \rho^*$
Discoid (platelets)	2	$\pi b v^2 N \rho^*$	3	$\frac{\pi}{3} b v^2 J \rho^*$
Fibrillar (rodlets)	1	$f v N \rho^*$	2	$\frac{f}{2} v J \rho^*$

b = thickness of platelet; f = cross section of rodlet; ρ^* = relative density ρ_c/ρ; N = number of nuclei per unit volume; J = rate of nucleation per unit volume; v = rate of crystal growth.

of the following equation:

$$K = \ln 2(t_{1/2}^{-1})^n . \tag{19.14}$$

Theoretical values of n and K are summarized in table 19.5.

When a polymer sample has been quenched from the molten state to the temperature of measurement, crystallization is very slow at first. After an "induction" period the process speeds up to a maximum rate and slows down again as it approaches the final equilibrium state.

Most polymers crystallize at measurable rates over a range of temperatures which is characteristic of each polymer. It may extend from about 10°C below the melting point T_m to about 30°C above the glass temperature T_g.

The rate of crystallization increases as the temperature decreases below T_m, reaching a maximum at about T_k and decreasing again when the temperature is lowered still further.

There is hardly a class of materials in which bulk properties are as kinetically determined as in that of the macromolecules. The consequences of the nature of nucleation and that of growth are so long-lived that virtually no amount of subsequent annealing can eradicate their effects.

B. DISSOLUTION

The first phase of the process of polymer dissolution is the penetration of solvent molecules into the polymer structure. This results in a *quasi-induction period*, i.e. the time necessary to build up a swollen surface layer. The relationship between this "swelling time" Θ_{sw} and the thickness of the swollen surface layer δ is:

$$\Theta_{sw} = \frac{\delta^2}{6\bar{D}} \tag{19.15}$$

where $\bar{D}$ is the mean diffusion coefficient of the penetrating molecule.

After this quasi-induction period a *steady state* may develop. During this steady state the volume-diffusion fluxes of the solvent and of the polymer will be equal. Then the rate of dissolution will be:

$$\dot{s} = \frac{\bar{D}}{\delta}\Delta\phi_S \tag{19.16}$$

where ϕ_S is the volume fraction of the solvent and $\Delta\phi_S$ is the total gradient in solvent concentration (expressed in volume fractions) between liquid and polymer surface.

If the dissolution takes place in a pure solvent, $\Delta\phi_S$ is unity, so that (19.16) becomes:

$$\dot{s} = \frac{\bar{D}}{\delta} . \tag{19.17}$$

The diffusion layer
According to Ueberreiter (1968) the integral surface layer (δ) on glassy polymers is

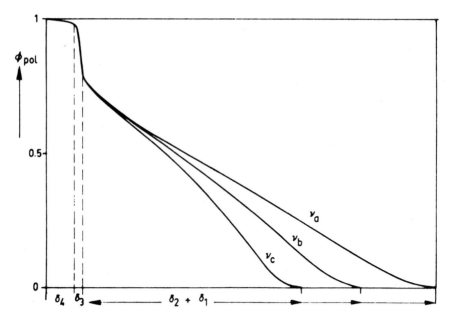

Fig. 19.5. Polymer concentration in the surface layer vs. layer thickness δ. δ_4 = infiltration layer; δ_3 = solid swollen layer; $\delta_2 + \delta_1$ = gel and liquid layer; ν_{a-c} = frequency of the stirrer (Ueberreiter, 1968).

composed of four sublayers:

δ_1, the *hydrodynamic liquid layer,* which surrounds every solid in a moving liquid

δ_2, the *gel layer,* which contains swollen polymer material in a rubber-like state

δ_3, the *solid swollen layer,* in which the polymer is in the glassy state

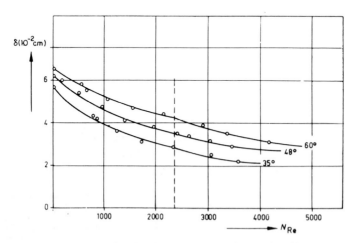

Fig. 19.6. Thickness of surface layer δ vs. Reynolds number, N_{Re}. Temperatures of dissolution are indicated (Ueberreiter and Kirchner, 1965).

δ_4, the *solid infiltration layer*, i.e. the channels and holes in the polymer filled with solvent molecules.

Fig. 19.5 gives an impression of the size of these sublayers and of the polymer concentration in them. Quantitatively, δ_1 and δ_2 are by far the most important sublayers. It is obvious that the thickness of the surface layer (δ) will be influenced by the degree of turbulence in the liquid. Since the latter is characterized by the Reynolds number ($N_{Re} = vL\rho/\eta$), one may expect a correlation between δ and N_{Re}. This has been found indeed, as is shown in fig. 19.6. Below the glass transition temperature the influence of the temperature on δ follows the relation:

$$\delta = \delta_0 \exp(-A/T) \tag{19.18}$$

and indicates a dependence of the stability of the gel layer on the viscosity within it; δ increases with temperature! The value of A is of the order of 1000 (K).

Finally, as can also be expected, δ is dependent on the molecular weight of the polymer. In the normal range of molecular weights a relationship of the form

$$\delta = kM^{1/2} \tag{19.19}$$

has been found. For molecular weights higher than 6×10^5, δ increases rapidly, possibly due to increasing entanglement of the macromolecules.

The overall expression for δ (integral surface layer) for polymers of the "normal" molecular weight range becomes:

$$\delta(\text{cm}) \approx 0.35 \times 10^{-2} M^{1/2} \frac{\exp(-A/T)}{1 + 0.35 \times 10^{-3} N_{Re}} \tag{19.20}$$

δ itself is of the order of $10^{-2} - 10^{-1}$ cm at usual temperatures and molecular weights. Asmussen and Ueberreiter (1962) showed that the quantity

$$\frac{\text{layer thickness } (\delta)}{\text{coil diameter of polymer molecule } \langle h^2 \rangle^{1/2}} \tag{19.21}$$

is nearly constant ($\approx 1.2 \times 10^4$ at room temperature).

According to Chapter 9

$$\langle h^2 \rangle^{1/2} = \alpha M^{1/2} \left(\frac{K_\Theta}{\Phi_o} \right)^{1/3}$$

and $\Phi_o \approx 2.5 \times 10^{23}$ mol^{-1}.

Diffusivity

In Chapter 18 (on permeability) we have shown that the diffusion coefficient of liquid penetrants appears to be determined by the viscosity of the solvent (at room temperature) as a measure of molecular size. This conclusion is confirmed by experiments of Ueberreiter (1965) on plasticizers where $\dot{s}$ and δ were measured simultaneously and $\bar{D}$ could be calculated from (19.17).

Types of dissolution

Ueberreiter (1968) demonstrated that the state of a polymer influences the type of dissolution to a great extent.

If an amorphous polymer is dissolved at a sufficiently high temperature, viz. higher than the "flow temperature" (which is the limit of the rubbery state), the surface layer will consist of δ_1 only: the dissolution process is reduced to a simple mixing of two liquids.

If the polymer is in its rubber-elastic state, the surface layer will contain δ_1 and δ_2. Solvent molecules are able to penetrate faster into the polymer matrix than the macromolecules can be disentangled and transported into the solution.

Most of the amorphous polymers are dissolved when they are in the glassy solid state. In this case the surface layer is "fully developed". The solid state of the polymer permits the existence of all four layers. The gel layer δ_2 is very important because it heals the cracks and holes which have been created by the penetrating front of dissolving macromolecules.

In some cases dissolution without a gel layer is found, especially at low temperatures. It appears that dissolution by stress cracking is the cause of this phenomenon. Cracks are observed which run into the polymer matrix, combine to form small blocks of the polymer, which leave the surface in a kind of eruption process. Large amounts of stored stress energy, frozen in in the glass transition interval and concentrated along the wider channels and hole systems, seem to be responsible for this process. In the extreme case of the original sublayers only δ_1 remains. In this process no induction period exists.

Different from the dissolution of amorphous polymers is that of semi-crystalline ones. Dissolution of these polymers is much more difficult than that in the glassy state, as the enthalpy of melting has to be supplied by the solvent. Many solvents which are able to dissolve tactic but glassy polymers, are unable to dissolve the same polymer in the crystalline state. Asmussen et al. (1965) have found that the velocity of dissolution of crystalline polymers as a function of temperature closely resembles the velocity of crystallization versus temperature curves. Polymers formed at the highest rate of growth also dissolve at the highest rate.

Example 19.2

Estimate the rate of dissolution of polystyrene in toluene at 35°C (308 K)
a) at a very low Reynolds number ($N_{Re} \approx 0$), b) at a Reynolds number of 1000.
The molecular weight of polystyrene is 150,000; the diffusivity of toluene in polystyrene at 35°C is about 1.5×10^{-6} cm^2/s (for estimation see Chapter 18).

Solution

We apply formula (19.20)
a) at $N_{Re} \approx 0$:

$$\delta \approx 0.35 \times 10^{-2} \times (150,000)^{1/2} \times \exp(-1000/308)$$

$$= 0.35 \times 10^{-2} \times 3.87 \times 10^2 \times 3.88 \times 10^{-2} = 5.25 \times 10^{-2} \text{ cm.}$$

b) at $N_{Re} = 1000$:

$$\delta \approx 0.35 \times 10^{-2} \times 3.87 \times 10^2 \times \frac{3.88 \times 10^{-2}}{1 + 0.35} = 3.9 \times 10^{-2} \text{ cm.}$$

We check this value with formula (19.21):
From Chapter 9 we know that K_Θ of polystyrene is 0.08 cm$^3 \cdot$ mol$^{1/2} \cdot$ g$^{-3/2}$. So

$$\langle h^2 \rangle^{1/2} = \alpha M^{1/2} \left(\frac{K_\Theta}{2.5 \times 10^{23}}\right)^{1/3} = \alpha \times 3.87 \times 10^2 \left(\frac{0.08}{2.5 \times 10^{23}}\right)^{1/3}$$

$$= \alpha \cdot 3.87 \times 10^2 \times (0.32 \times 10^{-24})^{1/3} = \alpha \cdot 2.65 \times 10^{-6} \text{ cm.}$$

Since $\alpha \approx 1.4$, we get

$\delta \approx 1.2 \times 10^4 \langle h^2 \rangle^{1/2} = 1.2 \times 10^4 \times 1.4 \times 2.65 \times 10^{-6} \approx 4.5 \times 10^{-2}$ cm (at 25°C)

in good agreement.

The rate of dissolution is

$\dot{s} = \dfrac{\bar{D}}{\delta} = \dfrac{1.5 \times 10^{-6}}{5.25 \times 10^{-2}} \approx 3 \times 10^{-5}$ cm/s at $N_{Re} \approx 0$.

Ueberreiter and Kirchner (1965) measured a value of 5×10^{-5} cm/s. The agreement may be considered fair.

At $N_{Re} = 1000$

$\dot{s} = \dfrac{\bar{D}}{\delta} = \dfrac{1.5 \times 10^{-6}}{3.9 \times 10^{-2}} \approx 4 \times 10^{-5}$ cm/s.

BIBLIOGRAPHY, CHAPTER 19

General references

Crank, J. and Park, G.S. (Eds.), "Diffusion in Polymers", Academic Press, London, New York, 1968.
Geil, P.H., "Polymer Single Crystals", Interscience, New York, 1963.
Gibbs, J.W., "Collected Works", Vol. I, p. 94, Longmans, New York, 1928.
Gornick, F. and Hoffman, J.D., "Nucleation in Polymers", Ind. Eng. Chem. 58 (1966) 41.
Keller, A., "Growth and Perfection of Crystals", Wiley, New York, 1958.
Mandelkern, L., "Crystallization of Polymers", McGraw-Hill, New York, 1964.
Sanchez, I.C., "Modern Theories of Polymer Crystallization", J. Macromol. Sci. C.-Rev. Macromol. Chem. 10 (1974) 114–148 (772 refs.).
Sharples, A., "Introduction to Polymer Crystallization", Edw. Arnold, London, 1966.
Stuart, H.A., "Die Physik der Hochpolymeren", Vol. IV, Springer, Berlin, 1956.
Ueberreiter, K., "Kristallisieren, Kristallzustand und Schmelzen" in "Struktur und physikalisches Verhalten der Kunststoffe" (Nitsche und Wolf, Eds.), Vol. I, Springer, Berlin, 1962.
Uhlmann, D.R. and Chalmers, B., "Energetics of Nucleation", Ind. Eng. Chem. 57 (1965) 19.
Volmer, M., "Kinetik der Phasenbildung", Steinkopf, Dresden, Leipzig, 1939.
Wunderlich, B., Angew. Chem. 80 (1968) 1009.
Wunderlich, B., "Macromolecular Physics", Academic Press, New York, 1973.

Special references

Asmussen, F. and Ueberreiter, K., J. Polymer Sci. 57 (1962) 199, Kolloid-Z. 185 (1962) 1.
Asmussen, F., Ueberreiter, K. and Naumann, H., in Diplomarbeit, Fr. Univ. Berlin, 1965.
Avrami, M., J. Chem. Phys. 7 (1939) 1103; 8 (1940) 212; 9 (1941) 177.
Becker, R., Ann. Physik 32 (1938) 128.
Becker, R. and Döring, W., Ann. Physik 24 (1935) 719.
Boon, J., Doctoral Thesis, Delft Univ. of Technology, 1966.
Boon, J., Challa, G. and Van Krevelen, D.W., J. Polymer Sci. A2,6 (1968) 1791, 1835.
Gandica, A. and Magill, J.H., Polymer 13 (1972) 595.
Hoffman, J.D., J. Chem. Phys. 28 (1958) 1192; SPE Trans. 4 (1964) 315; Ind. Eng. Chem. 58 (2) (1966) 41.
Hoffman, J.D. and Weeks, J.J., J. Chem. Phys. 37 (1962) 1723; 42 (1965) 4301.
Hoffman, J.D., Weeks, J.J. and Murphey, W.M., J. Research N.B.S. 63A (1959) 67.
Kavesh, S. and Schultz, J.M., Polymer Eng. Sci. 9 (1969) 5.

Maddock, B.H., S.P.E. Journal 15 (1959) 383.

Magill, J.H., Polymer 2 (1961) 221; Polymer 3 (1962) 43; J. Appl. Phys. 35 (1964) 3249; J. Polymer Sci. A-2,5 (1967) 89.

Mandelkern, L., Jain, N.L. and Kim, H., J. Polymer Sci. A-2,6 (1968) 165.

Steiner, K., Lucas, K.J. and Ueberreiter, K., Kolloid-Z. 214 (1966) 23.

Suzuki, T. and Kovacs, A.J., Polymer J. 1 (1970) 82.

Turnbull, D. and Fisher, J.C., J. Chem. Phys. 17 (1949) 71.

Ueberreiter, K., "Advances in Chemistry Series" 48 (1965) 35.

Ueberreiter, K., "The Solution Process", in "Diffusion in Polymers" (Crank, J. and Park, G.S., Eds.), 1968 (see General references).

Ueberreiter, K. and Kirchner, P., Makromol. Chem. 87 (1965) 32.

Van Antwerpen, F., Doctoral Thesis, Delft Univ. of Technology, 1971.

Van Antwerpen, F. and Van Krevelen, D.W., J. Polymer Sci.: Polymer Phys. 10 (1972) 2409, 2423.

Van Krevelen, D.W. and Hoftyzer, P.J. (1970). See Van Krevelen, D.W., "Properties of Polymers", Elsevier, Amsterdam, London, New York, 1st ed., 1972, p. 305.

PART V

PROPERTIES DETERMINING THE CHEMICAL STABILITY AND
BREAKDOWN OF POLYMERS

CHAPTER 20

THERMOCHEMICAL PROPERTIES

In this chapter it will be demonstrated that the *free enthalpy of reactions* can be calculated by means of additive group contributions.

A. THERMODYNAMICS AND KINETICS

All polymers are formed and changed by chemical reactions.

Chemical Reaction Science has two domains: *chemical thermodynamics*, dealing with equilibrium states; and *chemical kinetics*, dealing with reaction rates.

Thermodynamic potentials constitute the driving forces causing every natural process to proceed in the direction of its eventual state of equilibrium. Thermodynamics therefore determines whether a reaction is possible or not.

Whether or not a reaction will actually proceed depends on kinetic factors. A certain amount of activation energy and activation entropy is necessary to keep up practically any reaction. However, in many of the cases in which a reaction is thermodynamically feasible it has also proved possible to find a catalyst, active and selective enough to realize this reaction. A classical example is the polymerization of ethylene, either under high pressure with radical initiators or at low pressure with Ziegler-type catalysts.

Thermodynamics determines the possibility, kinetics the actuality of the conversion.

The *equilibrium constant* K_{eq} is connected with thermodynamic data, viz. the enthalpy of reaction ΔH^o and the entropy of reaction ΔS^o:

$$-RT \ln K_{eq} = \Delta H^o - T\Delta S^o = \Delta G^o \qquad (20.1)$$

where ΔG^o is the so-called standard "free" enthalpy change of the reaction.

Expression (20.1) can be written in a well-known form (*Van 't Hoff equation*):

$$\ln K_{eq} = -\frac{\Delta H^o}{RT} + \frac{\Delta S^o}{R} \qquad (20.2)$$

which describes the temperature dependence of the equilibrium constant.

Analogous to the Van 't Hoff equation for equilibria is the *Arrhenius equation* for the *reaction rate constant*:

447

448

$$\ln k = -\frac{E_{act}}{RT} + \ln A \tag{20.3}$$

where E_{act} is the activation energy and A is a constant ("frequency factor")

Modern transition state theories formulate eq. (20.3) in a form analogous to (20.2):

$$\ln k = -\frac{\Delta H_o^*}{RT} + \frac{\Delta S_o^*}{R} + \ln \frac{kT}{h} \tag{20.4}$$

where ΔH_o^* is the enthalpy of activation, ΔS_o^* is the entropy of activation, while k and h are the constants of Boltzmann and Planck respectively. Fig. 20.1 shows the interrelation of ΔH^o and ΔH_o^* (or E_{act}).

If the same reaction is studied with different catalysts or if analogous reactions are compared, it is usually found that the quantities E_{act} and A of the Arrhenius equations are interrelated. An increase in E_{act} is then "compensated" by an increase in A according to the formula:

$$\ln A = \frac{E_{act}}{RT_R} + \ln B \tag{20.5}$$

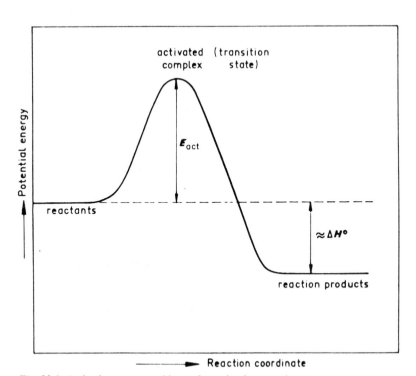

Fig. 20.1. Activation energy and heat of reaction in a reaction system.

where T_R is a characteristic constant with the dimension of temperature (the *"isokinetic" temperature*). Substitution in (20.3) then gives:

$$\ln k = -\frac{E_{act}}{R}\left(\frac{1}{T} - \frac{1}{T_R}\right) + \ln B \tag{20.6}$$

This is the generalized Arrhenius equation for families of related reactions.

Formula (20.5) is the mathematical form of the *"compensation effect"*, already mentioned in the treatment of diffusion constants.

Since chemical thermodynamics and chemical kinetics are vast domains of science, we will select some special topics, viz. calculation of free enthalpies of reactions from group contributions and thermodynamics of free radical formation.

B. CALCULATION OF THE FREE ENTHALPY OF REACTION FROM GROUP CONTRIBUTIONS

Unfortunately, the application of chemical thermodynamics is often handicapped by a lack of sufficient data. In these cases it is important to have a simple method for calculating these data, if only by approximation.

Given the reaction of formation of a compound C from its composing elements E_i

$$\sum_i n_i E_i \rightleftharpoons C$$

the equilibrium of this reaction at a given temperature is described by the equilibrium constant K_f:

$$K_f = \frac{[C]}{\Pi[E]^n} \tag{20.7}$$

where Π means a product of concentrations.

Thermodynamics provides the relation between the equilibrium constant and the free enthalpy of formation (ΔG_f^o)

$$\Delta G_f^o = -RT \ln K_f \tag{20.8}$$

From (20.7) we see that the equilibrium mentioned is shifted to the right if $K_f > 1$ and to the left if $K_f < 1$, from which it follows (according to (20.8)) that the equilibrium lies on the right if ΔG_f^o is negative and on the left if ΔG_f^o is positive. In other words: at a given temperature a compound is stable compared with its elements if at that temperature $\Delta G_f^o < 0$. *The actual value of* ΔG_f^o *is a quantitative measure of the stability of a compound (with respect to its elements).*

For any arbitrary chemical reaction

$$\sum n_A A \rightleftharpoons \sum n_B B$$

the equilibrium at a given temperature is determined by the constant:

$$K_{eq} = \frac{\Pi[B]^{nB}}{\Pi[A]^{nA}} \tag{20.9}$$

The equilibrium constant K_{eq} is related to the change in free enthalpy caused by the reaction

$$\Delta G^o = -RT \ln K_{eq} \tag{20.10}$$

This change of free enthalpy may also be written as a difference in free enthalpies of formation of the compounds considered:

$$\Delta G^o = \sum n_B \Delta G^o_{fB} - \sum n_A \Delta G^o_{fA} \tag{20.11}$$

Therefore, if the free enthalpies of formation of the compounds participating in any reaction are known, it is possible to calculate the position of the equilibrium of this reaction.

From the preceding it follows that it is of great practical importance, for polymerization as well as for degradation and substitution reactions, to know the numerical value of the free enthalpy of formation.

Only a very small part of the overwhelming number of known organic compounds have been examined for their thermodynamic behaviour. Hence it is obvious that methods have been sought to calculate these data.

Theoretically it is possible to calculate thermodynamical data by means of statistical-mechanical methods. However, these are laborious and moreover the (empirical!) spectroscopic data required to this end are usually lacking.

Also in this case the use of group contributions provides a powerful tool. Developments in this direction were made by Anderson et al. (1944), Bremner and Thomas (1948), Souders et al. (1949) and by Franklin (1949). The most elaborate system of group contributions was developed by Van Krevelen and Chermin (1951). A somewhat simplified version of this system is given in table 20.1 [1].

Group contributions

In the system of Van Krevelen and Chermin the free enthalpy of formation is calculated from group contributions, with some corrections due to structural influences:

$$\Delta G^o_f = \sum \text{contributions of} \atop \text{component groups} + \sum \text{structural} \atop \text{corrections} \tag{20.12}$$

The group contributions are considered as linear functions of the temperature:

$$\Delta G^o_{f\,group} = A + BT \tag{20.13}$$

which assumption is based on an argumentation by Scheffer (1945). Eq. (20.13) shows a strong similarity to the general thermodynamic equation:

$$\Delta G = \Delta H - T\Delta S \tag{20.14}$$

If (20.13) and (20.14) are compared it follows that **A** has the dimension of a heat of formation and **B** that of an entropy of formation. According to Ulich (1930):

$$\mathbf{A} \approx \Delta H_f^o(298)$$
$$\mathbf{B} \approx -\Delta S_f^o(298) \tag{20.15}$$

It is not possible to describe accurately the temperature dependence of the free enthalpy

TABLE 20.1

Free enthalpy of formation of some small molecules and related group contributions to the free enthalpy of formation of large molecules

Group	$\Delta G_f^o(T)$(J/mol)	Group	$\Delta G_f^o(T)$(J/mol)
CH_4	$-79,000 + 92.5\,T$	H_2O	$-243,000 + 48.2\ T$
$-CH_3$	$-46,000 + 95\ T$	$-OH$	$-176,000 + 50\quad T$
$-CH_2-$	$-22,000 + 102\ T$	$-O-$	$-120,000 + 70\quad T$
$\diagup CH-$	$-2,700 + 120\ T$		
$\diagup C \diagdown$	$20,000 + 140\ T$	$H_2C=O$	$-118,000 + 26\quad T$
		$-HC=O$	$-125,000 + 26\quad T$
$=CH_2$	$23,000 + 30\quad T$	$\diagup C=O$	$-132,000 + 40\quad T$
$=CH-$	$38,000 + 38\quad T$	HCOOH	$-381,000 + 100\ T$
$=C\diagdown$	$50,000 + 50\quad T$	$-COOH$	$-393,000 + 118\ T$
$=C=$	$147,000 - 20\quad T$	$-COO-$	$-337,000 + 116\ T$
$\equiv CH$	$112,500 - 32.5\,T$	NH_3	$-48,000 + 107\quad T$
$\equiv C-$	$115,000 - 25\quad T$	$-NH_2$	$11,500 + 102.5\,T$
CH_{ar}	$12,500 + 26\quad T$	$-NH-$	$58,000 + 120\quad T$
C_{ar}	$25,000 + 38\quad T$	$\diagup N-$	$97,000 + 150\quad T$
C_{ar}	$21,000 + 21.5\,T$	N	$69,000 + 50\quad T$
		H_2S	$-25,000 - 30\quad T$
	$75,000 + 156\ T$	$-SH$	$13,000 - 33\quad T$
		$-S-$	$40,000 - 24\quad T$
		S	$60,000 - 60\quad T$
	$87,000 + 167\ T$	$-S-S-$	$46,000 - 28\quad T$
		$\diagup S=O$	$-63,000 + 63\quad T$
		$-SO_2-$	$-282,000 + 152\ T$
	$100,000 + 180\ T$	$-NO_2$	$-41,500 + 143\ T$
		$-ONO$	$-21,000 + 130\ T$
HF	$-270,000 - 6\quad T$	$-ONO_2$	$-88,000 + 213\ T$
$-F$	$-195,000 - 6\quad T$	3-ring	$100,000 - 122\ T$
HCl	$-93,000 - 9\quad T$	4-ring	$100,000 - 110\ T$
$-Cl$	$-49,000 - 9\quad T$	5-ring	$20,000 - 100\ T$
HBr	$-50,000 - 14\ T$	6-ring	$-3,000 - 70\quad T$
$-Br$	$-14,000 - 14\ T$	Conjugation of	
HI	$12,000 - 41\ T$	double bonds	$-18,000 + 16\quad T$
$-I$	$40,000 - 41\ T$	cis-trans conversion	$-6,000 + \ 7\quad T$
HCN	$130,000 - 34.5\,T$		
$-CN$	$123,000 - 28.5\,T$		

(Continued on p. 452)

TABLE 20.1 (continued)

Molecule	$\Delta G_f^0(T)(J/mol)$	Molecule	$\Delta G_f^0(T)(J/mol)$
C_3O_2	$-92,000 - 59\ T$	N_2O	$81,000 + 75\ T$
CO	$-111,000 - 90\ T$	NO	$90,500 - 13\ T$
CO_2	$-394,500 - 2\ \ \ T$	NO_2	$33,000 + 63\ T$
$COCl_2$	$-221,000 + 47\ T$	HNO_3	$-130,000 + 208T$
COS	$-140,000 - 85\ T$	$NOCl$	$53,000 + 48\ T$
CS_2	$-111,500 - 152T$	N_2H_4	$92,000 + 223T$
$S_2(g)$	$130,000 - 164T$	$Br_2(g)$	$31,000 - 93\ T$
SO_2	$-300,000 + 0\ \ \ T$	$I_2(g)$	$63,000 - 144T$
SO_3	$-400,000 + 95\ T$	$(CN)_2$	$310,000 - 44\ T$
$SOCl_2$	$-215,000 + 59\ T$	H_2O_2	$-138,000 + 108T$
SO_2Cl_2	$-360,000 + 158T$	O_3	$142,000 + 70\ T$

of formation by the simple expression (20.13) over a very large temperature interval, but it is sufficiently accurate in the temperature interval of 300–600 K.

All group contributions and structural corrections are based on experimental data of organic compounds published in the literature.

For hydrocarbons, where the group contributions are based on experimental data of Rossini et al. (1953), the free enthalpies of formation calculated agree with the literature values within 3 kJ. For non-hydrocarbons the accuracy is less good and deviations up to 12 kJ may occur.

All values for the free enthalpy of formation are as a rule standardized for the ideal gaseous state of a fugacity of 1 (bar), (Standard State). This also holds for the group contributions given.

Example 20.1

Estimate the free enthalpy of formation of gaseous 1,3-butadiene and of the (imaginary)gaseous polybutadiene.

Solution

The structural units are:

monomer: $CH_2=CH-CH=CH_2$

and

polymer: $-CH_2-CH=CH-CH_2-$

For the monomer we calculate

$2(=CH_2)$	$46,000 + 60T$
$2(=CH-)$	$76,000 + 76T$
conjugation	$-18,000 + 16T$
	$104,000 + 152T$

At 300 K this becomes: 149,600 J/mol; the literature value is 152,900. At 600 K we calculate: 195,200; the literature value is 197,800.

For the (imaginary) gaseous polymer unit we calculate:

$$2(-CH_2-) \qquad -44,000 + 204T$$
$$2(-CH=) \qquad 76,000 + 76T$$
$$\overline{\qquad\qquad 32,000 + 280T}$$

The molar free enthalpy of polymerization will be:

$$32,000 + 280T - (104,000 + 152T) = -72,000 + 128T.$$

The literature value for $\Delta H_{gg}(pol)$ is -73.000 (Polymer Handbook) which is in excellent agreement with our calculation.

Thermodynamically the polymerization is possible at temperatures below

$$\frac{72,000}{128} = 562 \text{ K (ca } 300°\text{C)}.$$

Corrections for other physical states

If the reactants or the reaction products are not in the (ideal) gaseous state, but in a condensed state (the latter is always true for polymers), corrections have to be made (see Dainton and Ivin, 1950).

The corrections are clearly visualized by means of the diagrams of enthalpy and entropy levels, as shown in fig. 20.2 for polymerization reactions. The formulae to be used can easily be deduced from these diagrams and are summarized in table 20.2.

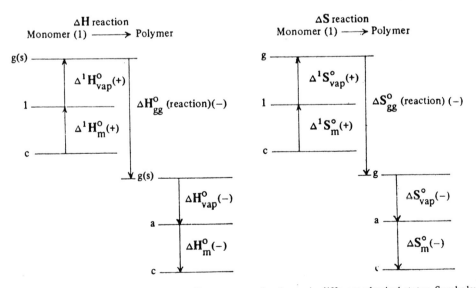

Fig. 20.2. Enthalpy and entropy levels of monomer and polymer in different physical states. Symbols: g = gaseous; l = liquid; a = amorphous; c = crystalline; s = dissolved; vap = vaporization (condensation); m = melting (crystallization); o = standard state (25°C, 1 bar).

TABLE 20.2

ΔH^o- and ΔS^o-corrections for the non-gaseous state

$\Delta H^o_{polymerization}$	$\Delta S^o_{polymerization}$
$\Delta H^o_{ga} = \Delta H^o_{gg} - \Delta H^o_{vap}$	$\Delta S^o_{ga} = \Delta S^o_{gg} - \Delta S^o_{vap}$
$\Delta H^o_{gc} = \Delta H^o_{gg} - \Delta H^o_{vap} - \Delta H^o_{m}$	$\Delta S^o_{gc} = \Delta S^o_{gg} - \Delta S^o_{vap} - \Delta S^o_{m}$
$\Delta H^o_{la} = \Delta H^o_{gg} + \Delta^l H^o_{vap} - \Delta H^o_{vap}$	$\Delta S^o_{la} = \Delta S^o_{gg} + \Delta^l S^o_{vap} - \Delta S^o_{vap}$
$\Delta H^o_{lc} = \Delta H^o_{gg} + \Delta^l H^o_{vap} - \Delta H^o_{vap} - \Delta H^o_{m}$	$\Delta S^o_{lc} = \Delta S^o_{gg} + \Delta^l S^o_{vap} - \Delta S^o_{vap} - \Delta S^o_{m}$
$\Delta H^o_{cc} = \Delta H^o_{gg} + \Delta^l H^o_{vap} - \Delta H^o_{vap} + \Delta^l H^o_{m} - \Delta H^o_{m}$	$\Delta S^o_{cc} = \Delta S^o_{gg} + \Delta^l S^o_{vap} - \Delta S^o_{vap} + \Delta^l S^o_{m} - \Delta S$

Notation:

ΔH^o_{xy} means: standard molar heat effect when monomer in state x is transformed into polymer in state y.

ΔS^o_{xy} means: standard molar entropy change, when monomer in state x is transformed into polymer in state y.

The experimental data available to deduce these correction factors are extremely scarce.

The following empirical rules of thumb may be used for the corrections to be made for polymerization reactions:

$$\Delta G^o_{ga} \approx \Delta G^o_{gg} - 7{,}000 + 15T \tag{20.16}$$

$$\Delta G^o_{gc} \approx \Delta G^o_{gg} - 17{,}000 + 40T \tag{20.17}$$

$$\Delta G^o_{la} \approx \Delta G^o_{gg} - 40T \tag{20.18}$$

$$\Delta G^o_{lc} \approx \Delta G^o_{gg} + 8{,}000 - 30T \tag{20.19}$$

$$\Delta G^o_{cc} \approx \Delta G^o_{gg} - 40T \tag{20.20}$$

where the symbol ΔG^o_{xy} means the molar free enthalpy change when a monomer in state x is transformed into a polymer in state y.

Example 20.2

Estimate the free enthalpy of polymerization of 1,3-butadiene to polybutadiene (1 : 4) when the monomer is in the liquid state and the polymer is in the amorphous solid state.

Solution

From example 20.1 we derive:

$$\Delta G^o_{gg}(pol) = -72{,}000 + 128T$$

Eq. (20.18) gives

$$\Delta G^o_{la} = \Delta G^o_{gg} - 40T$$

so that

$$\Delta G^o_{la} = -72{,}000 + 88T$$

or

$$\Delta H^o_{la} \approx -72{,}000 \quad \text{and} \quad -\Delta S^o_{la} \approx 88.$$

Y ←

Bond dissociation energies (kJ·mol⁻¹). X–Y matrix (lower-left triangle).

X \ Y	-H	-F	-Cl	-Br	-I	-CH3	-CH2(C)	-CH(C)(C)	-C(C)(C)(C)	-Ø	-CH2-Ø	-CH=CH2	-C≡CH	-CF3	-CCl3	-OH	-O-(C)	-C(=O)H	-C(=O)(C)	-C(=O)O-	-O-C(=O)	-NH2	-NH(C)	-N(C)(C)	-CN	-SH	-S-(C)
-H	432																										
-F	566	159																									
-Cl	428	251	239																								
-Br	363	235	218	190																							
-I	296	218	208	180	149																						
-CH3	436	453	352	293	235	369																					
-CH2(C)	111	444	339	289	222	356	337																				
-CH(C)(C)	394	440	339	285	222	348	327	318																			
-C(C)(C)(C)	381	427	331	264	210	335	314	306	293																		
-Ø	469	524	419	335	272	427	381	348	327	432																	
-CH2-Ø	335	377	285	214	168	302	260	230		323	197																
-CH=CH2	436		360		230	377	377	356	339	423	293	423															
-C≡CH	507					419	457	432		499			(461)														
-CF3	414	541	356	293	226	419								406													
-CCl3	402	444	306	226											365												
-OH	199					381	381	385	381	469					323	214											
-O-(C)	127	247	205			335	335	339	327	423							142										
-C(=O)H	365					314	297			377					210	419	251	251									
-C(=O)(C)	360		344	281	214	344	323	264								247	251		251								
-C(=O)O-	360									230																	
-O-C(=O)	169																				126						
-NH2	432					331	327	323	323	419								411	377?	272							
-NH(C)	385																						155				
-N(C)(C)	360																							176			
-CN						461				545		398	507												608		
-SH	377																									(126)	
-S-(C)	369		(272)																								(264)

NB. The dissociation energy is lowered
if the dissociating bond is in conjugation
with a π-electron system.

system	decrease of bond diss. energy
-C-C=C-	≈ 67
(phenyl)	≈ 67
-C=O	≈ 42

The literature value (Polymer Handbook) is:

$$\Delta H^o_{la} = -73,000; \qquad\qquad -\Delta S^o_{la} = 88.8$$

so that the agreement is excellent.

C. THERMODYNAMICS OF FREE RADICALS

Many polymerization and polymer degradation reactions proceed by radical mechanisms. Therefore it is important to know the thermodynamical data of free radicals in comparison with the bonded groups.

For the simple radicals these data are known from studies of flame reactions. Furthermore the dissociation energies of chemical bonds have been determined by thermochemical measurements. Table 20.3 provides the full information on these bond dissociation energies.

Finally, it is empirically known that the entropy change of simple bond breaking reactions is about 160 entropy units, so that the entropy change per free radical formed is about 80 entropy units (for atoms the latter value is about 40 e.u.).

By means of these empirical data it is possible to estimate the free enthalpy of radicals. These data are summarized in table 20.4 for those radicals which are of interest in polymer chemistry (see Sawada, 1969).

TABLE 20.4

Free enthalpies of free radicals and radical groups

Radical or radical group	$\Delta G^o(T)$(J/mol)
·H	$218,000 - 49.4T$
·F	$80,000 - 57\ T$
·Cl	$121,000 - 54\ T$
·Br	$112,000 - 99\ T$
·I	$107,000 - 112\ T$
·CH$_3$	$134,000 + 9\ \ T$
·CH$_2-$	$142,000 - 4\ \ T$
·CH$\diagdown$	$150,000 + 38\ T$
·C$\diagdown$	$159,000 + 63\ T$
·OH	$38,000 - 6\ \ T$
·O$-$	$33,500 - 8\ \ T$
·C$\diagup\diagdown$O	$21,000 - 42\ T$
·OC$\diagdown$	$-11,000 + 42\ T$
·NHC$\diagdown$O	$17,000 + 42\ \ T$
·CN	$460,000 - 63\ \ T$
·O$-$O$-$	$31,500$

Example 20.3

As an illustration of its use, we shall estimate the thermodynamic preference for two mechanisms of interradical reactions, viz. recombination and disproportionation.

Solution

The reactions are:

$$\sim\!\!CH_2\!\cdot + \cdot CH_2 - CH_2\!\!\sim \rightarrow \sim\!\!CH_2 - CH_2 - CH_2\!\!\sim \qquad\qquad \text{a)}$$

or

$$\sim\!\!CH_2\!\cdot + \cdot CH_2 - CH_2\!\!\sim \rightarrow \sim\!\!CH_3 + CH_2 = CH\!\!\sim \qquad\qquad \text{b)}$$

From the group contributions can be calculated

for reaction a) $\Delta G^O = -328,000 + 212T$

for reaction b) $\Delta G^O = -247,000 + 69T$

so that the free enthalpy difference between the two reactions is:

$$\Delta(\Delta G^O) = -81,000 + 143T$$

$$\Delta(\Delta G^O) = 0 \text{ at } 567 \text{ K.}$$

So above 567 K = 294°C disproportionation is preferred, below 567 K recombination.

BIBLIOGRAPHY, CHAPTER 20

General references

Chemical thermodynamics

Janz, G.J., "Estimation of Thermodynamic Properties of Organic Compounds", Academic Press, New York, 1958.

Lewis, G.N. and Randall, M., "Thermodynamics", 2nd ed., Rev. by Pitzer, K.S. and Brewer, L., McGraw-Hill, New York, 1961.

Parks, G.S. and Huffman, H.M., "The Free Energies of Some Organic Compounds", Chem. Cat. Co., New York, 1932.

Reid, R.C. and Sherwood, Th.K., "The Properties of Gases and Liquids", McGraw-Hill, New York, 1st ed., 1958; 2nd ed., 1966.

Rossini, F.D., "Chemical Thermodynamics", Wiley, New York, 1950.

Rossini, F.D. et al., "Selected Values of Chemical Thermodynamic Properties", Natl. Bur. Standards Circ. 500, U.S. Printing Office, Washington, 1952.

Rossini, F.D. et al., "Selected Values of Physical and Thermodynamic Properties of Hydrocarbons and Related Compounds", Carnegie Press, Pittsburgh, 1953.

Stull, D.R., Westrum, E.F. and Sinke, G.C., "The Chemical Thermodynamics of Organic Compounds", Wiley, New York, 1969.

Thermodynamics of polymerization

Ivin, K.J., "Heats and Entropies of Polymerization, Ceiling Temperatures and Equilibrium Monomer Concentrations", in "Polymer Handbook" (Brandrup, J. and Immergut, E.H., Eds.), Interscience, New York, 2nd ed., 1975, Part II, pp. 421–450.

Sawada, H., "Thermodynamics of Polymerization", J. Macromol. Sci., Revs. Macromol. Chem. C3 (2) (1969) 313–396; C5 (1) (1970) 151–174; C7 (1) (1972) 161–187; C8 (2) (1972) 236–287.

458

Chemical kinetics

Bamford, C.H. and Tipper, C.F.H. (Eds.), "Comprehensive Kinetics", Elsevier, Amsterdam, 1969.
Boudart, M., "Kinetics of Chemical Processes", Prentice-Hall, Englewood, N.J., 1968.
Burnett, G.M., "Mechanism of Polymer Reactions", Interscience, New York, 1954.
Glasstone, S., Laidler, K.J. and Eyring, H., "The Theory of Rate Processes", McGraw-Hill, New York, 1941.
Lefler, J.E. and Grunwald, E., "Rates and Equilibria of Chemical Reactions", Wiley, New York, 1963.

Bond strength and formation free radicals

Mortimer, C.T., "Reaction Heats and Bond Strengths", Pergamon Press, London, New York, 1962.
Franklin, J.L., "Prediction of Rates of Chemical Reactions Involving Free Radicals", Brit. Chem. Eng. 7 (1962) 340.

Special references

Anderson, J.W., Beyer, G.H. and Watson, K.M., Natl. Petr. News 36R (1944) 476.
Bremner, J.G.M. and Thomas, G.D., Trans. Faraday Soc. 44 (1948) 230.
Dainton, F.S. and Ivin, K.J., Trans. Faraday Soc. 46 (1950) 331.
Franklin, J.L., Ind. Eng. Chem. 41 (1949) 1070.
Scheffer, F.E.C., "De Toepassing van de Thermodynamica op Chemische Processen", Waltman, Delft, 1945.
Souders, M., Matthews, C.S. and Hurd, C.O., Ind. Eng. Chem. 41 (1949) 1037.
Ulich, H., "Chemische Thermodynamik", Dresden, Leipzig, 1930.
Van Krevelen, D.W. and Chermin, H.A.G., Chem. Eng. Sci. 1 (1951) 66; 1 (1952) 238.

CHAPTER 21

THERMAL DECOMPOSITION

> The heat resistance of a polymer may be characterized by its temperature of half decomposition. The latter quantity is closely related to the dissociation energy of the weakest bond.
>
> The amount of char on pyrolysis of a polymer can be estimated by means of an additive quantity, the char-forming tendency.

Introduction

The way in which a polymer degrades under the influence of thermal energy in an inert atmosphere is determined, on the one hand, by the chemical structure of the polymer itself, on the other hand by the presence of traces of unstable structures (impurities or additions).

Thermal degradation does not occur until the temperature is so high that primary chemical bonds are separated. Pioneering work in this field was done by Madorsky and Straus (1954–1961), who found that some polymers (poly(methyl methacrylate), poly-(α-methylstyrene) and poly(tetrafluoroethylene)) mainly form back their monomers upon heating, while others (like polyethylene) yield a great many decomposition products. These two types of thermal polymer degradation are called *chain depolymerization* and *random degradation.*

Temperature of half decomposition

For many polymers thermal degradation is characterized by the breaking of the weakest bond and is consequently determined by a bond dissociation energy. Since the change in entropy is of the same order of magnitude in almost all dissociation reactions, it may be assumed that also the activation entropy will be approximately the same. This means that, in principle, the bond dissociation energy determines the phenomenon. So it may be expected that the temperature at which the same degree of conversion is reached will be virtually proportional to this bond dissociation energy. The numerical values of the bond dissociation energy are given in Chapter 20 (table 20.4).

Table 21.1 summarizes the most important data about the thermal degradation of vinyl polymers. The temperature at which the polymer loses half its weight when heated in vacuo for 30 minutes has been chosen as the characteristic temperature $(T_{1/2})$ for the thermal stability. In fig. 21.1 these data, supplemented with those of some other polymers (Korshak and Vinogradova, 1968) and of a number of radical initiators (peroxides and azo compounds), are plotted against the bond dissociation energy.

459

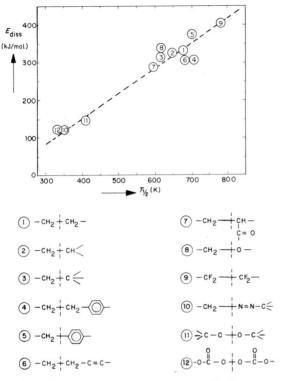

Fig. 21.1. Correlation between temperatures of half decomposition and dissociation energy of weakest bond.

In accordance with expectation a practically linear relationship is found, for which approximately holds:

$$T_{1/2}(K) = 1.6\, E_{diss} + 140 \tag{21.1}$$

in which E_{diss} = bond dissociation energy in kJ/mol.

Mechanism of thermal decomposition

As mentioned earlier, there are two types of thermal decomposition: chain depolymerization and random decomposition.

Chain depolymerization is the successive release of monomer units from a chain end or at a weak link, which is essentially the reverse of chain polymerization; it is often called *depropagation* or *unzipping*. This depolymerization begins at the ceiling temperature. Random degradation occurs by chain rupture at random points along the chain, giving a disperse mixture of fragments which are usually large compared with the monomer unit. The two types of thermal degradation may occur separately or in combination; the latter case is rather normal. Chain depolymerization is often the dominant degradation process in vinyl polymers, whereas the degradation of condensation polymers is mainly due to random chain rupture.

TABLE 21.1

Thermal degradation of polymers

Polymer	$T_{1/2}$ $(°C)^1$	k_{350} $(\%/min)^2$	Monomer yield (%)	E_{act} (kJ/mol)
poly(tetrafluoroethylene)	509	0.000002	>95	339
poly(p-xylylene)	432	0.002	0	306
poly(p-phenylene methylene)	430	0.006	0	209
polymethylene	414	0.004	<0.1	301
poly(trifluoroethylene)	412	0.017	<1	222
polybutadiene	407	0.022	2	260
polyethylene (branched)	404	0.008	<0.025	264
polypropylene	387	0.069	<0.2	243
poly(chlorotrifluoroethylene)	380	0.044	27	239
poly(β-deuterostyrene)	372	0.14	39	234
poly(vinylcyclohexane)	369	0.45	0.1	205
polystyrene	364	0.24	40	230
poly(α-deuterostyrene)	362	0.27	68	230
poly(m-methylstyrene)	358	0.90	45	234
polyisobutylene	348	2.7	20	205
poly(ethylene oxide)	345	2.1	4	193
poly(α,β,β-trifluorostyrene)	342	2.4	7.4	268
poly(methyl acrylate)	328	10	0	142
poly(methyl methacrylate)	327	5.2	>95	218
poly(propylene oxide) (isot.)	313	20	1	147
poly(propylene oxide) (atact.)	295	5	1	84
poly(α-methylstyrene)	286	228	>95	230
poly(vinyl acetate)	269	–	0	71
poly(vinyl alcohol)	268	–	0	–
poly(vinyl chloride)	260 [3]	170 [3]	0 [3]	134 [3]

[1] Temperature at which the polymer loses 50% of its weight, if heated in vacuum for 30 minutes.
[2] Rate of volatilization (weight loss) at 350°C.
[3] Determined from the loss of HCl.

The overall mechanism of thermal decomposition of polymers has been studied by Wolfs et al. (1959, 1960). They used polymers in which the link between the structural units (CH_2 bridges) was radioactive, so that the course of decomposition could be traced by radioactivity measurements in gas and residue, together with chemical and elementary analysis.

The basic mechanism of pyrolysis is sketched in fig. 21.2

In the first stage of pyrolysis (<550°C) a *disproportionation* takes place. Part of the decomposing material is enriched in hydrogen and evaporated as tar and primary gas, the rest forming the primary char. In the second phase (>550°C) the primary char is further decomposed, i.e. mainly dehydrogenated, forming the secondary gas and the final char. During the disproportionation reaction, hydrogen atoms of the aliphatic parts of the structural units are "shifted" to "saturate" part of the aromatic radicals, as is visualized

462

by the simplified scheme:

$$(-Ⓐ-CH_2-Ⓐ-CH_2-)_n \longrightarrow 2\left[\cdot Ⓐ-CH_2\cdot\right] \longrightarrow H Ⓐ CH_3 + -Ⓐ-\overset{\mid}{\underset{\mid}{C}}-$$

polymer   tar   residue

where Ⓐ is an aromatic nucleus.

The hydrogen shift during disproportionation is highly influenced by the nature of the structural groups. Groups which are capable of reacting with H atoms of the aromatic nucleus give rise to postcondensation (cross-linking); this occurs if the aromatic nucleus also contains −OH or =O groups. The char residue then is higher than in the case of non-substituted aromatic units. On the other hand, if the aromatic nucleus contains alkyl groups, the alkyl hydrogen may act as an extra source of hydrogen atoms; the formation of tar is enhanced in this case.

Char-forming tendency and char residue

The results of pyrolysis experiments with nearly 100 polymers enabled van Krevelen (1975) to quantify the char-forming tendency, defined as the amount of char per structural unit divided by 12 (the atomic weight of carbon), i.e. the amount of C equivalents in the char per structural unit of polymer.

This char-forming tendency proved to be an additive quantity. Each structural group in principle contributes to the char residue in its own characteristic way. Aliphatic groups, connected to aromatic nuclei, show a negative char-forming tendency, since they supply hydrogen for the disproportionation reaction ("H shift"). Table 21.2 gives the char-forming tendency (**CFT**) of the different structural groups.

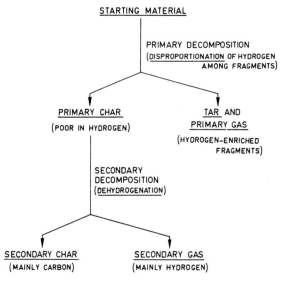

Fig. 21.2. Basic mechanism of pyrolysis.

TABLE 21.2

Group contributions to char formation

GROUP	CFT in C-equiv.	GROUP	CFT in C-equiv.
ALIPHATIC GROUPS		**HETEROCYCLIC GROUPS**	
—CHOH—	1/3	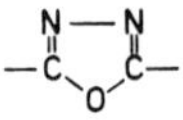 [N—N / C—O—C structure]	1
ALL OTHER *)	0	[—C=C— / N—NH—CH structure]	3½
AROMATIC GROUPS		[HC—S / C—N—C structure]	3½
[phenyl]	1	[HC=CH / C=N—N structure]	3½
[structure]	2	[HN—C—N benzimidazole structure]	7
[structure]	3	[—C—O—N benzoxazole structure]	7
[structure]	4	[—C=N / HC=N quinazoline structure]	9
[structure]	6	[O=C—N / —N—C=O structure]	11
[naphthalene structure]	6	[H-N / N-C double ring structure]	10
[structure]	10	[—N—C=O / C=O—N— pyromellitimide structure]	12
[anthracene structure]	14	[—N=C / N—C=N— structure]	10
—O—C—⟨O⟩—C—O— (with =O groups)	1¼	[—C=N—O—N=C— structure]	15
CORRECTIONS DUE TO DISPROPORTIONING (H-SHIFT): **GROUPS DIRECTLY CONNECTED TO AROMATIC NUCLEUS**		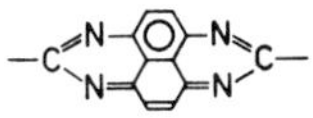	
>CH₂ and >CH—CH₂—	−1		
—CH₃	−1½		
>C(CH₃)₂	−3		
—CH(CH₃)₂	−4		
*) NO HALOGEN GROUPS INCLUDED N.B. SYSTEM IS NOT VALID FOR HALOGEN-CONTAINING POLYMERS			

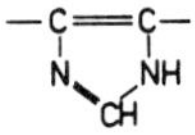

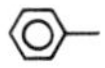

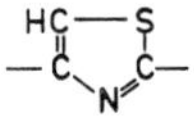

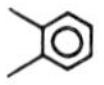

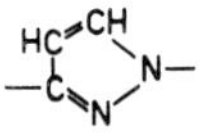

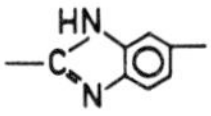

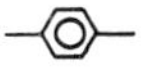

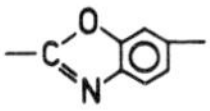

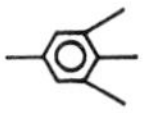

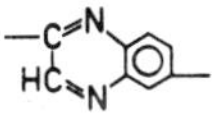

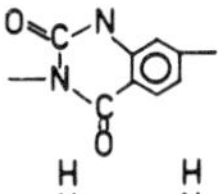

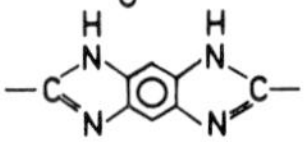

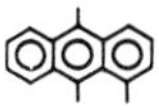

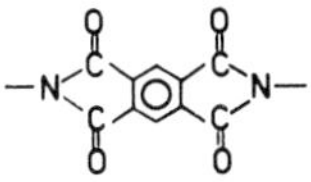

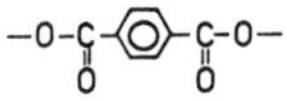

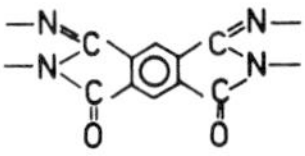

We want to emphasize that the char-forming tendency is a statistical concept! The fact that the phenyl group has a **CFT** value of 1 C equivalent means that on the average only one out of six phenyl groups in the polymer goes into the residue (five going into the tar and gas). If the benzene ring contains four side groups (i.e. if four hydrogen atoms are substituted), all the rings land in the residue, etc.

By means of the group contributions to the char-forming tendency the char residue on

464

pyrolysis can be estimated:

$$CR = \frac{\sum(CFT)_i}{M} \times 1200$$

where CR is expressed as a (weight) percentage. The average deviation from the experimental values for the polymers investigated is 3.5%. Fig. 21.3 shows the CR values experimentally found and calculated by means of table 21.2. The agreement is satisfactory.

Example 21.1

Estimate the char residue on pyrolysis of polycarbonate.

Solution. The structural unit of polycarbonate is:

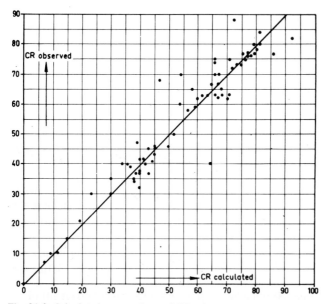

The molecular weignt per unit is 254.3.
The following group contributions may be taken from table 21.2:

groups	CFT
2 (benzene ring)	8
$-C(CH_3)_2-$	-3
$-O-$	0
$-O-CO-$	$\underline{0}$
	5

Fig. 21.3. Calculated versus observed CR-values.

So the char residue will amount to 5 × 12 = 60 g per structural unit. This is

60 × 100/254.3 = 24%

This is in agreement with the experimental value (24%).

Kinetics of thermal degradation

Random thermal degradation can usually be described as a first-order reaction (loss of weight as a parameter) if the decomposition products are volatile. For the mathematical treatment we refer to Van Krevelen et al. (1951), Reich (1963, 1967) and Broido (1969).

Chain depolymerization has been extensively studied (Simha and Wall, 1952). The two factors that are important for the course of the depolymerization are:
(1) the reactivity of depropagating radical and
(2) the availability of a reactive hydrogen atom for chain transfer.

All polymers containing α-hydrogens (such as polyacrylates, polyolefins, etc.) give poor yields of monomer; conversely, polymethacrylates and p-α-methylstyrenes give high yields of monomer, due to the blocking of chain transfer by the α-methyl group. Poly(tetrafluoroethylene) gives high yields of monomer because the strong C–F bonds are resistant to transfer reactions.

Also this type of degradation can be described by an overall quasi-first-order reaction, but the kinetic scheme may be complicated. Besides the rate constant two other parameters can be obtained by kinetic analysis:

$$\text{the transfer constant} = k_{tr} = \frac{\text{probability of transfer}}{\text{probability of initiation}}$$

$$\text{the kinetic chain length} = \Lambda_{kin} = \frac{\text{probability of propagation}}{\text{probability of (termination + transfer)}}$$

For polyethylene $\Lambda_{kin} \approx 0$ (no monomer produced); for poly(methyl methacrylate) $\Lambda_{kin} \approx 200$ (nearly 100% monomer produced).

BIBLIOGRAPHY, CHAPTER 21

General references

Behr, E., "Hochtemperaturbeständige Kunststoffe", Carl Hanser Verlag, Munich, 1969.
Conley, R.T. (Ed.), "Thermal Stability of Polymers", M. Dekker, New York, 1970.
Grassie, N., "Chemistry of High Polymer Degradation Processes", Interscience, New York, 1956.
Korshak, V.V., "The Chemical Structure and Thermal Characteristics of Polymers", (Translation), Israel Program for Scientific Translations, Jerusalem, 1971.
Madorsky, S.L. and Straus, S., "High Temperature Resistance and Thermal Degradation of Polymers", S.C.I. Monograph 13 (1961) 60–74.
Madorsky, S.L., "Thermal Degradation of Organic Polymers", Interscience, New York, 1964.
Voigt, J., "Die Stabilisierung der Kunststoffe gegen Licht und Wärme", Springer, Berlin, 1966.

Special references

Broido, A., J. Polymer Sci. A2, 7 (1969) 1761.

Korshak, V.V. and Vinogradova, S.V., Russian Chemical Series 37 (1968) 11.

Madorsky, S.L. and Straus, S., J. Research Natl. Bur. Standards 53 (1954) 361; 55 (1955) 223; 63A (1959) 261.

Reich, L., Makromol. Chem. 105 (1967) 223.

Reich, L. and Levi, D.W., Makromol. Chem. 66 (1963) 102.

Simha, R. and Wall, L.A., J. Phys. Chem. 56 (1952) 707.

Van Krevelen, D.W., "Coal", Ch. 25 and 26, Elsevier, Amsterdam, 1962.

Van Krevelen, D.W., Polymer 16 (1975) 615.

Van Krevelen, D.W., Van Heerden, C. and Huntjens, F.J., Fuel 30 (1951) 253.

Wolfs, P.M.J., Thesis, Delft University of Technology, 1959.

Wolfs, P.M.J., Van Krevelen, D.W. and Waterman, H.I., Brennstoff Chemie 40 (1959) 155, 189, 215, 241, 314, 342, 371; Fuel 39 (1960) 25.

CHAPTER 22

CHEMICAL DEGRADATION OF POLYMERS

Degradation of polymers by chemical reactions is a typical constitutive property. No methods of prediction exist in this field.

The rate of chemical degradation can often be measured by means of physical quantities, e.g. stress relaxation measurements.

Introduction

A polymer may be degraded by chemical changes due to reaction with components in the environment. The most important of these degrading reagents is oxygen. Oxidation may be induced and accelerated by radiation (photooxidation) or by thermal energy (thermal oxidation).

Besides the oxidative degradation, also other forms of chemical degradation play a part, the most important of which is the hydrolytic degradation.

Degradation under the influence of light

Of the electromagnetic energy emitted by the sun only a small portion reaches the earth's surface, namely, rays with a wavelength above 290 nm. X rays are absorbed in the outermost part of the atmosphere and UV rays with wavelengths up to 290 nm in the ozone atmosphere. Although the total intensity is subject to wide variations according to geographical and atmospheric conditions, the overall composition of sunlight is practically constant.

In photochemical degradation the energy of activation is supplied by sunlight. Most ordinary chemical reactions involve energies of activation between 60 and 270 kJ/mol. This is energetically equivalent to radiation of wavelengths between 1900 and 440 nm. The energies required to break single covalent bonds range, with few exceptions, from 165 to 420 kJ/mol, which corresponds to radiation of wavelengths from 710 to 290 nm (see fig. 22.1). This means that the radiation in the near ultraviolet region (300–400 nm) is sufficiently energetic to break most single covalent bonds, except strong bonds such as C–H and O–H.

Only the part of the radiation which is actually absorbed by the material can become chemically active. Most pure, organic synthetic polymers (polyethylene, polypropylene, poly(vinyl chloride), polystyrene, etc.) do not absorb at wavelengths longer than 300 nm owing to their ideal structure, and hence should not be affected by sunlight. However, these polymers often do degrade when subjected to sunlight and this has been attributed to the presence of small amounts of impurities or structural defects, which absorb light

468

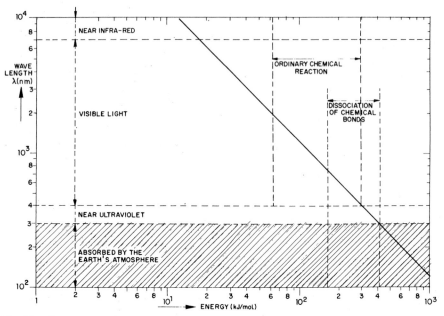

Fig. 22.1. Energy equivalence of light waves.

and initiate the degradation. Much of the absorbed light energy is usually dissipated by either radiationless processes (rotations and vibrations) or by secondary emission (fluorescence).

Although the exact nature of the impurities or structural defects responsible for the photosensitivity is not known with certainty, it is generally accepted that these impurities are various types of carbonyl groups (ketones, aldehydes) and also peroxides. The primary chain rupture or radical formation in the various photochemical processes is often followed by embrittlement due to cross-linking, but secondary reactions, especially in the presence of oxygen, cause further degradation of the polymer. Mechanical properties, such as tensile strength, elongation and impact strength, may deteriorate drastically. Coloured degradation products are often developed. Surface crazing can also be a sign of UV-induced degradation.

Some polymers show discoloration as well as reduction of the mechanical properties (e.g. aromatic polyesters, aromatic polyamides, polycarbonate, polyurethanes, poly-(phenylene oxide), polysulphone), others show only a deterioration of the mechanical properties (polypropylene, cotton) or mainly yellowing (wool, poly(vinyl chloride)). This degradation may be less pronounced when an ultraviolet absorber is incorporated into the polymer. The role of the UV-absorbers (usually o-hydroxybenzophenones or o-hydroxyphenylbenzotriazoles) is to absorb the radiation in the 300–400 nm region and dissipate the energy in a manner harmless to the material to be protected. A current development in the UV-protection of polymers is the use of additives (e.g. nickel chelates) which, by a transfer of excitation energy, are capable of quenching electronically excited states of impurities (e.g. carbonyl groups) present in the polymer (e.g. polypropylene).

Oxidative degradation

At normal temperature polymers generally react so slowly with oxygen that the oxidation only becomes apparent after a long time. For instance, if polystyrene is stored in air in the dark for a few years, the UV spectrum does not change perceptibly. On the other hand, if the same polymer is irradiated by UV light under similar conditions for 12 days, there appear strong bands in the spectrum. The same applies to other polymers such as polyethylene and natural rubber.

Therefore, in essence the problem is not the oxidizability as such, but the synergistic action of factors like electromagnetic radiation and thermal energy on the oxidation. By the action of these factors on the polymer free radicals are formed, which together with oxygen initiate a chain reaction. Hence most oxidation reactions are of an autocatalytic nature.

If the oxidation is induced by light, the phenomenon is called photooxidation. If the oxidation is induced by purely thermal factors, the term thermal oxidation is used.

Photooxidation

The most thoroughly investigated oxidative degradation is that of natural rubber. In 1943 Farmer and Sundralingham found that in the photochemical oxidation of this polymer a hydroperoxide is formed, the number of double bonds in the chain remaining constant. The oxygen was found to act on an activated methylene group, not on a double bond, as had previously been assumed.

Later the mechanism of the rubber oxidation was studied extensively by Bolland and coworkers (1946–1950), who mainly used model substances. In his first publication Bolland proposed the following mechanism for the propagation reaction:

$$R^\cdot + O_2 \rightarrow ROO^\cdot \tag{a}$$

$$ROO^\cdot + RH \rightarrow ROOH + R^\cdot \tag{b}$$

where RH is the olefin, $R^\cdot$ a radical obtained by abstraction of hydrogen in the allyl position, and $ROO^\cdot$ the peroxy radical obtained by addition of oxygen to this radical. According to Bolland the reaction chains are terminated by the combination of allyl and peroxy radicals, and the length of the main reaction chains is of the order of 50–100. This reaction could be initiated by any type of reaction in which free radicals are formed. The autocatalytic nature of the reaction is due to the decomposition of the hydroperoxides:

$$ROOH \overset{h\nu}{\rightarrow} RO^\cdot + {}^\cdot OH \tag{c}$$

The hydroperoxides also give rise to secondary reactions in which coloured resinous products are formed (via carbonyl compounds).

Stabilization to photooxidation can be achieved by the use of suitable UV absorbers in combination (synergistic action) with antioxidants (AH) which are capable of preventing reactions (a) and (b):

$$R^\cdot + AH \rightarrow RH + A^\cdot \tag{d}$$

$$ROO^\cdot + AH \rightarrow ROOH + A^\cdot \tag{e}$$

$$A^\cdot \rightarrow \text{inactive products} . \tag{f}$$

Thermal oxidation

Especially above room temperature many polymers degrade in an air atmosphere by oxidation which is not light-induced (heat ageing). A number of polymers already show a deterioration of the mechanical properties after heating for some days at about 100°C and even at lower temperatures (e.g. polyethylene, polypropylene, polyformaldehyde and poly(ethylene sulphide)).

The rate of oxidation can be determined by measuring volumetrically the oxygen uptake at a certain temperature. Such measurements have shown that the oxidation at 140°C of low-density polyethylene increases exponentially after an induction period of two hours. It can be concluded from this result that the thermal oxidation, like photo-oxidation, is caused by autoxidation, the difference merely being that the radical formation from the hydroperoxide is now activated by heat.

The primary reaction can be a direct reaction with oxygen

$$RH + O_2 \rightarrow R^{\cdot} + {}^{\cdot}OOH . \tag{g}$$

The thermal oxidation can be inhibited by antioxidants as before (eqs. (d), (e), (f)).

Effects of oxidative degradation

The principal effects of oxidative degradation of polymers are the decay of good mechanical properties (strength, elongation, resilience, etc.) and discoloration (mainly yellowing).

The behaviour of polymers may vary widely. A polymer may be resistant to mechanical decay but not to colour decay, or the reverse. Often the two go together. Table 22.1 gives a survey of these effects for the different polymer families in the case of photo-degradation.

Stabilization

The oxidative degradation of a polymer can be retarded or even practically prevented by addition of stabilizers. The following types of stabilizers may be used:

a. *UV absorbers*

A good UV absorber absorbs much UV light but no visible light. It should dissipate the absorbed energy in a harmless manner by transforming the energy into heat. Other requirements are: compatibility with the polymer, nonvolatility, light fastness, heat stability and, for textiles, also resistance to washing and dry cleaning.

The optimum effect of a UV absorber in a polymer film can be calculated from the absorbancy of the UV absorber and the thickness of the film. Such calculations show that the effect of UV absorbers is small in thin films and in yarns.

b. *Antioxidants*

The degradation of polymers is mostly promoted by autoxidation. The propagation of autoxidation can be inhibited by antioxidants (e.g. hindered phenols and amines).

c. *Quenchers*

A quencher induces harmless dissipation of the energy of photoexcited states. The only quenchers applied in the polymer field are nickel compounds in the case of polyolefins.

TABLE 22.1

Photodegradation of polymers

Polymer	Mechanical properties	Discoloration (yellowing)
Poly(methyl methacrylate)	0	0
Polyacrylonitrile	0	0
Cotton	–	+
Rayon	–	–
Polyoxymethylene	–	–
Polyethylene	– –	0
Poly(vinyl chloride)	0	– –
Qiana	– –	–
Terlenka	– –	–
Nylon 6	–	– –
Polystyrene	–	– –
Polypropylene	– – – –	0
Polycarbonate	– –	– –
Wool	–	– – –
Polyurethanes	–	– – –
Polysulphone	– – –	– – – –
Poly(2,6-dimethylphenylene oxide)	– – –	– – – –
Poly(2,6-diphenylphenylene oxide)	– – –	– – – –

Meaning of symbols: + = improvement   – = slight
                     0 = no change   – – = moderate
                                       – – – = strong } deterioration
                                       – – – – = very strong

Stress relaxation as a measure of chemical degradation

Stress relaxation occurs when a molecular chain carrying a load breaks. This occurs, e.g., during the oxidation of rubbers. When a stretched chain segment breaks, it returns to a relaxed state. Only stretched chains carry the load, and a load on a broken chain in a network cannot be shifted to other chains. It may be assumed that the rate at which stretched network chains are broken is proportional to the total number of chains (n) carrying the load:

$$-\frac{dn}{dt} = kn \qquad (22.1)$$

From the theory of rubber elasticity one can then derive in a simple way that:

$$\frac{\sigma}{\sigma_0} = \frac{\sigma(t)}{\sigma_0} = e^{-kt} \qquad (22.2)$$

This expression is of the same shape as that of stress relaxation of viscoelastic materials (Chapter 13). By analogy $1/k$ is called the "relaxation time" (Θ). Since chemical reactions normally satisfy an Arrhenius type of equation in their temperature dependence, the variation of relaxation time with temperature may be expressed as follows:

$$\ln \Theta = \ln \frac{1}{k} = \ln A + \frac{E_{act}}{RT} \tag{22.3}$$

where E_{act} is the activation energy of the chemical reaction. A typical value of E_{act} is 125 kJ/mol for the oxidative degradation of rubbers.

Hydrolytic degradation

Hydrolytic degradation plays a part if hydrolysis is the potential key reaction in the breaking of bonds, as in polyesters and polycarbonates. Attack by water may be rapid if the temperature is sufficiently high; attack by acids depends on acid strength and temperature. Degradation under the influence of basic substances depends very much on the penetration of the agent; ammonia and amines may cause much greater degradation than substances like caustic soda, which mainly attack the surface. The amorphous regions are attacked first and the most rapidly; but crystalline regions are not free from attack.

BIBLIOGRAPHY, CHAPTER 22

General references

Conley, R.T., (Ed.), "Thermal Stability of Polymers", M. Dekker, New York, 1970.
Grassie, N., "Chemistry of High Polymer Degradation Processes", Interscience, New York, 1956.
Jellinek, H.H.T., "Degradation of Vinyl Polymers", Academic Press, New York, 1955.
Neimann, M.B. (Ed.), "Aging and Stabilization of Polymers", Consultants Bureau, New York, 1965.
Reich, L. and Stivala, S.S., "Autoxidation of Hydrocarbons and Polymers", M. Dekker, New York, 1969.
Reich, L. and Stivala, S.S., "Elements of Polymer Degradation", McGraw-Hill, New York, 1971.
Scott, G., "Atmospheric Oxidation and Antioxidants", Elsevier, Amsterdam, 1965.

Special references

Bergen, R.L., S.P.E. Journal 20 (1964) 630.
Bolland, J.L., Proc. Roy. Soc. (London) A 186 (1946) 218.
Bolland, J.L. et al., Trans. Faraday Soc. 42 (1946) 236, 244; 43 (1947) 201; 44 (1948) 669; 45 (1949) 93; 46 (1950) 358.
Farmer, E.H. and Sundralingham, A., J. Chem. Soc. (1943) 125.
Hagan, R.S. and Thomas, J.R., "Plastic Part Properties and their Relationship to End-use Performance", 67th Annual Meeting ASTM, June 21–26, 1964.

PART VI

POLYMER PROPERTIES AS AN INTEGRAL CONCEPT

CHAPTER 23

INTRINSIC PROPERTIES IN RETROSPECT

Introduction

In the preceding 22 chapters all important intrinsic properties have been discussed. They depend in essence on two really fundamental characteristics of polymers (Chapter 2): the chemical structure of their repeating units and their molecular-weight-distribution pattern. The latter is of major importance for those cases where the molecular translational mobility is developed, i.e. for polymer properties in melts and solutions.

We have shown that the molecular structure is reflected in all the properties; ample use has been made of the empirical fact that many intrinsic quantities or combinations of

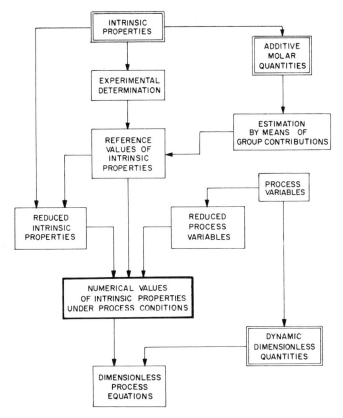

Fig. 23.1. Relationships of intrinsic properties.

476

quantities, if related to the structural molar unit, have additive properties, so that these quantities can be estimated in a simple manner from empirically derived group contributions or increments.

We repeat what has been said in Chapter 1: *reliable* experimental data are always to be preferred to values obtained by an estimation method. But in many cases they are not available; then estimation methods are of great value.

There is one additional virtue of our estimation method: if a predicted value shows a serious discrepancy with a measured one, there possibly is a theoretical problem. In this way the semi-empirical estimation method may also give incentives to theoretical scientists.

The philosophy of this book is clearly represented in fig. 23.1. Of practical significance are the numerical values of intrinsic properties under the prescribed experimental conditions. For this purpose one needs *reference values* under standard conditions and their *dependence* on certain variables, such as time, temperature, pressure and concentration.

The reference values may be estimated by means of additive molar quantities; often the values at 298 K and atmospheric pressure are used as such. Division of an intrinsic quantity by its reference value gives the reduced, dimensionless, intrinsic quantity.

The reduced intrinsic quantities in turn are functions of dimensionless process variables. If these functional correlations are known, every value of the required intrinsic quantity under arbitrary experimental conditions can be estimated. In this procedure the systems of dynamic dimensionless quantities may be of great help.

Finally the process equations may be formulated in dimensionless form.

A. REFERENCE VALUES OF INTRINSIC PROPERTIES EXPRESSED AS A FUNCTION OF ADDITIVE QUANTITIES

In retrospect we shall give a summary of all additive relationships that have been found. We use the sequence followed in this book.

1. Volumetric and calorimetric intrinsic properties (Chapters 4 and 5)

specific volume $\qquad v = \dfrac{V}{M}$

density $\qquad \rho = \dfrac{M}{V}$

specific expansivity $\qquad e = \dfrac{E}{M}$

thermal expansion coefficient $\qquad \alpha = \dfrac{E}{V}$

specific heat $\qquad c_p = \dfrac{C_p}{M}$

specific entropy of fusion $\qquad \Delta s_m = \dfrac{\Delta S_m}{M}$

2. Other thermophysical properties (Chapters 6–9)

crystalline melting temperature $\qquad T_m = \dfrac{Y_m}{M}$

glass transition temperature $\qquad T_g = \dfrac{Y_g}{M}$

cohesive energy density $\qquad e_{coh} = \dfrac{E_{coh}}{V}$

solubility parameter $\qquad \delta = \dfrac{F}{V}$

surface tension $\qquad \gamma = \left(\dfrac{P_S}{V}\right)^4$

unperturbed viscosity coefficient $\qquad K_\Theta \left(= \dfrac{[\eta]_\Theta}{M^{1/2}}\right) = \left(\dfrac{K}{M}\right)^2$

3. Optical and other electromagnetic properties (Chapters 10–12)

refraction index $\qquad n = \left[\dfrac{1 + 2\dfrac{R_{LL}}{V}}{1 - \dfrac{R_{LL}}{V}}\right]^{1/2} = 1 + \dfrac{R_{GD}}{V} = \dfrac{R_V}{M}$

specific refractive index increment $\qquad \dfrac{dn}{dc} = \dfrac{V}{M}\left(\dfrac{R_V}{M} - n_S\right)$

dielectric constant $\qquad \epsilon = \dfrac{1 + 2\dfrac{P_{LL}}{V}}{1 - \dfrac{P_{LL}}{V}} = \dfrac{P_V}{M}$

magnetic susceptibility $\qquad \chi = \dfrac{X}{M}$

4. Mechanical and rheological properties (Chapters 13–16)

longitudinal sound velocity $\qquad u_{long} = \left(\dfrac{U}{V}\right)^3 \left(\dfrac{3(1-\nu)}{1+\nu}\right)^{1/2}$

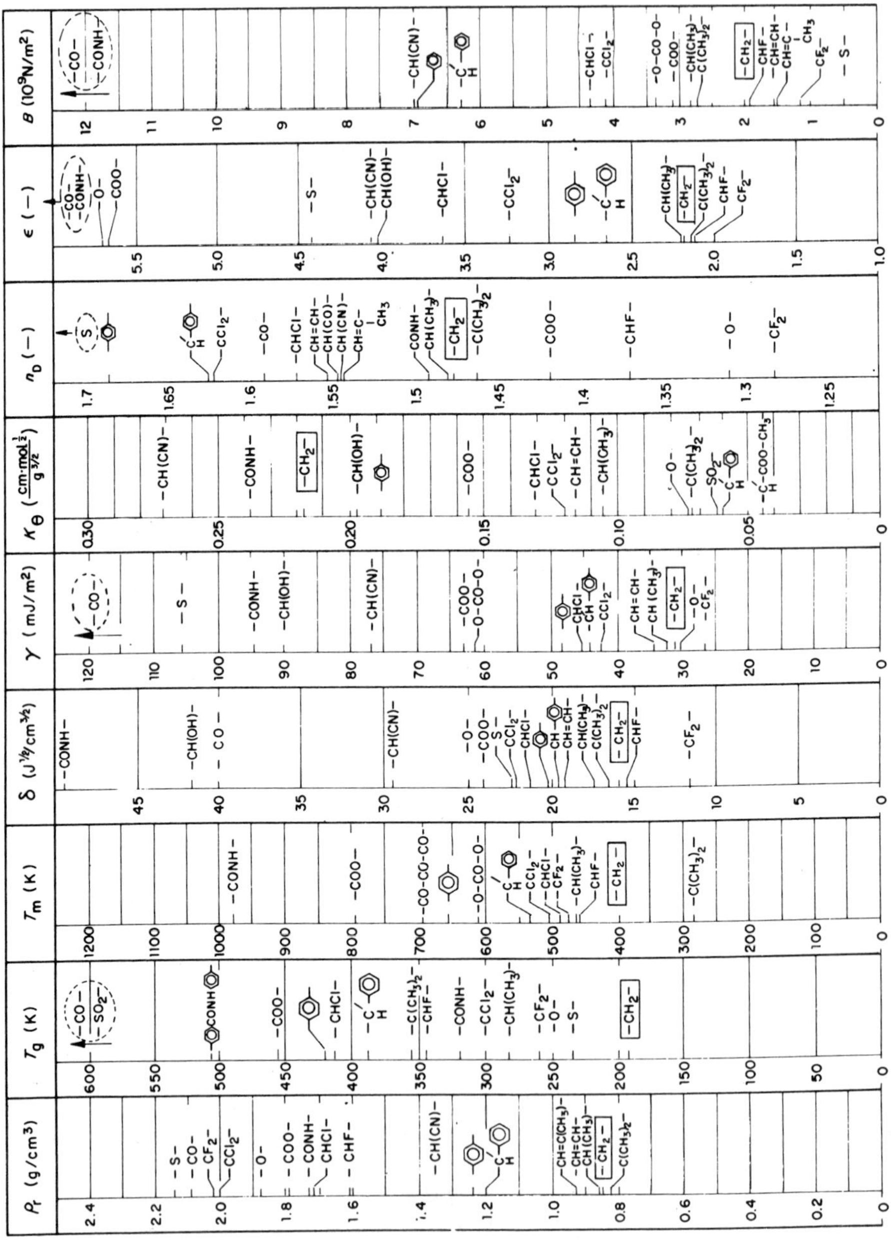

Fig. 23.2. Effect of structural groups on properties.

specific bulk modulus

$$\frac{B}{\rho} = \left(\frac{U}{V}\right)^6$$

activation energy of viscous flow

$$E_\eta(\infty) = \left(\frac{H_\eta}{M}\right)^3$$

5. Thermochemical properties (Chapters 20–22)

molar free enthalpy of formation

$$\Delta G_f^o = (A + BT)$$

carbon residue on pyrolysis (%)

$$CR = \left(\frac{CFT}{M}\right) \times 1200$$

In Part VII, Table VII, a comprehensive tabulation of numerical group contributions to the different additive quantities is given. The table contains the data needed for calculating the reference values of the intrinsic properties.

B. EFFECT OF STRUCTURAL GROUPS ON PROPERTIES

The degree to which properties are influenced by characteristic groups can best be assessed as follows. All groups can be so combined as to form exclusively bivalent units, e.g.

$[-CH_2-]$,

$[-CH_3] + [\ \rangle CH-] = [-CH(CH_3)-]$,

$2[-Cl] + [\ \rangle C \langle\ ] = [-CCl_2-]$,   etc.

From the additive quantities of these bivalent groups one can calculate the properties of a *hypothetical* polymer entirely consisting of these bivalent groups. In this way one finds the surface tension, solubility parameter, refractive index, etc., of this hypothetical polymer and consequently, of the constituting bivalent group. Thus a clear numerical insight is gained into the quantitative influence of the group on the properties.

In fig. 23.2 this has been done for a number of important quantities.

With some audacity one may say that fig. 23.2 reflects the "spectra" of the properties; by way of the additive quantities the composite "colour" of a substance (the "average value") is as it were split up into spectral lines, the system of additive quantities functioning as prism or grating.

C. DEPENDENCE OF INTRINSIC PROPERTIES ON PROCESS VARIABLES

1. Dimensionless expressions for temperature dependence

Every intrinsic quantity can be made dimensionless by dividing it by its value in the

480

reference state. The reduced quantity obtained in this way can be expressed as a dimensionless function of a reduced temperature.

The temperature dependence of "non-activated" processes differs from that of "activated" processes. In the latter the temperature dependence is in essence determined by an activation energy which determines the probability of the process.

a. *Non-activated processes.* These are found in thermal expansion and related phenomena. The general expression has the following form:

$$\frac{A(T)}{A_R} = 1 + \frac{B}{A_R}(T - T_R)$$

A may be a volume, a specific heat, etc.; B is an expansion property. B/A_R usually is nearly constant. As an example, the molar volume in the glassy state was expressed (Chapter 4) as:

$$\frac{V_g(T)}{V_g(298)} = 1 + \frac{E_g}{V_g(298)}(T - 298) = 1 + 0.29 \times 10^{-3}(T - 298) = 0.914 + 0.29 \times 10^{-3}\, T$$

b. *Activated processes.* These are found in all rate phenomena. The general expression is:

$$\frac{A(T)}{A_R} = \exp\left[-\frac{E_{act}}{R}\left(\frac{1}{T} - \frac{1}{T_R}\right)\right]$$

The ratio E_{act}/R has the dimension of a temperature. Sometimes it is related to characteristic temperatures which play a part in the process. We have, for instance, seen that in the shift factor of relaxation processes (Chapter 13) the following correlation is valid:

$$\frac{E_{act}}{R} \approx \frac{T_m T_R}{T_m - T_R}$$

In the crystallization phenomena we have found (Chapter 19):

$$\frac{E_{act}}{R} \sim \frac{T_m^2}{T_m - T_g}$$

2. Dimensionless expressions for time dependence

Many reduced intrinsic quantities are correlated with a reduced time quantity; usually the expression can be written in the following form:

$$-\log\frac{A(t)}{A_R} = f(t/t_R)$$

The reference time may be an arbitrarily chosen time, but normally it is connected with the nature of the phenomenon observed. In these cases the reference time has a very specific meaning:

Phenomenon	Characteristic reference time	Chapter
relaxation phenomena ("natural" time)	$\dfrac{\eta}{G} (= \Theta)$	15
heat transfer	$\dfrac{L^2 c_p \rho}{\lambda}$	17
diffusion phenomena	$\dfrac{L^2}{D}$	18
crystallization	$\dfrac{1}{\upsilon N^{1/3}} (\approx t_{1/2}$	19
effluence	$\dfrac{\eta}{\Delta p}$	
sedimentation	$\dfrac{\eta}{g \rho L}$	
centrifugation	$\dfrac{\eta \rho}{\omega^2}$	
surface levelling	$\dfrac{\eta L}{\gamma}$	

The last-mentioned characteristic time plays a part in coating processes, e.g. formation of films and paint levelling (L is a characteristic length).

3. Dimensionless expressions for concentration dependence

In Chapters 9, 16 and 18 we have met expressions for the concentration dependence of intrinsic properties. They have the general form:

$$\frac{A(c)}{A_0} = f(Bc)$$

B in this case is a quantity with the dimension c^{-1}.

Again we may distinguish between non-activated and activated processes.

a. *Non-activated processes.* Here the expression has the form:

$$\boxed{\frac{A(c)}{A_0} = 1 + f(Bc) \approx 1 + Bc + ...}$$

We have seen (Chapter 16) that the Huggins equation for the viscosity of a dilute solution has this form; it can be expressed in the following way:

$$\frac{\eta_{red}}{[\eta]} = 1 + k_H [\eta] c$$

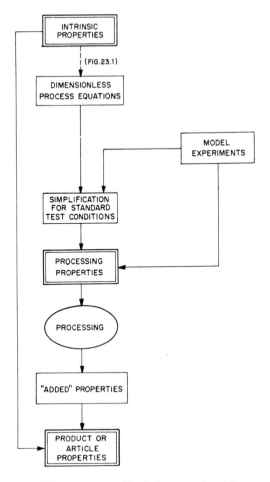

Fig. 23.3. Importance of intrinsic properties with respect to processing and product (article) properties.

Analogous equations have been found for the osmotic pressure, the diffusion coefficient and the sedimentation coefficient (Chapter 16).

b. *Activated processes,* i.e. phenomena that are controlled by an activation energy barrier. Here the equation takes the form:

$$\frac{A(c)}{A_0} = \exp(Bc)$$

We met this case in Chapter 18 for the penetration of vapours into polymers.

D. OUTLOOK

In fig. 23.1 the relevance of the intrinsic properties and their relations to process equations have been outlined.

In the following chapters (24–27) the most important process and product properties will be discussed along the lines sketched in Chapter 1.

Processing properties are mostly determined in specific standard tests; often they are the result of model experiments. In the scientific analysis of these model experiments the dimensionless process equations can be of considerable help.

By processing, the material receives "added" properties, desired as well as undesired ones. It is the combination of the intrinsic properties with the added properties which determines the product or article properties, often in a very complex and still obscure way.

Fig. 23.3 illustrates the interrelations between the different types of properties.

CHAPTER 24

PROCESSING PROPERTIES

Most of the common polymers are processed by a treatment in the molten state, followed by cooling. Dimensionless groups may be derived which control these processing steps.

Criteria of *extrudability, mouldability, spinnability* and *stretchability* as used in practice are described (melt index, spiral length, mouldability index, melt strength, ultimate thread length, etc.). These criteria are based on the dimensionless parameters (numerics) of the processes.

A. CLASSIFICATION OF PROCESSES

The aim of polymer processing is to convert the polymer – usually in the form of powder or granules – into a more useful form. Usually the change involved is largely physical, although in some conversion processes chemical reactions play a part.

The variety of conversion processes is very large.

One class of processes involves *simple extrusion*; by using different dies it is possible to make sheets, tubes, monofil, other special shapes and also plastic-coated wires.

Another class consists of *extrusion immediately followed by an additional phase.* This includes blow moulding, film blowing, quenched film forming, fibre spinning, and extrusion coating.

The third large class involves the processes of *moulding* (injection and compression moulding).

The fourth class is a miscellaneous collection of *shaping processes,* such as vacuum forming, calendering, rotation casting, and foaming.

As we have remarked in Chapter 1, the common features of all these processes may be summarized under four headings:
(a) mixing, melting and homogenization } (*transportation* and *conditioning*)
(b) transport and extrusion
(c) drawing and blowing (*forming* proper)
(d) cooling and finishing (*setting*)

The rheological conditions of these processing techniques are different. The shear rates, for instance, show enormous differences, as will be clear from the following survey (table 24.1)

TABLE 24.1

Processing conditions

Operation	Shear rate (s^{-1})
Calendering (rubber)	$<5.10^1$
Mixing rollers (rubber)	$5.10^1 - 5.10^2$
Banbury mixer (rubber)	$5.10^2 - 10^3$
Extrusion of pipes	$10 - 10^3$
Extrusion of film	$10 - 10^3$
Extrusion of cable	$10 - 10^3$
Extrusion of filaments	$10^3 - 10^5$
Injection moulding	$10^3 - 10^5$

Each processing technique has to fulfil certain requirements of economy. Often the most economic (i.e. the cheapest) method is the worst from the technological point of view. Commercial processing is always a compromise between the best quality and the lowest cost.

Three questions of particular importance claim attention:
1. the processability (and reprocessability) of the polymer as such
2. the controllability of the processing
3. the influence of the processing on the ultimate properties of the product.

Constancy of the processing conditions is essential for quality. This applies first of all to the uniformity and constancy of the starting material. Equally important, however, is the constancy of processing itself. To achieve quality control, the speed of the operations is a critical factor. The filling of dies, for instance, should take place rapidly. In the case of highly crystalline materials also the cooling should proceed rapidly, to prevent the formation of large spherulites. For glassy polymers, annealing is mostly beneficial (tension relaxation), for crystalline plastics it is mostly harmful (growth of secondary crystallites). The constancy of the *processing* should also·be analysed by careful *checking* of the product, which can be done by *control tests.* Measurements of the strength perpendicular and parallel to the direction of flow are essential to evaluate the *orientation sensitivity* of a material.

In this chapter we shall discuss some important unit operations as far as the processing properties are concerned, viz. extrusion, injection moulding, spinning and stretching.

B. SOME IMPORTANT PROCESSING PROPERTIES

EXTRUDABILITY

In the extrusion process a polymer melt is *continuously* forced through a die shaped to give the final object after cooling. In the extruder proper the polymer is propelled along a screw through sections of high temperature and pressure where it is compacted and melted. A wide variety of shapes can be made by extrusion: rods, tubes, hoses, sheets, films and filaments.

Shear viscosity (η) is the most important intrinsic property determining extrudability. Since the apparent viscosity is highly dependent on temperature and shear stress (hence on pressure gradient), these variables, together with the extruder geometry, determine the output of the extruder.

According to the considerations in Chapter 3 the most important dimensionless quantities in extrusion will be

$$\frac{\Delta p d}{\eta v}, \quad \frac{d}{L} \text{ and } \frac{\eta}{\eta_0}$$

where Δp is the pressure drop, v is the average linear velocity of the melt (directly connected with the flow rate), d and L are characteristic diameter and length dimensions, η is the shear viscosity and η_0 the viscosity at zero shear rate.

In order to assess the extrudability of a polymer two practical tests are applied: the melt flow index test and the flow rate test at various pressures (and temperatures).

Melt flow index (MI)

The melt (flow) index has become a widely recognized criterion in the appraisal of extrudability of thermoplastic materials, especially polyolefins. It is standardized as the weight of polymer (polyolefin) extruded in 10 minutes at a constant temperature (190°C) through a tubular die of specified diameter (0.0825 in. = 2.2 mm) when a standard weight (2160 g) is placed on the driving piston (ASTM D 1238).

Although commonly used, the melt flow index is not beyond criticism.

First, the rate of shear, which is not linear with the shearing stress due to the non-Newtonian behaviour, varies with the different types of polymer. The processability of different polymers with an equal value of the MI may therefore differ widely. Furthermore the standard temperature (190°C) was chosen for polyethylenes; for other thermoplastics it is often less suitable. Finally, the deformation of the polymer melt under the given stress is also dependent on time, and in the measurements of the melt index no corrections are allowed for entrance and exit abnormalities in the flow behaviour. The corrections would be expected to vary for polymers of different flow characteristics. The length–diameter ratio of the melt indexer is too small to obtain a uniform flow pattern.

Nevertheless, due to its relative simplicity the melt flow index is one of the most popular parameters in the plastics industry, especially for polyethylenes. Here the melt index is a good indicator of the most suitable (end) use. Table 24.2 gives some data.

A melt flow index of 1.0 corresponds to a melt viscosity of about 1.5×10^{-4} N· s/m^2 (= 1.5×10^5 poises).

Busse (1967) gives the following relationship between melt flow index and inherent viscosity:

$$(\text{MI}) \sim \eta_{\text{inh}}^{-4.9} \tag{24.1}$$

From this it follows that:

$$(MI) \sim [\eta]^{-4.9} \sim (\overline{M}_v)^{-3.5} \sim \eta_0^{-1} \tag{24.2}$$

where η_0 is the melt viscosity at zero shear rate.

Boenig (1966) gives a similar correlation (for polyethylenes) between melt index and melt viscosity (at 190°C):

$$\log (MI) = const - \log \eta_0 \tag{24.3}$$

Melt flow rate diagram

A more informative test is the measurement of the melt flow rate at varying temperature and pressure (fig. 24.1)

The results of this test may be generalized by plotting $\dfrac{32}{\pi d^3} \Phi \eta_0 \ (= \dot{\gamma}\eta_0)$ versus $\dfrac{\Delta p}{4L/d}$ $(= \tau)$ (fig. 24.2, data from Vinogradov and Malkin (1966)), where Φ is the volume flow rate, d the diameter of the circular capillary, L its length, $\dot{\gamma}$ the shear rate and τ the shear stress.

From this figure the influence of pressure and geometry of the apparatus on the flow rate can be derived if the $\eta_0 - T$ relationship is known.

Die swell

The phenomenon of post-extrusion swelling or "ballooning" has been discussed in Chapter 15. It is related to the so-called Barus effect (according to which the diameter of polymer extrudates is not equal to the capillary diameter when the melt is forced through an orifice). All materials with any degree of melt elasticity display this effect. The origin of the effect is related to the elasto-viscous nature of polymer melts.

Die swell is dependent upon the L/d ratio of the die. The phenomenon is a limiting factor in the drive to reduce moulding cycles, since the conditions which lead to excess

TABLE 24.2

Melt flow index values

Unit process	Product	Melt flow index required
Extrusion	Pipes	<0.1
	Sheets, bottles	} 0.1–0.5
	Thin tubes	
	Wire, cable	0.1–1
	Thin sheets	} 0.5–1
	Monofilaments (rope)	
	Multifilaments	≈1
	Bottles (high glass)	1–2
	Film	9–15
Injection Moulding	Moulded articles	1–2
	Thin-walled articles	3–6
Coating	Coated paper	9–15
Vacuum Forming	Articles	0.2–0.5

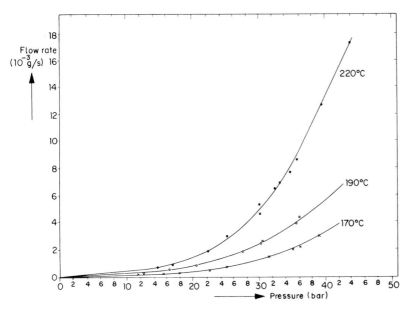

Fig. 24.1. Melt flow rate of polypropylene at different temperatures. Capillary d = 1.05 mm, L/d ratio = 4.75 (after Vinogradov and Malkin, 1966).

swelling lead also to quality deficiencies in appearance, form and properties of the extrudate.

In order to control the swelling the temperature of the melt can be increased, which causes a decrease in relaxation time. A long tapered die has also been found to reduce post-swelling.

On the basis of the melt viscosity and viscoelasticity discussed in Chapter 15 the amount of die swell under processing conditions can be estimated.

MOULDABILITY

During moulding a polymer melt is *discontinuously* extruded and immediately cooled in a mould of the desired shape.

Mouldability depends on the polymer and the process conditions, of which the rheological and thermal properties of the polymer as well as the geometry and the temperature and pressure conditions of the (test) mould are the most important.

Dimensional analysis (see Chapter 3) shows that the following dimensionless quantities must be expected to determine the process:

$$\frac{\Delta p d}{\eta \upsilon}, \ \frac{c_p \rho \upsilon d}{\lambda} \left(= \frac{\Delta H}{\Delta T} \frac{\rho \upsilon d}{\lambda} \right), \ \frac{L}{d} \text{ and } \frac{\eta}{\eta_0}$$

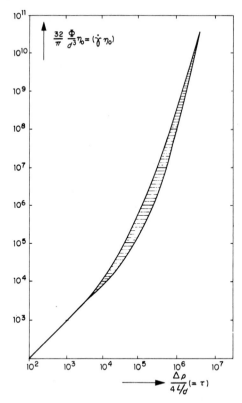

Fig. 24.2. Generalized melt flow rate diagram for commercial polymers (after Vinogradov and Malkin, 1966).

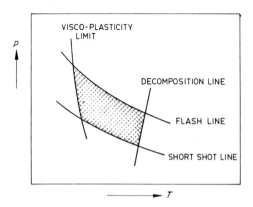

Fig. 24.3. Moulding area diagram.

where λ is the thermal conductivity and ΔH the change in heat content over a temperature change ΔT.

A well-known type of (purely empirical) processability characteristic is the *moulding area diagram* (fig. 24.3).

In the moulding area diagram the limits of pressure and temperature are indicated for the processing of a defined polymer in a given moulding press. The maximum temperature is determined by (visible) decomposition, the lower temperature limits by the development of too high viscosity and melt elasticity. The higher pressure limits are given by the start of "flashing": the polymer is then pressed through the clearance between the parts of the mould; the lower pressure limits are determined by "short shots", incompletely filling the mould.

It is clear that this diagram as such gives very little information of a general nature and is completely dependent on the accidental combination of material, machine and die.

Therefore other criteria have been developed which are of a more general value and are based on the intrinsic polymer properties and the processing variables.

Spiral flow length

A widely used test for mouldability evaluation is the *spiral flow test* (fig. 24.4). In this test the mould has the form of a spiral; the polymer melt flows into this mould under pressure and freezes in the spiral, the length of the polymer spiral being the test result. Mould geometry, temperature and pressure are standardized.

Holmes et al. (1966) made an engineering analysis of the test and found that the ultimate length of the spiral is a function of two groups of variables, one describing the process conditions $(\Delta p d^2/\Delta T)$, the other being representative of the polymer's rheological and thermal properties $(\rho\Delta H/\lambda\eta)$.

The following dimensionless relationship was obtained:

$$\left(\frac{L}{d}\right)^2 = C\left(\frac{\Delta p d^2}{\Delta T}\right)\left(\frac{\rho\Delta H}{\lambda\eta}\right) = C\left(\frac{\Delta p d}{\eta\upsilon}\right)\left(\frac{\Delta H}{\Delta T}\frac{\rho\upsilon d}{\lambda}\right) \tag{24.4}$$

In this equation

L = spiral length
d = effective diameter, characteristic of the channel cross section
ΔT = temperature difference between melt and channel wall
Δp = pressure drop
ρ = density of the solid polymer
λ = heat conductivity of the solid polymer
η = viscosity of the melt
ΔH = enthalpy difference between melt and solid

The constant C in equation (24.4) is determined by the geometry of the cross section. Equation (24.4) indeed contains the product of the dimensionless quantities predicted (Chapter 3).

492

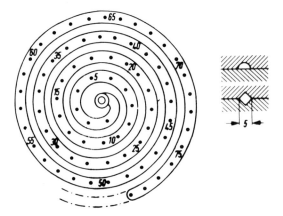

Fig. 24.4. The spiral flow test. The inlet cone is in the middle of the spiral.

In their analysis Holmes et al. demonstrated that the spiral length is limited by heat transfer (see fig. 24.5). The fluid entering the cavity solidifies upon contact with the wall, resulting in a reduced cross section for flow. This freezing on the wall continues until the solid layers meet in the centre of the channel, stopping the flow. In the tip of the spiral a core of liquid is left which freezes after the flow has stopped. This core solidifies stress-free and is optically isotropic, whereas the rest of the spiral solidifies under stress and is birefringent.

If during the experiment the plunger is withdrawn, eliminating the pressure difference before the heat transfer has resulted in flow stoppage, the spiral length becomes shorter. By varying the "plunger forward time" Holmes et al. were able to determine the time necessary to *just* obtain the maximum value of L; this time was called *freeze-off time* (t_f). The following approximate relation was found:

$$t_f \approx C' \left(\frac{\Delta H}{\Delta T}\right)\frac{\rho d^2}{\lambda} = f\ \left(\frac{T_{\text{solidif}} - T_{\text{mould}}}{T - T_{\text{mould}}}\right) \tag{24.5}$$

In this equation pressure and viscosity do not appear because they are factors related to the flow but not to the heat transfer. This analysis clearly shows the significance of dimensionless quantities to polymer processing.

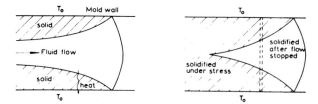

Fig. 24.5. Flow and solidification in mold channel.

Mouldability index

Another criterion of mouldability is the *mouldability index* (α_{STV}) developed by Weir (1963). (The index STV stands for shear–temperature–viscosity.)

It is defined as follows:

$$\alpha_{STV} = \frac{10^9}{\eta_0} \frac{\dfrac{\partial \ln \eta}{\partial \ln \dot{\gamma}}}{\dfrac{\partial \ln \eta}{\partial (1/T)}} \approx \frac{10^9}{\eta_0} \frac{|(n-1)|}{E_\eta/R} \quad (m^2/N \cdot s \cdot K) \tag{24.6}$$

where
- η_0 = apparent melt viscosity at low shear rates ($\approx 10 \; s^{-1}$)
- $\dot{\gamma}$ = shear rate
- n = exponent in the power law expression for non-Newtonian viscosity (see Ch. 15)
- E_η = activation energy of viscous flow (see Ch. 15)

Weir et al. (1963) have shown that for a series of polypropylenes there is a significant relation between α_{STV} and the spiral length (in the spiral flow test).

They also demonstrated that minimum cycle times are obtained at α_{STV}-values between 2 and 2.5. Boundary temperatures are found at $\alpha_{STV} \approx 2$ for "short shot" and at $\alpha_{STV} \approx 4.5$ for flashing (fig. 24.6).

Consequently, evaluation and selection of polymers is possible by determining the α_{STV} vs T relation from the $\eta = f(\dot{\gamma}, T, M)$ relationship (see Chapter 15). Then the working constraints, i.e. the temperature range, can be adapted to the critical T-values (see fig. 24.6).

For a number of other polymers Deeley and Terinzi (1965) have confirmed that there is an unambiguous relation between α_{STV} and the spiral length, which indeed permits a good polymer selection. This does not mean that the mouldability index is beyond

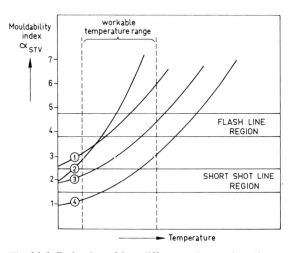

Fig. 24.6. Evaluation of four different polypropylenes by means of their mouldability index (after Weir et al., 1963).

criticism. It is found, for instance, that the critical values mentioned do not apply to high-melting aromatic thermoplastics.

Nevertheless, the mouldability index is a valuable criterion, which provides a rational basis for the construction of the moulding area diagram.

Control testing of processing conditions on moulded samples

In moulding operations both the size and the shape of the products are determined by the rather complicated thermal and mechanical history of the material. Due to viscoelastic stress relaxation, post-moulding cure and aftercrystallization, slow changes may occur after moulding which may be promoted by the (high) temperature during use. Factors such as moulding pressure, temperature, (and their variations), injection speed, etc., have a profound effect. The pressure in the mould is probably the most important variable; it is not only needed for flow but also for the compensation of shrinkage.

It has been found that moulding conditions can affect almost every property of moulded parts. Among the properties affected are *impact strength, crack resistance,* and appearance features such as *sink marks* and *voids, weld lines, clear spots, delamination* and *skinning, inhomogeneous pigment dispersion,* and *warping.*

The appearance of the article is one of the obvious criteria in evaluating the quality of processing. Measurements of gloss, clarity, etc., may help to quantify the assessment. But while appearance is an important aspect, it does not give us sufficient quantitative information about processing. Sometimes a better appearance may even mean less good mechanical properties!

One of the most important aspects of the processing conditions during moulding is the *orientation* in the mould.

Van Leeuwen (1965) describes a special test mould developed for studying these orientation effects (see fig. 24.7). The moulded object consists of two flat plates with a common runner. The plates can be tested as a whole, e.g. for falling-weight impact or for birefringence. Also, specimens may be cut out in two mutually perpendicular directions, e.g. for tensile impact and for "reversion" on heating.

The so-called *reversion test* is carried out by heating specimens floating on talcum powder to above the glass transition temperature. Reversion is then defined as follows:

$$\text{length reversion} = \frac{L_0}{L} - 1$$

$$\text{width reversion} = 1 - \frac{W_0}{W}$$

where L_0 and W_0 are the original length and width and L and W the same parameters after the reversion test.

No unique relationship between width and length reversion has been found (Paschke, 1967). The reversion runs parallel with birefringence up to a limiting value.

Van Leeuwen showed that a distinct relationship exists between the drop weight impact strength and the birefringence; the impact strength is very sensitive to orientation. A less satisfactory correlation with reversion was found.

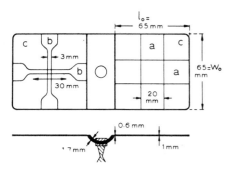

a: Reversion test
b: Tensile impact
c: Birefringence, drop weight impact
   and bending strength (whole plates)

Fig. 24.7. Test mould for orientation.

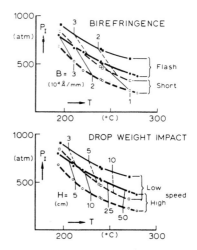

Fig. 24.8. Moulding diagrams for PS-R.

Test programs like the one described here permit an increase of the information in the moulding area diagram. Fig. 24.8 gives Van Leeuwen's data for rubber-modified polystyrenes. Curves of constant birefringence and constant impact strength have been drawn at two different injection speeds, for both short shot and flash. In the upper diagram birefringence was used as a criterion of quality, in the lower one impact strength. It makes a significant difference which of the two criteria is used. A high temperature and a high injection speed appear to be favourable for impact strength (a measure of brittleness and internal stresses). As to birefringence (as a measure of potential reversion and warping), moulding near the flash condition gives better results than marginal mould filling.

It is obvious that (apart from processing conditions) the degree of warping, the reversion and the impact strength are also determined by intrinsic properties of the polymer. Goppel and Van der Vegt (1966) showed that the first two effects increase with molecular weight and with broader molecular weight distribution. On the other hand, the impact strength increases with molecular weight and with narrower molecular weight distribution.

In conclusion, it may be said that the degree of orientation (and therefore the tendency to deformation under the influence of temperature and time) and the resistance to impact will be dependent partly on material properties, partly on process conditions.

SPINNABILITY

Spinnability is the ability of a polymer to be transformed into long continuous solid threads by a *melt-spinning* process. Therefore a spinnable polymer must conform to three requirements:
1. the polymer should be thermally and chemically stable under the spinning conditions, that is, at a temperature sufficiently high to permit flow through a nozzle

2. the liquid thread produced should remain intact at least until it has solidified

3. the thread should be highly extendable during the process.

Spinnability, although a necessary prerequisite for fibre formation, by no means guarantees that the polymer will be suitable as a fibre.

One of the earliest conventional methods for the assessment of spinnability was the *"pulling rod"* test: drawing a thread from the melt by means of a glass rod. Of course this very simple and convenient method is qualitative, since the drawing speed and the heat transfer are not controlled. Yet the thread length gives an immediate impression of the spinnability.

The first requirement of spinnability, thermal stability, has been discussed in Chapter 21. The other two requirements are closely related with the flow stability of fluid jets.

Stability of fluid threads in melt spinning

There is extensive literature on the stability of liquid jets. The subject was discussed by Lord Rayleigh as early as 1878, while the first quantitative description of the disintegration of a liquid jet was given by Weber (1931). A general survey of the stability of jets of Newtonian liquids with constant velocity (constant diameter) was given by Ohnesorge (1936). Even with the two restrictions mentioned the phenomenon is rather complicated because, depending on the velocity, four regions can be distinguished in which different mechanisms of disintegration prevail. In the order of increasing velocity these regions are:

1. formation of separate drops
2. formation of a liquid thread, which eventually disintegrates by the formation of successive beadlike swellings and contractions along the length of the thread (symmetrical drop breakup)
3. formation of a liquid thread which assumes the shape of a wave before disintegration (transverse wave breakup)
4. direct atomization.

A complete description of this theory will not be given here. The most important fact is that under the conditions mentioned the stability of a liquid jet is determined by two dimensionless groups:

$$N_{Re} = \frac{vd\rho}{\eta}$$

$$N_{We} = \frac{v^2 d\rho}{\gamma}$$

where
v = velocity of jet
d = diameter of jet
ρ = density
η = viscosity
γ = surface tension

In the second region of disintegration, which is the most important for viscous liquids, the stability criterion is

$$\frac{L_{max}}{d} = 12(N_{We}^{1/2} + 3 N_{We}/N_{Re}) \tag{24.7}$$

where L_{max} = maximum stable jet length
In many cases, this equation can be simplified to:

$$\frac{L_{max}}{d} = 36 \frac{v\eta}{\gamma} \tag{24.8}$$

Under actual melt-spinning conditions, the situation is far more complicated as the velocity always increases (d decreases), while the fluid generally does not show Newtonian behaviour. Moreover, the temperature decreases, so that the physical properties change in the course of the process.

Stability conditions for a jet showing increasing velocity, but having a constant temperature and Newtonian behaviour, have been derived by Ziabicki and Takserman-Krozer (1964). Their formula has no direct practical use, however, as it contains the amplitude of the original distortion as a parameter; this quantity is generally not known. But also in this treatment the stability is largely determined by the dimensionless group $v\eta/\gamma$.

The stability of melt spinning under non-isothermal conditions and for non-Newtonian fluids has been discussed by Pearson and Shah (1972, 1974). Their results cannot be summarized in a few words, but again the quantity $v\eta/\gamma$ plays an important part.

In most cases a sufficient stability criterion is that eq. (24.8) is satisfied over the whole spinning zone.

Table 24.3 shows an application of the stability criterion to three different types of melt. Completely different values are calculated for the ratio η/γ. It is an empirical fact that glass can be spun whereas metals cannot. Table 24.3 shows that impractically high velocities would be necessary to stabilize a jet of liquid metal [1], i.e. in satisfying expression (24.8).

Another conclusion is that the high viscosity of polymer melts is an important requirement for their spinnability.

TABLE 24.3

Application of stability criterion to different types of melt

Melt	η (N $\cdot$ s/m^2)	γ (N/m)	η/γ
metal	0.02	0.4	0.05
glass	100	0.3	300
polymer	10^4	0.025	4×10^5

Self-stabilizing effects in polymer spinning

A number of incorrect opinions about the stability of melt spinning have been expressed in the past. Nitschmann and Schrade (1948) suggested that an increase of the extensional viscosity with increasing extension rate was essential for spinnability. As was stated in Chapter 15, the underlying supposition is uncorrect, as in many cases the ex-

---

[1] Spinning of metals such as steel is only possible in gaseous atmospheres where a reaction takes place on the surface of the metal jet (Monsanto, 1972).

tensional viscosity does not increase during extension.

It is also incorrect to assume that the increase of viscosity due to the decrease of temperature during the spinning process is essential for the stability. Nevertheless, both factors mentioned may have a very favourable effect on the process since they promote the stability: the process becomes "self-stabilizing" by them.

The reverse may also be true, however, as the viscosity may decrease with increasing rate of deformation. This subject has been discussed by Pearson and Shah (1974).

Another effect of the variation of the extensional viscosity is the maximum extendibility. For polymers like high-density polyethylene, the rapid increase of the extensional viscosity during the spinning process limits the obtainable spin–draw ratio, that is the ratio between the winding velocity and the velocity in the orifice. Examples can be found in an article of Han and Lamonte (1972).

Melt strength

Liquid jet instability is only one possible cause of thread fracture during melt spinning. The other breaking mechanism is cohesive fracture. The importance of this phenomenon has been stressed by Ziabicki and Takserman-Krozer (1964).

For *isothermal* deformation of Newtonian fluids, Ziabicki and Takserman-Krozer derived the formula:

$$L_{max} = \frac{1}{\xi} \ln[(2e_{coh}E)^{1/2}/3\eta v_0 \xi] \tag{24.9}$$

where L_{max} = maximum length of jet
ξ = deformation gradient ($\xi = d \ln v/dx$)
e_{coh} = cohesive energy density
E = modulus of elasticity
η = viscosity
v_0 = initial velocity

It can easily be derived that for extensional deformation of a Newtonian fluid due to a constant tensile force the following expression holds:

$$\xi = \frac{\sigma_0}{3\eta v_0} = \text{constant} \tag{24.10}$$

where σ_0 = initial tensile stress.

Example 24.1

The application of eq. (24.9) may be elucidated by a numerical example. For the quantities involved, the following order of magnitude may be assumed

$$\left.\begin{array}{l} \sigma_0 = 10^4 \text{ N/m}^2 \\ \eta = 2 \times 10^4 \text{ N} \cdot \text{s/m}^2 \\ v_0 = 0.02 \text{ m/s} \\ e_{coh} = 3 \times 10^8 \text{ J/m}^3 \\ E = 3 \times 10^4 \text{ N/m}^2 \\ L_{max} \approx 0.7 \text{ m} \end{array}\right\} \xi = 8 \text{ m}^{-1}$$

This is an order of magnitude which will permit spinning under normal conditions. A relatively small variation in the magnitude of the parameters involved, however, may lead to cohesive fracture.

A rapid method for determining the *melt strength* has been developed by Busse (1967). He extruded a polymer melt through a standard orifice at a given temperature and a standard rate. The thread obtained was taken up on a pulley with variable speed. During a test the take-up speed was gradually increased until the thread broke, while the tension was recorded as a function of time.

Different polymers showed considerable differences both in melt strength and in maximum extension ratio. For a given polymer, the melt strength increased with the melt viscosity (decreasing temperature).

This test may be useful for a rapid comparison of a number of polymers. A theoretical interpretation of the results is almost impossible, however, because temperature and stress history of the polymer are completely undefined.

STRETCHABILITY

Stretchability denotes the suitability of a polymer in the solid state (amorphous or semicrystalline) to be stretched in one direction (occasionally in two directions). Of course, this processing step only serves a useful purpose in a specimen with a large aspect (i.e. length to diameter) ratio (fibres, films, sheets). The purpose of this operation generally is to achieve an improvement of mechanical properties, especially in the direction of stretching.

Although some operations in the plastics industry, such as calendering, could be described as stretching processes, the most important application of stretching is usually called *drawing* (of fibres and films).

There exists extensive literature on the drawing of synthetic polymers, of which only very broad outlines can be given here.

A phenomenon often encountered in drawing is *necking,* which may be described as a discontinuity in the reduction of the diameter of the specimen in the direction of stretching. The name "neck" has been chosen because in fibres the shape of this discontinuity often shows some similarity with the neck of a bottle.

A criterion of the appearance of a discontinuity during stretching was given by Considère in 1885. If a cylindrical body is subjected to a force F, the local mean tensile stress in an arbitrary cross section (area A) is

$$\sigma = \frac{F}{A}$$

For constant density

$$\frac{A_0}{A} = \frac{\Delta L}{\Delta L_0} \equiv \Lambda$$

where
A_0 = original area
ΔL = length of a small part
ΔL_0 = original length of this part
Λ = local draw ratio

500

Combination of the above equations gives:

$$\sigma = \frac{F}{A_0} \times \Lambda$$

So for constant F, σ is proportional to Λ. This expression is represented by the straight line in figs. 24.9 and 24.10. The deformation mechanics of the polymer, however, do not allow arbitrary combinations of σ and Λ.

If the stress–strain curve of a given material has a shape as sketched in fig. 24.9, the tensile force in a drawing experiment can be increased to a maximum value F_{max}. This force corresponds to the tangent to the curve from the origin. A further increase of the tensile force causes breakage of the specimen.

A number of materials, however, show stress–strain curves of the shape sketched in fig. 24.10. After the normal convex first part, the stress–strain curve shows an inversion point, after which the stress increases rapidly with strain. This phenomenon is sometimes called "strain hardening". In this case, a straight line through the origin can intersect the stress–strain curve at two points A and B. This means that only the intersection points A and B are possible conditions. The intermediate intersection point C is instable. So in this case two parts of the specimen, e.g. a fibre, with different draw ratios and hence different cross sections can coexist. If the fibre is stretched, part of the material with a cross section of point A is converted into material with a cross section of point B.

These considerations lead to a criterion of the stretchability of a material: *the stress–strain curve should show an inversion point (strain hardening)*. This is not a sufficient criterion, however, as under some experimental conditions these materials simply break on extension.

The second criterion is that the material should have sufficient molecular mobility to withstand a rapid reduction in diameter. The nature of the molecular mobility that permits drawing depends on the structure of the material. As a general rule, semi-crystalline polymers are drawn at temperatures from somewhat below the melting point, down to the glass transition temperature, while amorphous polymers are drawn at temperatures in the neighbourhood of the glass transition temperature. In this connection it should be mentioned that at high rates of deformation the temperature of the fibre can be considerably higher than the temperature of the surroundings.

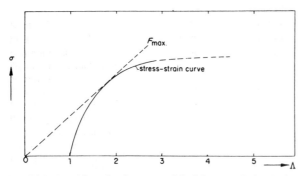

Fig. 24.9. Considère plot for a material without strain hardening.

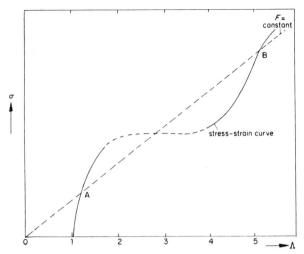

Fig. 24.10. Considère plot for a material with strain hardening.

The drawing of semi-crystalline polymers is a very complicated morphological phenomenon. According to Peterlin (1971) and Wada (1971) at least three stages can be distinguished:

1. plastic deformation of the original semi-crystalline structure
2. transformation of this structure into a fibre structure by a mechanism called "micro-necking"
3. plastic deformation of the fibre structure

Macroscopically, a sharp neck can generally be observed.

In the drawing of amorphous polymers, the structural changes involved principally result in an increasing degree of orientation, followed or not by partial crystallization.

As was described by Marshall and Thompson (1954) and by Müller and Binder (1962), drawing of amorphous polymers may involve two different molecular mechanisms. At a given rate of deformation of a given polymer there exists a transition temperature in the neighbourhood of the glass transition temperature, below which drawing takes place with the formation of a rather sharp neck. Above the transition temperature, there is a more gradual decrease in diameter. The transition temperature increases with the rate of deformation. Marshall and Thompson introduced the names "cold drawing" and "hot drawing" for these phenomena. For poly(ethylene terephthalate), for instance, the transition temperature is about 80° for low rates of deformation, as used in a tensile test. But the transition temperature can exceed $100°C$ under the high rates of deformation used in technical yarn drawing apparatus.

A recent confirmation of these phenomena has been given by Spruiell et al. (1972).

That cold drawing and hot drawing involve different deformation mechanisms can be concluded from the accompanying changes in physical properties. The increase of birefringence with draw ratio, for instance, is different for cold drawing than for hot drawing. Hot drawing is the type of deformation which already occurs during the spinning process.

After the spinning process, synthetic fibres are generally subjected to a cold-drawing process, followed or not by annealing.

An interesting example of the difference in drawing behaviour between amorphous and crystalline yarn is the drawing of crystalline poly(ethylene terephthalate). It is often stated that crystalline PETP cannot be drawn. It is true that the material breaks if drawn at a temperature of 80°C, which is a drawing temperature normal for the amorphous polymer. Mitsuishi and Domae (1965), however, were able to draw crystalline PETP to a draw ratio of 5.5 at a temperature of 180°C.

A quantity often used in the description of drawing phenomena is the "*natural draw ratio*". As can be seen in fig. 24.10, simple drawing of a material with the given stress—strain curve results in a fixed draw ratio corresponding to point B on the curve. This is called the natural draw ratio.

The natural draw ratio is not constant, but dependent on experimental conditions: temperature, rate of deformation, etc. Nevertheless, the order of magnitude of the natural draw ratio gives an indication of the stretchability of a given material. Very broadly speaking, the polymers can be divided into three categories:
1. typically amorphous polymers, such as polystyrene and polysulphone. They generally show a weak strain-hardening effect. The natural draw ratio is about 1.5—2.5.
2. polymers with a certain degree of crystallinity in the drawn state. To this group belong the important synthetic fibres like polyesters and polyamides. The natural draw ratio is about 4—5.
3. the typically high-crystalline polymers, such as polyethylene and polypropylene. Here high natural draw ratios (5—10) are found.

In principle, a simple bench drawing test may be used to obtain an impression of the stretchability and of the natural draw ratio of a given polymer. However, as the rate of deformation in the bench test is appreciably lower than under technical drawing conditions, testing should be done below the technical drawing temperature. An impression of the order of magnitude of this temperature difference may be obtained by application of the Williams—Landel—Ferry equation (see Chapter 13). The temperature difference may be more than 20°C.

To summarize: the stretchability of a polymer depends on the occurrence of strain hardening. It is limited to a temperature region where the polymer shows a specific magnitude of molecular mobility. A bench drawing test may be used to determine stretchability experimentally, but it should be performed at a temperature substantially below the technical drawing temperature.

C. IMPLEMENTATION OF PROCESSING RESEARCH

In order to bridge the gap between research data and the behaviour of products in actual practice, systematic application research has to be carried out. Fig. 24.11 shows what is meant by this.

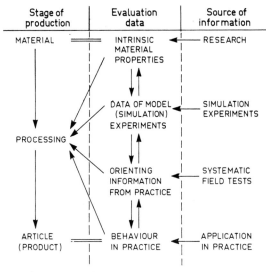

Fig. 24.11. Application research.

Usually so-called *simulation experiments* are carried out first. As regards *processing,* these simulation experiments should approach practice as closely as possible. (It stands to reason that the conditions applied in *testing* should also correspond closely to those in practice.)

The simulation experiments are followed by systematic *processing experiments* on a *model machine* (which is a small, well-equipped production machine). This gives data that are still closer to practice, because they have been obtained under practically equal, though carefully watched, circumstances.

Practice itself will afterwards supply the *feed back information,* which may even be more important. It will be clear that the practical knowledge of the processer is essential here. Mostly, however, this knowledge has no background in the research data available. In the introduction of new plastics, but also in the technical applications of existing material this may be a strongly limiting factor. In this connection, a scientific analysis of processing practice is very important.

BIBLIOGRAPHY, CHAPTER 24

General references

Brydson, J.A., "Flow Properties of Polymer Melts", Iliffe Books, Ltd., London, 1970.
Elden, R.A. and Swan, A.D., "Calendering of Plastics", Iliffe Books Ltd., London, 1971.
Fisher, E.G., "Extrusion of Plastics", Iliffe Books Ltd, London, 1964.
Fisher, E.G. and Chard, E.D., "Blow Moulding of Plastics", Iliffe Books Ltd, London, 1971.
Holmes-Walker, W.A., "Polymer Conversion", Applied Science Publishers, London, 1975.
Kobayashi, A., "Machining of Plastics", McGraw Hill, New York, 1967.
McKelvey, J.M., "Polymer Processing", Wiley, New York, 1962.

504

Martin, E.R., "Injection Moulding of Plastics", Iliffe Books Ltd, London, 1964.
Ogorkiewicz, R.M. (Ed.), "Engineering Properties of Thermoplastics", Wiley-Interscience, New York, 1970.
Pearson, J.R.A., "Mechanical Principles of Polymer Melt Processing", Pergamon Press, Oxford, 1966.
Pye, R.G.W., "Injection Mould Design", Iliffe Books Ltd, London, 1968.
Schenkel, G., "Plastics Extrusion Technology and Theory", Iliffe Books Ltd, London, 1966.
Tadmor, Z. and Klein, I., "Engineering Principles of Plasticating Extrusion", Van Nostrand, New York, 1970.
Thiel, A., "Principles of Vacuum Forming", Iliffe Books Ltd, London, 1965.
Westover, R.F. and Bernhardt, E.C., "Processing of Thermoplastic Materials", Reinhold, New York, 1959.

Special references

ASTM D 1238–70, "Measuring Flow Rates of Thermoplastics by Extrusion Plastometer".
Boenig, H.V., "Polyolefins", Elsevier, Amsterdam, 1966, Ch. 8, p. 262.
Busse, W.F., J. Polymer Sci. A2, 5 (1967) 1219 and 1261.
Considère, A., Ann. Ponts Chaussées 6 (1885) 9.
Deeley, C.W. and Terinzi, J.F., Modern Plastics 42 (1965) 111.
Goppel, J.M. and Van der Vegt, A.K., "Processing Polymers to Products", Proc. Internat. Congress, Amsterdam (1966), 't Raedthuys, Utrecht, 1967, p. 177.
Han, C.D. and Lamonte, R.R., Trans. Soc. Rheol. 16 (1972) 447.
Holmes, D.B., Esselink, B.P. and Beek, W.J., "Processing Polymers to Products", Proc. Intern. Congress, Amsterdam (1966), 't Raedthuys, Utrecht, 1967, p. 131.
Marshall, I. and Thompson, A.B., Proc. Royal Soc. (London), A 221 (1954) 541; J. Appl. Chem. 4 (1954) 145.
Müller, F.H. and Binder, G., Kolloid-Z. 183 (1962) 120.
Mitsuishi, Y. and Domae, H., Sen-i Gakkaishi 21 (1965) 528.
Monsanto Co., US Patent 3,645,657 (1972).
Nitschmann, H. and Schrade, J., Helv. Chim. Acta 31 (1948) 297.
Ohnesorge, W., Z. angew. Math. Mech. 16 (1936) 355.
Paschke, E., "Processing Polymers to Products", Proc. Internat. Congress, Amsterdam (1966), 't Raedthuys, Utrecht, 1967, p. 123; see also Kunststoffe 57 (1967) 645.
Pearson, J.R.A. and Shah, Y.T., Ind. Eng. Chem. Fund. 11 (1972) 145; 13 (1974) 134.
Peterlin, A., J. Mat. Sci. 6 (1971) 490.
Powell, P.C., "Processing Methods and Properties of Thermoplastic Melts", Ch. 11 in "Thermoplastics" (R.M. Ogorkiewicz, Ed.), John Wiley, London, 1974.
Rayleigh, J.W. Strutt, Lord, Proc. London Math. Soc. 10 (1878) 7.
Spruiell, J.E., McCord, D.E. and Beuerlein, R.A., Trans. Soc. Rheol. 16 (1972) 535.
Van der Vegt, A.K., Trans. Plastics Inst. 32 (1964) 165.
Van Krevelen, D.W., "Processing Polymers to Products", Proc. Intern. Congress, Amsterdam (1966), 't Raedthuys, Utrecht, 1967.
Van Leeuwen, J., Kunststoffe 55 (1965) 491; "Processing Polymers to Products", Proc. Intern. Congress, Amsterdam (1966), 't Raedthuys, Utrecht, 1967, p. 40.
Vinogradov, G.V. and Malkin, A.Ya., Kolloid-Z. 191 (1963) 1; J. Polymer Sci. A2 (1964) 2357; A-2, 4 (1966) 137.
Wada, Y., J. Appl. Polymer Sci. 15 (1971) 183.
Weber, C., Z. angew. Math. Mech. 11 (1931) 136.
Weir, F.E., SPE Trans. (1963) 32.
Weir, F.E., Doyle, M.E. and Norton, D.G., SPE Trans. (1963) 37.
Ziabicki, A. and Takserman-Krozer, R., Kolloid-Z. 198 (1964) 60; 199 (1964) 9.

CHAPTER 25

PRODUCT PROPERTIES (I)

MECHANICAL BEHAVIOUR AND FAILURE

Product (article) properties are in principle determined by combinations of intrinsic and "added" properties. However, the correlations between these basic properties and the (more or less subjectively defined) product properties are often complex and only partly understood. They are "system-related".

None of the mechanical product properties can be estimated directly from additive quantities. There exist, however, several quantitative relationships that connect the mechanical product properties with intrinsic mechanical properties.

Introduction

Product or article properties (also called *end-use properties*) are very complex. They depend not only on the material of which the product or article is made, but also – and mainly – on the system of which the article forms part: product properties are "*system-related*".

Friction, abrasion and wear, for instance, are – mathematically – "operators" of a system, i.e. they depend on the parameters of a system, such as the geometry of the surface, the temperature, the load, the relative velocities, the composition of the environmental atmosphere, etc. The operational character of wear, for example, depends on the physico-chemical interaction of surfaces and on *their* interaction with the lubricant and the atmosphere.

As far as the article itself is concerned, the product or article properties are in principle determined by combinations of intrinsic and "added" properties; the latter are obtained by processing. However, the correlations between these basic material properties and the more or less subjectively defined article properties have often been only partly investigated or are not yet fully understood.

It is, of course, impossible to give a general survey of product properties: every article has to be considered in its specific application as part of a system. So in this chapter *we shall give only some general lines of approach*.

The mechanical product properties are characteristic parameters for mechanical behaviour and failure under use conditions. They can roughly be divided into two categories, viz.:

a. properties connected with *high stress levels* and *short periods*

b. properties connected with *low stress levels* and *long periods*

Table 25.1 gives a classification of the mechanical end use properties.

TABLE 25.1

Mechanical end use properties

Class	Short-term behaviour	Long-term behaviour
Deformation properties	*Stiffness*	*Creep*
	Stress–strain behaviour	Uniaxial and flexural deformation
	Modulus	Creep behaviour
	Yield stress	
Durability properties	*Toughness*	*Endurance*
Bulk	Ductile and brittle fracture	Creep rupture
	Stress and elongation at break	Crazing (and cracking)
	Impact strength	Flexural resistance
		Fatigue failure at cyclic stress
	Hardness	*Friction* and *Wear*
Surface	Scratch resistance	Coefficient of friction
	Indentation hardness	Abrasion resistance

A. DEFORMATION PROPERTIES

Polymers are used in many applications where substantial loads have to be carried. A good designer tries to ensure that a given article will not break, deflect or deform, bearing in mind the economic penalties of overdesign.

Considerable quantities of design data are now becoming available, making major contributions to the resolution of many design problems. But these data can only resolve part of the problems, since many of them are extremely complicated and defy rigorous or even approximate analysis.

The most serious obstacle in the design of plastic articles is the influence of stress concentrations, *which should therefore be reduced to a minimum.*

In the category of deformation properties the phenomena of stress–strain behaviour, modulus and yield, stress relaxation and creep have been discussed already in Chapter 13.

Here we want to give special attention to the long-term deformation properties.

For a good design we need sufficiently reliable creep data (or stress–strain curves as a function of time and temperature).

Uniaxial deformation under constant load

The usual design procedure is to couple a specific value of design stress with a conventional stress or strain analysis of the assumed structural idealization. The uniaxial deformation behaviour is of special importance in thin-walled pipes, circular tanks and comparable systems under simple stress.

We confine ourselves here to cylindrical tanks as an example. For free-standing liquid storage tanks the following formula applies to the design stress σ_D:

$$\sigma_D(\text{at } \epsilon = 1\%) \geqslant \frac{pR}{d}\mu \ (\approx \frac{g\rho HR}{d}\mu) \tag{25.1}$$

where p is the hydrostatic pressure, R the radius and d the wall thickness of the tank, H the height of liquid above the base of the tank, and μ a shape factor of the order of 1.

If one knows σ as a function of ϵ, t and T, or the Young's modulus as a function of t and T, then the geometrical data can be calculated, e.g. the wall thickness at a given tank capacity.

Example 25.1

What is the minimum wall thickness of a cylindrical tank, 5 m in height, 1.5 m in radius, made of polypropylene and capable of storing aqueous solutions for a year, if the allowed maximum design strain is 1%.

Solution

The modulus of polypropylene at room temperature (100 s creep modulus) is 15×10^8 N/m^2 (see Chapter 13). Applying (13.57) we find

$$\log \frac{E_R}{E} = \log \frac{15 \times 10^8}{E} \approx 0.08 \log \frac{t}{t_R} \approx 0.08 \log \frac{3.16 \times 10^7}{10^2}$$

(1 year = 3.16×10^7 s)

This gives $E = 5.5 \times 10^8$ N/m^2

so that $\sigma_D = E\epsilon = 5.5 \times 10^8 \times 10^{-2} \geqslant \dfrac{9.81 \times 1000 \times 5 \times 1.5 \times \mu}{d}$

or $d \geqslant \dfrac{7.4 \times 10^4}{5.5 \times 10^6}\mu \approx 13.5 \times 10^{-3}$

So the wall thickness has to be at least 13.5 mm.

Flexural deformation under constant load

Again, reliable creep modulus data have to be available in order to apply the deflection formulae. Tables 25.2 and 25.3 give the expression for the deflections and torsional deformations of bars [1].

In practice the strain involved in the flexure of beams and struts is normally small; a practical limit of 0.5% has been suggested.

Example 25.2

Estimate the deflection after one year at 25°C at the free end of a nylon cantilever beam, 150 mm long, 10 mm wide and 12 mm thick, when it is subjected to a constant load of 2.5 N at the free end. Make the calculation for the following cases:

    a. nylon 66 in equilibrium with a dry atmosphere

---

[1] By means of these formulae the modulus of engineering materials may be determined from deflection and torsion experiments.

TABLE 25.2

Summary of flexural formulas (After Schmitz and Brown (1965–1969), Vol. 2, p. 329)

Sample geometry	Type of support	Type of loading	Maximum tensile stress σ_{max}	Modulus [1] E	Strain [1] ϵ
Rectangular beam of width b and thickness d	Two simple supports at distance L	Single concentrated load P at midpoint $L/2$	$\dfrac{3PL}{2bd^2}$	$\dfrac{PL^3}{4bd^3y}$	$\dfrac{6dy}{L^2}$
Rectangular beam of width b and thickness d	Two simple supports at distance L	Two equal loads $P/2$ at $1/3$ points $L/3$ and $2L/3$	$\dfrac{PL}{bd^2}$	$\dfrac{23PL^3}{108bd^3y}$	$\dfrac{108dy}{23L^2}$
Rectangular beam of width b and thickness d	Two simple supports at distance L	Two equal loads $P/2$ at $1/4$ points $L/4$ and $3L/4$	$\dfrac{3PL}{4bd^2}$	$\dfrac{11PL^3}{64bd^3y}$	$\dfrac{48dy}{11L^2}$
Rectangular beam of width b and thickness d	Fixed cantilever	Single concentrated load at free end	$\dfrac{6PL}{bd^2}$	$\dfrac{4PL^3}{bd^3y}$	$\dfrac{3dy}{2L^2}$
Rod of diameter D	Two simple supports at distance L	Single concentrated load at midpoint	$\dfrac{8PL}{\pi D^3}$	$\dfrac{4PL^3}{3\pi D^4y}$	$\dfrac{6Dy}{L^2}$
Rod of diameter D	Fixed cantilever	Single concentrated load at free end	$\dfrac{32PL}{\pi D^3}$	$\dfrac{64PL^3}{3\pi D^4y}$	$\dfrac{3Dy}{2L^2}$
Tube of outside diameter D and inside diameter d	Two simple supports at distance L	Single concentrated load at midpoint	$\dfrac{8PLD}{\pi(D^4-d^4)}$	$\dfrac{4PL^3}{3\pi(D^4-d^4)y}$	$\dfrac{6Dy}{L^2}$

[1] Note: y = maximum beam deflection in all cases.

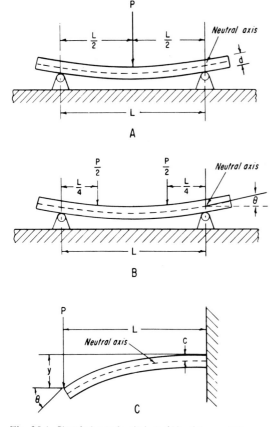

Fig. 25.1. Simple beam loaded at: (A) midspan; (B) one-quarter points; (C) cantilever beam loaded at free end. (Reproduced from Schmitz and Brown (1965–69), Vol. 2, p. 323.)

b. ditto at 65% relative humidity (RH)
c. for glass-reinforced nylon (dry)
d. for glass-reinforced nylon under water
Estimate also the maximum fibre strain in the beam.

The following data for the 100 s creep modulus are known:

Nylon 66: $E(298 \text{ K}, 100 \text{ s}) \approx [25 - 20(\text{RH}/100)] \times 10^8 \text{ N/m}^2$

Nylon 66, glass fibre reinforced: $E(298 \text{ K}, 100 \text{ s}) \approx [100 - 55(\text{RH}/100)] \times 10^8 \text{ N/m}^2$

Solution
The following expression is available for the deflection (see table 25.2):

$$y = \frac{4 \, PL^3}{bd^3E}$$

TABLE 25.3

Summary of torsion formulas

Bar cross section	Shear modulus	
	G (static)	G (dynamic)
Circular	$\dfrac{2\mathcal{I}L}{\pi r^4 \vartheta}$	$\dfrac{8\pi LI}{r^4 t_0{}^2}$
Equilateral triangle	$\dfrac{26\mathcal{I}L}{b^4 \vartheta}$	$\dfrac{104\pi^2 LI}{b^4 t_0{}^2}$
Square	$\dfrac{7.11\mathcal{I}L}{d^4 \vartheta}$	$\dfrac{28.5\pi^2 LI}{d^4 t_0{}^2}$
Rectangular	$\dfrac{16\mathcal{I}L}{\mu b d^3 \vartheta}$	$\dfrac{64\pi^2 LI}{\mu b d^3 t_0{}^2}$
Circular tube	$\dfrac{2\mathcal{I}L}{\pi(r_1{}^4 - r_2{}^4)\vartheta}$	$\dfrac{8\pi LI}{(r_1{}^4 - r_2{}^4)t_0{}^2}$

Nomenclature	Value of shape factor	
	b/d ratio	μ
L = Length of straight bar	1.0	2.25
b = Width or side	2.0	3.66
d = Diameter or thickness	3.0	4.21
r = Radius	5.0	4.66
μ = Shape factor	10	5.0
$\mathcal{I}$ = Torque (torsion couple)	20	5.17
ϑ = Angle of twist	50	5.27
I = Moment of inertia of the oscillatory system	100	5.30
	∞	5.33
t_0 = Oscillation period		

So the deflection is:

$$y = \frac{4 \times 2.5 \times (150 \times 10^{-3})^3}{10 \times 10^{-3} \times (12 \times 10^{-3})^3 \times E} = 1.95 \times 10^6 / E$$

The formula for the modulus of nylon (see Chapter 13, eq. (13.57)) is:

$$\log \frac{E_R}{E} \approx 0.1 \log \frac{t}{t_R} \approx 0.1 \log \frac{3.16 \times 10^7}{10^2} \qquad \text{or } E \approx \frac{E_R}{3.55}$$

The following values for E_R have to be substituted:

dry nylon	$E_R \approx 25 \times 10^8$ N/m²,	so $E \approx 7.1 \times 10^8$
nylon 65% RH	$E_R \approx 12 \times 10^8$ N/m²,	so $E \approx 3.4 \times 10^8$
glass-reinforced nylon	$E_R \approx 100 \times 10^8$ N/m²,	so $E \approx 28 \times 10^8$
glass-reinforced nylon, wet	$E_R \approx 45 \times 10^8$ N/m²,	so $E \approx 12.6 \times 10^8$

The maximum tensile stress in the beam is

$$\sigma_{max} = \frac{6\,PL}{bd^2} = \frac{6 \times 2.5 \times 150}{10 \times 10^{-3} \times (12 \times 10^{-3})^2} \approx 1.57 \text{ MN/m}^2$$

The maximum fibre strain is $\epsilon_{max} \approx \dfrac{1.57 \times 10^6}{E}$

This leads to the following values:

Sample	y (mm)	ϵ_{max} (%)
nylon, dry	2.85	0.22
nylon, 65% RH	5.80	0.46
nylon, dry, glass-reinf.	0.70	0.056
nylon, wet, glass-reinf.	1.55	0.12

B. TOUGHNESS AND ENDURANCE

The phenomena of ductile and brittle fracture and of ultimate stress and elongation have been discussed in Chapter 13.

The ultimate stress is very much time-dependent, as may be understood from the viscoelastic behaviour of polymers. At very high velocities there is, even in ductile materials, a change from ductile to brittle fracture.

Impact strength

Impact strength is the resistance to breakage under high-velocity impact conditions. This property is of great practical importance, but extremely difficult to define in scientific terms.

Many impact tests measure the energy required to break a standard sample under certain specified conditions. The most widely used tests are the *Izod test* (pendulum-type instrument with notched sample, which is struck on the free end), the *Charpy test* (pendulum-type instrument with sample supported at the two ends and struck in the middle), the *falling-weight test* (standard ball dropped from known height), and the *high-speed stress–strain test*.

The impact strength is temperature-dependent; near the glass temperature the impact strength of glassy polymers increases dramatically with temperature. Secondary transitions play an important role; a polymer with a strong low-temperature secondary transition in the glassy state is nearly always much tougher than a polymer which has no such transition.

Crystalline polymers have high impact strengths if their glass transition temperature is well below the test temperature. With increasing crystallinity and especially with increasing size of the spherulites the impact strength decreases.

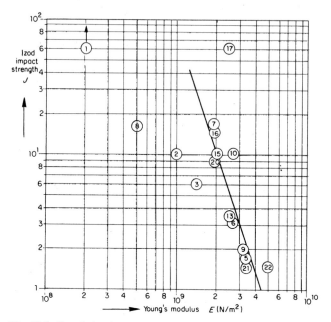

Fig. 25.2. Correlation between impact strength (J) and modulus (E). (See tables 13.10 and 25.4 for reference numbers.)

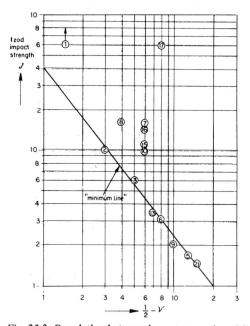

Fig. 25.3. Correlation between impact strength and Poisson ratio. (See tables 13.10 and 25.4 for reference numbers.)

The impact strength of thermosetting polymers varies little with temperature over a wide range.

The Izod impact strength of a number of common polymers at room temperature is listed in table 25.4. Plotted versus the modulus at room temperature, as is shown in fig. 25.2 it gives a rough correlation for first estimations.

Some polymers show large deviations. Polycarbonate (nr. 17) is an extremely tough polymer, with a high modulus; polyethylene l.d. (nr. 1) and poly(tetrafluoroethylene) (nr. 8) combine a high impact strength with a low modulus. The other polymers are spread around the drawn line.

The impact strength is also roughly correlated with the Poisson ratio, as shown by fig. 25.3. The drawn line in this figure gives *minimum* values of the impact strength as a function of $(\frac{1}{2} - \nu)$; the typical tough polymers such as polycarbonate and polyamides are above the line.

Creep rupture

Creep tests are normally carried out with small loads, so that the sample does not break. If the loads approach the breaking strength, rupture will occur after some time. The following expression has been derived both theoretically and experimentally (Coleman, 1956):

$$\ln t_{br} = A + \frac{E_{act} - B\sigma}{RT} \qquad (25.2)$$

where t_{br} is the time required for creep rupture, σ is the applied stress, E_{act} is the energy of activation of the fracture process, A and B are constants.

The formula shows that the applied stress lowers the activation energy E_{act} to a value $E_{act} - B\sigma$.

Crazing

Brittle fracture is normally preceded by crazing, i.e. a running crack is preceded by a zone of crazed material (see Chapter 13). Like cracks, crazes in isotropic materials grow at right angles to the principal tensile stress and only propagate if the stress at their tip exceeds a certain value. The craze can be described as an "open cell foam" with voids of the order of 10–20 nm in diameter and center-to-center distances of 50–100 nm.

Crazes usually form under tensile stress when a *critical strain* is surpassed; they do not occur under compressive stress; their development can even be inhibited by applying hydrostatic pressure during tensile deformation. Crazes always nucleate preferentially at points of stress concentration.

As already remarked in Chapter 13, craze formation is now considered to be a mode of plastic deformation peculiar to glassy polymers (or to glassy regions in the polymer) that is competitive with shear ductility in reducing stress. The strength of specimens that are crazed completely through their cross-sections is a manifestation of the degree of residual mechanical integrity of the polymer in the craze. Craze formation appears to be a plastic deformation in the tensile stress direction without lateral contraction.

In this respect the behaviour of vulcanized natural rubber, preoriented above T_g and

TABLE 25.4

Data on impact strength, hardness, friction and abrasion

Polymer	Izod impact strength ASTM D256 (kJ/m²)	Rockwell hardness		Ball indentation hardness (10^7 N/m²)	Shore D hardness	Friction coefficient (—)	Abrasion resistance (ASTM-D1044) (Taber) (mg/1000c)	Abrasion loss factor (DIN 53516) (mg)	Polymer ref. nr. in figures (cf. table 13.10)
		R scale	M scale						
Polyethylene (low d.)	>50	(10)		1.35	59	(0.5)			1
Pclyethylene (high d.)	10	40		5.35	71	0.23		2	2
Polypropylene	6	100		7.25	74	0.67			3
Polystyrene	1.7	(125)	75	11	78	0.38		640	5
Poly(vinyl chloride)	3.2	115	60	11.5	80	0.50			6
Poly(chlorotrifluoroethylene)	16	110		7.0	74	0.56		160	7
Poly(tetrafluoroethylene)	16	85		3.1	66	0.10		470	8
Poly(methyl methacrylate)	2	125	95	17.2	85	0.4			9
Polyoxymethylene	10	120	94	14.0	80		20		10
Poly(ethylene terephthalate)	3.5	120	106	12.0		0.25	3		13
Nylon 6,6	10	114	(70)	7.25	75	0.36		25	15
Nylon 6	15	85		6.25	72	0.39	8	15	16
Poly(bisphenol carbonate)	60	118	78	9.75	75	0.25	10		17
Cellulose acetate	9	100	25	4.3		0.55			20
Phenol formaldehyde resin	1.5	125		(19)	82	0.61		60	21
Melamine formaldehyde resin	1.5	130		>17	90				21a
Unsaturated polyester resin	1.5	125	75	17	82				22

Sources of data: "Technical data on plastics", Manufact. Chem. Assoc., Washington, 1957; B. Carlowitz, "Kunststoff Tabellen", Schiffmann, Bensberg-Frankenfort, 1963; "Plastics Materials Guide 1970–1971", British Plastics, Jan. 1970.

rapidly quenched, is interesting (Natarajan and Reed, 1972). At temperatures immediately below T_g necking can be observed. At slightly lower temperatures the material becomes brittle. But as the temperature is further reduced a new region of ductility is found, the plastic deformation now taking place by cavitation, beginning as narrow crazes but developing by lateral growth of the craze to give homogeneous voiding over a large volume.

Fatigue resistance

Failure and decay of mechanical properties after repeated applications of stress or strain are known as fatigue. Generally the "fatigue life" is defined as the number of cycles of deformation required to bring about rupture.

Many types of fatigue tester are used (flexing beams, rotating beams, constant amplitude of cyclic stress or strain, constant rate of increase in amplitude of stress or strain, etc.).

The results are reported as the number of cycles to failure versus the stress level used. The limiting stress below which the material will "never" fail is called the *fatigue or endurance limit; for many polymers this fatigue limit is about one-third of the static tensile strength.* Therefore, in practice it is important to design constructions subjected to vibrations in such a way that the maximum stresses to which they are subjected are below the fatigue limit rather than below the static tensile strength.

Also in this case there is a kind of temperature–time equivalence; the fatigue life of a polymer is generally reduced by an increase of temperature. The temperature-dependence can usually be expressed by:

$$\log t_{\text{fat}} = A + \frac{B}{T}. \tag{25.3}$$

Mechanical damping is important in the fatigue life determination. High damping (in the neighbourhood of a transition temperature) may be largely responsible for the fatigue failure, due to heat buildup. On the other hand damping is favourable, since without damping resonance vibrations may cause failure.

Very little is known about the effect of molecular structure on fatigue life.

C. HARDNESS

Two categories of hardness definitions can be distinguished:
    a. the scratch resistance
    b. the indentation hardness

Scratch resistance

The oldest criterion for scratch resistance, the Mohs' scale of hardness was originally devised more than 150 years ago. It is still used to classify the various minerals and consists of a list so selected and arranged that each mineral is able to scratch the ones preceding in the list shown in table 25.5

TABLE 25.5

Mohs' scale of hardness

Hardness number	Mineral	Hardness number	Mineral
1	Talc	6	Orthoclase
2	Gypsum	7	Quartz
3	Calcite	8	Topaz
4	Fluorite	9	Corundum
5	Apatite	10	Diamond

The Mohs' scale is useful for defining the scratch resistance of plastics relative to those things with which the plastic may come in contact during its service life. It is of limited value, however, for differentiating between the scratch resistance of the various plastics, since practically all of them, including both the thermosetting and the thermoplastic types, are in the range of 2–3 Mohs. Many of the materials with which the plastic will come in contact during service are higher than 3 on the Mohs' scale.

In examining new polymers, the hardness may be estimated by using one's fingernail (Mohs 2), a brass scribe (Mohs 3), a knife blade (Mohs 4), or a piece of glass (Mohs 5).

The relative scratch resistance of two polymers may be readily determined by scratching the surface of one with the corner of the other.

The scratch resistance of rigid polymers is related to abrasion. In general, for rigid polymers scratch resistance runs parallel with modulus. Rubber, if cross-linked, shows a high scratch resistance, however, which is due to easy deformation combined with complete resilience.

Indentation hardness

Indentation hardness is a very common determination in materials testing. In this test a very hard indenter (a hard steel sphere in the *Brinell test*, a diamond pyramid in the *Vickers test*) is pressed under a load into the surface of the material.

The mechanism of the indentation process has been clearly defined by Tabor (1947). When a ball presses on a metal surface, the material deforms elastically. As the load increases, the stresses soon exceed the elastic limit and plastic flow starts. By increasing the load still further the material directly beneath the penetrator becomes completely plastic. On release of the load there is an amount of elastic recovery.

From the theory of the stress field around the indenter it follows that almost two thirds of the mean pressure is in the form of a hydrostatic component and therefore plays no part in producing plastic flow. Thus as an approximation

$$p_y = \frac{W}{A} \approx 3\sigma_y \tag{25.4}$$

where
W = load applied
A = surface area under indentation

σ_y = uniaxial yield stress of the material
p_y = pressure at which plastic flow starts
So the yield stress of a material may be determined by a hardness measurement.

The original theory of the Brinell hardness test was developed by Hertz (1881) and revised by Timoshenko (1934); their treatment was based on the elasticity theory.

Starting from Tabor's concepts of plastic deformation and analysing the recovery process after the load release in terms of the elastic concepts, Baer et al. (1961) derived the following formula:

$$\frac{W}{E} \approx 3(d_1-d_2)(d_1 D)^{1/2} \qquad (25.5)$$

where
W = load applied
E = Young's modulus
d_1 = indentation depth
$d_1 - d_2$ = distance of recovery
D = diameter of penetrator (ball)

By measuring the initial distance of indentation and the distance of recovery the modulus E can be determined.

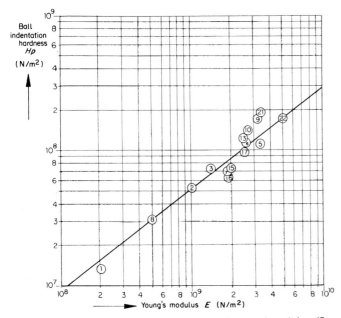

Fig. 25.4. Correlation between indentation hardness and modulus. (See tables 13.10 and 25.4 for reference numbers.)

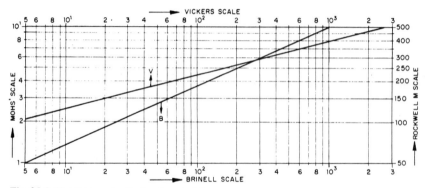

Fig. 25.5. Hardness scales for hard materials.

TABLE 25.6

Comparative hardness scales for soft materials

Hardness scale							Types of product
Mohs	Brinell	Rockwell		Shore			
		M	α (≈R)	D	C	A (≈IRHD)	
2	25	100					Hard plastics
	16	80					
	12	70	100	90			
	10	65	97	86			
	9	63	96	83			Moderately hard plastics
	8	60	93	80			
	7	57	90	77			
	6	54	88	74			
1	5	50	85	70			
	4	45		65	95		
	3	40	(50)	60	93	98	Soft plastics
	2	32		55	89	96	
	1.5	28		50	80	94	
	1	23		42	70	90	
	0.8	20		38	65	88	Rubbers
	0.6	17		35	57	85	
	0.5	15		30	50	80	
				25	43	75	
				20	36	70	
				15	27	60	
				12	21	50	
				10	18	40	
				8	15	30	
				6.5	11	20	
				4	8	10	

The hardness is defined as:

$$\frac{W}{\pi D d_1} = H_p. \tag{25.6}$$

Since $Dd \sim A$ (area under indentation) and σ_y is closely related to the modulus ($\sigma_y \sim E^n$), combination of (25.4) and (25.6) gives the following proportionality for a standard load and a standard indenter

$$H_p \sim E^n. \tag{25.7}$$

Table 25.4 gives some values for polymers investigated. Fig. 25.4 shows that the expression (25.7) is approximately confirmed. The empirical expression is:

$$\boxed{H_p \approx 10 \, E^{3/4}} \tag{25.8}$$

(H_p and E both expressed in N/m^2).

For very soft materials such as elastomers (rubbers) other hardness testers are used, the so-called *Shore Hardness testers*. As indenting body a steel pencil is used in the form of a truncated cone (Shore A and C) or of a rounded cone (Shore D). With a certain force exerted by a spring the pencil is pressed into the material and the indentation depth is measured on a scale ranging from 0 to 100.

Correlation between the hardness tests

Between the different hardness tests a rather good correlation exists. Fig. 25.5 shows this for hard materials, table 25.6 for soft materials.

D. FRICTION AND WEAR

Friction

The *coefficient of friction* μ is defined as the ratio of the tangential force F to the normal load W when the surface of a material is moved relative to another surface

$$\mu = \frac{F}{W}. \tag{25.9}$$

The coefficient of friction is by no means a constant, since it still depends on the load, the contact area, the surface structure, the velocity of sliding, the temperature and, above all, on lubricants.

Of the intrinsic properties the molecular adhesion, the softening temperature and the relative hardness of the two materials are the most important. Friction is high when molecular adhesion is high; therefore friction of a material with itself is usually higher than that with a dissimilar material.

According to the studies of Bowden and Tabor (1954) friction is a complex summation of different factors:

1. internal friction, caused by mechanical damping

2. surface shear friction, i.e. shearing of the junction where the surfaces are in intimate contact; the extreme form of this shearing is ploughing of the harder material into the softer.

1. Internal friction

This type of friction is most important in cyclic processes like rolling friction and automobile tires. Mechanical damping and delayed recovery cause dissipation of energy; consequently, rolling friction and mechanical damping are well correlated. For a hard ball rolling on a plastic surface the following expression was found by Flom (1961):

$$\mu = 0.115\left(\frac{G''}{G'}\right)\left(\frac{W}{G'r^2}\right)^{1/2} \tag{25.10}$$

where
W = load on the rolling ball of radius r
G' = shear modulus of polymer surface on which the ball is rolling
G''/G' = dissipation factor
Expression (25.10) clearly demonstrates that rolling friction is large if $G''/G' = \tan \delta$ is large; so friction will be large in transition regions.

2. Surface friction

Even the smoothest surfaces are rough on a submicroscopic scale. The contacting surfaces touch each other on the relatively few points only. Sliding of one surface over the other produces large forces at the contact points. In many cases plastic deformation will occur; junctions will be welded together, so that shearing can take place even below the surface of the softer material. Sliding will cause periodic rupture of temporary junctions formed.

If shearing is the largest factor in friction, the coefficient of friction is roughly determined by

$$\mu_{sh} = \frac{\tau}{p_y} \tag{25.11}$$

where τ is the shear strength of the softer material, p_y is the yield pressure of the softer material.

The yield pressure p_y is related to the modulus:

$$p_y \sim E^n. \tag{25.12}$$

In the extreme case where the asperities of the harder material plough grooves into the softer material, strong abrasion and wear will occur. Since polymers are relatively soft materials, this "ploughing" term in the total friction may be important.

Slip-stick motion

If the static friction is greater than the kinetic friction, slip-stick motion may be the result. In rigid plastics the kinetic friction coefficient is normally lower than the static coefficient, in elastomers the reverse applies. At high velocities it is sometimes difficult to separate the effects of velocity and temperature.

Abrasion

Abrasion is closely related to friction, especially the "ploughing component" of the frictional force; it is, of course, also closely related to the scratch resistance. Zapp (1955) found that the abrasion loss was proportional to the kinetic coefficient of friction and to the dynamic modulus, and inversely proportional to the tensile strength. One of the well-known abrasion testers is the Taber Abraser (ASTM D 1044 and 1300).

Table 25.4 gives a survey of the coefficients of friction of a number of plastics together with the relative abrasion losses.

BIBLIOGRAPHY, CHAPTER 25

General references

Bowden, F.P. and Tabor, D., "The Friction and Lubrication of Solids", Clarendon Press, Oxford, 1954.
Kausch, H.H., Hassel, J.A. and Jaffee, R.J. (Eds.), "Deformation and Fracture of High Polymers", Plenum Press, New York, 1973.
Ku, P.M. (Ed.), "Interdisciplinary Approach to Friction and Wear", NASA SP-181, US Government Printing Office, Washington, DC, 1968.
Laeis, W., "Einführung in die Werkstoffkunde der Kunststoffe", Carl Hanser Verlag, München, 1972.
Nielsen, L.E., "Mechanical Properties of Polymers", Reinhold, New York, 1962.
Nielsen, L.E., "Mechanical Properties of Polymers and Composites", 2 volumes, Marcel Dekker, New York, 1974.
Ogorkiewicz, R.M. (Ed.), "Thermoplastics, Properties and Design", Wiley-Interscience, London, 1974.
Ogorkiewicz, R.M. (Ed.), "Engineering Properties of Thermoplastics", Wiley-Interscience, London, 1970.
Rabinowicz, E., "Friction and Wear of Materials", John Wiley & Sons, New York, 1974.
Roff, W.J. and Scott, J.R., "Fibres, Films, Plastics and Rubbers", Butterworths, London, 1971.
Rosen, B. (Ed.), "Fracture Processes in Polymeric Solids", Interscience, New York, 1964.
Schmitz, J.V. and Brown, W.E. (Eds.), "Testing of Polymers", 4 volumes, Interscience, New York, 1965–1969.
Timoshenko, S., "Theory of Elasticity", McGraw-Hill, New York, 1934.

Special references

Baer, E., Maier, R.E. and Peterson, R.N., SPE Journal 17 (1961) 1203.
Coleman, B.D., J. Polymer Sci. 20 (1956) 447; Textile Research J. 27 (1957) 393; 28 (1958) 393, 891.
Flom, D.G., J. Appl. Phys. 32 (1961) 1426.
Griffith, A.A., Phil. Trans. Roy. Soc. (London) A221 (1921) 163.
Hertz, H., J. reine angew. Mathem. 92 (1881) 156.
Natarajan, R. and Reed, P.E., J. Polymer Sci. A2, 10 (1972) 585.
Smith, T.L., J. Appl. Phys. 35 (1964) 27.
Tabor, D., Proc. Roy. Soc. (London) 192 (1947) 247.
Zapp, R.L., Rubber World 133 (1955) 59.

CHAPTER 26

PRODUCT PROPERTIES (II)

ENVIRONMENTAL BEHAVIOUR AND FAILURE

The environmental product properties comprise the heat stability, flammability and resistance to organic solvents and detergents.

The *heat stability* is closely related to the transition and decomposition temperatures, i.e. to intrinsic properties.

The *degree of flammability* of a polymeric material may be predicted from its chemical structure. One of the most valuable criteria in fire research, the so-called Oxygen Index (OI), may be estimated either from the specific heat of combustion or from the amount of char residue on pyrolysis. Since both quantities can be determined if the chemical structure is known, also the oxygen index can be estimated. An approximate assessment of the OI value direct from the elementary composition of the polymer is also possible.

The *environmental decay* of polymers in liquids is primarily dependent on the solubility parameters of polymer and liquid and on the hydrogen bond interaction between polymer and liquid.

Introduction

The properties which determine the "environmental behaviour" of polymers after processing into final products may be divided into three categories: the thermal end use properties, the flammability, and the properties determining the resistance of polymers to decay in liquids.

A. THERMAL END USE PROPERTIES

Heat stability

By heat stability is exclusively understood the stability (or retention) of properties (weight, strength, insulating capacity, etc.) under the influence of heat. The melting point or the decomposition temperature invariably form the upper limit; the "use temperature" may be appreciably lower.

All intrinsic properties are influenced by temperature; these relationships have been treated in the relevant chapters of this book. Especially the influence of temperature on the mechanical properties proved to be of great importance (Chapters 13 and 25). Sometimes the expression "maximum temperature in long-term use" is found in the literature.

It is rather vaguely defined but gives a certain impression of heat stability, especially in comparison with the melting point or decomposition temperature. Table 26.1 gives some values.

Heat distortion

The heat distortion test is similar to a creep test, except that the temperature is increased at a uniform rate rather than being kept constant. At the softening or heat distortion temperature the polymer begins to deform at a rapid rate over a narrow temperature interval.

For amorphous polymers the softening temperature is near the glass transition temperature, whereas for highly crystalline polymers it is close to the melting point.

The heat distortion curve is shifted by a change in the applied stress. The higher the load, the lower is the heat distortion temperature.

Frozen-in stresses due to molecular orientation may be measured by this technique,

TABLE 26.1

Heat stability of polymers

Polymer	Ultimate end-use temperature range in 200 h (°C)	Ultimate end-use temperature range in 1000 days (°C)
poly(vinyl chloride)	60– 90	60
polystyrene	60– 90	60
polyisoprene	60– 90	60– 80
poly(meth)acrylates	70–100	60– 80
polyolefins	70–100	60– 90
polyamides	100–150	80–100
linear polyurethanes	130–180	70–110
unsaturated polyurethanes	130–220	80–110
epoxy resins	140–250	80–130
cross-linked polyurethanes	150–250	100–130
polycarbonate	140	100–135
linear polyester (PETP)	140–200	100–135
cross-linked arom. polyester	180–250	120–150
poly(phenylene oxide) (PPO)	160–180	130–150
polysulphone	160–180	130–150
fluor elastomers	200–260	130–170
siloxane elastomers	200–280	130–180
polyester imides	200–280	150–180
polyamide imide	200–280	150–180
silicone resins	200–300	150–200
polyfluorocarbons	230–300	150–220
diphenyloxide resins	230–300	180–220
aromatic polyamides	250–300	180–230
polyimides	300–350	180–250
poly(tetrafluoroethylene)	300–350	180–250
polybenzimidazole	350–400	250–300

since oriented polymers shrink rapidly above the softening temperature. Non-homogeneously oriented parts cause deformations.

The polymer will only shrink if the applied stress is less than the frozen-in stress. If the external stress is greater than the internal stress, the sample will never shrink. Therefore distortion curves at different applied stresses are useful in the study of oriented polymer samples (e.g. drawn fibres) and the effect of heat treatments.

B. FLAMMABILITY OF POLYMERS

What happens in broad outline when a material burns is schematically indicated in fig. 26.1. Fundamentally there are two consecutive chemical processes – *decomposition* and *combustion*, connected by *ignition* and *thermal feedback*.

Primarily the material decomposes (pyrolysis), which normally *requires* heat. The decomposition products are combusted, which involves generation of heat. This heat of combustion is (partly) used to support the decomposition. *An ignition mechanism is essential.* Of great importance are the heat effects, Q_1 and Q_2, as well as the available area, A, of exchange of heat and matter.

To be fire resistant, a material should have a low Q_2 value and a low A value; another possibility is that the material contains elements which, on decomposition, form combustion inhibitors (Cl- and Br-containing polymers). Q_2 will be low if only small amounts of combustible gases develop in the pyrolysis, for instance, because the material chars considerably and mainly splits off carbon dioxide and water. The *residue of pyrolysis* or the sum of this residue and the weight of carbon dioxide and water formed by pyrolysis may be used as a rough measure of non-flammability.

A more direct criterion of flame resistance is the *Oxygen Index* (OI).

The Oxygen Index
The OI (at 25°C) as a criterion of flame resistance was introduced by Fenimore and

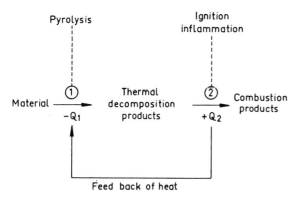

Fig. 26.1. Consecutive reactions during burning.

TABLE 26.2

Oxygen indices of polymers

Polymer	OI	Polymer	OI
Polyformaldehyde	0.15	Wool	0.25
Poly(ethylene oxide)	0.15	Polycarbonate	0.27
Poly(methyl methacrylate)	0.17	Nomex ®	0.285
Polyacrylonitrile	0.18	PPO ®	0.29
Polyethylene	0.18	Polysulphone	0.30
Polypropylene	0.18	Phenol−formaldehyde resin	0.35
Polyisoprene	0.185	Neoprene ®	0.40
Polybutadiene	0.185	Polybenzimidazole	0.415
Polystyrene	0.185	Poly(vinyl chloride)	0.42
Cellulose	0.19	Poly(vinylidene fluoride)	0.44
Poly(ethylene terephthalate)	0.21	Poly(vinylidene chloride)	0.60
Poly(vinyl alcohol)	0.22	Carbon	0.60
Nylon 66	0.23	Poly(tetrafluoroethylene) (Teflon ®)	0.95
Penton ®	0.23		

Martin (1966). It is the minimum fraction of oxygen in the test atmosphere which will just support combustion (after ignition). The test is performed under standardized conditions, at 25°C. In their initial description of the OI technique they reported that OI values are constant at linear flow rates of 3−10 cm/s. The current standard method for OI determinations specifies linear flow rates of 4 ± 1 cm/s. Table 26.2 gives the OI value of some polymeric materials.

A material must be considered flammable as long as the OI value is smaller than 0.26. Later investigations (e.g. Hendrix et al., 1973) have shown that the OI value is dependent on the weight, construction, moisture content and purity of the sample, on the temperature of the testing environment, and on the size and construction of the sample holder. Yet under standardized conditions the method is very precise, highly reproducible and applicable to a wide variety of materials (plastics, films, textiles, etc.). At the moment it is probably the most valuable test in fire research, although it cannot be considered as a replacement for all existing fire test methods. For instance, it cannot be used for assessing glow and flow (droplet) factors. The specific advantage of the Oxygen Index Test is that it gives numerical results and generally shows linear relationships to the flame-retardant level, whereas the other assessment tests (Tunnel Test, Underwriters Lab. Test) do not.

Since the flammability of materials increases with the ambient temperature, the oxygen index may be expected to decrease with increasing temperature. Johnson (1974) derived a quantitative experimental expression for OI-retention as a function of temperature. This is illustrated by fig. 26.2.

The OI value decreases by the 3/2 power of temperature, which indicates that diffusional processes are more important than chemical activation of pyrolysis.

From fig. 26.2 the temperature can be derived at which any given oxygen index, measured at room temperature, will be reduced to 0.21. This will be the temperature at which the flammability of a material with a given OI will permit candle-like burning in ordinary air. The result is given in fig. 26.3.

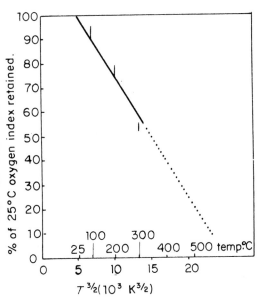

Fig. 26.2. Effect of temperature on oxygen index (after Johnson, 1974).

Relationships between OI and parameters of the combustion process

   Two interesting relationships have been found between the oxygen index and the parameters of the combustion process.

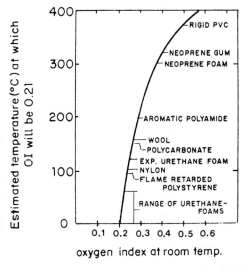

Fig. 26.3. Temperature for candle-like burning in air (after Johnson, 1974).

1. OI and heat of combustion

It is not surprising that a relationship exists between the heat evolved during combustion and the OI, the more so as ΔH_{comb} is closely correlated with the oxygen demand during combustion.

The molar heat of combustion can be calculated from the difference between the heat of formation of the carbon dioxide and water formed by complete combustion and the heat of formation of the substance combusted. The data for this calculation are provided in Chapter 20.

Much easier is the application of a simple rule, viz.

$$\Delta H_{comb} = \Delta(O_2) \times 435 \text{ kJ/mol} \tag{26.1}$$

where $\Delta(O_2)$ is the number of oxygen molecules needed for complete combustion of the structural unit (*molar oxygen demand*).

If we divide ΔH_{comb} by M, we obtain Δh_{comb}, the specific heat of combustion.

$$\Delta h_{comb} = \frac{\Delta(O_2)}{M} \times 435 \tag{26.2}$$

Table 26.3 shows how well Δh_{comb} is predicted by equation (26.2).

According to Johnson (1974) the OI values of many common materials can be reasonably well predicted by the expression:

$$OI = \frac{8000}{\Delta h_{comb}} \tag{26.3}$$

where Δh_{comb} is the *specific heat of combustion* in J/g.
Combination of the equations (26.2) and (26.3) gives:

$$OI = 0.184 \times \frac{M}{10 \, \Delta(O_2)} \tag{26.4}$$

Johnson states that the expression (26.3) is valid only as long as the atomic C/O ratio is larger than 6.

Fig. 26.4 shows the OI values in comparison with the drawn line calculated according to (26.3). It is clear that not only oxygen-rich polymers show large deviations, but also nitrogen-rich polymers such as polyacrylonitrile. Materials poor in hydrogen, such as carbon chars, graphites, etc., deviate as well. As a rule one may say that if the atomic C/O ratio or the C/N ratio is smaller than 6, the material is more flammable than is predicted by (26.4). If the C/H ratio is larger than about 1.5, the material will be less flammable than is predicted by (26.4). Halogen-containing polymers fit more or less into the scheme if their C/O and C/H ratios are appropriate.

2. OI and the char residue on pyrolysis

Pyrolysis being the first step in the combustion process of polymers, one may expect a relationship between OI and the parameters of pyrolysis.

An interesting correlation between OI and *char residue* (CR) on pyrolysis was found

TABLE 26.3

Specific heat of combustion of some polymers; comparison of calculation values

Polymer	Elementary composition of structural unit	M	$\Delta(O_2)$	Δh_{comb} (kJ/g)	
				calc.	exp.
Polyformaldehyde	CH_2O	30.0	1.0	14.5	16.7
Poly(methyl methacrylate)	$C_5H_8O_2$	100.1	6.0	26.1	–
Polyacrylonitrile	C_3H_3N	53.1	3.75	30.8	30.6
Polyethylene	C_2H_4	28.1	3.0	46.3	46.5
Polypropylene	C_3H_6	42.1	4.5	46.5	46.5
Polyisoprene	C_5H_8	68.1	7.0	44.7	44.9
Polybutadiene	C_4H_6	54.1	5.5	44.2	45.2
Polystyrene	C_8H_8	104.1	10.0	41.7	41.5
Cellulose	$C_6H_{10}O_5$	162.2	6.0	16.1	16.7
Poly(ethylene terephthalate)	$C_{10}H_8O_4$	192.2	10.0	22.7	22.2
Poly(vinyl alcohol)	C_2H_4O	44.1	2.5	24.7	25.1
Nylon 66	$C_{12}H_{22}O_2N_2$	226.3	16.5	31.7	31.4
Polycarbonate	$C_{16}H_{14}O_3$	254.3	18.0	30.8	31.0
Nomex®	$C_{14}H_{10}O_2N_2$	238.3	15.5	28.3	28.7
Polychloroprene (Neoprene®)	C_4H_5Cl	88.5	5.0	24.5	24.3
Poly(vinyl chloride)	C_2H_3Cl	62.5	2.5	17.5	18.0
Poly(vinylidene chloride)	$C_2H_2Cl_2$	97.0	2.0	9.0	10.45

by Van Krevelen (1974):

$$OI = \frac{17.5 + 0.4\,CR}{100} \qquad (26.5)$$

where CR is expressed as a weight percentage. This expression is valid for halogen-free polymers only.

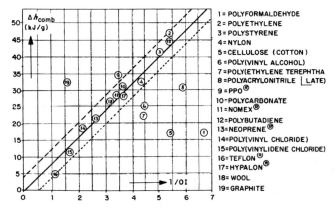

Fig. 26.4. Heat of combustion vs. OI (after Johnson, 1974).

530

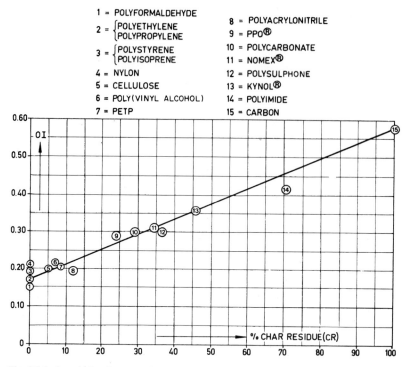

1 = POLYFORMALDEHYDE
2 = { POLYETHYLENE / POLYPROPYLENE }
3 = { POLYSTYRENE / POLYISOPRENE }
4 = NYLON
5 = CELLULOSE
6 = POLY(VINYL ALCOHOL)
7 = PETP

8 = POLYACRYLONITRILE
9 = PPO®
10 = POLYCARBONATE
11 = NOMEX®
12 = POLYSULPHONE
13 = KYNOL®
14 = POLYIMIDE
15 = CARBON

Fig. 26.5. Correlation between OI and CR.

Fig. 26.5 shows the relationship for a number of polymers.

Since the char residue on pyrolysis can be estimated by means of group contributions (see Chapter 21), also the value of OI may be estimated by means of eq. (26.5).

Oxygen index and elementary composition

Since the heat of combustion of a material and its char residue can be calculated from its elementary structure, it seemed logical to ascertain whether there is a direct relation between the Oxygen Index and the elementary composition.

Van Krevelen and Hoftyzer (1974) succeeded in finding such a relationship by using the following composition parameter (CP):

$$CP = \frac{H}{C} - 0.65\left(\frac{F}{C}\right)^{1/3} - 1.1\left(\frac{Cl}{C}\right)^{1/3} \tag{26.6}$$

where $\frac{H}{C}, \frac{F}{C}$ and $\frac{Cl}{C}$ are the atomic ratios of the respective elements in the polymer composition.

For the oxygen index the following correlations could be derived:

For CP $\geqslant$ 1: OI $\approx$ 0.175 \hfill (26.7a)

For CP $\leqslant$ 1: OI $\approx$ 0.60 – 0.425 CP \hfill (26.7b)

The equations give fairly good results for many polymers, as is shown in fig. 26.6

Estimation of the Oxygen Index

We now have three relations which — with some limitations — enable us to make an estimation of the Oxygen Index:

1. $OI = \dfrac{8000}{\Delta h_{comb}} \approx 0.184 \dfrac{M}{10\,\Delta\,(O_2)}$

2. $OI = \dfrac{1}{100}(17.5 + 0.4\,CR)$

3. $OI \approx 0.60 - 0.425\,CP$ for $CP \leqslant 1$
   $OI \approx 0.175$ for $CP \geqslant 1$
   with CP defined as given in equation (26.6)

Table 26.4 shows the results of OI estimation by these three relations in comparison with the experimental values.

Example 26.1

Estimate the specific heat of combustion of polycarbonate and its oxygen index by means of equation (26.3).

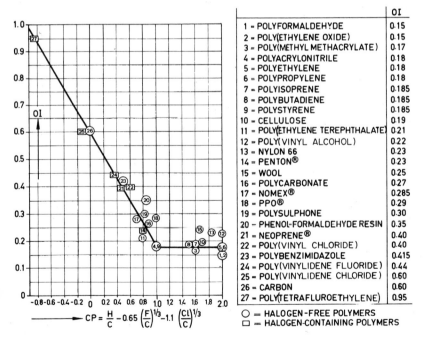

	OI
1 = POLYFORMALDEHYDE	0.15
2 = POLY(ETHYLENE OXIDE)	0.15
3 = POLY(METHYL METHACRYLATE)	0.17
4 = POLYACRYLONITRILE	0.18
5 = POLYETHYLENE	0.18
6 = POLYPROPYLENE	0.18
7 = POLYISOPRENE	0.185
8 = POLYBUTADIENE	0.185
9 = POLYSTYRENE	0.185
10 = CELLULOSE	0.19
11 = POLY(ETHYLENE TEREPHTHALATE)	0.21
12 = POLY(VINYL ALCOHOL)	0.22
13 = NYLON 66	0.23
14 = PENTON®	0.23
15 = WOOL	0.25
16 = POLYCARBONATE	0.27
17 = NOMEX®	0.285
18 = PPO®	0.29
19 = POLYSULPHONE	0.30
20 = PHENOL-FORMALDEHYDE RESIN	0.35
21 = NEOPRENE®	0.40
22 = POLY(VINYL CHLORIDE)	0.40
23 = POLYBENZIMIDAZOLE	0.415
24 = POLY(VINYLIDENE FLUORIDE)	0.44
25 = POLY(VINYLIDENE CHLORIDE)	0.60
26 = CARBON	0.60
27 = POLY(TETRAFLUOROETHYLENE)	0.95

$CP = \dfrac{H}{C} - 0.65\left(\dfrac{F}{C}\right)^{1/3} - 1.1\left(\dfrac{Cl}{C}\right)^{1/3}$

○ = HALOGEN-FREE POLYMERS
□ = HALOGEN-CONTAINING POLYMERS

Fig. 26.6. Correlation between oxygen index and elementary composition.

Solution

The elemental formula of polycarbonate is $C_{16}H_{14}O_3$ (M = 254.3), so that the combustion equation reads:

$$C_{16}H_{14}O_3 + 18\ O_2 \rightarrow 16\ CO_2 + 7\ H_2O$$

The molar oxygen demand is 18.
For the specific heat of combusion we get:

$$\Delta h_{comb} = \frac{\Delta(O_2) \times 435}{254.3} = \frac{78300}{254.3} = 30.8\ kJ/g$$

The experimental value is 30.9, so there is an excellent agreement. The C/O ratio of polycarbonate is 16/3 = 5.35. So equation (26.3) may be applied. We find

$$OI = \frac{8000}{30800} = 0.26$$

TABLE 26.4

Comparison of experimental and calculated OI values

Polymer	OI exp.	OI calculated from		
		CR	Δh_{comb}	$\frac{H}{C}$ etc.
Polyformaldehyde	0.15	0.175	–	0.175
Poly(ethylene oxide)	0.15	0.175	–	0.175
Poly(methyl methacrylate)	0.17	0.175	–	0.175
Polyacrylonitrile	0.18	0.175	0.26!	0.175
Polyethylene	0.18	0.175	0.17	0.175
Polypropylene	0.18	0.175	0.17	0.175
Polyisoprene	0.185	0.175	0.18	0.175
Polybutadiene	0.185	0.175	0.18	0.175
Polystyrene	0.185	0.175	0.19	0.175
Cellulose	0.19	0.195	–	0.175
Poly(ethylene terephthalate)	0.21	0.205	–	0.26!
Poly(vinyl alcohol)	0.22	0.21	–	0.175!
Nylon 66	0.23	0.175!	0.25	0.175!
Penton®	0.23	–	0.44!	0.27
Wool	0.25	0.175!	0.30!	0.175!
Polycarbonate	0.27	0.27	0.26	0.23!
Nomex®	0.285	0.295	0.28	0.295
PPO®	0.29	0.295	0.23!	0.175!
Polysulphone	0.30	0.315	0.26!	0.255!
Phenol–formaldehyde resin	0.35	0.355	0.25!	0.235!
Neoprene®	0.40	–	0.34!	0.36
Polybenzimidazole	0.415	0.445	(0.25)	0.39
Poly(vinyl chloride)	0.42	–	0.45	0.34!
Poly(vinylidene fluoride)	0.44	–	0.59!	0.45
Poly(vinylidene chloride)	0.60	–	(0.8)	0.64
Carbon (graphite)	0.60	0.575	–	0.60
Poly(tetrafluoroethylene) (Teflon®)	0.95	–	0.95	0.95

The experimental values mentioned in the literature vary from 0.25 to 0.28, with a most probable value of 0.27.

Example 26.2
Estimate the char residue on pyrolysis of polycarbonate and its oxygen index.

Solution
In example (21.1) we have already estimated the char-forming tendency and the char residue of polycarbonate. A CR value of 24% was found.
By means of equation (26.5) we calculate the OI value:

$$OI = \frac{17.5 + 0.4 \times 24}{100} = \frac{17.5 + 9.6}{100} = 0.27$$

This is in excellent agreement with the experimental value (0.27).

Example 26.3
Estimate the oxygen index of polycarbonate from its chemical composition.

Solution
From the elementary formula $C_{16}H_{14}O_3$ the H/C value of 0.875 is derived. Since the polymer does not contain halogen, also the CP value is 0.875. So equation (26.7b) gives OI $\approx 0.60 - 0.425 \times 0.875 \approx 0.23$.

The relationships mentioned lead to some interesting general conclusions:
1. The flame resistance increases according as the heat of combustion (and hence the oxygen demand during combustion) is smaller.
2. The flame resistance increases with the pyrolysis residue in thermal decomposition. This is the case when the polymer structure comprises more groups with a high char-forming tendency value (see table 21.2).
3. The flame resistance increases as the hydrogen content is lower and the halogen content higher. In this respect the atomic ratios are decisive. In the first instance the oxygen and nitrogen contents do not play a role!

Flame-retardant additives
Flame-retardant additives — often used to make polymers more fire resistant — may be based on different functions:
   a. They may reduce the area of contact between the material and oxygen, either by mechanical sealing of the surface (e.g. by melting or by the formation of a glassy film) or by splitting off non-combustible gases which temporarily seal the surface from the air.
   b. They may influence the pyrolysis, e.g. by "steering" the polymer decomposition, promoting char formation and/or formation of non-combustible gases such as carbon dioxide and water vapour.
   c. They may influence the combustion by disturbing the ignition or the combustion mechanism itself, e.g. by capturing OH radicals. For instance, as in the following reaction scheme:

TABLE 26.5

Average requirements for fire-retardant elements to render common polymers self-extinguishing (Lyons, 1970)

Polymer	%P	%Cl	%Br	%P + %Cl	%P + %Br	%Sb$_4$O$_6$ + %Cl	%Sb$_4$O$_6$ + %Br
Cellulose	2.5–3.5	>24	–	–	1 + 9	12–15 + 9–12	–
Polyolefins	5	40	20	2.5 + 9	0.5 + 7	5 + 8	3 + 6
Poly(vinyl chloride)	2–4	40	–	NA	–	5–15% Sb$_4$O$_6$	–
Acrylates	5	20	16	2 + 4	1 + 3	–	7 + 5
Polyacrylonitrile	5	10–15	10–12	1–2 + 10–12	1–2 + 5–10	2 + 8	2 + 6
Styrene	–	10–15	4–5	0.5 + 5	0.2 + 3	7 + 7–8	7 + 7–8
Acrylonitrile–butadiene–styrene	–	23	3	–	–	5 + 7	–
Urethane	1.5	18–20	12–14	1 + 10–15	0.5 + 4–7	4 + 4	2.5 + 2.5
Polyester	5	25	12–15	1 + 15–20	2 + 6	2 + 16–18	2 + 8–9
Nylon	3.5	3.5–7	–	–	–	10 + 6	–
Epoxies	5–6	26–30	13–15	2 + 6	2 + 5	–	3 + 5
Phenolics	6	16	–	–	–	–	–

Combustion chain:

$$CO + HO\cdot \rightarrow CO_2 + H\cdot$$
$$H_2 + HO\cdot \rightarrow H_2O + H\cdot$$
$$H\cdot + O_2 \rightarrow HO\cdot + O\cdot \quad \text{etc.}$$

Radical capturing:

$$HXBr \quad \rightarrow X' + HBr$$
$$HBr + HO\cdot \rightarrow H_2O + Br\cdot$$
$$Br\cdot + RH \rightarrow R\cdot + HBr$$
$$2R\cdot \rightarrow R_2$$

The most important flame retardants are compounds of phosphorus and/or halogen, or are based on synergisms of these elements with nitrogen and antimony. Hoke (1973) gave a handy classification scheme which is reproduced in fig. 26.7, while table 26.5 gives the average concentrations required to render the common polymers self-extinguishing.

Very often a linear relationship between the oxygen index and the concentration of the flame-retardant additive is observed:

$$OI = (OI)_0 + K(FR) \tag{26.8}$$

where K is a constant of the order of 0.005 and (FR) is the flame-retardant additive concentration (% by weight).

Smoke formation

Smoke generation may be a serious factor in a fire.

Normally polymer structures containing aliphatic backbones are low in smoke-generating character and are generally not self-extinguishing. Addition of additives to such systems to achieve flame-retardancy often enhances smoke generation!

Polymers with aromatic side groups such as polystyrene have a considerable tendency to generate smoke.

Polymers with an aromatic group in the main chain, however, such as polysulphones, polycarbonates and poly(phenylene oxides) proved to be intermediate in their smoke

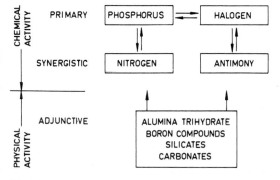

Fig. 26.7. Classification of flame retardants (after Hoke, 1973).

generation, possibly due to their considerable charring tendency. Also the unexpected drop in smoke density observed when poly(vinyl chloride) is partially chlorinated may be attributed to the high char yield. Einhorn et al. (1968) concluded that smoke development decreases with increasing degree of aromaticity in the polymer main chain, with increasing amount of chlorine- and phosphorus-containing additives, and with increasing cross-link density.

Gross et al. (1967) and Imhof and Stueben (1973) developed a smoke density index (D_m) based on the maximum specific optical density, ranging from 0 to 1000. High D_m values are found for polymers with Oxygen Index values between 0.18 and 0.30.

C. ENVIRONMENTAL DECAY OF POLYMERS IN LIQUIDS

While a given polymer may be quite resistant to some organic liquids, it may be attacked more or less severely by others. The effect of organic liquids on polymers can take several forms:

a. *dissolution*
b. *swelling*
c. *environmental stress cracking*
d. *environmental crazing*

Solubility and swelling have already been discussed in Chapter 7.

In *environmental stress cracking* the material fails by breaking when exposed to mechanical stress in the presence of organic liquids or wetting agents (soap solutions, etc.).

In *environmental crazing* the specimen fails by the development of a multitude of very fine cracks in the presence of an organic liquid or its vapour. This phenomenon may manifest itself even without the presence of mechanical stress: the internal stresses, always present in plastic specimens, can be sufficient.

The phenomena of stress cracking and crazing in the presence of a wide variety of organic liquids occur in both amorphous and semi-crystalline materials. They can lead to catastrophic failure at stresses far below the tensile strength and the critical stress for crazing of the materials tested in air. Especially solvent crazing may be regarded as an inherent material weakness of glassy polymers; in semi-crystalline polymers the problem is somewhat less serious.

It is not always possible to distinguish clearly between the phenomena a. to d., as they are dependent on the way the experiment is performed, on the time scale, the molecular weight of the polymer, etc. So the same polymer–solvent combination may be classed into different categories by different investigators.

Mechanism of solvent cracking and solvent crazing

Dissolution, swelling and solvent cracking are closely related phenomena. The initial action of an aggressive agent is to swell the polymer. The resulting lowering of the T_g causes a reduction of the stress required to initiate plastic flow at a given temperature. Whether dissolving or cracking will dominate is determined by the rate of solvent penetration on one hand and the rate of crack formation on the other. These phenomena are dependent on a number of properties of polymer and solvent and on the applied stress.

The phenomenon of solvent crazing cannot be explained from swelling, as many liquids which cause crazing do not show any swelling effect. Some authors assumed that the effect was caused by a lowering of the surface energy of the polymer in the presence of a solvent. Andrews and Bevan (1972) calculated values for the minimum surface energy of poly(methyl methacrylate) in different solvents that caused crazing.

Recent work of Kambour et al. (1973), however, raises doubts about the surface energy hypothesis. Although the last word has not been said in this matter, the effect of crazing solvents must probably be attributed to plasticization. This means that crazing agents, although present in minute concentrations, lower the stress level at which void propagation takes place.

According to MacNulty (1974), failure by solvent crazing occurs by brittle fracture, even when the failure is slow. Always a small liquid penetration zone appears to initiate the break.

Prediction of solvent cracking and solvent crazing

The foregoing considerations about the mechanism of solvent cracking and solvent crazing suggest that the solubility parameter difference, as a quantitative measure of the interaction between polymer and solvent, will play an important part in these phenomena.

This was confirmed in an investigation by Bernier and Kambour (1968) into the effect of different solvents on poly(dimethylphenylene oxide). (In this investigation, liquids thought to interact via hydrogen bonding were left out of consideration.) The authors demonstrated that the *critical strain* plotted against the solubility parameter of the solvent shows a minimum, while the equilibrium solubility against the solubility parameter shows a maximum at the same value (see figs. 26.8 and 26.9). It may be assumed that at the minimum critical strain (maximum solubility) the solubility parameter of the polymer

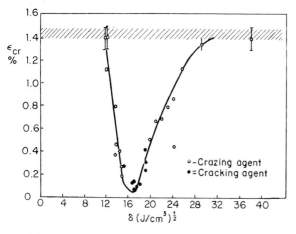

Fig. 26.8. Critical strain of poly(2,6-dimethyl-1,4-phenylene oxide) vs. solubility parameter δ of crazing and cracking liquids. Minimum in ϵ_{cr} occurs at δ equal to that of the polymer. Band at top indicates critical strain of polymer in air (Bernier and Kambour, 1968; reproduced by permission of the American Chemical Society).

538

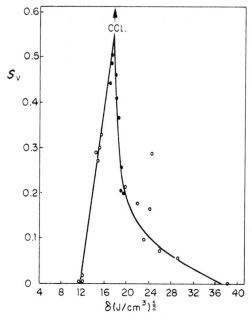

Fig. 26.9. Equilibrium solubilities of crazing fluids in poly(2,6-dimethyl-1,4-phenylene oxide) (Bernier and Kambour, 1968; reproduced by permission of the American Chemical Society).

δ_P equals that of the solvent δ_S. Small differences between δ_P and δ_S give rise to solvent cracking, larger differences are attended with solvent crazing.

This picture becomes more complicated, however, if liquids which can participate in hydrogen bonding are taken into account. This was done by Vincent and Raha (1972) for poly(methyl methacrylate), poly(vinyl chloride) and polysulphone. They plotted their results as a function of solubility parameter and *hydrogen-bonding parameter* [1]. Their graphs are reproduced in fig. 26.10. In each graph a solubility region is indicated as a shaded area. The solvents which cause cracking are near the periphery of the solubility region, the crazing solvents at a greater distance.

So attempts to correlate solvent cracking and solvent crazing with solvent properties lead to the same conclusion as was drawn in Chapter 7 for the solubility of polymers, viz. that besides the solubility parameter at least one other solvent property must be taken into account. The method proposed by Vincent and Raha is one of several possible two-dimensional correlation methods.

It was demonstrated in Chapter 7 that solubility data could effectively be represented in a $\delta_v - \delta_h$ diagram, where $\delta_v = \sqrt{\delta_d^2 + \delta_p^2}$ and δ_d, δ_p and δ_h are the solubility parameter components according to Hansen, representing disperse forces, polar forces and hydrogen bonding, respectively.

A good correlation is obtained if the results of Vincent and Raha are plotted in a

[1] The hydrogen-bonding parameter is the shift of the infrared absorption band in the 4-μm range occurring when a given liquid is added to a solution of deuterated methanol in benzene.

$\delta_v - \delta_h$ diagram. The results for the three polymers can be made to coincide if $\delta_{vS} - \delta_{vP}$ and $\delta_{hS} - \delta_{hP}$ are used as parameters, where the capital subscripts S and P denote solvent and polymer. The difficulty in this approach is that the solubility parameter components of the polymers are not readily available. For poly(methyl methacrylate) and poly(vinyl chloride), values of δ_v and δ_h as determined by Hansen (1969) have been men-

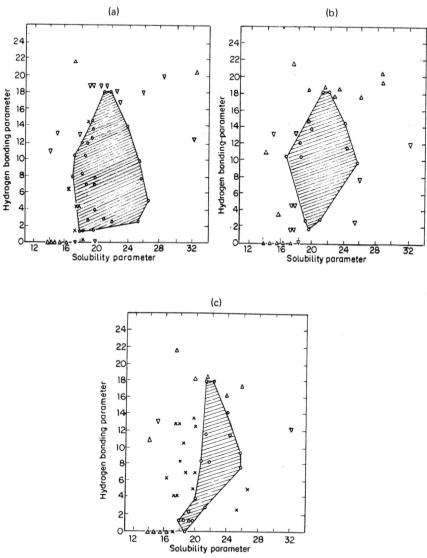

Fig. 26.10. Plot of data of Vincent and Raha (1972). (a) Solvents (o), cracking agents (x), low-strain crazing agents (▽) and high-strain crazing agents (△) for PMMA. (b) Solvents and swelling agents (o), low-strain crazing agents (▽) and high-strain crazing agents (△) for PVC. (c) Solvents, cracking and craz ing agents for polysulphone. Symbols are as in (a). (Reproduced by permission of the publishers, IPC Business Press Ltd.)

TABLE 26.6

Solubility parameter components of some polymers ($J^{1/2}/cm^{3/2}$)

Polymer	δ_v	δ_h
poly(vinyl chloride)	21.3	7.2
poly(methyl methacrylate)	21.4	8.6
polysulphone	22.0	8.0

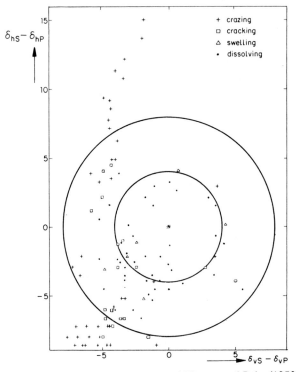

Fig. 26.11. Generalized plot of data of Vincent and Raha (1972).

TABLE 26.7

Parameters and effects of environment

Parameters	Effects
Stress and strain	Dissolution
Nature of environment	Softening
Temperature	Stress-cracking
Molecular weight	Embrittlement
Molecular architecture	Chemical degradation
Crystallinity	Photochemical degradation
Orientation	Biological degradation

tioned in Chapter 7; these values are used here. For polysulphone the values of δ_v and δ_h have been chosen in such a way that a good correlation was obtained. The solubility parameter components used are mentioned in table 26.6.

The data of Vincent and Raha for the three polymers mentioned have been plotted in fig. 26.11. Additional experimental data on polysulphone by Henry (1974) and MacNulty (1974) proved to be in good agreement with those of Vincent and Raha.

There is a small zone near the centre ($\delta_{vS} = \delta_{vP}$; $\delta_{hS} = \delta_{hP}$), where all solvents dissolve the polymer. At a large distance from the centre, crazing is generally found. In the intermediate zone, the main phenomenon is solvent cracking, although dissolving, swelling or crazing are observed with some solvents.

In principle, fig. 26.11 permits the prediction of solvent behaviour. The essential difficulty is the choice of proper values of the solubility parameter components δ_{vP} and δ_{hP} for a given polymer. As literature data are lacking, experimental determination of the solubility region for each new polymer cannot be avoided.

Life of a polymer in a liquid environment

Table 26.7 gives a survey of the parameters influencing the time to failure and the effects of environment on polymers. Ways to reduce the effects are to be found in the use of the parameters.

Several attempts have been made to quantitatively predict the lifetime of polymers in different liquid environments. Suezawa et al. (1963) showed that lifetimes under load in different liquids can be fitted to a mastercurve and that, in addition to stress also the environment can be considered a reduced variable.

Fulmer (1967) demonstrated that for a specific polymer every environment (liquid) shows a constant shift factor versus another environment. Next to his own experiments on (filled) polyethylene he used data obtained by Bergen (1964) in creep investigations. Table 26.8 lists some of these environmental shift factors for different polymers in two liquids. Comparative data for other polymer–liquid combinations are scarce.

TABLE 26.8

Environmental shift factors

(Hexane = 1)	
Polymer	Shift factor for isopropyl alcohol
Acrylonitrile–butadiene–styrene copolymer	120
Poly(vinyl chloride)	0.08
Polycarbonate	3
Styrene–acrylonitrile copolymer	1500

542

BIBLIOGRAPHY, CHAPTER 26

General references

Bradley, J.N., "Flame and Combustion Phenomena", Methuen, London, 1969.
Einhorn, I.N., "Fire Retardance of Polymeric Materials", J. Macromol. Sci., Revs. Polymer Technol. D 1 (2) (1971) 113–184.
Haward, R.N. (Ed.), "The Physics of Glassy Polymers", Applied Science Publishers, London, 1973.
Korshak, V.V., "The Chemical Structure and Thermal Characteristics of Polymers", Israel Program for Scient. Transl., Jerusalem, 1971.
Lyons, J.W., "The Chemistry and Uses of Fire Retardants", Wiley-Interscience, New York, 1970.
Thiery, P., "Fire Proofing", Elsevier, Amsterdam, 1970.

Special references

Abbott, C., Combustion Inst.; European Symposium 1973 (F.J. Weinberg, Ed.), p. 165 (Paper No. 28).
Andrews, E.H. and Bevan, L., Polymer 13 (1972) 337.
Bergen, R.L., SPE Journal 20 (1964) 630.
Bernier, G.A. and Kambour, R.P., Macromolecules 1 (1968) 393.
Einhorn, I.N., Mickelson, R.W., Shah, B. and Craig, R., J. Cell. Plast. 4 (1968) 188.
Emmons, H.W., J. Heat Transfer 95 (1973) (2) 145.
Fenimore, C.P. and Martin, F.J., Modern Plastics 44 (1966) 141; Combustion and Flame 10 (1966) 135.
Fulmer, G.E., Polymer Eng. Sci. 7 (1967) 280.
Gross, D., Loftus, J.J. and Robertson, A.F., ASTM STP-422 (1967) 166.
Hansen, C.M., Ind. Eng. Chem. Prod. Res. Dev. 8 (1969) 2.
Hendrix, J.F., Drake, G.L. and Reeves, W.A., (J. Am. Assoc.) Textile Chemist and Colourist 5 (1973) 144.
Henry, L.F., Polymer Eng. Sci. 14 (1974) 167.
Hoke, Ch.E., Soc. Plast. Eng. Techn. Pap. 19 (1973) 548; SPE Journal 29 (1973) (5) 36.
Imhof, L.G. and Stueben, K.C., Polymer Eng. Sci. 13 (1973) 146.
Johnson, P.R., J. Appl. Polymer Sci. 18 (1974) 491.
Kambour, R.P., Gruner, C.L. and Romagosa, E.E., J. Polymer Sci., Polymer Phys. Ed. 11 (1973) 1879.
MacNulty, B.J., British Polymer J. 6 (1974) 39.
Nametz, R.C., "Flame Retarding Synthetic Textile Fibres", Ind. Eng. Chem. 62 (1970) 41–53.
Suezawa, Y., Hojo, H., Ideda, T. and Okamura, Y., Materials and Research Standards 3 (1963) 550.
Vincent, P.I. and Raha, S., Polymer 13 (1972) 283.
Van Krevelen, D.W., "New Developments in the Field of Flame-Resistant Fibres", Angew. Makromol. Chem. 22 (1972) 133–158.
Van Krevelen, D.W., "Correlation between Flame Resistance and Chemical Structure of Polymers", Paper No. IV.5-2, IUPAC Conference on Macromolecules, Madrid, 1974; Polymer 16 (1975) 615.
Van Krevelen, D.W. and Hoftyzer, P.J., (1974) Unpublished results.

CHAPTER 27

AN ILLUSTRATIVE EXAMPLE OF END USE PROPERTIES:
ARTICLE PROPERTIES OF TEXTILE PRODUCTS

There is no category of products made from polymeric materials in which the article properties play such a predominant role — and are so varied — as in textile products; therefore the emphasis in this last chapter is on textile applications.

An integral method of evaluating polymeric materials for specific end uses is given: the so-called *profile method.*

Introduction

Textile articles are more or less unique by the wide and varied range of product properties which prove to be important. This is the reason why this product category will be discussed in more detail.

As described in Chapter 1, the article properties can be distinguished into three groups:
the aesthetic properties
the use or performance properties
the maintenance or care properties
In this order the article properties of textile products will be discussed.

A. AESTHETIC PROPERTIES

In this category belong the properties which determine the reactions (*perceptions*) of the senses: the eye (colour, lustre, covering power, appearance), and the tactile sense, viz. the tactile corpuscles of the skin (handle).

While the aesthetic properties are influenced by the intrinsic properties, they depend much more on the "added" properties, that is to say on those obtained during processing, as is clearly shown in table 27.1.

The correlation of the aesthetic properties with the intrinsic and added properties is very complex and only partly understood. (As matters stand at present, they are more qualitative than quantitative.)

The main aesthetic properties are considered below.

1. Colour and whiteness

Colour is very important, but it normally is an added property; it is obtained by a

TABLE 27.1

General correlation of aesthetic properties with intrinsic and added properties

Properties	Whiteness and colour	Lustre and gloss	Covering power	Handle and drape
Intrinsic properties				
Chemical structure	x			
Physical morphology	x	x	x	
Thermal stability	x			
Bending modulus				x
Stress relaxation				x
Added properties				
Fibre and yarn fineness		x	xx	x
Fibre cross-section		xx		x
Fibre microstructure	x	xx	x	x
Fibre and yarn surface				x
Yarn construction		x	xx	xx
Fabric construction		xx	xx	xx
Fabric finish				
(heat treatment)	x			xx

x = statistically significant; xx = (very) important.

dyeing process. Brilliant colours are the most popular but the most difficult to obtain. They can be realized only if the polymer itself is "water-white" (colourless). It is necessary that the whiteness is also maintained during processing and aftertreatment; yellowing of the polymer as such severely affects the appearance of the coloured product.

Whether a polymer can be suitably coloured depends on:

a. the chemical structure of the polymer; functional groups determine which class of pigments or dyestuffs is preferable. Basic dyestuffs lead to the highest brilliance but the colour often has a poor fastness. In acrylic fibres basic dyestuffs are more brilliant and much faster than in other polymeric fibres, such as polyesters.

b. the fine structure of the polymer; a smooth compact fibre, for instance, is more favourable than a microporous structure (although with regard to accessibility or *ease* of dyeing the reverse is true).

c. the *whiteness* of the polymer. *Whiteness means that the spectrum of the polymer shows no absorption bands in the visual part.*

2. Lustre and gloss

Lustre is the integral effect of *reflection* and *diffraction.* The larger the size of the reflecting areas, the more pronounced the reflection (glittering). This is the reason why the morphology of the fibre, and its cross-section, play a dominating part in textiles. A silky lustre is highly appreciated. Combination of lustre and colour may produce very special effects (gold, copper, silver lustre, etc.).

3. Covering power

While transparency is preferred in polymeric films, the covering power is an important factor in textiles.

Unlike the transparency of fibres, the transparency of fabrics is strongly reduced by light diffraction and lustre: *the transparency of a fabric is almost entirely determined by the morphology of the fibre and by the construction of yarn and fabric. Additional influence is exerted by pigments and dyes.*

For films and paper there are standard methods for measuring the transparency; such standards are not yet available for fabrics.

4. Handle and drape

In the evaluation of a textile product the handle and drape, both subjective quantities, play an important part.

Handle may be defined as a subjective tactile evaluation of the textile quality.

Howorth (1958, 1964) concluded that three fundamental cloth properties determine the handle, viz. *stiffness, softness* and *bulkiness* (thickness per unit weight).

It appears that the effect of the yarn and fabric construction on these properties is at least as great as the effect of the differences resulting from the nature of the polymer.

The *stiffness* of a fabric can be objectively determined as the average of the flexural rigidities (in warp and weft direction). These depend on the shear modulus and the coefficient of friction; both are influenced by swelling and, therefore by humidity.

The *softness* of a textile material is presumably built up of two components: the smoothness of the fibre and the smoothness of the fabric; the latter is determined by the fabric construction and the yarn structure (bulkiness, etc.).

In regard to *bulkiness,* we distinguish between the bulkiness of a fabric and that of a yarn (thickness per unit weight). Yarns having a higher bulkiness will give fabrics with a better handle and drape, a higher covering power and greater comfort.

The influence of the intrinsic polymer properties on the yarn bulkiness is relatively small (low density and high stiffness are favourable) in contrast with that of the fibre, yarn and cloth constructions. Hence the significance of texturing (crimping) processes, which impart a greater bulkiness (crimp) to the compact filament yarn.

Drape is a visual quality characteristic, referring to the degree to which a fabric falls into folds under the influence of gravity. Paper and film have a very poor drape; fabrics generally have a drape varying from acceptable to excellent. In knitted fabrics the drapability is generally quite sufficient; for woven articles a proper drape can usually be realized by choosing a suitable weave and finish treatment. The drape of non-wovens presents problems because of the stiffness produced by the bonding of fibres and filaments.

Drape is determined by the same basic quantities as handle.

Both handle and drape are strongly influenced by the cloth construction and the aftertreatment (finish) of the article. The chemical structure of the polymer has a secondary influence.

B. USE OR PERFORMANCE PROPERTIES

Most of the use properties have to do with comfort or with the retention of desired properties (colour, shape, appearance, etc.).

Also this category of properties is much more dependent on added properties than on the intrinsic ones. Again, the correlations are of a complex nature and are qualitative rather than quantitative. Table 27.2 shows the interdependence.

TABLE 27.2

General correlation of use (performance) properties with intrinsic and added properties

Intrinsic/added properties	Use (performance) properties							
	Thermal comfort	Mechanical comfort	Shape retention (wrinkle fastness)	Retention of surface appearance (wear fastness)	Colour fastness	Soiling resistance	Resistance to static charging	Resistance to fatigue
Intrinsic properties								
Chemical structure	x				x	x	x	x
Physical morphology			x		x	x		x
Transition regions			xx					xx
Surface energy	x					x	x	
Moisture absorption	x		xx				xx	
Light fastness					x			
Thermal stability			x					x
Stress–strain pattern		x	x	x				
Stress relaxation			x					
Creep			xx					
Young's modulus		x	x	x				
Mechanical damping				x				xx
Elastic recovery		x	x					
Torsion relaxation		x	x					
Bending modulus		x	x					
Lateral strength				x				
Added properties								
Fibre and yarn fineness	x							
Fibre micro structure	x					x		
Fibre and yarn friction				xx				xx
Yarn construction	xx	xx	xx	xx		xx		
Fabric construction	xx	xx	xx	xx		xx		
Heat treatment ("finish")	x	x	xx		x	xx	xx	

x = statistically significant; xx = (very) important.

In the following, the use properties will be discussed in some detail.

1. Thermal comfort

Thermal comfort exists if the human body is in thermal equilibrium with its environment, implying a constant temperature of the body. Comfort is mainly determined by the *construction* of a garment, in particular by its thermal *insulation* and by *moisture transfer*. This means that — save in exceptional circumstances — the nature of the textile fibre is less material than the fabric construction.

Heat insulation is *mainly determined by the construction of the fabric,* is proportional to its thickness, and decreases with increasing air velocity (wind).

Moisture may be transferred via three mechanisms:

(1) *water vapour permeation,* which is inversely proportional to thickness and increases with air velocity

(2) *capillary moisture transfer,* which increases with the *wettability,* and therefore depends on *interfacial tension*

(3) *moisture transfer through fibres,* which increases with the *moisture absorption.* Of these mechanisms the water vapour permeation seems to be the most important.

In steady states, where the heat production of the human body is practically in equilibrium with the heat loss, discomfort is nevertheless felt if about 25% of the skin is moistured by perspiration.

Comfort is felt if the heat insulation and the water vapour permeability agree with the following key values, which are based on experience (See table 27.3).

Since the ratios of the heat and water vapour permeability coefficients do not differ much, it suffices to assess one of them.

TABLE 27.3

Average comfort data of textile articles

Textile product	Thickness (mm)	Weight (kg/m^2)	Air permeation $(m^3/m^2 \cdot s)$	Heat permeability coefficient $(J/m^2 \cdot s \cdot K)$ [1] (a)	Water vapour permeability coefficient $(g/m^2 \cdot s \cdot bar)$ (b)	a/b
Lingerie	0.8	0.17	55	17.5	0.58	30
Linings	0.15	0.11	10	22	0.65	34
Shirting	0.30	0.11	10–100	21.5	0.70	31
Pullovers	2.0	0.4	50	12.5	0.44	29
Suiting	0.75	0.25	5–50	18.5	0.57	32
Overcoating	1.5	0.4	15	14	0.45	31
Work clothing	0.8	0.17	50	17.5	0.58	30

[1] In clothing physiology a thermal resistance coefficient, the *Clo,* is often used: 1 Clo = 0.155 $m^2 \cdot s \cdot K/J$.

2. Mechanical comfort

A distinction may be made between:

a. comfort in the sense that there is no tight fitting: the garment shows a reversible stretch corresponding to the *movements* of the body

b. comfort derived from ready adaptation to the *shape* of the body; here the *resilience* of the fabric is important.

The *cloth elasticity,* determined by the fabric construction, is the principal factor. Knitted fabrics may have a recoverable stretch of 200—300%, while woven fabrics cannot have more than about 25%.

The *yarn elasticity* plays a *minor* role, *unless* the elasticity of the yarn is very low or very high (high-elastic falsetwist yarns, elastomeric yarns).

3. Shape retention

Shape retention is a factor in almost all articles made from polymeric materials (cf. warping of plastic articles, deformation of films, etc.). In textiles the lack of shape retention is reflected in the sagging of curtains, the bagging of trousers, etc.

Shape retention is determined by the viscoelastic properties of the polymer, especially under the influence of moisture: plastic deformation and creep are highly undesirable, resilience is favourable.

Special forms of shape retention are wrinkle recovery and pleat and crease retention.

3a. Wrinkle recovery (wrinkle fastness)

By wrinkling is understood any fabric deformation resulting from the formation of folds that is not immediately and completely reversible.

The wrinkling behaviour of textile fabrics is determined not only by factors such as cloth construction, yarn construction, yarn fineness, friction, but also by the viscoelastic behaviour of the yarn (Rawling et al., 1956; Van der Meer, 1970). As a result, wrinkling is dependent on humidity, temperature and load. On the basis of results obtained with many different textile materials we may assume that the wrinkling of textile fabrics is much worse within "transition" ranges than beyond these ranges. A purely amorphous polymer has a transition range around the glass transition temperature (T_g). In highly crystalline polymers we find such a range around the crystalline melting point (melt transition). Partly crystalline polymers (i.e. nearly all the polymers used for textiles) have transition ranges both around the T_g and the T_m.

The properties of yarns made from partly crystalline polymers are dependent, among other factors, on the degree of crystallization and the nature of the crystalline ranges. As a result, measurements on model yarns, etc., of factors such as T_g, T_m and loss factor as a function of temperature, are not nearly sufficient to serve as a basis for making predictions concerning the wrinkling of textiles. However, it seems likely that for a good wrinkling behaviour the transition ranges of the material must lie outside the range of temperatures to which it is subjected during use, i.e. roughly outside the temperature range of 0—100°C. For a polymer this means a T_g in water above 100°C or a T_g in air below 0°C. In pressing and ironing, when we do want clear, irreversible deformations (smoothing, sharp creases or pleats), a transition range will have to be passed, and the treatment will have to take place as much as possible within a dispersion range. For polymers with a high T_g the transition range around T_g can be used. For hydrophilic materials this range can be shifted to lower temperatures by means of water (ironing of cotton, wool, rayon, using steam). If the amorphous material is in the rubbery state, excessive shrinking or sticking occurs in the transition range around the T_g. Ironing and pressing of these materials is impossible or very critical. For partly crystalline material with a low T_g (below $0°C$), ironing and pressing will have to be carried out in the transition range around the crystalline melting point. This, too, may be risky.

It seems probable that information on wrinkling can be obtained not only from the *loss factor* but also from the curve of the *modulus of elasticity as a function of temperature in air and water.* In this connection it has to be ascertained whether the deformation in wrinkling is imposed or determined by the load. If the latter is true, the modulus of elasticity will be an important parameter.

3b. Pleat and crease retention

Pleat and crease retention may be defined as the spontaneous reversal to the original state of a purposely made pleat or crease after it has temporarily faded through wear or washing. This property very much resembles that of wrinkle recovery, both having in common that there is always a return to a specially imposed shape, whether flat or pleated. The pleat is made under conditions in which the material is soft, that is at an elevated temperature and — if desired — in the presence of water or steam. Subsequent recrystallization of the fibre will then restore the desired shape, which is so fixed that it is very difficult to remove at a lower temperature, or even in water. Only during use, for instance during washing, if the temperature rises to above the softening temperature (in water!) will the pleat more or less disappear, depending on the degree of deformation imposed and on the duration.

It may be concluded that shape retention, wrinkle recovery and pleat and crease retention depend on well-known viscoelastic properties: the existence of a transition range, tension relaxation, creep and permanent deformation, and a possible resilience by a change in external conditions.

4. Retention of surface appearance

The degradation of surface appearance is generally connected with wear, but in the case of textiles it has also secondary effects like "fluffing" and "pilling". (In *plastics* the surface appearance is mainly determined by scratching. *Scratch hardness* is the main parameter. In textiles the coefficient of friction is the main factor.)

4a. Resistance to wear

Loss by wear is dependent on the coefficient of friction, the stiffness, the resilience and the degree of brittleness.

In order to assess the resistance to wear it has to be ascertained whether this property is in equilibrium with other properties, e.g. colour fastness and shape retention. If the durability is determined by the resistance to wear, the aesthetic and use properties must remain virtually constant during the life of the product.

A high wear resistance is a special advantage if it permits a lower weight per unit product.

4b. Fluffing and pilling

Since fluffs (or hairiness) and fibre balls (pills) have an unfavourable influence on the appearance of the fabric, their formation must be avoided.

Hairiness precedes the formation of pills; whether it gives rise to pilling depends on the number and length of the protruding fibres or filament ends per unit surface area.

Among the fibre properties, the lateral strength (double loop strength) and the bending abrasion resistance are the decisive factors. But more important than the intrinsic properties are the yarn and fabric constructions. Pilling decreases with decreasing filament fineness, increasing fibre length, increasing twist, and increasing fabric density.

This whole complex of parameters is normally assessed in a pilling tester, e.g. Baird's Random Tumble Pilling Tester (Baird et al., 1956). In this test various specimens are compared with a standard by counting the pills per unit area or by determining the weight per unit area.

5. Colour fastness

A good colour fastness implies that the colour is maintained under different conditions (rubbing, washing, exposure to sunlight, seawater, etc.). Colour fastness has many aspects, but it is sufficient to mention the three main groups: *light fastness, wet fastness* (washing, seawater, sweat, cleaning liquids), and *heat* (sublimation) *fastness.*

Light fastness is mainly determined by the nature of polymer and dyestuff and by the interaction between the two. Additives like pigments and stabilizers (antioxidants) are important. The better the light fastness of the polymer, the greater the chance that it will have a good colour fastness.

The wet fastness is determined by the bond strength between polymer and dyestuff, and therefore by the presence of specific functional groups in the polymer.

The heat (sublimation) fastness increases with the bond strength between polymer and dyestuff and with the sublimation temperature of the dyestuff.

6. Resistance to soiling

The soiling tendency of textiles can only be determined properly by means of actual wear and wash tests.

Two factors have direct impact:
a. the affinity of the polymer for fatty substances; this affinity is determined by the relation between the solubility parameters of polymer and soiling substance.
b. the roughness of the yarn surface; a rough yarn surface may mechanically take up finely dispersed soil, which can hardly be removed by washing.

Static charging may play a role, since a charged surface (yarn, cloth) attracts oppositely charged dust particles.

7. Resistance to static charging

The background of static charging has been discussed in Chapter 11. In general a strongly hydrophilic material will cause no static charging, in contrast with a hydrophobic material. In the latter, static charging can be largely suppressed by antistatic agents.

8. Resistance to fatigue

Fatigue is the decay of mechanical properties after repeated application of stress and strain. Fatigue tests give information about the ability of a material to resist the development of cracks or crazes resulting from a large number of deformation cycles.

Fatigue resistance is a major factor in industrial applications of textile materials (conveyer belts, automobile tyres, etc.). The fatigue resistance depends on the viscoelastic properties (mechanical damping) of the material, but equally on the soundness of bonds between the surfaces or interfaces.

In composite materials, such as tyres (reinforced with textile canvas) and other reinforced materials, the adhesion between the two phases is of prime importance: poor adhesion may induce fatigue failure.

The main variable in the fatigue test is the *fatigue life* as a function of the total number of cycles. Generally, the fatigue life is reduced by an increase of temperature. Therefore mechanical damping is so important: high damping may raise the temperature. In polymers of which the strength decreases rapidly with increasing temperature, high damping may be largely responsible for fatigue failure.

C. MAINTENANCE OR CARE PROPERTIES

This aspect will only be briefly discussed. The general correlations are shown in table 27.4. The main properties in this category are:

1. Washability

   a. *Resistance to washing.* This is measured by the loss of strength after 10, 20 or 50 washes. Mechanical dispersion (transition) regions and environmental degradation are important.

   b. *Cleanability by washing.* Cleanability may be defined as the degree to which dirt and strains can be removed. This property is dependent on the *nature of the polymer* and that of the dirt, and on the detergent used (surface energy); furthermore it is determined by the geometrical structure of the fabric and the yarn construction. It is clear that also the washing method and the temperature have a great influence.

   c. *Shrinkage resistance during washing.* This property, which is mainly dependent on the chemical structure of the polymer, has long been in the centre of attention. Interest has somewhat diminished following the development of anti-shrink finish treatments and stabilization. The distance between washing temperature and glass—rubber transition temperature has a great effect on the property.

2. Dryability

   a. *Quick drying.* The rate of drying is determined by the cloth construction, the

TABLE 27.4

General correlation of maintenance properties with intrinsic and added properties

Intrinsic/added properties	Maintenance properties					
	Washability	Quick drying	Wrinkle-free drying	Shrinkage	Pressability	Suitability for dry cleaning
Intrinsic properties						
Chemical structure	x	x	x			x
Physical morphology					x	x
Transition regions	x		x			x
Moisture absorption		xx	x	x		
Light fastness	x					
Thermal stability					x	
Solubility parameter	x					xx
Surface energy	xx					
Stress relaxation	x		x		x	
Creep	x		x	xx		
Elastic recovery	x					
Torsion relaxation			x		x	
Bending modulus			x		x	
Added properties						
Yarn construction	xx	x	x	xx	x	
Fabric construction	xx	x	x	xx	x	
Heat treatment (finish)	x		x	xx		

x = statistically significant; xx = (very) important.

swelling value of the fibre (on moisture uptake), and the bulkiness of the yarn.
b. *Wrinkle-free drying.* Shape retention in the washing process is an adequate expression for this property. It has already been discussed under Use or Performance Properties.

3. Pressability (Ironability)

The ease of ironing (pressing) depends on the relative positions of glass transition temperature and heat distortion or decomposition temperature. Also the influence of moisture on T_g is very important.

4. Suitability for dry-cleaning

This property is closely connected with the solubility parameters of polymer and dry-cleaning agent. Furthermore the dry-cleaning temperature should be outside a mechanical dispersion (transition) region of the polymer, since otherwise deformation may occur.

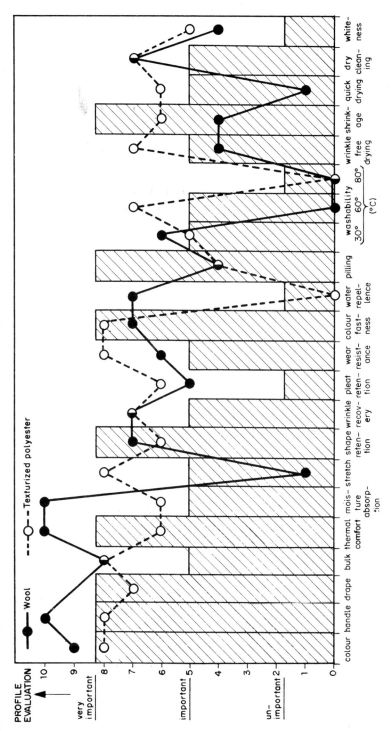

Fig. 27.1. Desirability profile (blocks) for a certain application (sweaters) compared with the product profile (lines) of wool and polyester.

D. INTEGRAL EVALUATION OF FIBRE POLYMERS, FIBRES AND YARNS BY THE CRITERIA MENTIONED (PROFILE METHOD)

The potential market for a polymer is primarily determined by its suitability for application in various fields. For a simple and rapid study of this qualitative aspect a selection method was developed which is referred to as *the profile method*. This method compares the properties required for the end product with those of the starting materials.

The *qualitative demands* made on the end product can be established by a study of consumer requirements. In an ideal situation the degree of importance would have to be established quantitatively, for instance as the d-function (desirability). By means of such a d-function the importance of the various properties can be measured and, consequently, also the influence of a change in one of the properties on the overall desirability. For practical reasons (practicability, time) the requirements to be satisfied by the end product in various applications usually are not indicated as d-functions, but are simple *rated* as *unimportant, important* and *very important.* This procedure is based on the results of consumer studies and gives the *desirability profile for the application.*

Also the article properties obtained by suitable processing form a profile, viz. the *product profile.*

The article properties are rated by experts, partly on the basis of quantitative measurements of intrinsic properties, partly on the basis of their experience.

By *comparison of the product profile with the desirability profile,* the strong and weak points of the product are immediately visible. By comparison of a starting material with materials that have already penetrated into a particular end use, the product's chances of capturing a market share by its qualitative aspects can be assessed.

Although the system is not perfect, it has been found to provide useful indications about the question in what applications the properties of some starting material are used to the best advantage and whether this starting material stands a chance in competition with other starting materials.

In fig. 27.1 an example is given of the position of wool and textured polyester in a well-defined application: sweaters. Almost the only points in favour of wool are its appearance and comfort; textured polyester does not score such high marks in these properties, but its care properties are considerably better than those of wool.

Textured polyester has mainly penetrated into a consumer category where, in addition to appearance, special value is attached to ease of care properties (middle price class).

Woollen articles are particularly dominant in the higher price bracket, where greater demands are made on the appearance; the ease of care properties only play a minor role (dry-cleaning instead of domestic laundering).

The wool industry has introduced a system of attaching the wool market exclusively to shrink-free and washable woollen sweaters. By the special treatment carried out to realize these properties it has been possible to reduce one of the greatest disadvantages of wool relative to synthetic fibres: its lack of shrink fastness.

In the same way any product may be rated for a specific end use of which the desirability profile can be designed.

BIBLIOGRAPHY, CHAPTER 27

General references

Fourt, L. and Hollies, N.R.S., "Clothing, Comfort and Function", M. Dekker, New York, 1970.
Hearle, J.W.S., Grosberg, P. and Backer, S., "Structural Mechanics of Fibers, Yarns and Fabrics", Wiley-Interscience, New York, 1969.
Kaswell, E.R., "Textile Fibers, Yarns and Fabrics", Reinhold Publ. Corp., New York, 1953.
Renbourn, E.T., "Materials and Clothing in Health and Disease", H.K. Lewis & Co., London, 1972.

Special references

Baird, E.M., Legere, L.E. and Stanley, H.E., Text. Res. J. 26 (1956) 731.
Howorth, W.S., J. Textile Inst. 55 (1964) T 251.
Howorth, W.S. and Oliver, P.H., J. Textile Inst. 49 (1958) T 540.
Rawling, G.D., Stanley, H.E. and Wilkinson, P.R., Text. Res. J. 26 (1956) 974.
Tippets, E.A., Text. Res. J. 37 (1967) 527.
Van der Meer, S.J., "Dynamic mechanical properties and permanent deformation of yarns, cords and fabrics", Thesis, University of Technology, Delft, 1970.

PART VII

COMPREHENSIVE TABLES

TABLE I

THE INTERNATIONAL SYSTEM OF UNITS (SI)

1. Basic SI units

Physical quantity	Unit	Symbol
Length	metre	m
Mass	kilogramme	kg
Time	second	s
Electric current	ampere	A
Thermodynamic temperature	kelvin	K
Amount of substance	mole	mol
Luminous intensity	candela	cd

2. Supplementary SI units

Physical quantity	Unit	Symbol
Plane angle	radian	rad
Solid angle	steradian	sr

3. Derived SI units (examples)

Physical quantity	Unit	Definition
Area (surface)	square metre	m^2
Volume	cubic metre	m^3
Velocity	metre per second	$m \cdot s^{-1}$
Angular velocity	radian per second	$rad \cdot s^{-1}$
Acceleration	metre per square second	$m \cdot s^{-2}$
Wave number	reciprocal metre	m^{-1}
Density	kilogramme per cubic metre	$kg \cdot m^{-3}$
Mass concentration	kilogramme per cubic metre	$kg \cdot m^{-3}$
Molar concentration	mol per cubic metre	$mol \cdot m^{-3}$
Intensity of electric current	ampere per square metre	$A \cdot m^{-2}$
Luminance	candela per square metre	$cd \cdot m^{-2}$

N.B. $kg \cdot m^{-3}$ may be written as kg/m^3, etc.

3a. Derived SI units with special names and symbols

Common derived units

Physical quantity	Unit	Symbol	Definition
Frequency	hertz	Hz	s^{-1}
Energy	joule	J	$kg \cdot m^2 \cdot s^{-2}$
Force	newton	N	$kg \cdot m \cdot s^{-2} = J \cdot m^{-1}$
Pressure	pascal	Pa	$kg \cdot m^{-1} \cdot s^{-2} = N \cdot m^{-2}$
Power	watt	W	$kg \cdot m^2 \cdot s^{-3} = J \cdot s^{-1}$
Electric charge	coulomb	C	$A \cdot s$
Electric potential difference	volt	V	$kg \cdot m^2 \cdot s^{-3} \cdot A^{-1} = J \cdot A^{-1} \cdot s^{-1}$
Electric resistance	ohm	Ω	$kg \cdot m^2 \cdot s^{-3} \cdot A^{-2} = V \cdot A^{-1}$

(Continued on p. 560)

TABLE I (continued)

Electric conductance	siemens	S	$kg^{-1} \cdot m^{-2} \cdot s^3 \cdot A^2 = \Omega^{-1}$
Electric capacitance	farad	F	$A^2 \cdot s^4 \cdot kg^{-1} \cdot m^{-2} = A \cdot s \cdot V^{-1}$
Magnetic flux	weber	Wb	$kg \cdot m^2 \cdot s^{-2} \cdot A^{-1} = V \cdot s$
Inductance	henry	H	$kg \cdot m^2 \cdot s^{-2} \cdot A^{-2} = V \cdot A^{-1} \cdot s$
Magnetic flux density (magnetic induction)	tesla	T	$kg \cdot s^{-2} \cdot A^{-1} = V \cdot s \cdot m^{-2}$

3b. Derived SI units formed by combination of (1) and (3a) (examples)

Physical quantity	Unit	Definition
Moment of force	newton metre	$N \cdot m$
Surface tension	newton per metre	$N \cdot m^{-1}$
Dynamic viscosity	newton second per square metre	$N \cdot s \cdot m^{-2}$
Thermal conductivity	watt per metre per kelvin	$W \cdot m^{-1} \cdot K^{-1}$
Molar energy	joule per mol	$J \cdot mol^{-1}$
Electric field strength	volt per metre	$V \cdot m^{-1}$

4. Decimal fractions and multiples

Fraction	Prefix	Symbol	Multiple	Prefix	Symbol
10^{-1}	deci	d	10	deca	da
10^{-2}	centi	c	10^2	hecto	h
10^{-3}	milli	m	10^3	kilo	k
10^{-6}	micro	μ	10^6	mega	M
10^{-9}	nano	n	10^9	giga	G
10^{-12}	pico	p	10^{12}	tera	T
10^{-15}	femto	f	10^{15}	peta	P
10^{-18}	atto	a	10^{18}	exa	E

TABLE II

SURVEY OF CONVERSION FACTORS

| Quantity | | Expressed in (units) | | Multiplication | Expressed in |
Name	Symbol	Name	Symbol	factor	S.I. units
1. Space and time					
Length	l, L	kilometer	km	10^3	m
or width	b	centimeter	cm	10^{-2}	
height	h	millimeter	mm	10^{-3}	
thickness	d, δ	micron	μm	10^{-6}	
radius	r	nanometer	nm	10^{-9}	
diameter	$d(D)$	Angström	Å	10^{-10}	
path length	s	inch	in	0.0254	
wavelength	λ	foot	ft	0.3048	
		yard	yd	0.9144	
		mile	mile	1.609×10^3	
		nautical mile	n mile	1.852×10^3	
Area (surface)	$A, (S)$	hectare	ha	10^4	m^2
		are	a	10^2	
		square centimeter	cm^2	10^{-4}	
		square millimeter	mm^2	10^{-6}	
		square Angström	$Å^2$	10^{-20}	
		square inch	in^2	0.645×10^{-3}	
		square foot	ft^2	9.29×10^{-2}	
		square yard	yd^2	0.836	
		acre	acre	4.047×10^3	
		square mile	$mile^2$	2.590×10^6	
Volume	V	cubic decimeter	dm^3	10^{-3}	m^3
		cubic centimeter	cm^3	10^{-6}	
		litre	l	10^{-3}	
		decilitre	dl	10^{-4}	
		millilitre	ml	10^{-6}	
		cubic inch	in^3	1.639×10^{-5}	

(Continued on p. 562)

TABLE II (continued)

Quantity		Expressed in (units)		Multiplication factor	Expressed in S.I. units
Name	Symbol	Name	Symbol		
Volume (continued)	V	cubic foot	ft^3	2.832×10^{-2}	m^3
		cubic yard	yd^3	0.765	
		barrel (US)	barrel	0.159	
		gallon (US)	gal (US)	3.785×10^{-3}	
		gallon (UK)	gal (UK)	4.546×10^{-3}	
Angle	$\alpha, \beta, \delta, \vartheta, \theta, \varphi$	radian	rad	1	rad
		degree ($= 2\pi/360$ rad)	1°	1.743×10^{-2}	
		minute ($= 1/60°$)	1'	2.9×10^{-4}	
		second ($= 1/60'$)	1''	4.85×10^{-6}	
Time	t, Θ	year	a	3.16×10^7	s
		month	month	2.63×10^6	
		day	d	8.64×10^4	
		hour	h	3.6×10^3	
		minute	min	0.6×10^2	
Frequency	$\nu, \omega (= 2\pi\nu)$	cycles per minute	c/min	0.6×10^2	Hz = s^{-1}
		cycles per hour	c/h	3.6×10^3	(hertz)
Velocity	$v(u)$	kilometers per hour	km/h	0.278	m/s
		foot per minute	ft/min	5.08×10^{-3}	
		foot per second	ft/s	0.3048	
		mile per hour	mile/h	0.4470	
		knot	kn	0.514	
Acceleration	a, g	foot per square second	ft/s^2	0.3048	m/s^2
Volumetric flow rate	Φ	litre per second	l/s	10^{-3}	m^3/s
		litre per minute	l/min	1.667×10^{-5}	
		cubic meter per minute	m^3/min	1.667×10^{-2}	
		cubic meter per hour	m^3/h	0.2778×10^{-3}	
		cubic foot per second	ft^3/s	2.832×10^{-2}	
		cubic foot per hour	ft^3/h	7.87×10^{-6}	

Quantity	Symbol	Unit	Abbr.	Conversion factor	SI unit
Volumetric flow (rate) density	v	barrel (US) per day	barrel/d	1.840×10^{-6}	
		gallon (US) per minute	gal (US)/min	6.31×10^{-5}	
		gallon (UK) per minute	gal (UK)/min	7.58×10^{-5}	
		cub foot per square foot sec = foot per second	$ft^3/ft^2 \cdot s$ = ft/s	0.3048	m/s
2. Mechanics					
Mass	m	ton	t	10^3	kg
		gram	g	10^{-3}	
		milligram	mg	10^{-6}	
		microgram	μg	10^{-9}	
		carat		2×10^{-4}	
		grain	gr	6.48×10^{-5}	
		ounce (avoirdupois)	oz	2.83×10^{-2}	
		pound (avoirdupois)	lb	0.4536	
		stone		6.35	
		slug		14.59	
		hundred weight (UK)	cwt	50.8	
		short hundred weight	sh cwt	45.36	
		short ton (US)	sh tn	0.907×10^3	
		long ton (UK)	ton	1.016×10^3	
Density (mass density)	ρ	gram per cubic centimeter	g/cm^3	10^3	kg/m^3
		grain per cubic foot	gr/ft^3	2.288×10^{-3}	
		pound per cubic foot	lb/ft^3	16.02	
		pound per cubic inch	lb/in^3	2.768×10^4	
		pound per gallon (US)	lb/gal	0.120×10^3	
Specific volume	$v = 1/\rho$	cubic centimeter per gram	cm^3/g	10^{-3}	m^3/kg
		cubic foot per pound	ft^3/lb	6.24×10^{-2}	
Fineness (linear density) of yarns and fibres	Td	denier	den = g/9000 m	0.111	tex = 10^{-6} kg/m
		tex	tex = g/1000 m	1	
		decitex	dtex = g/10,000 m	0.1	
Mass flow rate (production capacity)	Φ_m	kilogram per hour	kg/h	2.778×10^{-4}	kg/s
		ton per day	t/d	1.157×10^{-2}	
		ton per month	t/mth	3.79×10^{-4}	

(Continued on p. 564)

TABLE II (continued)

Quantity		Expressed in (units)		Multiplication factor	Expressed in S.I. units
Name	Symbol	Name	Symbol		
Mass flow rate (continued)	Φ_m	ton per year	t/a	3.17×10^{-5}	kg/s
		pound per minute	lb/min	7.56×10^{-3}	
		short ton per day	shtn/d	1.050×10^{-2}	
		(long) ton per day	ton/d	1.176×10^{-2}	
Mass flow density	ϕ_m	kilogram per sq meter p.h	$kg/m^2 \cdot h$	2.778×10^{-4}	$kg/m^2 \cdot s$
		pound per square foot p. min	$lb/ft^2 \cdot min$	8.14×10^{-2}	
Force or weight	F $(W)(P)$	dyne	$dyn\ (= g \cdot cm/s^2)$	10^{-5}	N (newton) $(= kg \cdot m/s^2)$
		gram-force	gf	9.81×10^{-3}	
		kilogram-force	kgf	9.81	
		ton-force	tf	9.81×10^3	
		poundal	pdl	0.1383	
		pound force	lbf	4.448	
Specific weight (Force per unit volume)	γ	gram-force per cubic cm	gf/cm^3	9.81×10^3	N/m^3
		pound-force per cubic foot	lbf/ft^3	157.1	
Moment of force or bending moment; torque moment of a couple	M (S)	dyne centimeter	$dyn \cdot cm$	10^{-7}	$N \cdot m$ $(N \cdot m = J)$
		kilogram force meter	$kgf \cdot m$	9.81	
		foot poundal	$ft \cdot pdl$	4.214×10^{-2}	
		pound-force foot	$lbf \cdot ft$	1.356	
Moment of inertia	I	gram square centimeter	$g \cdot cm^2$	10^{-7}	$kg \cdot m^2$
		pound foot squared	$lb \cdot ft^2$	4.214×10^{-2}	
Second moment of area	(axial) I_a (polar) I_p	inch to the fourth	in^4	4.162×10^{-7}	m^4
Section modulus (moment of resistance)	$Z(W)$	inch cubed	in^3	1.639×10^{-5}	m^3
Force per unit surface pressure	p	dyne per square centimeter	dyn/cm^2	10^{-1}	N/m^2 $\left(\dfrac{N}{m^2} = \dfrac{J}{m^3} = Pa \right)$
normal stress	σ	kilogram-force per sq. meter	kgf/m^2	9.81	
shear stress	τ	technical atmosphere	at	9.81×10^4	
		atmosphere	atm	1.013×10^5	

Quantity	Symbol	Unit	Unit symbol	Factor	SI unit
Young's or elasticity m.	E	millimeter mercury	mmHg	133.3	
Rigidity or shear m.	G	millimeter water	mmH$_2$O	9.81	
Bulk m. or compression m.	B	bar (= 10^6 dyn/cm^2)	bar	10^5	
		poundal per square foot	pdl/ft^2	1.488	
		pound-force per square foot	lbf/ft^2	47.88	
		pound-force per square inch	lbf/in^2	6.89×10^3	
		inch of water	inH$_2$O	2.491×10^2	
		foot of water	ftH$_2$O	2.989×10^3	
		inch of mercury	inHg	3.386×10^3	
Specific strength of yarns and fibres		gram force per denier	gf/den	0.0883	N/tex
		rupture kilometer	Rkm	0.981×10^{-2}	
		centinewton per tex	cN/tex	10^{-2}	
		gram force per tex	gf/tex	0.981×10^{-2}	
		gram force per decitex	gf/dtex	0.0981	
Tensile stress in yarns and fibres	σ	newton per tex	N/tex	$10^6\,\rho$	N/m^2 (ρ = density in kg/m^3)
		gram force per tex	gf/tex	$0.981 \times 10^4\,\rho$	
		gram force per denier	gf/den	$0.883 \times 10^5\,\rho$	
Stiffness factor	EI	kilogram-force centimeter squared	kgf·cm^2	9.81×10^{-4}	N·m^2
Surface tension	γ, σ	dyne per centimeter	dyn/cm	10^{-3}	N/m
		pound-force per foot	lbf/ft	14.59	$\left(\dfrac{N}{m} = \dfrac{J}{m^2}\right)$
Viscosity (dynamic)	$\eta(\lambda)$	poise	P = dyn·s/cm^2	10^{-1}	N·s/m^2
		centipoise	cP	10^{-3}	
		kilogram-force sec p. sq. meter	kgf·s/m^2	9.81	
		kilogram-force hour p. sq. meter	kgf·h/m^2	3.531×10^4	
		poundal second p. sq. foot	pdl·s/ft^2	1.488	
		pound-force sec per sq. foot	lbf·s/ft^2	47.88	
		pound-force sec per sq. in.	lbf·s/in^2	6.90×10^3	
Kinematic viscosity	ν	square centimeter per second	cm^2/s	10^{-4}	m^2/s
Diffusion coefficient	D	square meter per hour	m^2/h	2.778×10^{-4}	
Thermal diffusivity	a	stokes	cm^2/s	10^{-4}	
		centistokes	cm^2/100s	10^{-6}	
		square inch per second	in^2/s	0.645×10^{-3}	
		square foot per second	ft^2/s	9.29×10^{-2}	

(Continued on p. 566)

TABLE II (continued)

Quantity		Expressed in (units)		Multiplication factor	Expressed in S.I. units
Name	Symbol	Name	Symbol		
Energy	E	erg (= dyne · cm)	dyn · cm	10^{-7}	J
or work	W, A	kilogram-force meter	kgf · m	9.81	$(J = N \cdot m = W \cdot s)$
potential energy	E_p	foot poundal	ft · pdl	4.21×10^{-2}	
kinetic energy	E_k	foot pound-force	ft · lbf	1.356	(joule)
		litre atmosphere	l · atm	1.013×10^2	
		cubic foot atmosphere	$ft^3 \cdot atm$	2.869×10^3	
		horse power hour	hph	2.685×10^6	
		kilowatt hour	kWh	3.60×10^6	
		kilocalorie	kcal	4.19×10^3	
		calorie	cal	4.19	
		British thermal unit	Btu	1.055×10^3	
Power	P	erg per second	erg/s	10^{-7}	W
		kilogram-force meter p. sec	kgf · m/s	9.81	(watt)
		horse power (UK)	hp	7.46×10^2	$(W = J/s)$
		horse power (metric)	hp	7.36×10^2	
		foot pound-force per second	ft · lbf/s	1.356	
		foot poundal per second	ft · pdl/s	4.214×10^{-2}	

3. General thermodynamics

Quantity		Expressed in (units)		Multiplication factor	Expressed in S.I. units
Name	Symbol	Name	Symbol		
Temperature	T	degree Centigrade	°C	1	K
		degree Fahrenheit	°F	0.55555	(kelvin)
Energy	E	erg	erg = dyn · cm	10^{-7}	J
or Heat quantity	Q	litre atmosphere	l · atm	1.013×10^2	(joule)
Internal energy	U	cubic foot atmosphere	$ft^3 \cdot atm$	2.869×10^3	$\left(\begin{array}{c} J = N \cdot m \\ = W \cdot s \end{array}\right)$
Enthalpy	H	calorie	cal	4.19	
Free energy	F	kilocalorie	kcal	4.19×10^3	
Free enthalpy	G	British thermal unit	Btu	1.055×10^3	
Latent heat	L	therm	$Btu \times 10^5$	1.055×10^8	

Quantity	Symbol	Name	Unit	Factor	SI unit
Specific energy					
sp. internal energy	u	calorie per gram	cal/g	4.19×10^3	J/kg
specific enthalpy	h	Br. therm. unit per pound	Btu/lb	2.326×10^3	
sp. free energy	f				
sp. free enthalpy	g				
sp. latent heat	l				
Heat capacity	C	kilocalorie per °C	kcal/°C	4.19×10^3	J/K
Entropy	S	calorie per °C	cal/°C	4.19	
		Br. therm. unit p. degree Fahrenheit	Btu/°F	1.90×10^3	
Specific heat capacity	c	calorie p. gram degree Centigrade	cal/g·°C	4.19×10^3	J/kg·K
Specific entropy	s	Brit. therm. unit per pound degree Fahrenheit	Btu/lb·°F	4.19×10^3	
Heat flow (power)	Φ_h	erg per second	erg/s	10^{-7}	W (watt) (W = J/s)
		kilocalorie per hour	kcal/h	1.163	
		calorie per second	cal/s	4.19	
		Br. therm. unit per second	Btu/s	1.055×10^3	
		Br. therm. unit per hour	Btu/h	0.293	
Heat flow density	ϕ_h	calorie p. sq. centimeter p. sec	cal/cm²·s	4.19×10^4	W/m²
		kilocalorie p. sq. meter p. hour	kcal/m²·h	1.163	
		Brit. therm. unit p. sq. foot sec	Btu/ft²·s	1.136×10^4	
		Brit. therm. unit p. sq. foot hour	Btu/ft²·h	3.16	
Thermal conductivity	$\lambda(k)$	calorie per centimeter second degree Centigrade	cal/cm·s·°C	4.19×10^2	J/m·s·K (= W/m·K)
		kilocalorie per meter hour degree Centigrade	kcal/m·h·°C	1.163	
		British thermal unit per hour foot degree Fahrenheit	Btu/ft·h·°F	1.73	
		British thermal unit inch per hour square foot degree F	Btu·in/ft²·h·°F	0.144	
		British thermal unit per second square foot degree F	Btu/ft·s·°F	6.23×10^3	

(Continued on p. 568)

TABLE II (continued)

Quantity		Expressed in (units)		Multiplication factor	Expressed in S.I. units
Name	Symbol	Name	Symbol		
Overall coefficient of heat transfer	U, K	calorie per square centimeter second degree Centigrade	$cal/cm^2 \cdot s \cdot °C$	4.19×10^4	$J/m^2 \cdot s \cdot K$ $(= W/m^2 \cdot K)$
Heat transfer coefficient	h, α	kilocalorie per square meter hour degree Centigrade	$kcal/m^2 \cdot h \cdot °C$	1.163	
		British thermal unit per hour square foot degree Fahrenheit	$Btu/ft^2 \cdot h \cdot °F$	5.68	
		British thermal unit per second square foot degree F	$Btu/ft^2 \cdot s \cdot °F$	2.044×10^4	
Concentration	c	gram per litre	g/l	1	kg/m^3
		gram per decilitre	g/dl	10	
		gram per cubic centimeter	g/cm^3	10^3	
		grain per cubic foot	gr/ft^3	0.2288×10^{-2}	
		pound per cubic foot	lb/ft^3	16.02	
4. Chemical thermodynamics					
Amount of substance	n	grammole	mol	1	mol
Concentration	c	molarity	mol/l	10^3	mol/m^3
		—	$mol/100\ g$ solvent	10	mol/kg solvent
		molality	$mol/1000\ g$ solvent	1	mol/kg solvent
Molecular energy	(E)	calorie per mole	cal/mol	4.19	J/mol
		electron volt p. molecule	$eV/molecule$	0.965×10^5	
		erg per molecule	$erg/molecule$	6.025×10^{16}	
		wave number	cm^{-1}	11.96	
5. Optics					
Stress optical coefficient	C	brewster	$\equiv 10^{-13}\ cm^2/dyn$	10^{-12}	m^2/N

Quantity	Symbol	Unit system	CGS dimensions	Factor	SI unit
Hydrogen bonding number	$\Delta\nu$	gordy ≡ shift of 10 wave numbers in spectroscopic OD absorption band			

6. Electricity and magnetism

Quantity	Symbol	Unit system	CGS dimensions	Factor	SI unit
Electric current (flow rate)	$I(i)$	electrostatic cgs unit electromagnetic cgs unit	$cm^{3/2} \cdot g^{1/2}/s^2$ $cm^{1/2} \cdot g^{1/2}/s$	3.333×10^{-10} 10	A (ampere)
Quantity of electricity (Electric charge)	Q (e)	electrostatic cgs unit electromagnetic cgs unit	$cm^{3/2} \cdot g^{1/2}/s$ $cm^{1/2} \cdot g^{1/2}$	3.333×10^{-10} 10	C (coulomb) ($C = A \cdot s$)
Electric field strength	F (E)	electrostatic cgs unit electromagnetic cgs unit	$g^{1/2}/cm^{1/2} \cdot s$ $cm^{1/2} \cdot g^{1/2}/s^2$	3.00×10^{4} 10^{-6}	V/m $\left(\dfrac{N}{A \cdot s} = \dfrac{V}{m}\right)$
Potential Electric motive force	V (E)	electrostatic cgs unit electromagnetic cgs unit	$cm^{1/2} \cdot g^{1/2}/s$ $cm^{3/2} \cdot g^{1/2}/s^2$	3.00×10^{2} 10^{-8}	V (volt) $\left(V = \dfrac{N \cdot m}{A \cdot s}\right)$
Resistance	R	electrostatic cgs unit electromagnetic cgs unit	s/cm cm/s	9.00×10^{11} 10^{-9}	Ω (ohm) ($\Omega = V/A$)
Specific resistance	ρ	electromagnetic cgs unit ohm centimeter	cm^2/s $\Omega \cdot cm$	10^{-11} 10^{-2}	$\Omega \cdot m$
Conductance		electrostatic cgs unit electromagnetic cgs unit	cm/s s/cm	0.11×10^{-11} 10^{9}	S (siemens) ($S = 1/\Omega$)
Electric conductivity	γ	electromagnetic cgs unit	s/cm^2 $1/\Omega \cdot cm$	10^{11} 10^{2}	$1/\Omega \cdot m$
Power	P	electromagnetic cgs unit	$cm^2 \cdot g/s^3$	10^{-7}	W (watt) ($W = V \cdot A$)
Energy	E	electromagnetic cgs unit	$cm^2 \cdot g/s^2$	10^{-7}	J (joule) ($J = W \cdot s$)
Capacitance	C	electrostatic cgs unit electromagnetic cgs unit	cm s^2/cm	1.11×10^{-12} 10^{9}	F (farad) ($F = A \cdot s/V$)
Inductance	L	electromagnetic cgs unit	cm	10^{-9}	H (henry) ($H = V \cdot s/A$)

(Continued on p. 570)

TABLE II (continued)

Quantity		Expressed in (units)		Multiplication factor	Expressed in S.I. units
Name	Symbol	Name	Symbol		
Electric displacement	Γ	electrostatic cgs unit	$g^{1/2}/cm^{1/2} \cdot s$	2.653×10^{-7}	$A \cdot s/m^2$
		electromagnetic cgs unit	$g^{1/2}/cm^{3/2}$	7.958×10^{3}	
Electric moment	m	electrostatic cgs unit	$cm^{5/2} \cdot g^{1/2}/s$	3.333×10^{-12}	$A \cdot s \cdot m$
		electromagnetic cgs unit	$cm^{3/2} \cdot g^{1/2}$	0.1000	
		debye $= 10^{-18}$ esu $\cdot$ cm $= 10^{-18}$	$cm^{5/2} \cdot g^{1/2}/s$	3.333×10^{-30}	
Electrization		electrostatic cgs unit	$g^{1/2}/cm^{1/2} \cdot s$	3.333×10^{-6}	$A \cdot s \cdot m/m^3$
Electric polarizability		electrostatic cgs unit	cm^3	1.11×10^{-16}	$\dfrac{A \cdot s \cdot m}{V/m}$
Electric susceptibility	ϵ	dimensionless number	–	1	number
Magnetic flux	Φ	maxwell	$cm^{3/2} \cdot g^{1/2}/s$	10^{-8}	$V \cdot s = Wb$ (weber)
Magnetic field strength	H	oerstedt	$g^{1/2}/cm^{1/2} \cdot s$	79.58	$A/m = N/V \cdot s$
Magnetic induction	B	gauss	$g^{1/2}/cm^{1/2} \cdot s$	10^{-4}	$V \cdot s/m^2$
Magnetic moment	$m(\beta)$	gauss cubic centimeter	$cm^{5/2} \cdot g^{1/2}/s$	1.257×10^{-9}	$V \cdot s \cdot m$
Magnetization	J	gauss	$g^{1/2}/cm^{1/2} \cdot s$	1.257×10^{-3}	$V \cdot s \cdot m/m^3$
Magnetic polarizability	β	electromagnetic cgs unit	cm^3	1.58×10^{-11}	$\dfrac{V \cdot s \cdot m}{A/m}$
Magnetic susceptibility	χ	electromagnetic cgs unit	–	12.57	number
Hall-constant		electromagnetic cgs unit	$cm^{5/2}/g^{1/2}$	10^{-7}	$m^3/A \cdot s$

TABLE III

VALUES OF SOME FUNDAMENTAL CONSTANTS

Constant	Symbol	Value in S.I. units	Value in c.g.s. units
Volume of 1 mole gas at NTP	–	22.420×10^{-3} m^3	22.420×10^3 cm^3
Avogadro number	N_A	6.025×10^{23} mol^{-1}	6.025×10^{23} mol^{-1}
Gas constant	R	8.314 J/mol · K	8.314×10^7 erg/mol · K
			1.987 cal/mol · K
			82.057 cm^3 · atm/mol · K
Boltzmann constant	k	1.380×10^{-23} J/K	1.380×10^{-16} erg/K
Planck's constant	h	6.625×10^{-34} J · s	6.625×10^{-27} erg · s
Velocity of light	c	2.998×10^5 km/s	2.998×10^{10} cm/s
Faraday constant	$\mathcal{F}$	96.520 C/mol	2.894×10^{-13} e.s.u./mol
			96.52 C/equivalent
Charge of electron	e	1.602×10^{-19} C	4.803×10^{-10} e.s.u.
			1.602×10^{-20} e.m.u.
Mass of electron	m	9.108×10^{-31} kg	9.108×10^{-28} g
Mechanical equivalent of heat	J	1	4.186×10^7 erg/cal
Ratio proton: electron mass	m_p/m	1836	1836
Bohr magneton	μ_B	1.165×10^{-29} Wb/m	9.273×10^{-21} erg/gauss
Gravitational constant	G	6.67×10^{-11} N · m^2/kg^2	6.67×10^{-8} dyn · cm^2/g^2
Permeability of free space	μ_0	$4\pi \times 10^{-7}$ H/m	1
Permittivity of free space	ϵ_0	8.854×10^{-12} F/m	1
Standard gravity	g	9.81 m/s^2	980.665 cm/s^2
ln 10	–	2.302585	2.302585 ·

TABLE IV

CODE SYMBOLS FOR THE MOST IMPORTANT POLYMERS

ABS	Acrylonitrile–butadiene–styrene copolymer
AMMA	Acrylonitrile–methyl methacrylate copolymer
ASA	Acrylic ester–styrene–acrylonitrile copolymer
BR	Polybutadiene rubber
CA	Cellulose acetate
CAB	Cellulose acetobutyrate
CAP	Cellulose acetopropionate
CF	Cresol formaldehyde
CMC	Carboxymethyl cellulose
CN	Cellulose nitrate
CP	Cellulose propionate
CPE	Chlorinated polyethylene
CPVC	Chlorinated poly(vinyl chloride)
CS	Casein resin
EC	Ethyl cellulose
EP	Epoxide resin
EPR	Ethylene–propylene rubber
EPTR	Ethylene–propylene terpolymer rubber
ETFE	Ethylene–tetrafluoroethylene copolymer
EU	Polyether–urethane
EVA	Ethylene–vinyl acetate copolymer
HD-PE	High-density polyethylene
IR	Isoprene rubber
LD-PE	Low-density polyethylene
MBS	Methyl methacrylate–butadiene–styrene copolymer
MF	Melamin–formaldehyde resin
NBR	Acrylonitrile–butadiene rubber
NCR	Acrylonitrile–chloroprene rubber
NR	Natural rubber
PA	Polyamide
PA 6	Polycaprolactam
PA 66	Poly(hexamethylene adipamide)
PA 6.10	Poly(hexamethylene sebacamide)
PA 11	Polyamide of 11-aminoundecanoic acid
PA 12	Polylaurolactam
PAA	Poly(acrylic acid)
PAN	Polyacrylonitrile
PB	Polybutylene
PBTP	Poly(butylene glycol terephthalate)
PC	Polycarbonate
PCTFE	Poly(chlorotrifluoroethylene)
PDAP	Poly(diethyl phthalate)
PE	Polyethylene
PEC	Chlorinated polyethylene
PETP	Poly(ethylene terephthalate)
PF	Phenol–formaldehyde resin
PIB	Polyisobutylene
PMMA	Poly(methyl methacrylate)
PMP	Poly(4-methylpentene-1)
POM	Polyoxymethylene = polyacetal = polyformaldehyde

TABLE IV (continued)

PP	Polypropylene
PPO	Poly(2,6-dimethyl-1,4-phenylene oxide)
PS	Polystyrene
PTFE	Poly(tetrafluoroethylene)
PTMT	Poly(tetramethylene terephthalate)
PUR	Polyurethane
PVA(L)	Poly(vinyl alcohol)
PVAC	Poly(vinyl acetate)
PVB	Poly(vinyl butyral)
PVC	Poly(vinyl chloride)
PVCA	Vinyl chloride–vinyl acetate copolymer
PVDC	Poly(vinylidene chloride)
PVDF	Poly(vinylidene fluoride)
PVF	Poly(vinyl fluoride)
PVFM	Poly(vinyl formal)
PY	Unsaturated polyester resin
RF	Resorcinol–formaldehyde resin
RP	Reinforced plastic
SAN	Styrene–acrylonitrile copolymer
SB	Styrene–butadiene copolymer
SBR	Styrene–butadiene rubber
SI	Silicone rubber
SIR	Styrene–isoprene rubber
SMS	Styrene–α-methylstyrene copolymer
UE	Polyurethane rubber
UF	Urea–formaldehyde resin
UP	Unsaturated polyester resin
UR	Polyurethane rubber

TABLE V

PHYSICAL PROPERTIES OF THE MOST IMPORTANT POLYMERS

Polymers	M	ρ_a	ρ_c	e_g	e_l	c_p^s	c_p^l	ΔH_m
	g/mol	g/cm³	g/cm³	10^{-4} cm³·g⁻¹·K⁻¹		J·g⁻¹·K⁻¹		kJ/mol
Polyolefins								
polyethylene	28.1	0.85	1.00	2.4/3.6	7.5/9.6	1.55/1.76	2.26	7.6/8.7
polypropylene	42.1	0.85	0.95	2.2/(4.4)	5.5/9.4	1.62/1.78	2.13	1.9/10.9
poly(1-butene)	56.1	0.86	0.95	3.8	8.8	1.55/1.76	2.13	4.1/13.9
poly(3-methyl-1-butene)	70.1	<0.90	0.93					17.3
poly(1-pentene)	70.1	0.85	0.92		9.2			4.0/6.3
poly(4-methyl-1-pentene)	84.2	0.838		3.83	7.61	1.67		11.9/19.7
poly(1-hexene)	84.2	0.86	0.91					
poly(5-methyl-1-hexene)	98.2		0.84					
poly(1-octadecene)	252.5	0.86	0.95					
polyisobutylene	56.1	0.84	0.94	1.6/2.0	5.6/6.9	1.67	1.95	12.0
1,2-poly(1,3-butadiene) (iso)	54.1		>0.96					
1,2-poly(1,3-butadiene) (syndio)	54.1	<0.92	0.963					
Polystyrenes								
polystyrene	104.1	1.05	1.13	1.7/2.6	4.3/6.5	1.23	1.71	8.4/10.1
poly(α-methylstyrene)	118.2	1.065						
poly(2-methylstyrene)	118.2	1.027	1.07	2.6	5.3			
poly(4-methylstyrene)	118.2	1.04						
poly(4-methoxystyrene)	134.2		>1.12					
poly(4-phenylstyrene)	180.2							
poly(3-phenyl-1-propene)	118.2	1.046	>1.052					
poly(2-chlorostyrene)	138.6	<1.25						
poly(4-chlorostyrene)	138.6							
Polyhalo-olefins								
poly(vinyl fluoride)	46.0	<1.37	1.44					7.5
poly(vinyl chloride)	62.5	1.385	1.52	1.1/2.1	4.2/5.2	0.95	~1.21	2.8/11.3
poly(vinyl bromide)	107.0							
poly(vinylidene fluoride)	64.0	1.74	2.00	1.2	2.1/4.6			8.9
poly(vinylidene chloride)	97.0	1.66	1.95	1.2	5.7		0.86	~1.4
poly(tetrafluoroethylene) (Teflon)	100.0	2.00	2.35	(1.3)/3.0	4.8	0.96	0.96	5.7
poly(chlorotrifluoroethylene)	116.5	1.92	2.19	1.0/1.5	2.0/3.5	0.92		5.0/8.8
Polyvinyls								
poly(vinylcyclopentane)	96.2	<0.965	0.986					
poly(vinylcyclohexane)	110.2	0.95	0.982					
poly(α-vinylnaphthalene)	154.2		1.12					
poly(vinyl alcohol)	44.1	1.26	1.35	3		1.30/1.51		6.9/7.0
poly(vinyl methyl ether)	58.1	<1.03	1.175					
poly(vinyl ethyl ether)	72.1	0.94	>0.97					
poly(vinyl propyl ether)	86.1	<0.94						
poly(vinyl isopropyl ether)	86.1	0.924	>0.93					
poly(vinyl butyl ether)	100.2	<0.927	0.944					
poly(vinyl isobutyl ether)	100.2	0.93	0.94					
poly(vinyl sec.-butyl ether)	100.2	0.92	0.956					
poly(vinyl tert.-butyl ether)	100.2		0.978					
poly(vinyl hexyl ether)	128.2	0.925	>0.925					
poly(vinyl octyl ether)	156.3	0.914	>0.91					
poly(vinyl methyl ketone)	70.1	1.12	1.216					
poly(methyl isopropenyl ketone)	84.1	1.12/1.15	1.15/1.17					
poly(vinyl formate)	72.1	<1.35	1.49					
poly(vinyl acetate)	86.1	1.19	>1.194	1.8/2.4	5.0/6.0	1.34/1.47	1.97	
poly(vinyl propionate)	100.1	1.02						
poly(vinyl chloroacetate)	120.5	1.45		1.3	3.4			
poly(vinyl trifluoroacetate)	140.1		1.633					~7.5
poly(vinyl benzoate)	148.2							
poly(2-vinylpyridine)	105.1							
poly(vinylpyrrolidone)	111.1	1.25						
poly(vinylcarbazole)	193.2	<1.19/1.2	0.988					
Polyacrylates								
poly(acrylic acid)	72.1							
poly(methyl acrylate)	86.1	1.22		1.8/2.7	4.6/5.6	1.34	1.80	
poly(ethyl acrylate)	100.1	1.12		2.8	6.1	1.45	1.80	
poly(propyl acrylate)	114.1	<1.08	>1.18					
poly(isopropyl acrylate)	114.1		1.08/1.18	2.2/2.6	6.1/6.3			5.9
poly(butyl acrylate)	128.2	1.00/1.09		2.6	6.0	1.64	1.82	
poly(isobutyl acrylate)	128.2	<1.05	1.24					
poly(sec.-butyl acrylate)	128.2	<1.05	1.06	2.75	6.1			
poly(tert.-butyl acrylate)	128.2	1.00	1.04/>1.08					

Physical properties / Polymers	γ 10^{-3} N/m	T_g K	T_m K	δ $J^{1/2}/cm^{3/2}$	n	ϵ	λ_a $J \cdot s^{-1} \cdot m^{-1} \cdot K^{-1}$	λ_c	K_Θ $cm^3 \cdot mol^{1/2} \cdot g^{-3/2}$
Polyolefins									
polyethylene	31/36	195(150/253)	414	15.8/17.1	1.49/1.52	2.3	(0.16)/(0.48)	(0.74)	0.20/0.26
polypropylene	29/34	238/299	385/481	16.6/18.8	1.49	2.2	(0.09)/(0.22)		0.120/0.182
poly(1-butene)	34	228/249	379/415		1.5125				0.105/0.123
poly(3-methyl-1-butene)		<323	573/583						
poly(1-pentene)		223/287	384/403						0.113/0.120
poly(4-methyl-1-pentene)	25	295/315	501/523		1.459/1.465	2.1			
poly(1-hexene)		223	321						
poly(5-methyl-1-hexene)		<259	383/403						
poly(1-octadecene)		<328	341/353		1.471/1.507				
polyisobutylene	27/34	198/243	275/317	16.0/16.6	1.508		0.123/0.130		0.085/0.115
1,2-poly(1,3-butadiene) (iso)		208	398						
1,2-poly(1,3-butadiene) (syndio)			428						
Polystyrenes									
polystyrene	27/43	353/373	498/523	17.4/19.0	1.591	2.55	0.131/0.142	(0.110)	0.067/0.100
poly(α-methylstyrene)	36	443/465							0.064/0.084
poly(2-methylstyrene)		409	633		1.5874				
poly(4-methylstyrene)		366/379							0.066/0.070
poly(4-methoxystyrene)		~362	511		1.5967				0.062
poly(4-phenylstyrene)		434							
poly(3-phenyl-1-propene)		333	503/513						
poly(2-chlorostyrene)	42	392		18.2	1.6098	2.6			
poly(4-chlorostyrene)		383/399				2.6	0.116		0.050
Polyhalo-olefins									
poly(vinyl fluoride)	28/37	253/313	473						
poly(vinyl chloride)	26/42	247/356	485/583	19.2/22.1	1.539	2.8/3.05	0.16/0.17		0.095/0.335
poly(vinyl bromide)		373		19.6					0.040
poly(vinylidene fluoride)	25/33	233/286	410/511		1.42	8/13	0.13		
poly(vinylidene chloride)	40	255/288	463/483	20.3/25.0	1.60/1.63	2.85			
poly(tetrafluoroethylene)(Teflon)	16/22	160/400	292/672	12.7	1.35/1.38	2.1	(0.25)		
poly(chlorotrifluoroethylene)	31	318/373	483/533	14.7/16.2	1.39/1.43	2.5/2.8	(0.14)/0.25		
Polyvinyls									
poly(vinylcyclopentane)		<348	565						
poly(vinylcyclohexane)		<363	575/656						
poly(α-vinylnaphthalene)		408/435	633		1.6818				
poly(vinyl alcohol)	37	343/372	505/538	25.8/29.1	1.5	8/12			0.160/0.300
poly(vinyl methyl ether)	29	242/260	417/423		1.467				
poly(vinyl ethyl ether)	36	231/254	359		1.4540				
poly(vinyl propyl ether)			349						
poly(vinyl isopropyl ether)		270	464						
poly(vinyl butyl ether)		220	337		1.4563				
poly(vinyl sec.-butyl ether)		246/255	443		1.4507				
poly(vinyl tert.-butyl ether)		253	443		1.4740				
poly(vinyl hexyl ether)		361	533						
poly(vinyl octyl ether)		196/223			1.4591				
poly(vinyl methyl ketone)		194			1.4613				
poly(methyl isopropenyl ketone)		353/387	443		1.50				
poly(vinyl formate)		304/310	473/513		1.5200				
poly(vinyl acetate)	36/37	301		19.1/22.6	1.4757	3.25	0.159		0.078/0.110
poly(vinyl propionate)		283		18.0/18.5	1.467				
poly(vinyl chloroacetate)		304			1.4665				
poly(vinyl trifluoroacetate)		319	448		1.513				
poly(vinyl benzoate)		341			1.375				0.062
poly(2-vinylpyridine)		377	488		1.5775				0.082
poly(vinylpyrrolidone)		418/448			1.53				0.074/0.090
poly(vinylcarbazole)		473/481			1.683		0.126/0.155		0.074/0.076
Polyacrylates									
poly(acrylic acid)	29/35	379			1.527				0.076/0.165
poly(methyl acrylate)	41	281		19.8/21.3	1.479	4.4/5.5			0.054/0.081
poly(ethyl acrylate)	35	251		19.2	1.4685				0.090
poly(propyl acrylate)		229	388/435	18.4					
poly(isopropyl acrylate)		262/284	389/453						
poly(butyl acrylate)	28	221	320	18.0/18.5	1.466				
poly(isobutyl acrylate)		249/256	354	18.4/22.5					
poly(sec.-butyl acrylate)		250/256	403						
poly(tert.-butyl acrylate)		313/316	466/473						

(continued on p. 576)

TABLE V (continued)

Polymers / Physical properties	M g/mol	ρ_a g/cm³	ρ_c g/cm³	e_g 10^{-4} cm³·g⁻¹·K⁻¹	e_l	c_p^s J·g⁻¹·K⁻¹	c_p^l	ΔH_m kJ/mol
Polymethacrylates								
poly(methacrylic acid)	86.1					1.05/1.30		
poly(methyl methacrylate)	100.1	1.17	1.23	1.2/2.3	5.2/5.4	1.37	~1.80	
poly(ethyl methacrylate)	114.1	1.119		2.75	5.40/5.7	1.49		
poly(propyl methacrylate)	128.2	1.08		3.2	5.7			
poly(isopropyl methacrylate)	128.2	1.033		2.0/2.4	6.2			
poly(butyl methacrylate)	142.2	1.055			6.1	1.68	1.84	
poly(isobutyl methacrylate)	142.2	1.045		2.4	6.0			
poly(sec.-butyl methacrylate)	142.2	1.052		3.3	6.3			
poly(tert.-butyl methacrylate)	142.2	1.02		2.7	7.0			
poly(2-ethylbutyl methacrylate)	170.2	1.040			5.76			
poly(hexyl methacrylate)	170.2	1.01			6.3/6.6			
poly(octyl methacrylate)	198.3	0.971			5.8			
poly(dodecyl methacrylate)	254.4	0.929		3.8	6.8			
poly(octadecyl methacrylate)	338.6		>0.97					
poly(phenyl methacrylate)	162.2	1.21		1.3	4.4			
poly(benzyl methacrylate)	176.2	1.179		1.45	4.2			
poly(cyclohexyl methacrylate)	168.2	1.098		2.7	5.4			
Other polyacrylics								
poly(methyl chloroacrylate)	120.5	1.45/1.49						
polyacrylonitrile	53.1	1.184	1.27/1.54	1.4/(1.6)	2.9/(3.1)	1.26		4.9/5.2
polymethacrylonitrile	67.1	1.10	1.134					
polyacrylamide	71.1	1.302						
poly(N-isopropylacrylamide)	113.2	1.03/1.07	1.118					
Polydienes								
poly(1,3-butadiene)(cis)	54.1		1.01				1.84	8.4/9.2
poly(1,3-butadiene)(trans)	54.1		1.02				2.39	3.6/13.8
poly(1,3-butadiene)(mixt.)	54.1	0.892		2.0	6.4/7.7	1.65		
poly(1,3-pentadiene)(trans)	68.1	0.89	0.98					
poly(2-methyl-1,3-butadiene)(cis)	68.1	0.908	1.00	2.0	6.0/7.4			4.4
poly(2-methyl-1,3-butadiene)(trans)	68.1	0.904	1.05		8.3			12.8
poly(2-methyl-1,3-butadiene)(mixt.)	68.1					1.59	1.91	
poly(2-tert.-butyl-1,3-butadiene)(cis)	110.2	<0.88	0.906					
poly(2-chloro-1,3-butadiene) (tr. ?)	88.5		1.09/1.66					8.4
poly(2-chloro-1,3-butadiene) (i. ?)	88.5	1.243	1.356		4.2/5.0			
Polyoxides								
poly(methylene oxide)	30.0	1.25	1.54	1.8		~1.42	~2.09	3.7/10.0
poly(ethylene oxide)	44.1	1.125	1.33		6.4	~1.26	2.05	7.3/12.0
poly(tetramethylene oxide)	72.1	0.98	1.18		6.9	1.65	2.07	12.4/14.4
poly(ethylene formal)	74.1		1.325/1.414			1.29	1.84	16.7
poly(tetramethylene formal)	102.1		1.234			1.42	1.90	14.0/14.7
polyacetaldehyde	44.1	1.071	1.14	2.1	6.3			
poly(propylene oxide)	58.1	1.00	1.10/1.21		7.2	~1.423	1.917	8.4
poly(hexene oxide)	100.2	<0.92	>0.97					
poly(octene oxide)	128.2	<0.94	>0.97					
poly(trans-2-butene oxide)	72.1	<1.01	1.099					
poly(styrene oxide)	120.1	1.15	>1.18					
poly(3-methoxypropylene oxide)	88.1	<1.095						
poly(3-butoxypropylene oxide)	130.2	<0.982						
poly(3-hexoxypropylene oxide)	158.2	<0.966						
poly(3-phenoxypropylene oxide)	150.2	<1.21	1.305					
poly(3-chloropropylene oxide)	92.5	1.37	1.461		5.6			
poly[2,2-bis(chloromethyl)-trimethylene-3-oxide] (Penton)	155.0	1.39	1.47		3.2	0.96		23.0/24.0
poly(2,6-dimethyl-1,4-phenylene oxide) (PPO)	120.1	1.07	1.31			1.23	1.76	3.8/5.9
poly(2,6-diphenyl-1,4-phenylene oxide) (Tenax, P3O)	244.3	<1.15		1.3				12/87
Polysulphides								
poly(propylene sulphide)	74.1	<1.10	>1.12/1.234					
poly(phenylene sulphide)	108.2	<1.34	1.44					
Polyesters								
poly(glycolic acid)	58.0	1.60	1.70					12
poly(ethylene succinate)	144.1	1.175	1.358	3.16	4.0			
poly(ethylene adipate)	172.2	<1.183/1.221	1.25/1.45		5.9			15.9/21.0
poly(tetramethylene adipate)	200.2	<1.019						
poly(ethylene azelate)	214.3		1.17/1.22					

Physical properties / Polymers	γ 10^{-3} N/m	T_g K	T_m K	δ J$^{1/2}$/cm$^{3/2}$	n	ϵ	λ_a J·s^{-1}·m^{-1}·K^{-1}	λ_c	K_Θ cm^3·mol$^{1/2}$·g$^{-3/2}$
Polymethacrylates									
poly(methacrylic acid)									0.066
poly(methyl methacrylate)	27/44	266/399	433/473	18.6/26.4	1.490	2.6/3.7	0.15/0.20		0.042/0.090
poly(ethyl methacrylate)	33	285/338		18.3	1.485	2.7/3.4			0.047
poly(propyl methacrylate)		308/316			1.484	3.1			
poly(isopropyl methacrylate)		300/354			1.552	3.0			
poly(butyl methacrylate)		249/300		17.8/18.4	1.483	2.5/3.1			0.030/0.038
poly(isobutyl methacrylate)		281/326		16.8/21.5	1.477				
poly(sec.-butyl methacrylate)		333							
poly(tert.-butyl methacrylate)		280/387	377/438	17.0	1.4638				
poly(2-ethylbutyl methacrylate)		284							0.035
poly(hexyl methacrylate)		256/268			1.4813				0.042
poly(octyl methacrylate)		253							0.030
poly(dodecyl methacrylate)		208/218	239		1.4740				0.032/0.035
poly(octadecyl methacrylate)			309						
poly(phenyl methacrylate)		378/393			1.5706/ 1.7515				
poly(benzyl methacrylate)		327		20.3	1.5679				
poly(cyclohexyl methacrylate)		324/377			1.5065				0.034
Other polyacrylics									
poly(methyl chloroacrylate)		416			1.517	3.4			
polyacrylonitrile	44	353/378	591	25.6/31.5	1.514	3.1/4.2			0.225
polymethacrylonitrile		393	523	21.9	1.52				0.220
polyacrylamide	35/40	438							0.260
poly(N-isopropylacrylamide)		358/403	473	21.9					
Polydienes									
poly(1,3-butadiene)(cis)	32	171	277	17.6	1.516				0.145/0.185
poly(1,3-butadiene)(trans)	31	255/263	421						0.200
poly(1,3-butadiene)(mixt.)		188/215		17.0	1.518				
poly(1,3-pentadiene)(trans)		213	368						
poly(2-methyl-1,3-butadiene)(cis)	31	203	287/309	16.2/17.2	1.520				0.119/0.130
poly(2-methyl-1,3-butadiene)(trans)	30	205/220	347						0.230
poly(2-methyl-1,3-butadiene)(mixt.)		225				2.4	0.134		
poly(2-tert.-butyl-1,3-butadiene)(cis)		298	379		1.506				
poly(2-chloro-1,3-butadiene)(trans)		225	353/388	16.8/18.8					
poly(2-chloro-1,3-butadiene)(mixt.)	38/44	228	316	16.8/19.0	1.558		0.19		0.095/0.135
Polyoxides									
poly(methylene oxide)	29/38	190/243	333/471	20.9/22.5	1.510	3.1/3.6	(0.16)/(0.42)	(0.62)	0.130/0.380
poly(ethylene oxide)	43	206/246	335/345		1.4563/ 1.54	4.5			0.100/0.230
poly(tetramethylene oxide)	32	185/194	308/453	17.0/17.5					0.180/0.33
poly(ethylene formal)		209	328/347						0.200
poly(tetramethylene formal)		189	296						
polyacetaldehyde		243	438						
poly(propylene oxide)	3?	200/212	333/348	15.3/20.3	1.450/ 1.457	4.9			0.108/0.125
poly(hexene oxide)		204	345						
poly(octene oxide)		203	360		1.469				
poly(trans-2-butene oxide)		277	387						
poly(styrene oxide)		312	413/452						
poly(3-methoxypropylene oxide)		211	330		1.463				
poly(3-butoxypropylene oxide)		194	300		1.458				
poly(3-hexoxypropylene oxide)		188	317		1.459				
poly(3-phenoxypropylene oxide)		315	485						
poly(3-chloropropylene oxide)			390/408	19.2					
poly[2,2-bis(chloromethyl)-trimethylene-3-oxide] (Penton)		281	353/459			3.0			
poly(2,6 dimethyl-1,4-phenylene oxide) (PPO)		453/515	534/548	19.0	1.575	2.6			
poly(2,6-diphenyl-1,4-phenylene oxide) (Tenax, P30)		500	730/770	19.6	1.64/1.68	2.8			
Polysulphides									
poly(propylene sulphide)		221/236	313/326		1.596				
poly(phenylene sulphide)		358/423	527/563			3.1	(0.29)		
Polyesters									
poly(glycolic acid)		311/368	496/533						
poly(ethylene succinate)		272	379		1.4744	5.0/5.5			
poly(ethylene adipate)		203/233	320/338	~19.4		5.2			
poly(tetramethylene adipate)		205	327			3.1			
poly(ethylene azelate)		228	319			3.95			

(continued on p. 578)

TABLE V (continued)

Physical properties / Polymers	M g/mol	ρ_a g/cm³	ρ_c g/cm³	e_g 10⁻⁴ cm³·g⁻¹·K⁻¹	e_l	c_p^s J·g⁻¹·K⁻¹	c_p^l	ΔH_m kJ/mol
Polyesters (continued)								
poly(ethylene sebacate)	228.3	1.04/1.11	1.063/1.21	1.96	3.6/6.9		1.93/2.05	13.8/35
poly(decamethylene adipate)	284.4		1.16		7.3			15.9/45.6
poly(decamethylene sebacate)	340.5		1.13		7.5			30.2/56.5
poly(α,α-dimethylpropiolactone)	100.1	1.097	1.23					14.9
poly(para-hydroxybenzoate) (Ekonol)	120.1	<1.44	>1.48					
poly(ethylene oxybenzoate) (A-tell)	164.2	<1.34					2.2	10.5
poly(ethylene isophthalate)	192.2	1.34	>1.38	2.0	3.8/5.3			
poly(ethylene terephthalate)	192.2	1.335	1.46/1.52	1.4/2.4	6.0/7.4	1.13	1.55	9.2/27.8
poly(tetramethylene isophthalate)	220.2	1.268	>1.309					42.3
poly(tetramethylene terephthalate)	220.2		>1.08	2.9			1.8	(10.6)/31/32
poly(hexamethylene terephthalate)	248.3		1.146					33.5/35.6
poly(decamethylene terephthalate)	304.4		1.012?/1.022		5.3			43.5/48.6
poly(1,4-cyclohexane dimethylene terephthalate)(trans)	274.3	1.19	1.265					
poly(ethylene-1,5-naphthalate)	242.2	<1.37		1.56	3.43			
poly(ethylene-2,6-naphthalate)	242.2	<1.33	>1.35	1.41	4.86			
poly(1,4-cyclohexylidene dimethyleneterephthalate) (Kodel) (cis)	274.3	1.209	1.303					
poly(1,4-cyclohexylidene dimethyleneterephthalate) (Kodel) (trans)	274.3	1.19	1.265					
Polyamides								
poly(4-aminobutyric acid)(nylon 4)	85.1	<1.25	1.34/1.37					
poly(6-aminohexanoic acid)(nylon 6)	113.2	1.084	1.23	2.7	5.6	1.47/1.59	2.13/2.47	17.6/23.0
poly(7-aminoheptanoic acid) (nylon 7)	127.2	<1.095	1.21	3.5		>1.67/1.84		
poly(8-aminooctanoic acid)(nylon 8)	141.2	1.04	1.04/1.18	3.1				
poly(9-aminononanoic acid)(nylon 9)	155.2	<1.052	>1.066	3.6				
poly(10-aminodecanoic acid) (nylon 10)	169.3	<1.032	1.019	3.5				
poly(11-aminoundecanoic acid) (nylon 11)	183.3	1.01	1.12/1.23	3.6				41.4
poly(12-aminododecanoic acid) (nylon 12)	197.3	0.99	1.106	3.8		0.71		16.7
poly(hexamethylene adipamide) (nylon 6,6)	226.3	1.07	1.24			1.47		36.8/46.9
poly(heptamethylene pimelamide) (nylon 7,7)	254.4	<1.06	1.108					
poly(octamethylene suberamide) (nylon 8,8)	282.4	<1.09						
poly(hexamethylene sebacamide) (nylon 6,10)	282.4	1.04	1.19			1.59	2.18	30.6/58.6
poly(nonamethylene azelamide) (nylon 9,9)	310.5	<1.043						
poly(decamethylene azelamide) (nylon 10,9)	324.5	<1.044			6.6			36.2/68.2
poly(decamethylene sebacamide) (nylon 10,10)	338.5	<1.032	>1.063		6.7			32.7/51.1
poly[bis(4-aminocyclohexyl)methane-1,10-decanedicarboxamide] (Qiana) (trans)	404.6	1.034	1.040				2.8	12
poly(m-xylylene adipamide)	246.3	<1.22	1.22/1.251					
poly(p-xylylene sebacamide)	302.4	<1.14	1.169					
poly(2,2,2-trimethylhexamethylene terephthalamide)	288.4	1.12				1.47		
poly(piperazine sebacamide)	252.4				5.9			26.0/26.4
poly(metaphenylene isophthalamide) (Nomex)	238.2	<1.33	>1.36	0.45		1.42		
poly(p-phenylene terephthalamide) (Kevlar)	238.2		1.54					
Polycarbonates								
poly[methane bis(4-phenyl) carbonate]	226.2	1.24	1.303					
poly[1,1-ethane bis(4-phenyl)carbonate]	240.3		>1.22					
poly[2,2-propane bis(4-phenyl)carbonate]	254.3	1.20	1.31	2.4/2.9	4.8/5.9	1.19	1.61	36.8
poly[1,1-butane bis(4-phenyl)carbonate]	268.3		>1.17					
poly[1,1-(2-methyl propane) bis(4-phenyl)carbonate]	268.3		>1.18					
poly[2,2-butane bis(4-phenyl) carbonate]	268.3	<1.18						

Physical properties / Polymers	γ 10^{-3} N/m	T_g K	T_m K	δ $J^{1/2}/cm^{3/2}$	n	ϵ	λ_a $J \cdot s^{-1} \cdot m^{-1} \cdot K^{-1}$	λ_c	K_Θ $cm^3 \cdot mol^{1/2} \cdot g^{-3/2}$
Polyesters (continued)									
poly(ethylene sebacate)		243	351			4.1			
poly(decamethylene adipate)		217	343/355						
poly(decamethylene sebacate)			344/358			3.35			0.220
poly(α,α-dimethylpropiolactone)		258/315	513						
poly(para-hydroxybenzoate) (Ekonol)		>420	590/ >770			3.3/3.8	0.75		
poly(ethylene oxybenzoate) (A-tell)		355	475/500						
poly(ethylene isophthalate)		324	416/513						
poly(ethylene terephthalate)	40/43	342/350	538/557	19.8/21.9	1.64	2.9/3.2	0.22	(0.28)	0.15/0.20
poly(tetramethylene isophthalate)			426						
poly(tetramethylene terephthalate)		295/353	505			3.1			
poly(hexamethylene terephthalate)		264/318	427/434						
poly(decamethylene terephthalate)		268/298	396/411						
poly(1,4-cyclohexane dimethylene terephthalate)(trans)		365	591						
poly(ethylene-1,5-naphthalate)		344	503						
poly(ethylene-2,6-naphthalate)		386/453	533/541						
poly(1,4-cyclohexylidene dimethylene terephthalate) (Kodel) (cis)			530						
poly(1,4-cyclohexylidene dimethylene terephthalate) (Kodel) (trans)		365	590						
Polyamides									
poly(4-aminobutyric acid) (nylon 4)			523/538						
poly(6-aminohexanoic acid) (nylon 6)	40/47	323/348	487/506	22.5	1.53	4.2/4.5			0.190/0.230
poly(7-aminoheptanoic acid) (nylon 7)		325/335	490/506						
poly(8-aminooctanoic acid)(nylon 8)		324	458/482	26.0					
poly(9-aminononanoic acid)(nylon 9)		324	467/482						
poly(10-aminodecanoic acid) (nylon 10)		316	450/465						
poly(11-aminoundecanoic acid) (nylon 11)	33/43	319	455/493			3.7			
poly(12-aminododecanoic acid) (nylon 12)		310	452			2.8/3.6	(0.24/0.35)		
poly(hexamethylene adipamide) (nylon 6,6)	42/46	318/330	523/545	27.8	1.475/ 1.580	3.8/4.3			0.190/0.250
poly(heptamethylene pimelamide) (nylon 7,7)	43		469/487						
poly(octamethylene suberamide) (nylon 8,8)	34		478/498						
poly(hexamethylene sebacamide) (nylon 6,10)		303/323	488/506		1.475/ 1.565	3.5			
poly(nonamethylene azelamide) (nylon 9,9)	36		450						
poly(decamethylene azelamide) (nylon 10,9)			487						
poly(decamethylene sebacamide) (nylon 10,10)	32	319/333	469/489			3.4/3.8			
poly[bis(4-aminocyclohexyl)methane-1,10-decanedicarboxamide] (Qiana) (trans)		408/420	(548)/581						
poly(m-xylylene adipamide)		363	518						
poly(p-xylylene sebacamide)		388	541/573						
poly(2,2,2-trimethylhexamethylene terephthalamide)					1.566	3.1/3.5	(0.21)		
poly(piperazine sebacamide)		355	455						
poly(metaphenylene isophthalamide) (Nomex)		545	660/700						
poly(p-phenylene terephthalamide) (Kevlar)		580/620	770/870						
Polycarbonates									
poly[methane bis(4-phenyl) carbonate]		393/420	513/573						
poly[1,1-ethane bis(4-phenyl)carbonate]		403	468		1.5937	2.9			
poly[2,2-propane bis(4-phenyl)carbonate]	35/45	414/423	498/540	20.3	1.585	2.6/3.0	0.19/0.24		0.180/0.277
poly[1,1-butane bis(4-phenyl)carbonate]		396	443		1.5792	3.3			
poly[1,1-(2-methyl propane) bis(4-phenyl)carbonate]		422	453		1.5702	2.3			
poly[2,2-butane bis(4-phenyl)carbonate]		407	495		1.5827	3.1			

(continued on p. 580)

TABLE V (continued)

Polymers	M	ρ_a	ρ_c	e_g	e_l	c_p^s	c_p^l	ΔH_m
Physical properties	g/mol	g/cm³	g/cm³	$10^{-4}\ cm^3 \cdot g^{-1} \cdot K^{-1}$		$J \cdot g^{-1} \cdot K^{-1}$		kJ/mol
Polycarbonates (continued)								
poly[2,2-pentane bis(4-phenyl)carbonate]	282.3		>1.13					
poly[4,4-heptane bis(4-phenyl)carbonate]	310.4		>1.16					
poly[1,1-(1-phenylethane)bis-(4-phenyl)carbonate]	316.3		>1.21					
poly{diphenylmethane bis(4-phenyl)carbonate}	378.4	<1.27						
poly[1,1-cyclopentane bis(4-phenyl)carbonate]	280.3		>1.21					
poly[1,1-cyclohexane bis(4-phenyl)carbonate]	294.3		>1.20					
poly{thio bis(4-phenyl)carbonate]	244.3	1.355	1.500					
poly[2,2-propane bis-{4-(2-methyl phenyl)} carbonate]	282.3		>1.22					
poly[2,2-propane bis-{4-(2-chlorophenyl)}carbonate]	323.2		>1.32					
poly[2,2-propane bis-{4-(2,6-dichlorophenyl)}-carbonate]	392.1		>1.42					
poly[2,2-propane bis-{4-(2,6-dibromophenyl)}-carbonate]	569.9		>1.91					
poly[1,1-cyclohexane bis-{4-(2,6-dichlorophenyl)}-carbonate]	432.1		>1.38					
Other polymers								
poly(p-xylylene)	104.1	1.05/1.10	1.08/1.25					30.2
poly(chloro p-xylylene)	138.6	<1.28						
poly(α-α-α'-α'-tetrafluoro-p-xylylene)	176.1	<1.506	>1.597					
poly(4,4'-tetramethylene dioxy-dibenzoic anhydride)	312.3	<1.266	>1.301					
poly[4,4'-isopropylidene diphenoxy di(4-phenylene)sulphone] (polysulphone)	442.5	<1.24		1.35				
poly[N,N'(p,p'-oxydiphenylene)-pyromellitimide] (Kapton)	382.3	1.42				1.51		
poly(dimethylsiloxane)	74.1	0.98	1.07	2.7/3.2	9.14		1.47/1.59	1.3

Polymers \ Physical properties	γ 10^{-3} N/m	T_g K	T_m K	δ $J^{1/2}/cm^{3/2}$	n	ϵ	λ_a $J \cdot s^{-1} \cdot m^{-1} \cdot K^{-1}$	λ_c	K_Θ $cm^3 \cdot mol^{1/2} \cdot g^{-3/2}$
Polycarbonates (continued)									
poly[2,2-pentane bis(4-phenyl)-carbonate]		410	493		1.5745				
poly[4,4-heptane bis(4-phenyl)-carbonate]		421	473		1.5602				
poly[1,1-(1-phenylethane) bis-(4-phenyl)carbonate]		449/463	503		1.6130				
poly[diphenylmethane bis-(4-phenyl)carbonate]		394	503		1.6539				
poly[1,1-cyclopentane bis-(4-phenyl)carbonate]		440	523		1.5993				
poly[1,1-cyclohexane bis-(4-phenyl)carbonate]		446	533		1.5900	2.6			
poly[thio bis(4-phenyl)carbonate]		383	513						
poly[2,2-propane bis-{4-(2-methyl phenyl)}carbonate]		368/418	443		1.5783				
poly[2,2-propane bis-{4-(2-chlorophenyl)}carbonate]		420	483		1.5900				
poly[2,2-propane bis-{4-(2,6-dichlorophenyl)}-carbonate]		453/493	533		1.6056				
poly[2,2-propane bis-{4-(2,6-dibromophenyl)}-carbonate]		430	533		1.6147				
poly[1,1-cyclohexane bis {4-(2,6-dichlorophenyl)}-carbonate]		446	543		1.5858				
Other polymers									
poly(p-xylylene)		333/353	648/713		1.669	2.65			
poly(chloro-p-xylylene)		353/373	552/572		1.629	3.0			
poly(α-α-α'-α'-tetrafluoro-p-xylylene)		363	~773			2.35			
poly(4,4'-tetramethylene dioxy-dibenzoic anhydride)		348	477						
poly[4,4'-isopropylidene diphenoxy di(4-phenylene)sulphone] (polysulphone)		463/468	570	20.3	1.633	3.1	0.26		0.145
poly[N,N'(p,p'-oxydiphenylene)-pyromellitimide] (Kapton)		600/660	770			3.5			
poly(dimethylsiloxane)	20/24	150	234/244	14.9/15.6	1.4035/1.43		0.13/0.163		0.070/0.106

TABLE VI

PHYSICAL CONSTANTS OF THE MOST IMPORTANT SOLVENTS

Temperature 20°C except if other value is mentioned

Name	Formula	M	ρ	V	T_b	T_m	η	γ	n_D
			g/cm^3	cm^3/mol	°C	°C	(25°C) 10^{-3} $\frac{N \cdot s}{m^2}$	10^{-3} N/m	
Hydrocarbons									
hexane	$CH_3-(CH_2)_4-CH_3$	86.17	0.660	130.5	69	−94	0.29	18.43	1.3754
heptane	$CH_3-(CH_2)_5-CH_3$	100.21	0.684	146.6	98	−91	0.39	20.30	1.386
octane	$CH_3-(CH_2)_6-CH_3$	114.23	0.703	162.6	126	−57	0.51	21.14	1.396
cyclohexane		84.16	0.779	108.0	81	7	0.90	25.5	1.4290
benzene		78.11	0.879	88.9	80	6	0.60	28.85	1.501
methylbenzene (toluene)		92.13	0.867	106.3	111	−95	0.55	28.5	1.4969
1,2-dimethylbenzene (o-xylene)		106.16	0.880	120.6	144	−27/−29	0.77	30.10	1.5055
1,3-dimethylbenzene (m-xylene)		106.16	0.864	122.8	139	−47/−54	0.58	28.9	1.4972
1,4-dimethylbenzene (p-xylene)		106.16	0.861	123.2	138	13	0.61	28.37	1.4958
ethylbenzene		106.16	0.867	122.4	134−136	−93/−94	0.64	29.20	1.4983
ethenylbenzene (styrene)		104.14	0.907	114.7	146	−31	0.70	32.3	1.5434
1,2,3,4-tetrahydronaphthalene (Tetralin)		132.20	0.870/ 0.971	136.1 152.0	207	−30	2.0	35.46	1.539
decahydronaphthalene (Decalin)		138.25	0.870/ 0.896	154.3/ 158.9	186/195	−43/−31	2.1/3.4	29.9/ 32.2	1.470/
Hydrocarbons, halogenated									
dichloromethane (methylene chloride)	CH_2Cl_2	84.94	1.336	63.6	40	−97	0.42	26.52	1.4237
trichloromethane (chloroform)	$CHCl_3$	119.39	1.499	79.7	58−62	−64	0.54	27.14	1.4464
tetrachloromethane (carbon tetrachloride)	CCl_4	153.84	1.595	96.5	77	−21 to −29	0.88	26.95	1.4631
chloroethane (ethyl chloride)	CH_3-CH_2Cl	64.52	0.88	73.3	12	−139	~0.27	~19.5	(1.3738)
1,2-dichloroethane (ethylene chloride)	CH_2Cl-CH_2Cl	98.97	1.257	78.7	84	−35	(0.73)	24.15	1.4443
1,1-dichloroethane (ethylidene chloride)	CH_3-CHCl_2	98.97	1.174	84.3	57	−97	0.47	24.75	1.416
1,1,2-trichloroethane	$CH_2Cl-CHCl_2$	133.42	1.443	92.5	114	−37	0.11	33.75	1.4715
1,1,1-trichloroethane	CCl_3CH_3	133.42	1.325	100.7	74	−31	0.80	25.56	1.4375
1,1,2,2-tetrachloroethane	$CHCl_2-CHCl_2$	167.86	1.600	104.9	146	(−36)/−44	(1.75)	35.6	1.493
1-chloropropane (n-propyl chloride)	$CH_3-(CH_2)_2-Cl$	78.54	0.890	88.2	45−47	−123	(0.35)	21.78	1.386
1-chlorobutane (n-butyl chloride)	$CH_2Cl-(CH_2)_2-CH_3$	92.57	0.884	104.7	78	−123	0.43	23.75	1.400
chlorobenzene		112.56	1.107	101.7	132	−45/(−55)	(0.80)	33.56	1.5248
bromobenzene		157.02	1.499	104.7	155−156	−31	(0.99)	36.5	1.5598
1-bromonaphthalene		207.07	1.488	139.2	281	0/6	4.52	44.19	1.6586
1,1,2-trichloro-1,2,2-trifluoroethane (freon 113)	$CFCl_2-CF_2Cl$	187.38	(1.564)	119.8	48	−36	(0.71)	17.75	1.355
Ethers									
ethoxyethane (diethyl ether)	$CH_3-CH_2-O-CH_2-CH_3$	74.12	0.714	103.9	35	α −116 β −123	0.22	17.01	1.349
1-propoxypropane (dipropyl ether)	$C_3H_7-O-C_3H_7$	102.18	0.736/ 0.749	136.9/ 138.8	90	−123	(0.38)	20.53	1.3805
2-isopropoxypropane (diisopropyl ether)	$CH_3-CH-O-CH-CH_3$ $\quad\ \ CH_3\quad\ \ CH_3$	102.17	0.726	140.7	68−69	−60/−86	0.38	17.34	1.367

	Formula	ϵ	μ (debye)	$\Delta\nu$ (gordy)	δ ($J^{1/2}/cm^{3/2}$)	δ_d ($J^{1/2}/cm^{3/2}$)	δ_p ($J^{1/2}/cm^{3/2}$)	δ_h ($J^{1/2}/cm^{3/2}$)	δ_a ($J^{1/2}/cm^{3/2}$)	δ_v ($J^{1/2}/cm^{3/2}$)
...ons										
	$CH_3-(CH_2)_4-CH_3$	1.89	0–0.08	0	14.8–14.9	14.8	0	0	0	14.8
	$CH_3-(CH_2)_5-CH_3$	1.92	0.0	0	15.2	15.2	0	0	0	15.2
	$CH_3-(CH_2)_6-CH_3$	1.95	0	–	15.6	15.6	0	0	0	15.6
...ne	(cyclohexane)	2.02	0–1.78	0	16.7	16.7	0	0	0	16.7
	(benzene)	2.28	0–1.56	0	18.5–18.8	17.6–18.5	1.0	2.0	2.3–6.4	17.6–18.5
...zene (toluene)	(⬡)-CH_3	2.38	0.43	4.2/4.5	18.2–18.3	17.3–18.1	1.4	2.0	2.5–6.0	17.3–18.1
...ylbenzene (o-xylene)	(⬡)-CH_3, CH_3	2.57	0.44–0.62		18.4	16.8–17.6			5.3–7.4	16.9–17.7
...ylbenzene (m-xylene)	(⬡)-CH_3, CH_3	2.37	0.30–0.46	}4.5	18.0	16.7–17.4	1.0} 1.0		4.8–6.8	16.7–17.5
...ylbenzene (p-xylene)	CH_3-(⬡)-CH_3	2.27	0–0.23		17.9–18.0	16.6–17.3			4.7–6.8	16.7–17.3
...ene	(⬡)-CH_2-CH_3	2.41	0.35–0.58	1.5/4.2	17.9–18.0	16.7–17.8	0.6	1.4	1.6–6.8	16.7–17.8
...nzene (styrene)	(⬡)-CH·CH_2	2.43	0–0.56	1.5	18.0/ 19.0	16.8–18.6	1.0	4.1	4.2–9.0	16.9–18.6
...rahydronaphthalene (Tetralin)		2.77	0.49–1.67	–	19.5	19.1–19.2	2.0	2.9	3.1–3.5	19.3–19.4
...naphthalene (Decalin)		–	–	–	18.0	–				
...ons, halogenated										
...ethane (methylene chloride)	CH_2Cl_2	9.08	1.47–1.9	1.5	19.9	17.4–18.2	6.4	6.1	8.8–10.4	18.6–19.3
...ethane (chloroform)	$CHCl_3$	4.81	1.0–1.55	1.2/1.5	18.9–19.0	17.7–18.1	3.1	5.7	5.2–6.6	18.0–18.4
...omethane (carbon tetrachloride)	CCl_4	2.24	0	0	17.7	16.1–17.7	0.0	0.0	0–8.3	16.1–17.7
...ane (ethyl chloride)	CH_3-CH_2Cl	9.45	2.04	–	17.4	16.3	–	–	6.1	–
...roethane (ethylene chloride)	CH_2Cl-CH_2Cl	10.65	1.1–2.94	1.5	20.0–20.1	17.4–18.8	5.3	4.1	6.7–10.0	18.2–19.6
...roethane (ethylidene chloride)	CH_3-CHCl_2	10.15	1.97–2.63	–	18.3	16.8	–	–	8.2	–
...loroethane	$CH_2Cl-CHCl_2$	–	1.15–1.55	1.5	19.7–20.8	18.3	–	–	10.0	–
...loroethane	CCl_3CH_3	7.53	0.88–2.03	–	17.5	16.6–16.9	4.3	2.0	4.8–5.5	17.2–17.4
...trachloroethane	$CHCl_2-CHCl_2$	8.20	1.29–2.00	~1.5	19.9–20.2	18.7	–	–	7.3	–
...ropane (n-propyl chloride)	$CH_3-(CH_2)_2-Cl$	7.7	1.83–2.06	–	17.4	15.9	–	–	7.2	–
...utane (n-butyl chloride)	$CH_2Cl-(CH_2)_2-CH_3$	–	1.90–2.13	–	17.3	16.1–16.3	5.5	2.1	5.9–6.4	17.0–17.2
...zene	(⬡)-Cl	5.71	1.58–1.75	1.5/2.7	19.5–19.6	18.8–19.0	4.3	2.1	4.8–5.6	19.3–19.5
...zene	(⬡)-Br	5.4	1.36–1.79	0	20.0	18.9	–	–	6.8	–
...aphthalene	(naphthalene)-Br	5.12	1.29–1.59	–	21.0	18.8–20.4	3.1	4.1	5.1–9.3	19.0–20.6
...loro-1,2,2-trifluoroethane (113)	$CFCl_2-CF_2Cl$	(2.41)	–	–	14.8	14.5	–	–	3.0	–
...ane (diethyl ether)	$CH_3-CH_2-O-CH_2-CH_3$	4.33/ 4.34	1.15–1.30	13.0	15.2–15.6	14.4	2.9	5.1	5.9	14.7
...propane (dipropyl ether)	$C_3H_7-O-C_3H_7$	(3.39)	1.3	11.7	14.1	–	–	–	–	–
...oxypropane (diisopropyl ether)	$CH_3-CH-O-CH-CH_3$; CH_3 CH_3	3.88	1.13–1.26	12.3	14.4	13.7	–	–	4.4	–

(continued on p. 584)

TABLE VI (continued)

Name	Formula	M	ρ	V	T_b	T_m	η	γ	n_D
			g/cm³	cm³/mol	°C	°C	(25°C) 10^{-3} $\frac{N \cdot s}{m^2}$	10^{-3} N/m	

Ethers (continued)

Name	Formula	M	ρ	V	T_b	T_m	η	γ	n_D
1-butoxybutane (dibutyl ether)	$C_4H_9-O-C_4H_9$	130.23	0.769	169.3	142	−95/(−98)	~0.63	~22.9	1.3992
dimethoxymethane (methylal)	$CH_3-O-CH_2-O-CH_3$	76.09	0.856	88.9	44	−105	(0.33)	21.12	1.3534
methoxybenzene (anisole)	⬡– OCH₃	108.13	0.995	108.6	155	−37	(1.32)	(36.18)	1.515
1,4-epoxybutane (tetrahydrofuran)		72.10	0.888	81.2	64−66	−65/−109	0.36	26.4	1.4091
p-dioxane		88.10	1.035	85.1	102	(9−13)	1.2	36.9	1.4232
1,4-epoxy-1,3-butadiene (furan)		68.07	0.937	72.7	31	−86	0.36	24.10	1.4216
2,2'-dichlorodiethyl ether	$CH_2Cl-CH_2-O-CH_2-CH_2Cl$	143.02	1.222	117.0	178	−50	2.14	37.6	1.4575
1-chloro-2,3-epoxypropane (epichlorohydrin)	$CH_2-CH-CH_2Cl$	92.53	1.180	78.4	117	−26	1.03/ ~1.05	37.00	1.4420

Esters

Name	Formula	M	ρ	V	T_b	T_m	η	γ	n_D
ethyl formate	$HC-OC_2H_5$	74.08	0.924	80.2	54	−81	(0.40)	23.6	1.3598
propyl formate	$HC-OC_3H_7$	88.10	0.901	97.8	81	−93	(0.46)	24.5	1.3771
methyl acetate	$CH_3-C-OCH_3$	74.08	0.934	79.3	57	−98	0.36	24.6	1.3594
ethyl acetate	$CH_3-C-O-CH_2-CH_3$	88.10	0.901	97.8	77	−84	0.44	23.9	1.3722
propyl acetate	$CH_3-C-O(CH_2)_2-CH_3$	102.13	0.887	115.1	102	−93	0.55	24.3	1.382
isopropyl acetate	$CH_3-C-O-CH-CH_3$	102.13	0.873	116.9	89	−73	~0.47	22.10	1.375
butyl acetate	$CH_3-C-O-(CH_2)_3-CH_3$	116.16	0.882	131.7	(124−126)	−77	0.69	~24.8−27.6	1.3951
isobutyl acetate	$CH_3-C-O-CH_2-CH-CH_3$	116.16	0.871	133.3	115−117	−99	0.65	23.7	1.388
amyl acetate	$CH_3-C-OC_5H_{11}$	130.18	0.875	148.7	145−149	−79	0.86	25.68/25.8	1.4028
isoamyl acetate	$CH_3-C-O-(CH_2)_2-CH-CH_3$	130.18	0.867/0.872	149.3 150.1	138−143	−79	0.79	24.62	1.403
ethyl lactate	$CH_3-CHOH-C-OC_2H_5$	118.13	1.031	114.6	150−154	−25	2.44	29.9	1.412
butyl lactate	$CH_3-CHOH-C-OC_4H_9$	146.18	0.968	151.0	160−190	−43	3.18	30.6	1.4217
2-ethoxyethyl acetate (cellosolve acetate)	$CH_3-C-O(CH_2)_2-O-CH_2-CH_3$	132.16	0.973	135.8	156	−62	1.03/1.21	31.8	1.4023
diethylene glycol, monoethyl ether, acetate (carbitol acetate)	$CH_3-C-O(CH_2)_2-O-(CH_2)_2-O-C_2H_5$	176.21	1.009	174.6	218	−25	(2.8)	−	1.4213
1,2-ethanediol, carbonate (ethylene carbonate)		88.06	1.334	66.0	238	36	−	−	1.426
1,2-propanediol, carbonate (propylene carbonate)		102.09	1.201	85.0	242	−49	2.8	40.5	1.4209

Ketones and aldehydes

Name	Formula	M	ρ	V	T_b	T_m	η	γ	n_D
2-propanone (acetone)	CH_3-C-CH_3	58.08	0.792	73.3	57	−95	0.32	23.70	1.3589
2-butanone (methyl ethyl ketone)	$CH_3-C-CH_2-CH_3$	72.10	0.805	89.6	80	−86	(0.42)	~24.3	1.3807
3-pentanone (diethyl ketone)	$CH_3-CH_2-C-CH_2-CH_3$	86.13	0.816	105.6	103	−42	0.44	~24.8/25.26	1.3939
2-pentanone (methyl propyl ketone)	$CH_3-C-(CH_2)_2-CH_3$	86.13	0.812	106.1	102	−78	0.47	25.2	1.3895

	Formula	ϵ	μ (debye)	$\Delta\nu$ (gordy)	δ $J^{1/2}/cm^{3/2}$	δ_d $J^{1/2}/cm^{3/2}$	δ_p $J^{1/2}/cm^{3/2}$	δ_h $J^{1/2}/cm^{3/2}$	δ_a $J^{1/2}/cm^{3/2}$	δ_v $J^{1/2}/cm^{3/2}$
nued)										
ane (dibutyl ether)	$C_4H_9-O-C_4H_9$	3.08	1.09–1.26	11.0	14.5–15.9	15.2	–	–	4.5	–
ethane (methylal)	$CH_3-O-CH_2-O-CH_3$	2.65	0.67–1.14	–	17.4	~15.1	~1.8	~8.6	8.8	~15.2
ene (anisole)	$\langle\text{ring}\rangle-OCH_3$	(4.33)	1.25/1.4	7.0	~19.5 20.3	~17.8	~4.1	~6.8	~7.9	~18.3
ane (tetrahydrofuran)	[ring structure]	(7.58)	1.48–1.84	12.0	19.5	16.8/18.9	5.7	8.0	4.7/9.8	17.8/19.8
	[ring structure]	2.21	0–0.49	9.7/14.6	19.9–~20.5	17.5–~19.0	~1.8	~7.4	~7.6–9.5	~17.6–~19.1
3-butadiene (furan)	[ring structure]	2.95	0.63–0.72	–	18.6/18.7	17.3/17.8	1.8	5.3	5.6/6.9	17.4/17.9
diethyl ether	$CH_2Cl-CH_2-O-CH_2-CH_2Cl$	(38)	2.36–2.60	8.4	~21.1–21.2	17.2–~18.3	~9.0	~3.1	~9.5–12.2	~19.5/~20.9
epoxypropane (hydrin)	$CH_2-CH-CH_2Cl$ (epoxide O)	23/26	1.8	10.4	21.9	19.0	10.2	3.7	10.9	21.6
e	$HC(O)-OC_2H_5$	7.16/9.10	1.94–2.01	8.4	19.2/19.6	15.6	–	–	12.5	–
ate	$HC(O)-OC_3H_7$	7.72	1.91	–	19.6	15.0	–	–	12.5	–
te	$CH_3-C(O)-OCH_3$	6.68	1.45–1.75	8.4	19.4/19.7	15.5	–	–	11.7	–
e	$CH_3-C(O)-O-CH_2-CH_3$	6.02	1.76–2.05	8.4	18.6	15.2	5.3	9.2	10.6	16.1
te	$CH_3-C(O)-O(CH_2)_2-CH_3$	5.60–6.00	1.79–1.91	8.5/8.6	17.9–18.0	15.6	–	–	8.8	–
etate	$CH_3-C(O)-O-CH-CH_3$ (CH_3)	–	1.83–1.89	8.5/8.6	17.2–17.6	14.4–14.9	4.5	8.2	9.4–9.6	15.1–15.6
e	$CH_3-C(O)-O-(CH_2)_3-CH_3$	5.01	1.82–1.9	8.8	17.3–17.4	15.7	3.7	6.4	7.3	16.1
tate	$CH_3-C(O)-O-CH_2-CH-CH_3$ (CH_3)	5.29	1.87–1.89	8.7/8.8	17.0/17.2	15.1	3.7	7.6	8.4	15.5
	$CH_3-C(O)-OC_5H_{11}$	4.75	1.72–1.93	8.2/9.0	17.4	–	–	–	–	–
ate	$CH_3-C(O)-O-(CH_2)_2-CH-CH_3$ (CH_3)	(4.63)	1.76–1.86	–	17.0	15.3	3.1	7.0	7.6	15.6
	$CH_3-CHOH-C(O)-OC_2H_5$	13.1	1.9–2.34	7.0	20.5/21.6	16.0	7.6	12.5	14.6	17.7
	$CH_3-CHOH-C(O)-OC_4H_9$	–	1.9/2.4	7.0	19.2/19.8	15.7	6.6	10.2	12.2	17.0
yl acetate (e acetate)	$CH_3-C(O)-O(CH_2)_2-O-CH_2-CH_3$	(7.57)	2.24–2.32	10.1	19.7	15.9	4.7	10.6	11.5	16.6
lycol, monoethyl ether, acetate (acetate)	$CH_3-C(O)-O(CH_2)_2-O-(CH_2)_2-O-C_2H_5$	–	1.8	9.4	17.4/19.3	16.2	–	–	10.5	–
ol, carbonate (e carbonate)	[ring structure, O]	(89.6)	1.0–4.91	4.9	29.6–30.9	19.5–22.2	21.7	5.1	21.5–23.3	29.1–31.1
diol, carbonate (propylene e)	CH_3-[ring structure, O]	–	1.0/4.98	4.9	27.2	20.1	18.0	4.1	18.4	27.0
aldehydes										
e (acetone)	$CH_3-C(O)-CH_3$	20.70/21	2.86–2.9	9.7/12.5	20.0–20.5	15.5	10.4	7.0	12.6	18.7
(methyl ethyl ketone)	$CH_3-C(O)-CH_2-CH_3$	15.45/18.51	2.5–3.41	7.7/10.5	19.0	15.9	9.0	5.1	10.4	18.3
(diethyl ketone)	$CH_3-CH_2-C(O)-CH_2-CH_3$	17.00	2.5–2.82	7.7	18.0/18.1	15.7	–	–	9.5	–
e (methyl propyl ketone)	$CH_3-C(O)-(CH_2)_2-CH_3$	15.45	2.5–2.74	8.0	18.3	15.8	–	–	9.2	–

(continued on p. 586)

TABLE VI (continued)

Name	Formula	M	ρ g/cm³	V cm³/mol	T_b °C	T_m °C	η (25°C) 10^{-3} $\frac{N \cdot s}{m^2}$	γ 10^{-3} N/m	n_D
Ketones and aldehydes (continued)									
2-hexanone (methyl butyl ketone)	$CH_3-C(=O)-(CH_2)_3-CH_3$	100.16	0.808/ 0.812	123.4/ 123.9	127	−57	0.58	25.2	1.395
4-methyl-2-pentanone (methyl isobutyl ketone)	$CH_3-C(=O)-CH_2-CH(CH_3)-CH_3$	100.16	0.802	124.9	115–119	−85	0.54/ 0.57	23.64	1.394
2,6-dimethyl-4-heptanone (diisobutyl ketone)	$(CH_3-CH(CH_3)-CH_2)_2-C(=O)$	142.24	0.806	176.4	165–168	42	1.0	–	1.412
4-methyl-3-penten-2-one (mesityl oxide)	$CH_3-C(CH_3)=CH-C(=O)-CH_3$	98.14	0.854	114.9	129/(131)	−59	0.88	–	1.442
cyclohexanone	⬡=O	98.14	0.948/ 0.998	98.4/ 103.5	(155)/157	−16 −32	(1.80)	34.50	1.4507
4-hydroxybutanoic acid, lactone (butyrolactone)	(lactone ring)	86.09	(1.129)	76.3	206	−44	1.7	–	1.434
methyl phenyl ketone (acetophenone)	Ph-C(=O)-CH₃	120.14	1.026	117.1	202	20	1.62	39.8	1.5342
3,5,5-trimethyl-2-cyclohexen-1-one (isophorone)	(cyclohexenone, CH_3, $(CH_3)_2$)	138.20	0.923	149.7	215	−8	(2.62)	–	1.4789
ethanal (acetaldehyde)	$CH_3-C(=O)-H$	44.05	0.783	56.3	21	−124	0.22	21.2	1.3316
butanal (butyraldehyde)	$CH_3-(CH_2)_2-C(=O)-H$	72.10	0.817	88.3	76	−99	(0.46)	29.9	1.3791
benzenecarbonal (benzaldehyde)	Ph-C(=O)-H	106.12	(1.050)	101.0	180	−26 to −57	1.39	40.04	1.5463
Alcohols									
methanol	CH_3-OH	32.04	0.792	40.4	65	−98	0.55	22.61	1.3312
ethanol	C_2H_5-OH	46.07	0.789	58.4	(78)/79	−115/−117	1.08	22.75	1.3624
1-propanol	$CH_3-(CH_2)_2-OH$	60.09	0.780/ 0.804	74.7/ 77.1	97/(98)	−127	1.91/ 2.02	23.78	1.3854
2-propanol (isopropyl alcohol)	$CH_3-CHOH-CH_3$	60.09	0.785	76.5	82	−90	~1.9	21.7	1.3776
1-butanol	$CH_3-(CH_2)_3-OH$	74.12	0.810	91.5	118	(−88) −90	2.46/ 2.60	24.6	1.3993
2-methyl-1-propanol (isobutyl alcohol)	$CH_3-CH(CH_3)-CH_2OH$	74.12	0.801	92.5	106–108	−108	3.24/3.9	23.0	1.3968
2-butanol (sec.-butyl alcohol)	$CH_3-CHOH-CH_2-CH_3$	74.12	0.808	91.7	100	−89/−115	~3.1	23.47	1.397
1-pentanol (amyl alcohol)	$CH_3-(CH_2)_4-OH$	88.15	0.814	108.2	138	−79	3.19/ 3.35	25.6	1.4099
cyclohexanol	⬡-OH	100.16	0.962	104.0	162	22–25	56.2	33.91	1.4656
phenol	Ph-OH	94.11	1.072	87.8	182	41	(12.7)	40.9	1.5509
3-methylphenol (m-cresol)	(phenol, CH_3)	108.13	1.034	104.6	203	11–12	(20.8)	(38.01)	1.5398
phenyl methanol (benzyl alcohol)	Ph-CH_2OH	108.13	1.050	103.0	205	−15	(5.8)	39.0	1.5396
1,2-ethanediol (ethylene glycol)	CH_2OH-CH_2OH	62.07	1.109/ 1.116	55.6/ 56.0	198–200	(−12) −17	17.4	47.7	1.4274
1,2-propanediol (propylene glycol)	$CH_3-CHOH-CH_2OH$	76.09	1.040	73.2	189	−60	~30/43	~36.8/ 40.1	1.431
1,3-butanediol (butylene glycol)	$CH_3-CHOH-CH_2-CH_2OH$	90.12	1.005	89.7	204	<−50	98.3/ 110	37.8	1.441
1,2,3-propanetriol (glycerol)	$CH_2OH-CHOH-CH_2OH$	92.09	1.260	73.1	290	18	945/954	63.4	1.4729
2-methoxyethanol (methyl cellosolve)	$CH_3-O-CH_2-CH_2OH$	76.09	0.966	78.8	124	−85	1.60	35	1.400
2-ethoxyethanol (ethyl cellosolve)	$CH_3-CH_2-O-CH_2-CH_2OH$	90.12	0.930/ 0.931	96.8/ 97.0	135	−90	1.85	28.2/32	1.405

	Formula	ϵ	μ	$\Delta\nu$	δ	δ_d	δ_p	δ_h	δ_a	δ_v
			debye	gordy	$J^{1/2}/cm^{3/2}$	$J^{1/2}/cm^{3/2}$	$J^{1/2}/cm^{3/2}$	$J^{1/2}/cm^{3/2}$	$J^{1/2}/cm^{3/2}$	$j^{1/2}/cm^{3/2}$

ldehydes
)

	Formula	ϵ	μ	$\Delta\nu$	δ	δ_d	δ_p	δ_h	δ_a	δ_v
nethyl butyl ketone)	$CH_3-C(O)-(CH_2)_3-CH_3$	12.2	2.5–2.75	8.4	17.4/17.7	15.9	–	–	7.7	–
ntanone (methyl isobutyl	$CH_3-C(O)-CH_2-CH-CH_3$ (CH_3)	13.11	2.7	7.7/10.5	17.2/17.5	15.3	6.1	4.1	8.5	16.5
4-heptanone (diisobutyl	$(CH_3-CH-CH_2)_2-C(O)$ (CH_3)	–	2.66/2.7	8.4/9.8	16.0/16.7	15.9	3.7	4.1	5.4	16.3
nten-2-one (mesityl oxide)	$CH_3-C=CH-C(O)-CH_3$ (CH_3)	–	2.79–3.28	9.7/12.0	18.4/18.8	16.3	7.2	6.1	9.4	17.8
e	(cyclohexanone) =O	18.3	2.7–3.08	11.7/13.7	19.0–20.2	17.7	8.4	5.1	9.8	19.6
anoic acid, lactone tone)	(lactone)	39 ·	2.7/4.15	9.7	26.2–31.7	19.0/20.1	16.6	7.4	16.8/18.1	25.2/26.1
l ketone (acetophenone)	$C(O)-CH_3$	17.39	2.60–3.4	7.7	19.8	17.5–18.5	8.6	3.7	7.1–9.4	19.5–20.4
1-2-cyclohexen-1-one e)	O= (CH_3)($CH_3)_2$	–	3.99	14.9	19.9	16.6	8.2	7.4	11.0	18.5
dehyde)	$CH_3-C(O)-H$	21.8	2.55	–	20.1	–	–	–	–	–
aldehyde)	$CH_3-(CH_2)_2-C(O)-H$	13.4	2.45–2.74	11.7	–	–	–	–	–	–
al (benzaldehyde)	$C(O)-H$	16/17.8	2.72–2.99	8.4	19.2–21.3	18.2–18.7	8.6	5.3	10.1–10.2	20.2–20.6
	CH_3-OH	33.62	1.7–1.71	18.7/19.8	29.2–29.7	15.2	12.3	22.3	25.4	19.5
	C_2H_5-OH	24.3	1.7–1.73	17.7/18.7	26.0–26.5	15.8	8.8	19.5	21.4	18.1
	$CH_3-(CH_2)_2-OH$	20.1	1.54–3.09	16.5/18.7	24.4–24.5	15.9	6.8	17.4	18.6	17.2
propyl alcohol)	$CH_3-CHOH-CH_3$	13.8/18.3	1.48–1.80	16.7	23.6	15.8	6.1	16.4	17.5	16.9
	$CH_3-(CH_2)_3-OH$	17.8	1.7/1.81	18.0/18.7	23.1/23.3	16.0	5.7	15.8	16.8	17.0
panol (isobutyl alcohol)	$CH_3-CH-CH_2OH$ (CH_3)	17.7	1.42–2.96	17.9	22.9	15.2	5.7	16.0	17.0	16.2
butyl alcohol)	$CH_3-CHOH-CH_2-CH_3$	15.8	1.66	17.5	22.2	15.8	–	–	15.6	–
yl alcohol)	$CH_3-(CH_2)_4-OH$	13.9	0.89–1.8	18.2	21.7	16.0	4.5	13.9	14.7	16.6
	OH (cyclohexanol)	15.0	1.3–1.9	16.5/18.7	22.4–23.3	17.4	4.1	13.5	14.2	17.9
	OH (phenol)	(9.78)	1.48–1.55	7.0	25.6	–	–	–	–	–
ol	OH (CH_3)	11.8	1.55–2.39	–	22.7	18.1–19.4	5.1	12.9	12.0–13.9	18.8–20.0
nol (benzyl alcohol)	CH_2OH	13.1	1.67–1.79	18.7	22.1–24.8	18.5	–	–	16.1	–
(ethylene glycol)	CH_2OH-CH_2OH	34/37.7	2.20–4.87	20.6	29.1–33.4	16.9	11.1	26.0	28.7	20.2
ol (propylene glycol)	$CH_3-CHOH-CH_2OH$	32.0	2.2–3.63	20.0	30.3	16.9	9.4	23.3	25.1	19.3
(butylene glycol)	$CH_3-CHOH-CH_2-CH_2OH$	–	–	–	29.0	16.6	10.0	21.5	23.8	19.4
riol (glycerol)	$CH_2OH-CHOH-CH_2OH$	42.5	~2.3–4.21	~22.0	33.8–43.2	17.3	12.1	29.3	39.5	21.1
nol (methyl cellosolve)	$CH_3-O-CH_2-CH_2OH$	(16.93)	2.06–2.22	–	24.7	16.2	9.2	16.4	17.0	18.6
ol (ethyl cellosolve)	$CH_3-CH_2-O-CH_2-CH_2OH$	(29.6)	2.10–2.24	15.7	24.3	16.1	9.2	14.3	17.5	18.5

(continued on p. 588)

TABLE VI (continued)

Name	Formula	M	ρ	V	T_b	T_m	η	γ	n_D
			g/cm³	cm³/mol	°C	°C	(25°C) 10^{-3} $\dfrac{N \cdot s}{m^2}$	10^{-3} N/m	
Alcohols (continued)									
2-butoxyethanol (butyl cellosolve)	$CH_3-(CH_2)_3-O-CH_2-CH_2OH$	118.17	0.903	130.9	171	–	3.15	31.5	1.4
4-hydroxy-4-methyl-2-pentanone (diacetone alcohol)	$CH_3-\overset{O}{\overset{\|}{C}}-CH_2-\underset{CH_3}{\overset{\|}{C}OH}-CH_3$	116.16	0.938	123.8	164–166	–44 to –57	(2.9)	31.0	1.4
Acids									
formic acid	$H-\overset{O}{\overset{\|}{C}}-OH$	46.03	1.220	37.7	101	8	1.97	37.6	1.3
acetic acid	$CH_3-\overset{O}{\overset{\|}{C}}-OH$	60.05	1.049	57.2	118	17	1.16	27.8	1.3
butyric acid	$CH_3-(CH_2)_2-\overset{O}{\overset{\|}{C}}-OH$	88.10	0.959	91.9	163	–5/ –8	1.57	26.8	1.3
acetic acid, anhydride	$CH_3-\overset{O}{\overset{\|}{C}}-O-\overset{O}{\overset{\|}{C}}-CH_3$	102.09	1.082	94.4	140	–73	(0.78)/ (0.91)	32.7	1.3
Nitrogen compounds									
1-aminopropane (propylamine)	$CH_3-(CH_2)_2-NH_2$	59.11	0.719	82.2	49	–83	0.35	22.4	1.3
diethylamine	$CH_3-CH_2-NH-CH_2-CH_3$	73.14	0.707	103.5	56	(–39)/ –50	0.35/ 0.37	(20.63)	1.3
aminobenzene (aniline)	⬡–NH_2	93.12	1.022	91.1	184	–6	3.71	42.9/ 44.1	1.5
2-aminoethanol (ethanolamine)	$\underset{NH_2}{CH_2}-CH_2-OH$	61.08	1.018	60.0	172	11	19.35	48.89	1.4
nitromethane	CH_3-NO_2	61.04	1.130	54.0	101	–29	0.62	36.82	1.3
nitroethane	$CH_3-CH_2-NO_2$	75.07	1.052	71.4	115	< –50/–90	0.64	32.2	1.3
nitrobenzene	⬡–NO_2	123.11	1.204	102.3	211	6	(2.03)	43.9	1.5
ethanenitrile (acetonitrile)	CH_3-CN	41.05	0.783	52.4	82	–41 to –44	0.35	29.30	1.3
methanamide (formamide)	$HC\overset{O}{\overset{\|}{}}-NH_2$	45.04	1.134	39.7	211	3	3.30	58.2	1.4
dimethylformamide	$HC\overset{O}{\overset{\|}{}}-N(CH_3)_2$	73.09	0.949	77.0	153	–58	0.80	36.76/ ~38	1.4
dimethylacetamide	$CH_3-\overset{O}{\overset{\|}{C}}-N(CH_3)_2$	87.12	(0.937)	93.0	166	–20	~0.92	~34	1.4
1,1,3,3-tetramethylurea	$(CH_3)_2-N-\overset{O}{\overset{\|}{C}}-N-(CH_3)_2$	116.16	(0.969)	119.9	177	–1	–	–	·1.4
pyridine (azine)	⬡N	79.10	0.982	80.5	115	–42	0.88	38.0	1.5
morpholine	O⬡NH	87.12	1.0	87.1	126–130	–3	(1.79/ 2.37)	37.63	1.4
2-pyrrolidone	⬠NH	85.10	1.116	76.3	245–(251)	25	13.3	–	1.4
N-methyl-2-pyrrolidone	⬠N-CH_3	99.13	(1.028)	96.4	202	–16 to –24	1.67	41.83	1.4
Sulphur compounds									
dimethyl sulphide	CH_3-S-CH_3	62.13	0.846	73.5	38	–83	0.28	24.48	1.4
diethyl sulphide	$(C_2H_5)_2-S$	90.18	0.837	107.7	92	–102	0.42	25.2	1.4
carbon disulphide	CS_2	76.13	1.263	60.3	46	–109/–112	(0.36)	32.33	1.6
dimethyl sulphoxide	$CH_3-\overset{O}{\overset{\|}{S}}-CH_3$	78.13	1.102	71.0	189	19	2.0	43.54	1.4
Other substances									
triethyl phosphate	$(C_2H_5)_3-PO_4$	182.16	1.069	170.5	216	–56	–	(30.61)	1.4
hexamethyl phosphoramide	$[(CH_3)_2N]_3P=O$	179.20	1.027	174.5	233	7	(3.47)	33.8	1.4
water	H_2O	18.02	0.998	18.0	100	0	0.89	72.75	1.3

	Formula	ϵ	μ debye	$\Delta\nu$ gordy	δ $J^{1/2}/$ $cm^{3/2}$	δ_d $J^{1/2}/$ $cm^{3/2}$	δ_p $J^{1/2}/$ $cm^{3/2}$	δ_h $J^{1/2}/$ $cm^{3/2}$	δ_a $J^{1/2}/$ $cm^{3/2}$	δ_v $J^{1/2}/$ $cm^{3/2}$
tinued)										
nol (butyl cellosolve)	$CH_3-(CH_2)_3-O-CH_2-CH_2OH$	(9.30)	2.10	13.0	21.0	15.9	6.4	12.1	13.7	17.1
methyl-2-pentanone (diacetone	$CH_3-\overset{O}{\overset{\|}{C}}-CH_2-COH-CH_3$ $\overset{\|}{CH_3}$	(18.2)	2.5–3.24	13.0/16.3	18.8–20.8	15.7	8.2	10.9	13.5	17.7
	$H-\overset{O}{\overset{\|}{C}}-OH$	58.5	1.20–2.09	–	24.9– ~25.0	~14.3–15.3	~11.9	~16.6	19.8– ~20.4	~18.6– ~19.4
	$CH_3-\overset{O}{\overset{\|}{C}}-OH$	6.15	0.38–1.92	20.0	~18.8– ~21.4	~14.5–16.6	~8.0	~13.5	13.2– ~15.7	~16.6– ~18.4
	$CH_3-(CH_2)_2-\overset{O}{\overset{\|}{C}}-OH$	2.97	0–1.9	–	~18.8–23.1	~14.9–16.3	~4.1	~10.6	~11.4–16.3	~15.5– ~16.8
nhydride	$CH_3-\overset{O}{\overset{\|}{C}}-O-\overset{O}{\overset{\|}{C}}-CH_3$	20.7	2.7–3.15	–	21.3–22.2	15.4–16.0	11.1	9.6	14.7–15.1	18.9–19.5
npounds										
ane (propylamine)	$CH_3-(CH_2)_2-NH_2$	5.31	1.17–1.39	–	18.4	15.5	–	–	9.9	–
	$CH_3-CH_2-NH-CH_2-CH_3$	(3.58)	0.91–1.21	–	16.3	14.9	2.3	6.1	6.5	15.1
ne (aniline)	⬡$-NH_2$	6.89/7	1.5–1.56	18.1	22.6–24.2	19.5	5.1	10.2	11.4	20.2
nol (ethanolamine)	$\overset{CH_2-CH_2-OH}{\underset{NH_2}{\|}}$	(37.72)	2.59	–	31.7	17.1	15.6	21.3	26.4	23.1
e	CH_3-NO_2	38.57	2.83–4.39	2.5	25.1–26.0	15.8–16.4	18.8	5.1	19.0–19.5	24.6–25.0
	$CH_3-CH_2-NO_2$	28.0	3.22–3.70	2.5	22.7	16.0–16.6	15.6	4.5	15.5–16.2	22.3–22.8
e	⬡$-NO_2$	35.74/36	3.93–4.3	2.8	20.5–21.9	17.6–19.9	12.3	4.1	8.7–13.0	21.5–23.4
e (acetonitrile)	CH_3-CN	37	3.08–4.01	5.7/6.3	24.1–24.5	15.4–16.2	18.0	6.1	18.0–19.0	23.7–24.2
e (formamide)	$H\overset{O}{\overset{\|}{C}}-NH_2$	109	3.25–3.86	–	36.7	17.2	26.2	19.0	32.4	31.3
mamide	$H\overset{O}{\overset{\|}{C}}-N(CH_3)_2$	(26.6/ 36.71)	2.0–3.86	11.7/18.9	24.9	17.4	13.7	11.3	17.8	22.2
tamide	$CH_3-\overset{O}{\overset{\|}{C}}-N(CH_3)_2$	(37.78)	2.0–3.81	12.3	22.1/22.8	16.8	11.5	10.2	15.4	20.3
methylurea	$(CH_3)_2-N-\overset{O}{\overset{\|}{C}}-N-(CH_3)_2$	23.06	3.28–3.92	–	21.7	16.8	8.2	11.1	13.8	18.7
ne)	⬡$_N$	12.3	1.96–2.43	18.1	21.7–21.9	18.9–20.1	8.8	5.9	8.3–10.6	20.9–21.9
	⬡$_{NH}$ (O)	7.33	1.49–1.75	–	21.5	18.2–18.8	4.9	9.2	10.4–11.7	18.9–19.5
e	⬠$_{NH}$	–	2.3–3.79	–	28.4	19.5	17.4	11.3	20.7	26.1
pyrrolidone	⬠$_{N-CH_3}$	(32.0)	4.04–4.12	–	22.9	17.9	12.3	7.2	14.2	21.7
pounds										
phide	CH_3-S-CH_3	6.2	1.41–1.50	–	18.4	17.6	–	–	5.9	–
iide	$(C_2H_5)_2-S$	(5.72)	1.52–1.62	–	17.3	16.0–16.9	3.1	2.1	3.7–6.7	16.3–17.2
phide	CS_2	(2.64)	0–0.49	0	20.4/20.5	16.2–20.4	0	0	0–12.3	16.2–20.4
phoxide	$CH_3-\overset{O}{\overset{\|}{S}}-CH_3$	(46.68)	3.9	7.7	26.5–26.7	18.4–19.3	16.4	10.2	18.1–19.3	24.7–25.3
nces										
sphate	$(C_2H_5)_3-PO_4$	–	2.84–3.10	11.7	22.3	16.8	11.5	9.2	14.7	20.3
phosphoramide	$[(CH_3)_2N]_3P=O$	30	5.54	–	23.3	18.4	8.6	11.3	14.2	20.3
	H_2O	80.37	1.82–1.85	39.0	47.9–48.1	~12.3– ~14.3	~31.3	~34.2	~45.9– ~46.4	~16.4– ~16.8

TABLE VII

SURVEY OF GROUP CONTRIBUTIONS IN ADDITIVE MOLAR QUANTITIES

Group	Z	M	V_g	V_r	V_W	C_p^s	C_p^l	ΔH_m	Y_g	Y_m	E_{coh}
		g/mol	cm³/mol	cm³/mol	cm³/mol	J/mol·K	J/mol·K	J/mol	g·K/mol	g·K/mol	J/mol
Bifunctional hydrocarbon groups											
−CH₂−	1	14.03	15.85	16.45	10.23	25.35	30.4	3,800	2,700	5,700	4,190
−CH(CH₃)− {symm. / asymm.}	1	28.05	33.35	32.65	20.45	46.5	57.85	6,300	8,000	{13,000 / −7,000}	10,060
−CH(C₅H₉)−	1	82.14			53.28	110.8	147.5				
−CH(C₆H₁₁)−	1	96.17	100.15		63.58	121.2	173.9				
−CH(C₆H₅)−	1	90.12	82.15	74.5	52.62	101.2	144.15		35,000	48,000	31,420
−C(CH₃)₂−	1	42.08	52.4	50.35	30.67	68.0	81.2		{8,400 [2] / 15,000 / (50,000)}	12,000	13,700
−C(CH₃)(C₆H₅)−	1	104.14	101.20	92.2	62.84	122.7	167.5				35,060
−CH=CH− {cis / trans}	2	26.04		27.75	16.94	37.3	42.8	2,100			10,200
−CH=C(CH₃)− {cis / trans}	2	40.06		42.8	27.16	60.05	74,22	4,600			14,500
−C≡C−	2	24.02			16.1						
[cyclohexane ring] {cis / trans}	4	82.14	87.8		53.34	103.2	147.5		31,000	{26,000 / 50,000}	
[benzene ring, para]	4	76.09	65.5	61.4	43.32	78.8	113.1	22,200	32,000 [3]	50,000 [9]	25,140
[benzene ring, meta]	3	76.09			43.32	78.8	113.1		28,000	25,000	
[benzene ring, ortho]	2	76.09			43.32	78.8	113.1		7,000	13,000	
[benzene ring with 2 CH₃]	4	104.14	104.1		65.62	126.8	166.8		(55,000)	35,000	
[benzene ring with CH₃]	4	90.12	83.4		54.47	102.75	140.1		35,000		
[−C₆H₄−CH₂−] {symm. / asymm.}	5	90.12	81.35	77.85	53.55	104.15	143.5	26,000	{34,700 / 25,000}	55,700	29,330
−CH₂−[C₆H₄]−CH₂−	6	104.14	97.20	94.30	63.78	129.5	173.9	29,800	37,400	9	33,520
−[C₆H₄]−CH₂−[C₆H₄]−	9	166.21	146.85	139.25	96.87	182.95	256.6	48,200	79,700	90,000	54,470
−[C₆H₄]−[C₆H₄]−	8	152.18	131.0	122.8	86.64	157.6	226.2	44,400	77,000 [3]	100,000	50,280
[fused tricyclic ring structure]	4	228.28	(201.7)		129.96	236.2	339.4			153,000	
Other hydrocarbon groups											
−CH₃	0	15.03	23.9	22.8	13.67	30.9	36.9	2,500			9,640
−C₂H₅	0	29.06	39.75	39.25	23.90	56.25	67.3	6,300			13,830
−nC₃H₇	0	43.09	55.60	55.70	34.13	81.6	97.7	10,100			18,020
−iC₃H₇	0	43.09	63.65	55.45	34.12	77.4	94.75	8,800			19,700
−tC₄H₉	0	57.11	76.3	73.15	44.34	99.0	118.1				23,340
−CH	1	13.02	9.45	9.85	6.78	15.6	20.95	3,800			420
−C−	1	12.01	4.6	4.75	3.33	6.2	7.4				−5,580
=CH₂	0	14.03			11.94	22.6	21.8				
=CH−	1	13.02		13.88	8.47	18.65	21.4	1,050			5,100
=C<	1	12.01		(6.12)	5.01	10.5	15.9	1,050			(−240)
=C=	1	12.01			6.96						
−CH=C−	2	25.03		20.0	13.48	29.15	37.3	2,100			4,860
≡CH	0	13.02			11.55						
≡C−	1	12.01			8.05						

Group	F(Small)	P_S	K	R_LL	R_GD	R_V	P_LL	X	U	ΔG_f°
	$J^{1/2}\cdot cm^{3/2}/mol$		$g^{1/4}\cdot cm^{3/2}/mol^{3/4}$	cm^3/mol	cm^3/mol	g/mol	cm^3/mol	$10^{-6}\,cm^3/mol$ (cgs)	$cm^{10/3}/s^{1/3}\cdot mol$	J/mol
Bifunctional hydrocarbon groups										
$-CH_2-$	272	39.0	2.35	4.65	7.83	20.64	4.65	11.35	880	$-22{,}000 + 102\,T$
$-CH(CH_3)-$ {symm. asymm.}	495	78.0	4.7	9.26	15.62	41.15	9.26	23.5	1850	$-48{,}700 + 215\,T$
$-CH(C_5H_9)-$	1430	208.3		25.65	43.77	124.48				$-73{,}400 + 548\,T$
$-CH(C_6H_{11})-$	1680	244.9	11.15	30.30	51.75	146.15				$-118{,}400 + 680\,T$
$-,CH(C_6H_5)-$	1561	211.9	19.4	29.03	50.97	144.91	29.12	62	5100	$84{,}300 + 287\,T$
$-C(CH_3)_2-$	686	117.0	7.1	13.87	23.36	61.69	13.86	36	2850	$-72{,}000 + 330\,T$
$-C(CH_3)(C_6H_5)-$	1752	250.9	21.8	33.44	58.41	166.27	33.72	74.5	6100	$61{,}000 + 402\,T$
$-CH=CH-$ {cis trans}	454	67.0	0.5	8.88	15.50	40.62		13.2	1400	$\{76{,}000 + 76\,T$ / $70{,}000 + 83\,T\}$
$-CH=C(CH_3)-$ {cis trans}	(704)	106.0	2.9	13.49	23.24	61.16		25.6	2150	$\{42{,}000 + 183\,T$ / $36{,}000 + 190\,T\}$
$-C\equiv C-$		56.0						14		$230{,}000 - 50\,T$
(cyclohexylene) {cis trans}	1410	205.9	8.0	25.70	44.00	125.10				$\{-96{,}400 + 578\,T$ / $-102{,}400 + 585\,T\}$
(o-phenylene)	1346	172.9	16.3	25.03	44.8	128.6	25.0	50	4100	$100{,}000 + 180\,T$
(m-phenylene)	1346	172.9		25.00	44.7	128.6		50		$100{,}000 + 180\,T$
(p-phenylene)	1346	172.9		24.72	44.2	129.0		50		$100{,}000 + 180\,T$
(dimethylphenylene)	(1850)	250.9		34.8	61.0	169.8		75	6150	$33{,}000 + 394\,T$
(methylphenylene)	(1600)	211.9		29.9	52.7	149.2		63		$66{,}500 + 287\,T$
$-CH_2-$ (phenylene) {symm. asymm.}	1618	211.9	18.65	29.53	52.06	147.3	29.65	61	4980	$78{,}000 + 282\,T$
$-CH_2-$ (phenylene) $-CH_2-$	1890	250.9	21.0	34.03	59.32	166.0	34.3	73	5860	$56{,}000 + 384\,T$
(biphenylene) $-CH_2-$	2964	384.8	34.95	54.56	96.9	275.9	54.65	111	9080	$178{,}000 + 462\,T$
(biphenylene)	2692	345.8	32.6	50.06	89.6	257.2	50.0	100	8200	$200{,}000 + 360\,T$
(naphthylene)	(3980)	518.7		74.9	134.0	386.0		152	12650	$209{,}000 + 538\,T$
Other hydrocarbon groups										
$-CH_3$	438	56.1	3.55	5.64	8.82	17.66	5.64	14.5	1400	$-46{,}000 + 95\,T$
$-C_2H_5$	710	95.1	5.9	10.29	16.65	38.30	10.29	25.85	2280	$-68{,}000 + 197\,T$
$-nC_3H_7$	982	134.1	8.25	14.94	24.48	58.94	14.94	37.2	3160	$-90{,}000 + 299\,T$
$-iC_3H_7$	933	134.1	8.25	14.90	24.44	58.81	14.90	38	3250	$-94{,}700 + 310\,T$
$-tC_4H_9$	1124	173.1	10.65	19.51	32.18	79.35	19.50	50.5	4250	$-118{,}000 + 425\,T$
$-CH$	57	21.9	1.15	3.62	6.80	23.49	3.62	9	450	$-2{,}700 + 120\,T$
$-C-$	-190	4.8	0	2.58	5.72	26.37	2.58	7	50	$20{,}000 + 140\,T$
$=CH_2$	389	50.6		5.47	8.78	17.46		9		$23{,}000 + 30\,T$
$=CH-$	227	33.5	0.25	4.44	7.75	20.31		6.6	700	$38{,}000 + 38\,T$
$=C\big<$	39	16.4	-0.9	3.41	6.67	23.19		4.5	50	$50{,}000 + 50\,T$
$=C=$		28.0		4.23	7.62	20.01				$147{,}000 - 20\,T$
$-CH=C-$	266	49.9	-0.65	7.85	14.42	43.50		11.1	750	$88{,}000 + 88\,T$
$\equiv CH$	356	45.1						9		$112{,}500 - 32.5\,T$
$\equiv C-$	227	28.0						7		$115{,}000 - 25\,T$

(continued on p. 592)

TABLE VII (continued)

Group	Z	M	V_g	V_r	V_W	C_p^s	C_p^l	ΔH_m	Y_g	Y_m	E_{coh}
		g/mol	cm³/mol	cm³/mol	cm³/mol	J/mol·K	J/mol·K	J/mol	g·K/mol	g·K/mol	J/mol

Other hydrocarbon groups (continued)

Group	Z	M	V_g	V_r	V_W	C_p^s	C_p^l	ΔH_m	Y_g	Y_m	E_{coh}
–C=C– {cis/trans}	2	24.02		(12.24)	10.02	21.0	31.8	2,100			(–480)
CH_{ar}	1	13.02			8.06	15.4	22.2				
C_{ar}–	1	12.01			5.54	8.55	12.2				
[cyclopentane ring]	0	69.12			46.56	95.2	126.55				
[cyclohexane ring]	0	83.15	90.7		56.79	105.6	152.95				
[benzene ring]	0	77.10	72.7	64.65	45.84	85.6	123.2				31,000
[fused ring]	4	74.08	56.3		38.28	65.0	93.0				
[fused ring]	4	75.08	59.5		40.80	71.85	103.2				

Bifunctional oxygen-containing groups

Group	Z	M	V_g	V_r	V_W	C_p^s	C_p^l	ΔH_m	Y_g	Y_m	E_{coh}
–O–	1	16.00	10.0	8.5	3.7/[5.8][1]	16.8	35.6	1,700	4,000	9,10	6,290
–C– (=O)	1	28.01	13.4		11.7	23.05	52.8		27,000		
–O–C– (=O) {general/acrylic}	2	44.01	{23.0/18.25}	{24.6/21.0}	15.2/[17.0][1]	(46)	65.0	–4,200	4	11	13,410
–O–C–O– (=O)	3	60.01	31.4		18.9/[23.0][1]				5	12	
–C–O–C– (=O =O)	3	72.02			(27)				(20,000)	13	
–CH(OH)–	1	30.03	19.15		14.82	32.6	65.75		13,000	18,000	
–CH(COOH)–	1	58.04				(65.6)	119.85				
–CH(HC=O)–	1	42.14			21.92						
[benzene]–COO–	6	120.10	88.5	86.0	58.52	(124.8)	178.1	18,000			38,550
–O–CH₂–O–	3	46.03	35.85	33.45	17.63	58.95	101.6	7,200	10,700		16,770

Other oxygen-containing groups

Group	Z	M	V_g	V_r	V_W	C_p^s	C_p^l	ΔH_m	Y_g	Y_m	E_{coh}
–OH	0	17.01	9.7		8.04	17.0	44.8				
[benzene]–OH	0	93.10	75.2		51.36	95.8	157.9				
–C–H (=O)	0	29.02			15.14						
–C–OH (=O)	0	45.02				(50)	98.9				

Bifunctional nitrogen-containing groups

Group	Z	M	V_g	V_r	V_W	C_p^s	C_p^l	ΔH_m	Y_g	Y_m	E_{coh}
–NH–	1	15.02			8.08	14.25	(31.8)				
–CH(CN)–	1	39.04	28.95		21.48	(40.6)					25,420
–CH(NH₂)–	1	29.04			17.32	36.55					
[benzene]–NH–	5	91.11			(51.4)	93.05	(144.9)				

Other nitrogen-containing groups

Group	Z	M	V_g	V_r	V_W	C_p^s	C_p^l	ΔH_m	Y_g	Y_m	E_{coh}
–NH₂	0	16.02			10.54	20.95					
>N–	1	14.01			4.33	17.1	(44.0)				
N_{ar}	1	14.01									
–C≡N	0	26.02	19.5		14.7	(25)					25,000
[benzene]–NH₂	0	92.12			53.86	99.75					
[benzene]–N<	5	90.10			47.65	95.9	(157.1)				

Group	$F_{(Small)}$ $J^{1/2} \cdot cm^{3/2}/mol$	P_S	K $g^{1/4} \cdot cm^{3/2}/mol^{3/4}$	R_{LL} cm^3/mol	R_{GD} cm^3/mol	R_V g/mol	P_{LL} cm^3/mol	X 10^{-6} cm^3/mol (cgs)	U $cm^{10/3}$ $s^{1/3} \cdot mol$	ΔG_f° J/mol
Other hydrocarbon groups (continued)										
$-C=C-$ { cis / trans	78	32.8	-1.8	6.81	13.34	46.38		9	100	{ 100,000 + 100 T / 94,000 + 107 T
CH_{ar}		34.5						9.2		12,500 + 26 T
$C_{ar}-$		17.4						7		25,000 + 38 T
(cyclopentane ring)	1370	186.4		22.0	36.97	100.99				-70,700 + 428 T
(cyclohexane ring)	1620	223.0	10.0	26.69	44.95	122.66				-115,700 + 560 T
(benzene ring)	1504	190.0	18.25	25.51	44.63	123.51	25.5	53	4650	87,000 + 167 T
(fused benzene ring)	(970)	138.7		23.85	44.72	139.0		46.4	3350	125,000 + 204 T
(fused benzene ring)	(1160)	155.8		24.4	44.76	133.8		48.6		112,500 + 192 T
Bifunctional oxygen-containing groups										
$-O-$	143	20.0	0.1	1.59/ 1.77 [19]	2.75/ 2.96 [19]	22.6/ 23.85 [19]	5.2	5	400	-120,000 + 70 T
$-C(=O)-$	563	(48)		4.53/ 5.09 [20]	7.91/ 8.82 [20]	41.9/ 43.0 [20]	(10)	6.5	900	-132,000 + 40 T
$-O-C(=O)-$ { general / acrylic	634	64.8	{ 9.0 / 6.4	6.21/ 6.71 [21]	10.47/ 11.31 [21]	64.20/ 65.32 [21]	15	14	1250	-337,000 + 116 T
$-O-C(=O)-O-$		84.8	(27.5)	7.75 [22]	13.12/ 13.39 [22]	86.8/ 87.8 [22]	22		1600	
$-C(=O)-O-C(=O)-$		(113)		(10.7)	(18.4)	(107)	(25)		(2150)	
$-CH(OH)-$		59.0	(9.15)	6.07	10.75	47.4	(10)	16.5	1050	-178,700 + 170 T
$-CH(COOH)-$		103.8	9.15	10.83	18.79	87.75		28		-395,700 + 238 T
$-CH(HC=O)-$		(87)		9.45	16.43	64.2		17.4		-127,700 + 146 T
(phenyl)$-COO-$	1980	237.7	25.3	31.74	56.1	193.4	40	64	5350	-237,000 + 296 T
$-O-CH_2-O-$	558	79.0	2.55	7.93	13.45	67.0	15.05	21.35	1680	-262,000 + 242 T
Other oxygen-containing groups										
$-OH$		37.1	(8)	2.45/ 2.55 [23]	3.85/ 4.13 [23]	23.95/ 24.08 [23]	(6)	7.5	600	-176,000 + 50 T
(phenyl)$-OH$		210.0	(24.3)	27.30	48.33	151.3	(45)	57.5	4700	-76,000 + 230 T
$-C(=O)-H$		(65)		5.83	9.63	40.69		8.4		-125,000 + 26 T
$-C(=O)-OH$		81.9	8.0	7.21	11.99	64.26		19		-393,000 + 118 T
Bifunctional nitrogen-containing groups										
$-NH-$		29.6		3.59	6.29	24.30		9		58,000 + 120 T
$-CH(CN)-$	896	(86)	(16.15)	9.14	15.88	60.16	14.6	20		120,300 + 91.5 T
$-CH(NH_2)-$		68.6		7.97	14.05	46.13		21		8,800 + 222.5T
(phenyl)$-NH-$		202.5		29.56	53.48	155.5		59		158,000 + 300 T
Other nitrogen-containing groups										
$-NH_2$		46.7		4.36	7.25	22.64		12		11,500 + 102.5T
$\backslash N-$		12.5		2.80	5.70	26.66		6	100	97,000 + 150 T
N_{ar}								12		69,000 + 50 T
$-C\equiv N$	839	63.7	(15)	5.53	9.08	36.67	11	11		123,000 - 28.5 T
(phenyl)$-NH_2$		219.6		29.92	53.2	152.3		62		111,500 + 282.5T
(phenyl)$-N<$		185.4		29.08	53.5	159.3		56	4200	197,000 + 330 T

(continued on p. 594)

TABLE VII (continued)

Group	Z	M	V_g	V_r	V_W	C_p^s	C_p^l	ΔH_m	Y_g	Y_m	E_{coh}
		g/mol	cm³/mol	cm³/mol	cm³/mol	J/mol·K	J/mol·K	J/mol	g·K/mol	g·K/mol	J/mol
Bifunctional nitrogen- and oxygen-containing groups											
−C(=O)−NH−	2	43.03	24.9		19.56/ [18.1] [1]	(38/54)	(90.1)	2,900	[6]	[14]	60,760
−O−C(=O)−NH−	3	59.03			(23)				(25,000) [7]	[15]	
−NH−C(=O)−NH−	3	58.04			(27.6)				[8]	[16]	
−CH(NO₂)−	1	59.03			23.58	57.5					
C₆H₄−C(=O)−NH− (phenyl)	6	119.12	90.4		62.88	(116.8/ 132.8)	(203.2)	25,100			85,900
Other nitrogen- and oxygen-containing groups											
−C(=O)NH₂	0	44.03			(22.2)						
−C(=O)N (cyclic)	2	42.02			(16.0)						
−NO₂	0	46.01			16.8	41.9					
Bifunctional sulphur-containing groups											
−S−	1	32.06	17.8	15.0	10.8	24.05	44.8		−7,500	9,17	8,800
−S−S−	2	64.12	(35.6)	(30.0)	22.7	(48.1)	(89.6)			[18]	(17,600)
−SO₂−	1	64.06			20.3	(50)			(58,000)		
−S−CH₂−S−	3	78.15	51.45	46.45	31.8	73.45	120.0				21,790
Other sulphur-containing groups											
−SH	0	33.07			14.81	46.8	52.4				
Bifunctional halogen-containing groups											
−CHF−	1	32.02	20.35	19.85	13.0	(37.0)	(41.95)		11,000	14,700	4,890
−CF₂−	1	50.01	26.4	24.75	15.3	(49.0)	(49.4)		13,000	23,700	3,360
−CHCl−	1	48.48	29.35	28.25	19.0	42.7	(60.75)		20,000	23,700	13,410
−CCl₂−	1	82.92	44.4	41.55	27.8	60.4	(87.0)		25,000	41,700	20,400
−CH=CCl−	2	60.49		38.4	25.72	56.25	(77.1)				17,850
−CFCl−	1	66.47	35.4	33.15	21.57	(54.7)	(68.2)		23,000	32,700	11,880
−CHBr−	1	92.93	(39)		21.4	41.9					15,920
−CBr₂−	1	171.84	(46)		32.5	58.8					25,420
−CHI−	1	139.93			27.1	38.0					
−CI₂−	1	265.83			44.0	51.0					
Other halogen-containing groups											
−F	0	19.00	10.9	10.0	6.0	(21.4)	(21.0)				4,470
−CF₃	0	69.01	37.3	34.75	21.33	(70.4)	(70.4)				7,830
−CHF₂	0	51.02	31.25	29.85	18.8	(58.4)	(62.95)				9,360
−CH₂F	0	33.03	26.75	26.45	16.2	(46.75)	(51.4)				8,660
−Cl	0	35.46	19.9	18.4	12.2	27.1	(39.8)				12,990
−CCl₃	0	118.38	64.3	59.95	(40)	87.5	(126.8)				33,390
−CHCl₂	0	83.93	49.25	46.65	31.3	69.8	(100.55)				26,400
−CH₂Cl	0	49.48	35.75	34.85	22.5	52.45	(70.2)				17,180
C₆H₄−Cl (phenyl)	0	111.55	85.4	79.8	55.3	105.9	(152.9)				38,130
−Br	0	79.92			14.6	26.3					15,500
−CBr₃	0	251.76			(47.1)	85.1					40,920
−CHBr₂	0	172.85			36.0	68.2					31,420
−CH₂Br	0	93.94			24.8	51.65					19,690
−I	0	126.91			20.4	22.4					
−CI₃	0	392.74			(64.4)	73.4					
−CHI₂	0	266.84			47.5	60.4					
−CH₂I	0	140.94			30.6	47.75					

[1] Between brackets: V_W-value of Slonimskii.

[2] For −C(CH₃)₂− Y_{gi} = 8,400 in polyisobutylene only.

[3] For correction terms of Y_{gi} or special group contributions see table 6.2.

[4] For −COO− Y_{gi} = 8,000 + 12,000 I.

Group	F$_{(Small)}$	P$_S$	K	R$_{LL}$	R$_{GD}$	R$_V$	P$_{LL}$	X	U	ΔG$_f^\circ$
	$J^{1/2}\cdot cm^{3/7}/mol$		$g^{1/4}\cdot cm^{3/2}/mol^{3/4}$	cm^3/mol	cm^3/mol	g/mol	cm^3/mol	$10^{-6}\ cm^3/mol$ (cgs)	$cm^{10/3}/s^{1/3}\cdot mol$	J/mol
Bifunctional nitrogen- and oxygen-containing groups										
$-C(=O)-NH-$		(78)	12.6	7.23	15.15	69.75	30	14	1700	−74,000 + 160T
$-O-C(=O)-NH-$		(94)	(25)						(2100)	
$-NH-C(=O)-NH-$		(107)								
$-CH(NO_2)-$	960			10.28	17.81	89.49				−44,200 + 263T
⬡$-C(=O)-NH-$			28.9	33.5	62.9	201.6	55	64	5800	
Other nitrogen- and oxygen-containing groups										
$-C(=O)-NH_2$			(23)					17		
$-C(=O)-N<$			(8)					11	(1000)	
$-NO_2$	900			6.66	11.01	66.0				−41,500 + 143T
Bifunctional sulphur-containing groups										
$-S-$	460	48.2		8.07	14.44	53.33	8	16		40,000 − 24 T
$-S-S-$	(920)	(96.4)		16.17	29.27	107.63	16	(32)		46,000 − 28 T
$-SO_2-$			(12)						1250	−282,000 + 152T
$-S-CH_2-S-$	1192	135.4		20.8	36.71	127.3	21	43		58,000 + 54 T
Other sulphur-containing groups										
$-SH$	644	65.3		8.79/ 9.27[24]	15.14/ 15.66[24]	49.15/ 50.61[24]		18		13,000 − 33 T
Bifunctional halogen-containing groups										
$-CHF-$	(307)	47.6		4.51	7.68	45.7	(5.42)	15.6	(950)	−197,700 + 114T
$-CF_2-$	(310)	56.2		4.38	7.12	68.2	6.25	20.2	(1050)	−370,000 + 128T
$-CHCl-$	609	76.2	13.4	9.64	16.71	73.8	13.7	27.5	1600	−51,700 + 111T
$-CCl_2-$	914	113.4	24.5	14.63	25.54	127.0	17.7	44	2350	−78,000 + 122T
$-CH=CCl-$	818	104.2	11.6	13.87	24.33	93.8		29.6	1900	39,000 + 79 T
$-CFCl-$	(612)	84.8		9.50	16.3	97.6	(13.9)	32.1	(1700)	−224,000 + 125T
$-CHBr-$	753	89.9	(12.15)	12.57	22.06	141.9		36.5		−16,700 + 106T
$-CBr_2-$	1202	140.8	(22)	20.49	36.24	263.2		62		−8,000 + 112T
$-CHI-$	927	112.9		17.52	31.80			52		37,300 + 79 T
$-CI_2-$	1550	186.8		30.38	55.72			93		100,000 + 58 T
Other halogen-containing groups										
$-F$	(250)	25.7		0.90[25]	0.70/ 0.88[25]	20.92/ 22.20[25]	(1.8)	6.6	(500)	−195,000 − 6 T
$-CF_3$	(560)	81.9		5.27	7.83	89.1		25	(1550)	−565,000 + 122T
$-CHF_2$	(557)	73.3		5.41	8.20	65.3		22.2	(1450)	−392,700 + 108T
$-CH_2F$	(522)	64.7		5.55	8.71	42.84	(6.45)	18.0	(1380)	−217,000 + 96 T
$-Cl$	552	54.3	12.25	5.93/ 6.05[26]	9.84/ 10.07[26]	50.31/ 51.23[26]	(9.5)	18.5	1150	−49,000 − 9 T
$-CCl_3$	1344	167.7	36.75	20.7	35.93	180.1		60	3500	−127,000 + 113T
$-CHCl_2$	1121	130.5	25.65	15.7	26.94	126.0		46	2750	100,700 + 102T
$-CH_2Cl$	824	93.3	14.6	10.7	17.90	71.9	(14.15)	30	2030	−71,000 + 93 T
⬡$-Cl$	1898	227.2	28.55	30.63	53.62	177.0	(34.5)	68.5	5250	51,000 + 171T
$-Br$	696	68.0	(11)	8.90/ 9.03[27]	15.15/ 15.29[27]	118.4/ 119.1[27]		27.5		−14,000 − 14 T
$-CBr_3$	1898	208.8	(33)	29.3	51.2	381.9		89.5		−22,000 + 98 T
$-CHBr_2$	1449	157.9	(23.15)	21.4	37.10	260.5		64		−30,700 + 92 T
$-CH_2Br$	968	107.0	(13.35)	13.5	22.98	139.1		39		−36,000 + 88 T
$-I$	870	91.0		13.90	25.0			43		40,000 − 41 T
$-CI_3$	2420	277.8		44.3	80.7			136		140,000 + 17 T
$-CHI_2$	1797	203.9		31.4	56.8			95		77,300 + 38 T
$-CH_2I$	1142	130.0		18.5	32.83			54		18,000 + 61 T

(continued on p. 596)

[5] For $-OCOO-$ $Y_{gi} = 16,000 + 10,000\,I$.

[6] For $-CONH-$ $Y_{gi} = 12,000 + 1,800\,I^{-1} + 2 \times 10^6\,n_\phi/M$.

[7] For $-OCONH-$ $Y_{gi} = (25,000 \pm ?)$.

[8] For $-NHCONH-$ $Y_{gi} = 20,000 + 2,100\,I^{-1}$.

[9] For correction terms of Y_{mi} or special group contributions see tables 6.7 and 6.8.

[10] For $-O-$ $Y_{mi} = -3,300 + 33,000\,I$ * $Y_m(ODD) = -300$ **.

[11] For $-COO-$ $Y_{mi} = 5,000 + 30,000\,I$ $Y_m(ODD) = -1,500$ **.

[12] For $-OCOO-$ $Y_{mi} = 7,000 + 30,000\,I$ $Y_m(ODD) = -1,500$ **.

[13] For $-COOCO-$ $Y_{mi} = 14,000 + 36,000\,I$ $Y_m(ODD) = -1,500$ **.

[14] For $-CONH-$ $Y_{mi} = 48,000 - 6,000\,I^{-1/2}$ $Y_m(ODD) = -2,500$ **.

[15] For $-OCONH-$ $Y_{mi} = 42,000 - 6,000\,I^{-1/2}$ $Y_m(ODD) = -2,500$ **.

[16] For $-NHCONH-$ $Y_{mi} = 55,000 - 6,000\,I^{-1/2}$ $Y_m(ODD) = -2,500$ **.

[17] For $-S-$ $Y_{mi} = 1,700 + 60,000\,I$ * $Y_m(ODD) = -1,000$ **.

[18] For $-S-S-$ $Y_{mi} = 5,000 + 60,000\,I$ * $Y_m(ODD) = -1,000$ **.

[19] 1.59, 2.96, 23.85 for methyl ethers; 1.63, 2.75, 22.99 for acetals; 1.64, 2.81, 23.18 for higher ethers; 1.77, 2.84, 22.6 attached to benzene ring.

[20] 4.79, 8.42, 43.01 for methyl ketones; 4.53, 7.91, 43.03 for higher ketones; 5.09, 8.82, 41.9 attached to benzene ring.

[21] 6.24, 10.76, 65.32 for methyl esters; 6.38, 10.94, 64.49 for ethyl esters; 6.21, 10.47, 64.20 for higher esters; 6.71, 11.31, 64.8 attached to benzene ring; 6.31, 10.87, 64.90 for acetates.

[22] 7.75, 13.39, 87.8 for methyl carbonates; 7.74, 13.12, 86.8 for higher carbonates.

[23] 2.55, 4.13, 24.08 for primary alcohols; 2.46, 3.95, 23.95 for secondary alcohols; 2.45, 3.85, 24.05 for tertiary alcohols.

[24] 8.85, 15.22, 50.61 for primary thioalcohols; 8.79, 15.14, 50.33 for secondary thioalcohols; 9.27, 15.66, 49.15 for tertiary thioalcohols.

[25] 0.90, 0.88, 22.20 mono; 0.90, 0.70, 20.92 per.

[26] 6.05, 10.07, 51.23 primary; 6.02, 9.91, 50.31 secondary; 5.93, 9.84, 50.75 tertiary.

[27] 8.90, 15.15, 118.5 primary; 8.96, 15.26, 118.4 secondary; 9.03, 15.29, 119.1 tertiary.

* Not valid at $I = 1$.

** $Y_m(ODD)$ is correction per odd methylene chain.

AUTHOR INDEX

Abbott, C., 542
Abitz, W., 34
Acierno, D., 391, 392
Adamse, J.W.C., 350–354, 368
Albert, R., 58, 60, 79
Alcock, T.C., 34
Alfrey, T., 124, 126, 309, 418, 424
Allen, G., 76, 78, 158, 159
Allen, V.R., 338, 369
Altenburg, K., 34
Anderson, J.W., 450, 458
Andrade, E.N. da Costa, 339, 368
Andrews, E.H., 309, 537, 542
Andrews, R.D., 222, 229, 312, 327
Anet, F.A.L., 257
Angus, W.R., 244, 256
Armstrong, R.W., 203, 207
Arnett, R.L., 79
Arthur, J.B., 241
Askadskii, A.A., 79
Asmussen, F., 441–443
Avrami, M., 438, 443

Backer, S., 555
Baer, E., 517, 521
Bagley, E.B., 147, 159, 367, 368
Baird, E.M., 550, 555
Balazs, C.F., 292, 293, 310
Ballman, R.L., 313, 314, 327, 364, 368
Baltá-Calleja, F.J., 248, 256
Bamford, C.H., 458
Barnet, F.R., 272, 310
Barnett, S.M., 364, 368
Barrales-Rienda, J.M., 248, 256
Barrer, R.M., 424
Barrie, I.T., 366, 368
Barrie, J.A., 423–425
Barton, J.M., 100, 127
Bartos, O., 364, 368
Batchinski, A.J., 340, 368
Beaman, R.G., 122, 127
Becht, J., 34
Beck, R.H., 291, 310

Becker, R., 429, 443
Bedwell, M.E., 248, 256
Beek, W.J., 504
Beerbower, A., 146, 159
Behr, E., 465
Bell, C.L.M., 257
Bellamy, L.J., 228
Benbow, J.J., 364, 368
Benderskii, V.A., 79
Benoit, H., 199, 208
Beret, S., 77, 78
Bergen, R.L., 472, 541, 542
Bernhardt, E.C., 504
Bernier, G.A., 537, 538, 542
Bestul, A.B., 95, 97
Beuerlein, R.A., 504
Bevan, L., 537, 542
Beyer, G.H., 458
Bhatnagar, S.S., 244, 256, 257
Bianchi, U., 112, 127
Billmeyer, F.W., 34
Biltz, W., 65, 78
Binder, G., 501, 504
Birks, J.B., 241
Bitler, L.P., 79
Bitter, F., 244, 257
Bixler, H.J., 409, 425
Blake, T.D., 171
Blanks, R.F., 159
Blinova, N.K., 393
Blokland, R., 279, 280, 309
Boenig, H.V., 488, 504
Böttcher, C.J.F., 241
Bolland, J.L., 469, 472
Bolton, J.R., 256
Bonart, R., 34
Bondi, A., 4, 7, 45, 47, 62, 65, 67–69, 78, 90,
    92, 97, 131, 159, 248, 257, 392
Boon, J., 436, 437, 443
Boudart, M., 458
Bovey, F.A., 253, 256, 257
Bowden, F.P., 519, 521
Bowless, W.A., 369

597

SUBJECT INDEX

607

608

casting, rotation, 485
cavitation, 515
centrifugation, 481
CFT, 462, 463
chain backbone, 180
char-forming tendency, 462, 463
charge decay, 239
Charpy test, 511
char residue, 462, 463, 479, 525, 528
chemical shift, 249–252
chemical structure, 9
chromatography, gel permeation, 19, 199
Clausius–Clapeyron equation, 407
cleanability, 551
clustering, 420
CMR, 249, 251
coating, extrusion, 485
coating processes, 481, 488
coefficient, diffusion, 204, 391, 403, 404, 410
    416, 419, 420, 423, 439, 441
–, friction, 506, 519–521
–, mass extinction, 212, 428
–, permeation, 403
–, second virial, 180, 223
–, sedimentation, 204, 391, 392
–, self-diffusion, 419
–, solubility, 404
–, stress optical, 221, 222, 353
–, thermal expansion, 67, 70, 89, 111, 157,
    174, 316, 347, 476
cohesion, work, 162
cohesive energy, 100, 129, 130, 136, 142, 162
cohesive energy density, 129, 130, 158, 167,
    265, 477
cold drawing, 501
colligative properties, 42
colour, 543, 544
colour fastness, 550
comb polymers, 104, 117
combustion, 525
–, heat, 525, 528, 529
–, molar heat, 528
–, specific heat, 528
combustion chain, 535
comfort, mechanical, 548
–, thermal, 547
compatibility, 33
compensation effect, 410, 449
complex modulus, 282
complex notation, 31
complex shear modulus, 350
complex viscosity, 350
compliance, 259
–, bulk, 89, 111, 157, 158, 162, 259, 263, 265,

347
–-, creep, 288
–, retardation, 288, 296
–, shear, 259
–, tensile, 259
composition parameter, 530
compressibility, 89, 111, 157, 158, 162, 259,
    263, 265, 347
compression, isothermal, 77
–, isotropic (hydrostatic), 259
compressional wave, 263
compressive strength, 302, 303
concentration, critical, 376, 381
–, reduced, 378
concentration coefficient of diffusion, 392
concentration coefficient of sedimentation, 392
condensation polymers, 101, 103, 113, 114, 116
conditioning, 485
conducting media, 211
conductivity, 239
–, heat, 317, 395, 427
–, specific electric, 211
–, thermal, 316, 395, 427
conductor, electric, 231
cone-and-plate rheometer, 350
cone viscometer, 336
configuration, 10, 12, 16, 174
–, random coil, 173
conformation, 10, 174
conformational model, 175
conformational state, 174
conformations, macro-, 28
conservation equation, 40, 42
Considère criterion, 499
constitutive properties, 42
contact angle, 164
convergence, angle, 363
convergent flow, 333, 362
cooling, 485
copolymers, 32, 124
–, block, 33, 124
–, graft, 33
–, random, 33, 124
corona attack, 240
Cotton–Mouton effect, 222
couette flow, 332, 336
coupling constant, 252, 253
covering power, 544, 545
cracking, 152, 299, 301, 506, 513, 536, 537
–, environmental stress, 536
–, solvent, 152, 536, 537
–, stress, 442, 536
crack propagation, 299
crack resistance, 494

620

work of adhesion, 170
work of cohesion, 162
work-hardening, 299, 301
wormlike chain model, 175
wrinkle recovery, 548, 549
wrinkling, 548

X-ray diffraction, 23, 312
X-ray scattering, 173, 428

yellowing, 468
yielding, 288
yield pressure, 520
yield stress, 300, 506, 517
Young's equation, 164
Young's modulus, 259, 261, 266, 299, 302, 303,
      313, 315, 320, 322, 335, 507

zero point molar volume, 52, 65
Zimm plot, 224, 225